71st Highway Geology Symposium (HGS 2022)

Better Highways Through Applied Geology

Asheville, North Carolina, USA
23 - 25 May 2022

ISBN: 978-1-7138-5552-1

Printed from e-media with permission by:

Curran Associates, Inc.
57 Morehouse Lane
Red Hook, NY 12571

Highway Geology Symposium (HGS)
C/O John Pilipchuk
1589 Mail Service Center
Raleigh, NC, 27699-1589

Phone: (919) 707-6851
Fax: (919) 250-4237

jpilipchuk@ncdot.gov

Additional copies of this publication are available from:

Curran Associates, Inc.
57 Morehouse Lane
Red Hook, NY 12571 USA
Phone: 845-758-0400
Fax: 845-758-2633
Email: curran@proceedings.com
Web: www.proceedings.com

71st HIGHWAY GEOLOGY SYMPOSIUM
May 23-25, 2022

Renaissance Hotel
Asheville, North Carolina

Grateful Acknowledgments

We would like to thank the following people who helped make made this Symposium possible.

Jody Kuhne
Cheryl Youngblood
Peter Ingraham
Richard Lane
Marc Fish
Krystle Pelham
John Pilipchuk
HGS Steering Committee
North Carolina Geological Survey
Delaney Meeting and Event Management

On Cover – Asheville at Night.
Courtesy of ExploreAsheville.com. Andre Daugherty
Photographer

71st ANNUAL
HIGHWAY GEOLOGY SYMPOSIUM
Table of Contents

The Proceedings of the 71st Highway Geology Symposium are dedicated to Vernon (Vern) Bump

Vern Bump passed away on November 18, 2021 at the Dougherty Hospice House in Sioux Falls SD. Vern was born on January 13, 1938 in Rapid City SD and grew up attending schools in Rapid City. He graduated from the South Dakota School of Mines and Technology in 1961 with a BS in Geological Engineering which was the second greatest accomplishment in his life after marrying the love of his life Gloria Imsland in 1960. Being true to his South Dakota roots, Vern began a career with the South Dakota DOT which spanned 40 years.

Vern's career had a huge impact on the SDDOT as he guided all things geotechnical in the transportation system. Vern oversaw and participated in foundation investigations and construction support for hundreds of bridges throughout the state, including several large bridges crossing the Missouri River. He was very active in pile load testing research that was used to develop dynamic pile driving formulas that are still used today in SD. Vern worked on many challenging landslides over the years with majority of them being within the Pierre Shale at various locations along the Missouri River. His "White Whale" landslide was the Forest City

Landslide, which was a massive slide that affected an abutment of a large bridge over the Missouri River. Vern worked on various mitigations at this slide for 30+ years. The final remediation at this site involved the combination of stone columns and shear pins. It was the first time shear pins were used to mitigate a landslide of this magnitude in the United States. Vern's work at this slide was the subject of various papers at the HGS and Northwest Geotechnical Workshop (NWGW).

Vern was well known and respected statewide and nationally throughout the geotechnical community, as evidenced by the numerous honors he received, including the Highway Geology Symposium's Medallion Award, the NWGW "Mr. Northwest Geotech" and "Hats Off" award, and the Guy E. March Medal which is the highest award of achievement and service given by SDSM&T, his alma mater. Beyond his technical achievements, Vern will be remembered for his positive attitude, sense of humor and passion for geology, engineering, and highways. He was always willing to share his knowledge and experiences with others. Vern was a very practical engineer, he always sought the simplest and most common sense solutions to even the most complex geotechnical problems. One of the more well-known "Bumpisms" that Vern stressed to bridge engineers and highway designers that he worked with was "you must account for geologic conditions during design and construction because if you don't it will change your plans for you".

Vern served many years on the HGS Steering committee and he and Gloria traveled to HGS meetings all over the country, even in his retirement years. Vern was instrumental in making the HGS what it is today. He will be greatly missed and fondly remembered by everyone that knew him.

At a Glance Schedule of Events

71st Highway Geology Symposium
Asheville, North Carolina
May 23-25, 2022

Sunday, May 22

12:00 PM – 7:00 PM
Highway Geology Symposium Registration Open in Grand Ballroom Prefunction Area

12:00 PM – 7:00 PM
Exhibitor Set up in the Grand Ballroom

Monday, May 23

7:00 AM – 5:30 PM
Highway Geology Symposium Registration Open in Grand Ballroom Prefunction Area

7:00 AM – 12:00 PM
Exhibitor Set up in the Grand Ballroom

8:00 AM – 12:00 PM
Transportation Research Board Technical Session:
Improving Resiliency through Geotechnical Asset and Performance Management Approaches
Location: Windsor Ballroom

12:00 PM – 8:30 PM
Highway Geology Symposium Exhibitor Area Open
Location: Grand Ballroom

Highway Geology Symposium
Welcome and Opening Remarks 1:00 PM -1:45 PM

Location: Grand Ballroom
John Pilipchuk, HGS Organizing Committee
Dedication of Proceedings
Dr. Kenneth Taylor, North Carolina State Geologist - *The Geology and Mineral Resources of the Old North State.*

Monday, May 23 (Continued)

Technical Session 1 1:45 PM -3:05 PM

Location: Grand Ballroom
Chris Ruppen, GeoStabilization International, Moderator

1:45 PM – 2:05 PM
Young Author Presentation: Using Geophysics to Evaluate the Results of a Grouting Program in Karstic Geology
Authors: Christopher Michael Mayer, Jacob Sheehan, Mia Ann Painter, Jeremy J. Brown, and Sarah McInnes

2:05 PM – 2:25 PM
Young Author Presentation: Efficient Rock Slope Design during Construction of a State Highway Safety Enhancement Project State Highway 55, Idaho
Authors: Luke Ferguson and Ethan Guzek

2:25 PM – 2:45 PM
Young Author Presentation: Evolution of Midslope Rockfall Attenuator on Federal Lands Transportation Projects
Author: Nicholas J. Farny

2:45 PM – 3:05 PM
Young Author Presentation: Utilizing Cellular Concrete for Geohazard Mitigation Solutions
Author: José LuQuin

3:05 PM – 3:35 PM
Afternoon Coffee Break
Location: Grand Ballroom and Prefunction Area

Technical Session 2 3:35 PM -4:45 PM

Location: Grand Ballroom
Kyle Halverson, Kansas DOT, Moderator

3:35 PM – 3:55 PM
Young Author Presentation: Use of Smart Rocks to Improve Rock Slope Design
Authors: Bruma Souza and Jean Benoît

3:55 PM – 4:15 PM
Young Author Presentation: Geosynthetic-Reinforced Soil (GRS) vs. Mechanically-Stabilized Earth (MSE); An Overview of Practical Applications of GRS
Author: Jeffrey A. Stallings

4:15 PM – 4:35 PM
Flood Repairs Along the SR 187 Corridor
Author: Jason M. Gardner

4:35 PM – 4:45 PM
Field Trip Overview – Jody Kuhne

Monday, May 23 (Continued)

5:00 PM – 6:00 PM
HGS National Steering Committee Meeting
Location: Swannanoa Room

6:30 PM – 8:30 PM
Ice Breaker Social
Location: Grand Ballroom

Tuesday, May 24

Highway Geology Symposium Field Trip
7:00 AM – 8:00 AM
To-Go Continental Breakfast
Location: Highway Geology Symposium Registration Area

7:30 AM – 8:00 AM
Load buses for Field Trip
Pick-up Location: In front of hotel

8:00 AM – 5:00 PM **Field Trip**
Lunch—Sponsored by Geobrugg
Beverages and snacks - Sponsored by GeoStabilization International
Transportation – Sponsored by Ameritech Slope Constructors, Inc.

(NO GLASS ALLOWED INSIDE BUSES)

Free evening to explore and dine in Asheville

Wednesday, May 25

6:30 AM – 8:00 AM
Continental Breakfast
Location: Top of the Plaza

Guest Field Trip to Biltmore Estate

9:30 AM – 3:30 PM
Meet in hotel lobby, transportation will load at the front of hotel.
Lunch—Sponsored by CATLIN Engineers and Scientists
Transportation – Sponsored by Boulderscape, Inc.

Highway Geology Symposium
Technical Session 3   8:00 AM -9:40 AM

Location: Grand Ballroom
John Szturo, HNTB, Moderator

8:00 AM – 8:20 AM
Evaluation of Mine Subsidence Conditions using Borings and Downhole Investigation Techniques
Authors: David L. Knott, Richard E. Gray, John Lea and Hayden Streater

8:20 AM – 8:40 AM
Unstable Slope Inventory along the Blue Ridge Parkway, NC
Authors: Brian K. Banks, Jennifer Bauer, Majed Abdelhadi and Timothy Ramey

8:40 AM – 9:00 AM
Rock Slope Rockfall Risk Reduction – Little River Road (Forest Highway #69) Douglas County, Oregon
Authors: Brent Black, Evan Garich, and Adam Koslofsky

9:00 AM – 9:20 AM
Potential Applications of Steel Fin Piles in Highway Transportation Infrastructure
Authors: Sarah McInnes, Jonathan Hubler, Anthony LaRegina and Hannah M. Iezzoni

9:20 AM – 9:40 AM
Experience in the Face of Unknowns Bridge Foundation Alternatives for the Leesport Bridge, Pennsylvania
Authors: Bruce Shelly, Sarah McInnes and Jeff Rai

9:40 AM – 10:10 AM
Morning Break
Location: Grand Ballroom

Wednesday, May 25 (Continued)

Technical Session 4 10:10 AM – 11:50 AM

Location: Grand Ballroom
Ken Ashton, West Virginia Geological Survey, Moderator

10:10 AM – 10:30 AM
Geological assessment of the Westbound I-40 Slope Failure, Rockwood, Tennessee
Authors: David A. Hannam and Randy L. Kath

10:30 AM – 10:50 AM
Accelerated Geotechnical Investigation of the Sterling Highway Realignment – Cooper Landing, Alaska
Authors: Adam Koslofsky, Logan Allender, Darren Beckstrand, and Keri Nutter

10:50 AM – 11:10 AM
Potential Liability Associated with Unstable Slope Management Programs
Author: Timothy R. Wyatt

11:10 AM – 11:30 AM
Advancements in Investigating, Testing, and Treatment of Acid Producing Rock – SR 15 Section 088, Central Susquehanna Valley Thruway, Snyder County Pennsylvania
Authors: Andrew J. Smithmyer and Jason M. Gardner

11:30 AM – 11:50 AM
Investigation, Design, and Construction of a Debris Flow Barrier System for a Repetitively Failing Slope Along I-40 Near the Buncombe/McDowell County Line in North Carolina
Authors: Melissa E. Landon, Jay R. Smerekanicz, Peter C. Ingraham, D. Matthew Mullen, Jody Kuhne, and Roger Moore

11:50 AM – 1:00 PM
Lunch — Sponsored by Nector Natural Hazard Protection Systems
Location: Grand Ballroom and Prefunction Area

Lunchtime Keynote Speaker: AEG Jahns Lecturer Rick Wooten
2018-2020: Two Years, Eight Storms, 320+ landslides, and an Earthquake (What does it mean, and what do we do now?)

Technical Session 5 1:00 PM – 2:40 PM

Location: Grand Ballroom
Peter Ingraham, Scarptec, Moderator

1:00 PM – 1:20 PM
Geographic Information System (GIS) and Interpretation of Relative Geologic Risk Susceptibly For Proposed Roadway Alignments through Gates of the Arctic National Park, Alaska
Authors: Orion George and Douglas A. Anderson

Wednesday, May 25 (Continued)

Technical Session 5 (continued)

1:20 PM – 1:40 PM
Shallow Foundation Load-Settlement Behavior Assessed from Surface Geophysical Data
Authors: Gary Norris, Sherif Elfass, and Horng-Jyh (Tigra) Yang

1:40 PM – 2:00 PM
Back Calculation from a Plate Load Test on Cohesionless Soil
Authors: Horng-Jyh (Tigra) Yang, Gary Norris, Sherif Elfass

2:00 PM – 2:20 PM
Reliability Models for Roads Crossing Slow-Moving Landslides
Authors: Michael Porter, Scott Anderson, Mark Vessely, and Martin Devonald

2:20 PM – 2:40 PM
Challenges in Rock Slope Stabilization – SR 209, Section RSM, Rock Slope Stabilization Project, Jim Thorpe, Pennsylvania
Authors: Joseph T. Krupansky, Andrew J. Smithmyer, and Scott M. Cressman

2:40 PM – 3:10 PM
Afternoon Break — Sponsored by HDR, Inc.
Location: Grand Ballroom

Technical Session 6 3:10 PM – 4:50 PM

Location: Grand Ballroom
Cheryl Youngblood, NCDOT, Moderator

3:10 PM – 3:30 PM
Geophysical Applications for Highway Wall Design
Author: Edward D. (Ned) Billington and C. Ryan Pastrana

3:30 PM – 3:50 PM
GUARD - making flexible geohazard protection systems SMART
Authors: Tim Shevlin, and Helene Lanter

3:50 PM – 4:10 PM
S.R. 0081 Rock Slope Stabilization, Lackawanna County, Pennsylvania
Author: Daniel F. Martt and Sebastian Lobo-Guerrero

4:10 PM – 4:30 PM
Advancements and Unknowns in the Design of Flexible Facings for Slope Improvement
Authors: Jonathan D. Blanchard, John D. Duffy, and Michael S. Finegan

4:30 PM – 4:50 PM
Migrating Mud Pot - Emergency Responses to Protect Critical Transportation Infrastructure
Authors: Jim Bailey and R. Travis Deane

Wednesday, May 25 (Continued)

Highway Geology Symposium Banquet Dinner

6:00 PM – 7:00 PM

Highway Geology Symposium Social Hour – Sponsored by: Landslide Technology

Location: Grand Ballroom Prefunction Area

Everyone Welcome!

7:00 PM – 9:00 PM

Highway Geology Symposium Banquet – Sponsored by: Maccaferri Inc.

Location: Grand Ballroom

Ticketed Event

8:30 PM – 9:30 PM

Banquet Keynote Speaker - Sponsored by Access Limited Construction

Jennifer Bauer, Appalachian Landslide Consultants - *We're All on the Same Team – How Inter-agency Collaboration Can Lead to Greater Landslide Resilience*

Everyone Welcome!

Young Author Awards – Chris Ruppen

Next Year's Highway Geology Symposium – Marc Fish

Closing Remarks and Adjournment of the Symposium

Thursday, May 26

Geotechnical Asset Management Peer Exchange

8:00 AM – 4:00 PM
Location: Windsor Ballroom

Obstacles and Opportunities Recognized Through Geotechnical Asset Management Implementation

This meeting takes advantage of the participation by state DOTs and others that will be at the Highway Geology Symposium and the TRB midyear committee meeting to bring together people interested in the deployment of Geotechnical Asset Management (GAM) to improve safety and mobility on the nation's transportation corridors. The goal of this peer exchange is to increase awareness and knowledge of current GAM practices of participants through real-world examples and lessons learned.

The meeting will be held on Thursday May 26, 2022, from 8:00 am to 4:00 pm with a 1-hour lunch break (lunch included). We plan to hold a combination of breakout sessions and panel discussions of a handful of general topics including:

- Deployment of GAM and incorporation into TAM Plans.
- Evaluating life Cycle costs, deterioration rates, and models.
- Funding of GAM program – Moving from pilot or research into broader deployment.
- Overlapping efforts with other assets such as culverts, bridges, pavements, retaining walls.
- Climate change impact on geotechnical assets and examples incorporating resiliency in design.
- Risk analysis – Management of resources, prioritizing interventions, assessment of interventions.

GEOTECHNICAL ASSET MANAGEMENT SUBCOMMITTEE AKG00(1)

2022 TRB Midyear Meeting at the 71th Highway Geology Symposium (HGS), Asheville, North Carolina

Date: Monday, May 23, 2022, 8:00 AM – 11:30 AM

Session Theme: Improving Resiliency through Geotechnical Asset and Performance Management Approaches

Our transportation infrastructure has been repeatedly tested by an increase in extreme weather events. Improving resiliency at project and system level against these events will prevent harm and speed recovery and response efforts. Geotechnical Asset Management (GAM) efforts provide important insights to system vulnerabilities and performance and help target resiliency improvements using a risk-based approach and other methods. This session at HGS will highlight how application of GAM approaches will speed up efforts to reduce impact from increasing event severity and frequency.

Time	Topic	Discussion Lead/Presenter
8:00 – 8:25	Welcome, Self-Introduction and Introduction to the Theme and Hypothesis: GAM methods and practices help with understanding and managing a transportation network's resilience	Scott Anderson, BGC Engineering, AKG00(1) Co-Chair
8:25 – 8:35	GAM Subcommittee Business	Darren Beckstrand, Landslide Technology, AKG00(1) Co-Chair
Presentations		
8:35 – 8:50	North Carolina DOT's Resiliency Program *NCDOT has begun implementing a resiliency program to understand implications of changing climatic inputs.*	Colin Mellor and Jody Kuhne, NCDOT
8:50 – 9:05	Efforts to Quantify the Benefits of Implementing Resilience Measures for Geologic Hazards in Colorado	Matt Tello, CDOT
9:05 – 9:25	Observable effects on vulnerable highways: Examples from Alaska	Darren Beckstrand, Landslide Technology
9:25 – 9:40	Washington DOT Resiliency Efforts	Marc Fish, WSDOT
9:40 – 10:00	Break	
10:00 – 10:10	Status of Resilience Programs: States engaged early with the FHWA Peer Exchange were asked questions on resilience programs and the connection to geotechnical programs in their states	Scott Anderson, BGC Engineering
10:10 – 10:30	Tools to understand asset inventory, condition, and threats to resilience.	Zac Sala, BGC Engineering
10:30 – 11:25	Roundtable Discussion with DOTs: Testing the hypothesis • Does GAM relate to reliance on a practical level? • If so, how can DOTs use GAM to help manage resilience? • What methods and tools show most promise? • How can TRB Research Activities help DOTs?	Moderated Discussion
11:25 – 11:30	Actions and next steps – Minutes posted on TRB GAM Subcommittee Website	

Lunchtime Keynote Speaker

The Association of Environmental & Engineering Geologists 2021 - 2022 Jahns Distinguished Lecturer

Richard M. Wooten, P.G.

Richard (Rick) Wooten has over 40 years of experience in applied geology in the Cascade Mountains of Washington State and applied geologic research in the Piedmont and Blue Ridge Mountains of North Carolina. He earned his BS and MS degrees in geology at the University of Georgia in 1973 and 1980. Rick recently retired from the North Carolina Geological Survey where he was the Senior Geologist for Geohazards and Engineering Geology from 1990 to 2021. His previous work includes mapping geologic resources and conditions for land-use planning, landslide investigations, and applied geotechnical geology for the USDA Forest Service on the Gifford Pinchot National Forest in Washington State from 1980 to 1990. His work with the North Carolina Geological Survey includes the scientific regulatory review and field investigations for a low-level radioactive waste disposal project and bedrock geologic mapping in the Piedmont and Blue Ridge Mountains. Since 2003, his main focus has been on landslide hazard mapping and research and responding to landslide events North Carolina Blue Ridge. He has a special interest in the relationships of ductile and brittle bedrock structures with geomorphology and landslides processes and communicating landslide hazards information with stakeholders.

Banquet Keynote Speaker

"We're all on the same team – how inter-agency collaboration can lead to greater landslide resilience"

Jennifer Bauer, PG, Appalachian Landslide Consultants, PLLC

Jennifer Bauer, PG is a principal geologist and co-owner of Appalachian Landslide Consultants, PLLC in Asheville, NC. She started ALC in December of 2011, after working with the North Carolina Geological Survey's Landslide Hazard Mapping team since 2005. Prior to working for the state, Jennifer worked at MACTEC Engineering & Consulting (now Wood) in Raleigh, NC, after getting her geology degree from UNC-Chapel Hill in 2001. She is Past President of the Association of Environmental & Engineering Geologists, an international professional organization dedicated to applied geology. Jennifer has over 20 years of engineering geology experience and is passionate about applying that experience to help protect lives, property, and infrastructure.

Oftentimes state roads and interstate highway corridors are impacted by slope movements initiating outside of the right of way, particularly during extreme weather events. This was the case in Western NC during Tropical Storm Fred in August 2021. In many localities, other organizations or agencies have data on landslide occurrence and susceptibility adjacent to highway corridors. Through examples, this talk will focus on how inter-agency collaboration to assist with asset management can help highway departments prepare for, respond to, and mitigate these landslide hazards.

Debris flow in Cruso, NC that occurred during Tropical Storm Fred on August 17, 2021

Highway Geology Symposium History, Organization, and Function

Inaugural Meeting

Established to foster a better understanding and closer cooperation between geologists and civil engineers in the highway industry, the Highway Geology Symposium (HGS) was organized and held its first meeting on March 14, 1950, in Richmond Virginia. Attending the inaugural meeting were representatives from state highway departments (as referred to at that time) from Georgia, South Carolina, North Carolina, Virginia, Kentucky, West Virginia, Maryland, and Pennsylvania. In addition, a number of federal agencies and universities were represented. A total of nine technical papers were presented.

W.T. Parrott, an engineering geologist with the Virginia Department of Highways, chaired the first meeting. It was Mr. Parrott who originated the Highway Geology Symposium.

It was at the 1956 meeting that future HGS leader, A.C. Dodson, began his active role in participating in the Symposium. Mr. Dodson was the Chief Geologist for the North Carolina State Highway and Public Works Commission, which sponsored the 7th HGS meeting.

Symposium Locations

Since the initial meeting, 69 consecutive annual meetings have been held in 33 different states. Between 1950 and 1962, the meetings were east of the Mississippi River, with Virginia, West Virginia, Ohio, Maryland, North Carolina, Pennsylvania, Georgia, Florida, and Tennessee serving as host state.

In 1962, the symposium moved west for the first time to Phoenix, Arizona where the 13th annual HGS meeting was held. Since then it has alternated, for the most part, back and forth from the east to the west. The Annual Symposium has moved to different location as shown on the next page.

Organization

Unlike most groups and organizations that meet on a regular basis, the Highway Geology Symposium has no central headquarters, no annual dues and no formal membership requirements. The governing body of the Symposium is a steering committee composed of approximately 20 - 25 engineering geologist and geotechnical engineers from state and federal agencies, colleges and universities, as well as private service companies and consulting firms throughout the country. Steering committee members are elected for three-year terms, with their elections and re-elections being determined principally by their interests and participation in and contribution to the Symposium. The officers include a chairman, vice chairman, secretary, and treasurer. all of whom are elected for a two-year term. Officers, except for the treasurer, may only succeed themselves for one additional term.

A number of three-member standing committees conduct the affairs of the organization. The lack of rigid requirements, routing and relatively relaxed overall functioning of the organization is what attracts many participants.

List of Highway Geology Symposium Meetings

No.	Year	HGS Location	No.	Year	HGS Location
1st	1950	Richmond, VA	2nd	1951	Richmond, VA
3rd	1952	Lexington, VA	4th	1953	Charleston, WV
5th	1954	Columbus, OH	6th	1955	Baltimore, MD
7th	1956	Raleigh, NC	8th	1957	State College, PA
9th	1958	Charlottesville, VA	10th	1959	Atlanta, GA
11th	1960	Tallahassee, FL	12th	1961	Knoxville, TN
13th	1962	Phoenix, AZ	14th	1963	College Station, TX
15th	1964	Rolla, MO	16th	1965	Lexington, KY
17th	1966	Ames, IA	18th	1967	Lafayette, IN
19th	1968	Morgantown, WV	20th	1969	Urbana, IL
21st	1970	Lawrence, KS	22nd	1971	Norman, OK
23rd	1972	Old Point Comfort, VA	24th	1973	Sheridan, WY
25th	1974	Raleigh, NC	26th	1975	Coeur d'Alene, ID
27th	1976	Orlando, FL	28th	1977	Rapid City, SD
29th	1978	Annapolis, MD	30th	1979	Portland, OR
31st	1980	Austin, TX	32nd	1981	Gatlinburg, TN
33rd	1982	Vail, CO	34th	1983	Stone Mountain, GA
35th	1984	San Jose, CA	36th	1985	Clarksville, TN
37th	1986	Helena, MT	38th	1987	Pittsburg, PA
39th	1988	Park City, UT	40th	1989	Birmingham, AL
41st	1990	Albuquerque, NM	41st	1991	Albany, NY
43rd	1992	Fayetteville AR	44rd	1993	Tampa, FL
45th	1994	Portland, OR	46th	1995	Charleston, WV
47th	1996	Cody, WY	48th	1997	Knoxville, TN
49th	1998	Prescott, AZ	50th	1999	Roanoke, VA
51st	2000	Seattle, WA	52nd	2001	Cumberland, MD
53rd	2002	San Luis Obispo, CA	54th	2003	Burlington, VT
55th	2004	Kansas City, MO	56th	2005	Wilmington, NC
57th	2006	Breckinridge, CO	58th	2007	Pocono Manor, PA
59th	2008	Santa Fe, NM	60th	2009	Buffalo, NY
61st	2010	Oklahoma City, OK	62nd	2011	Lexington, KY
63rd	2012	Redding, CA	64th	2013	North Conway, NH
65th	2014	Laramie, WY	66th	2015	Sturbridge, MA
67th	2016	Colorado Springs	68th	2017	Marietta, GA
69th	2018	Portland, ME	70th	2019	Portland OR
71st	2022	Asheville, NC			

Meeting sites are chosen two to four years in advance and are selected by the Steering Committee following presentations made by representatives of potential host states. These presentations are usually made at the steering committee meeting, which is held during the Annual Symposium. Upon selection, the state representative becomes the state chairman and a member of the Steering Committee.

HGS History, Organization, and Function (continued)

The symposia are generally scheduled for two and one-half days, with a day-and-a-half for technical papers plus a full day for the field trip. The Symposium usually begins with a TRB session and an evening Ice-Breaker the first day, a full day of technical presentations the second day, a field trip on the third day followed by the annual banquet that evening, and a half day of technical presentations on the final day.

The Field Trip

The field trip is the focus of the meeting. In most cases, the trips cover approximately 150 to 200 miles, provide for six to eight scheduled stops, and require about eight hours. Occasionally, cultural stops are scheduled around geological and geotechnical points of interests. To cite a few examples: in Wyoming (1973), the group viewed landslides in the Big Horn Mountains; Florida's trip (1976) included a tour of Cape Canaveral and the NASA space installation; the Idaho and South Dakota trips dealt principally with mining activities; North Carolina provided stops at a quarry site, a dam construction site, and a nuclear generation site; in Maryland, the group visited the Chesapeake Bay hydraulic model and the Goddard Space Center. The Oregon trip included visits to the Columbia River Gorge and Mount Hood; the Central mine region was visited in Texas; and the Tennessee meeting in 1981 provided stops at several repaired landslide in Appalachia regions of East Tennessee.

In Utah (1988) the field trip visited sites in Provo Canyon and stopped at the famous Thistle Landslide, while in New Mexico, in 1990, the emphasis was on rockfall treatments in the Rio Grande River canyon and included a stop at the Brugg Wire Rope headquarters in Santa Fe.

Mount St, Helens was visited by the field trip in 1994 when the meeting was in Portland, Oregon, while in 1995 the West Virginia meeting took us to the New River Gorge Bridge that has a deck elevation of 876 feet above the water.

In Cody, Wyoming the 1996 field trip visited the Chief Joseph Scenic Highway and the Beartooth Uplift in northwest Wyoming. In 1997 the meeting in Tennessee visited the newly constructed future I-26 highway in the Blue Ridge of East Tennessee. The Arizona meeting in 1998 visited the Oak Creek Canyon near Sedona and a mining ghost town at Jerome, Arizona. The Virginia meeting in 1999 visited the "Smart Road" Project that was under construction. This was a joint research project of the Virginia Department of Transportation and Virginia Tech University. The Seattle Washington meeting in 2000 visited an ancient lahar in the Mount Rainier area. A stop during the Maryland meeting in 2001 was the Sideling Hill road cut for I-68 which displayed a tightly folded syncline in the Allegheny Mountains.

The California field trip in 2002 provided a field demonstration of the effectiveness of rock netting against rock falls along the Pacific Coast Highway. The Kansas City meeting in 2004 visited the Hunt Subtropolis which is said to be the "world's largest underground business complex". It was created through the mining of limestone by way of the room and pillar method. The Rocky Point Quarry provided an opportunity to search for fossils at the North Carolina meeting in 2005. The group also visited the US-17 Wilmington Bypass Bridge which was under construction. Among the stops at the Pennsylvania meeting were the Hickory Run Boulder Field, the No.9 Mine and Wash Shanty Museum, and the Lehigh Tunnel.

HGS History, Organization, and Function (continued)

The New Mexico field trip in 2008 included stops at a soil nailed wall along US-285/84 north of Santa Fe and a road cut through the Bandelier Tuff on highway 502 near Los Alamos where rockfall mesh was used to protect against rockfalls. The New York field trip in 2009 included the Niagara Falls Gorge and the Devil's Hole Trail. The Oklahoma field trip in 2010 toured the complex geology of the Arbuckle Mountains in the southern part of the state along with stops at Tucker's Tower and Turner Falls.

In the bluegrass state of Kentucky, the 2011 HGS field trip included stops at Camp Nelson which is the site of the oldest exposed rocks in Kentucky near the Lexington and Kentucky River Fault Zones. Additional stops at the Darby Dan Farm and the Woodford Reserve Distillery illustrated how the local geology has played such a large part in the success of breeding prized Thoroughbred horses and made Kentucky the "Birthplace of Bourbon".

In Redding, California, the 2012 field trip included stops at the Whiskeytown Lake, which is one in a series of lakes that provide water and power to northern California. Additional stops included Rocky Point, a roadway construction site containing Naturally Occurring Asbestos (NOA), and Oregon Mountain where the geology and high rainfall amounts have caused Hwy 299 to experience local and global instabilities since first constructed in 1920.

The 2013 field trip of New Hampshire highlighted the topography and geologic remnants left by the Pleistocene glaciation that fully retreated approximately 12,000 years ago. The field rip included stops at various overlooks of glacially-carved valleys and ranges; the Old Man of the Mountain Memorial Plaza, which is a tribute to the famous cantilevered rock mass in the Franconia Notch that collapsed on May 3, 2003; the lacustrine deposits and features of the Glacial Lake Ammonoosuc; views of the Presidential Range; bridges damaged during Tropical Storm Irene in August 2011; and the Willey Slide, located in the Crawford Notch where all members of the Willey family were buried by a landslide in 1826.

The 2014 field trip presented a breathtaking tour of the geology and history of southeast Wyoming, ascending from the high plains surrounding Laramie at 7000 feet to the Medicine Bow Mountains along the Snowy Range Scenic Byway. Visible along the way were a Precambrian shear zone, and glacial deposits and features. From the glacially carved Mirror Lake and the Snowy Range Ski Area, the path wound east to the Laramie Mountains and the Vedauwoo Recreational Area, a popular rock climbing and hiking area before returning to Laramie.

In Sturbridge, MA, the 2015 field trip focused on the Connecticut Valley, a Mesozoic rift basin that signaled the breakup of Pangea, and the Berkshires, which represents the collision and amalgamation of an island arc system with the North American Laurentian margin.

The field trip in 2016 was an urban setting along the western edge of Colorado Springs and around Manitou Springs. Stops included the Pikeview Quarry, Garden of the Gods Visitor Center, and several other locations where rockfall and debris flow mitigation, post-flooding highway embankment repair, and a nonconformity in the rock records that spans 1.3 billion years were observed.

The 2017 field trip provided an opportunity to view the geology of northern Georgia. Stops included the Bellwood Quarry, which, at one time was run by the City of Atlanta and also served as a prison labor camp. It will eventually serve as a 2.4 billion-gallon water storage facility for the City of Atlanta upon completion of a tunnel to connect the quarry to two water treatment plans and three pump stations. Additional stops included the Buzzi Unicem Cement Plant to get a close up view of the Clairmont Melange, The Cooper Furnace near the Allatoona Dam, and the New Riverside Ochre-Emerson Barite mine.

The 2018 field trip in Portland Maine provided a good overview of the geology of coastal Maine. Field trip stops included a stop at the Sherman Salt Marsh near Newcastle which was recently restored to its natural state after the dam that carried US Highway 1 washed out during a 2005 storm. Additional stops included the site of the 1996 landslide near Rockland Harbor that consumed several homes and the rock slope remediation project at the Penobscot Narrows Bridge near Prospect Maine. A lobster lunch along the shore of Penobscot Bay was one of several highlights of the field trip.

The 2019 field trip in Portland Oregon travelled the Columbia River Gorge west. Starting at the Crown Point Vista House and Portland Women's Forum State Scenic Viewpoint above the gorge to learn about the river highway. Descending into the gorge, we stopped at scenic Multnomah Falls and Benson Bridge, and saw flexible rockfall fence installed to protect the lodge and historic Columbia River Highway. Other stops included lunch at Cascade Locks, Bonneville Landslide and rockfall areas along the highway.

At the technical sessions, case histories and applied state-of-the-art papers are most common; with highly theoretical papers the exception. The papers presented at the technical sessions are published in the annual proceedings. All proceedings are available to download from www.HighwayGeologySymposium.org.

Banquet speakers are also a highlight and have been varied through the years.

Member Recognition: A Medallion Award was initiated in 1970 to honor those persons who have made significant contributions to the Highway Geology Symposium. The selection was- and is currently made from the members of the national steering committee of the HGS.

Emeritus Members: A number of past members of the national steering committee have been granted Emeritus status. These individuals, usually retired, resigned from the HGS Steering Committee, or are deceased, have made significant contributions to the Highway Geology Symposium. A total of 42 persons have been granted Emeritus status.

Dedications: Several Proceedings volumes have been dedicated to past HGS Steering Committee members who have passed away. The 36th HGS Proceedings were dedicated to David L. Royster (1931 - 1985, Tennessee) at the Clarksville, Indiana Meeting in 1985. In 1991 the Proceedings of the 42nd HGS held in Albany, New York were dedicated to Burrell S. Whitlow (1929 - 1990, Virginia). The 64th HGS Proceedings were dedicated to Earl Wright (1931 – 2012) at the North Conway, New Hampshire meeting. The 65th proceedings were dedicated to Nicholas Priznar (1952 – 2014) at the Laramie, Wyoming meeting. The 76th HGS held at Colorado Springs, Colorado dedicated the proceedings to Vern McGuffy (1934 – 2016). The proceedings for the 68th HGS held in Marietta, Georgia were dedicated to Richard (Dick) Cross (1944 – 2016). The proceedings for the 69th HGS are dedicated to Dave Bingham (1932-2018) and Joe Gutierrez (1926-2018). The Proceedings of the 71st HGS are dedicated to Vernon (Vern) Bump.

Young Author Award: The Highway Geology Symposium has always encouraged participation of Young Professionals, realizing that Young Professionals are the future of the Organization. This participation was taken formal in 2014, with the formation of an annual National Young Author Competition, where Young Authors have the opportunity to prepare papers and present their work. To participate, Young Author's must be up to 35 years old or younger, the principal author of the paper and the sole presenter of the paper at the Symposium. Papers are reviewed and judged based on Technical Presentation of the Paper (including Geology), Originality of the Work, Applicability of the Work to Others and Paper Layout. One Young Author is selected each year to receive the coveted Young Author Award, with presentation of the award conducted at the annual Symposium banquet

Young Author Award Winners

2014 Simon Boone, "Performance of Flexible Debris Flow Barriers in a Narrow Canyon"

2015 Cory Rinehart, "High Quality H20: Utilizing Horizontal Drains for Landslide Stabilization"

2016 Todd Hansen, "Geologic Exploration for Ground Classification: Widening of the I-70 Veterans Memorial Tunnels"

2017 James Arthurs, "Construction of Transportation Infrastructure in Weathered Volcanic Ash Soils"

2018 Brian Felber, "Geotechnical Challenges for Bridge Foundations & Roadway Embankment Design in Peats and Deep Glacial Lake Deposits"

2019 Anya Brose, "The Assessment and Remediation of Wabasha St. Rock Fall"

HGS Medallion Award Recipients

Hugh Chase	1970
Tom Parrott	1970
Paul Price	1970
K.B. Woods	1971
R.J. Edmondson	1972
C.S. Mullin	1974
A.C. Dodson	1975
Burrell Whitlow	1978
Bill Sherman	1980
Virgil Burgat	1981
Henry Mathis	1982
David Royster	1982
Terry West	1983
Dave Bingham	1984
Vernon Bump	1986
C.W. "Bill" Lovell	1989
Joseph A. Gutierrez	1990
Willard McCasland	1990
W.A. "Bill" Wisner	1991
David Mitchell	1993
Harry Moore	1996
Earl Wright	1997
Russell Glass	1998
Harry Ludowise	2000
Sam Thornton	2000
Bob Henthorne	2004
Mike Hager	2005
Joseph A. Fischer	2007
Ken Ashton	2008
A. David Martin	2008
Michael Vierling	2009
Dick Cross	2009
John F. Szturo	2010
Christopher Ruppen	2012
Jeff Dean	2012
John Pilipchuk	2015
Peter Ingraham	2016

Emeritus Members of the Steering Committee

Emeritus Status is granted by the Steering Committee

R.F. Baker
John Baldwin
David Bingham
Vernon Bump
Virgil E. Burgat
Robert G. Charboneau
Hugh Chase
Jim Coffin
Dick Cross
A.C. Dodson
Walter F. Fredricksen
Brandy Gilmore
Russell Glass
Robert Goddard
Joseph Gutierrez
Mike Hager
Rich Humphries
Charles T. Janik
John Lemish
Bill Lovell
A. David Martin
Henry Mathis
William McCasland
George S. Meadors, Jr.
David Mitchell
Harry Moore
W.T. Parrot
Paul H. Price
Nicholas Priznar
David L. Royster
Bill Sherman
Willard L. Sitz
Mitchell Smith
Jim Stroud
Steve Sweeney
Sam Thornton
Berke Thompson
Mike Vierling
Burrell Whitlow
W.A. "Bill" Wisner
Earl Wright
Ed J. Zeigler

HGS National Steering Committee Officers

Krystle Pelham - CHAIRMAN
New Hampshire Dept. of Transportation
Bureau of Materials and Research
PO Box 483
5 Hazen Drive
Concord, NH 03302-0483
Phone: (603) 271-1657
Email: Krystle.Pelham@dot.nh.gov

Bill Webster - VICE-CHAIRMAN
CalTrans
5900 Folsom Blvd.
Sacramento, CA 95819
Phone: (916) 662-1183
Email: bill_webster@dot.ca.gov

Kyle Halverson - SECRETARY
Kansas Department of Transportation
Bureau of Structures and Geotechnical Services
700 SW Harrison St.
Topeka, KS 66603
Office: 785-291-3860
Cell: 785-845-4332
Email: kyle.halverson@ks.gov

John Pilipchuk - TREASURER
NCDOT Geotechnical Engineering Unit
1020 Birch Ridge Drive
Raleigh, NC 27699-1589
Phone: (919) 707-6851
Email: jpilipchuk@ncdot.gov

HGS National Steering Committee Members

Ken Ashton – (Membership)
West Virginia Geological Survey
1 Mont Chateau Road
Morgantown, WV 26508
Phone: (304) 594-2331
Fax: (304) 594-2575
Email: ashton@wvgs.wvnet.edu

Vanessa Bateman
Engineering & Construction Headquarters
U.S. Army Corps of Engineers
441 G Street NW
Washington, DC 20314-1000
Phone: (202) 761-7423
Email: vanessa.c.bateman@usace.army.mil

Jeff Dean
Terracon
4701 North Stiles Avenue
Oklahoma City, OK 73015
Phone: (405) 445-3280
Email: jeff.dean@terracon.com

John D. Duffy
Caltrans (Retired)
128 Baker Ave.
Shell Beach, CA 93449
Phone: (805) 440-9062
Email: JohnDuffy@charter.net

HGS National Steering Committee Members (continued)

Mark Falk
Wyoming DOT
5300 Bishop Blvd.
Cheyenne, WY 82009
Phone: (307) 777-4205
Email: mark.falk@wyo.gov

Marc Fish
WSDOT Geotechnical Office
1655 S. 2nd Ave
Tumwater, WA 98512
Phone: (360) 709-5498
Email: FishM@wsdot.wa.gov

Kyle Halverson (Secretary)
Kansas Department of Transportation
Bureau of Structures and Geotechnical Services
700 SW Harrison St.
Topeka, KS 66603
Office: (785) 291-3860
Cell: (785) 845-4332
Email: kyle.halverson@ks.gov

Bob Henthorne
Kansas Department of Transportation
Bureau of Structures and Geotechnical Services
700 SW Harrison Street
Topeka, KS 66603-3754
Phone: (785) 296-3531
Email: bob.henthorne@ks.gov

Peter Ingraham
Scarptec Inc.
19 Lord Jeffrey Drive
Amherst, NH 03031
Phone: (603) 785-0262
Email: peter@scarptec.com

Jody Kuhne
North Carolina DOT
P. O. Box 3279
US Highway 74
Asheville, NC 28802
Phone: (828) 298-3874
Email: jkuhne@ncdot.gov

Richard Lane
NHDOT (Retired)
213 Pembroke Hill Rd.
Pembroke, NH 03275
Phone: (603) 485-3202
Email: lanetrisbr@hotmail.com

Sarah McInnes
PA DOT
District 6-0
7000 Geerdes Blvd.
King of Prussia, PA 19406
Phone: (610) 205-6544
Email: smcinnes@pa.gov

Krystle Pelham (Chairman)
New Hampshire Dept. of Transportation
Bureau of Materials and Research
PO Box 483
5 Hazen Drive
Concord, NH 03302-0483
Phone: (603) 271-1657
Email: Krystle.Pelham@dot.nh.gov

John Pilipchuk (Treasurer)
NCDOT Geotechnical Engineering Unit
1020 Birch Ridge Drive
Raleigh, NC 27699-1589
Phone: (919) 707-6851
Email: jpilipchuk@ncdot.gov

HGS National Steering Committee Members (continued)

Victoria Porto
PA DOT (Retired)
10 Pine Lake Drive
Carlisle, PA 17015
Phone: (717) 805-5941
Email: vamporto@aol.com

Erik Rorem
Geobrugg North America, LLC
20483 Whistle Punk Rd. 97702
Bend, OR 97702
Phone: 1 505 690 7144
Email: erik.rorem@geobrugg.com

Christopher A. Ruppen (Young Author Committee)
GeoStabilization International
3808 Sunflower Road
New Brighton, PA 15066
Phone: (724) 272-7532
Email: chris.ruppen@gsi.us

Stephen Senior
Ontario Min of Trans. (Retired)
11 Dewbourne Ave.
Richmond Hill, ON L4B 3G7 Canada
Phone: (416) 235-3734
Email: sa.senior@rogers.com

Tim Shevlin, R.G.
Geobrugg North America LLC
Salem, OR 97302
Phone: (503) 423-7258
Email: tim.shevlin@geobrugg.com

Deana Sneyd
Petrologic Solutions, Inc.
3997 Oak Hill Road
Douglasville, GA 30135
Phone: (678) 313-4147
Email: dsneyd@gmail.com

Steven Sweeney
NY Thruway (Retired)
105 Albert Rd.
Delanson, NY 12053
Email: 2ssweeney@gmail.com

John F. Szturo
HNTB Corporation
715 Kirk Drive
Kansas City, MO 64105
Phone: (816) 527-2275 (Direct Line)
Cell: (913) 530-2579
Email: jszturo@hntb.com

Bill Webster (VICE-CHAIRMAN)
CalTrans
5900 Folsom Blvd.
Sacramento, CA 95819
Phone: (916) 662-1183
Email: bill_webster@dot.ca.gov

Terry West (Medallion, Emeritus)
Earth and Atmospheric Science Dept.
Purdue University
West Lafayette, IN 47907-1297
Phone: (765) 494-3296
Email: trwest@purdue.edu

HIGHWAY GEOLOGY SYMPOSIUM
Past, Present, and Future Symposium Contact List

2013	New Hampshire	Krystle Pelham	603-271-1657	Krystle.Pelham@dot.state.nh.us
2014	Wyoming	Jim Coffin	307-777-4205	Jim.coffin@wyo.gov
2015	Massachusetts	Peter Ingraham	603-688-0880	peter_ingraham@golder.com
2016	Colorado	Ty Ortiz	303-921-2634	Ty.ortiz@state.co.us
2017	Georgia	Deana Sneyd	678-313-4147	Dsneyd61@gmail.com
2018	Maine	Krystle Pelham	603-271-1657	Krystle.Pelham@dot.state.nh.us
2019	Oregon	Scott Burns	503-725-3389	BurnsS@pdx.edu
2022	North Carolina	John Pilipchuk	919-707-6851	jpilipchuk@ncdot.gov
		Jody Kuhne	828-250-3285	jkuhne@ncdot.gov

71st ANNUAL HIGHWAY GEOLOGY SYMPOSIUM

Sponsors

The following companies have graciously contributed toward the sponsorship of the Symposium. The HGS relies on sponsor contributions for refreshment breaks, field trip lunches and other activities. We gratefully appreciate the contributions made by these sponsors.

Platinum Level Sponsors

Ameritech Slope Constructors, Inc.
P.O. Box 2702
Asheville, NC 28802
828-633-6352
www.ameritech.pro

Ameritech Slope Constructors, Inc. is a Geohazard Mitigation contractor. We provide slope stabilization services for rock and soil slopes for a wide variety of clients. Our services include rock scaling, rock bolting, rockfall barriers, rockfall drapes and attenuators, pinned mesh systems, boulder lashing, soil nailing, anchored mesh systems, anchored shotcrete walls, rock and soil drains, and high angle drilling.

Geobrugg
8004 Windspray Drive
Summerfield, NC 27358
336-337-0945
www.geobrugg.com

Design test and manufacture geohazard solutions.

Maccaferri Inc.
10303 Governor Lane Blvd. 220
Williamsport, MD 21795-3115
301-641-8072
www.maccaferri.com

Established in 1879, Maccaferri has more than 100 companies worldwide and has become a global technical reference in the research, design and implementation of innovative solutions within civil, geotechnical and environmental engineering. The company operates within numerous market sectors including infrastructure, mining, river control and environmental protection. In addition to geohazard mitigations, solutions offered to these markets include soil reinforcement, hydraulic works, ground stabilization, retaining structures and erosion protection. Maccaferri does not simply supply products but works in partnership with clients, offering technical expertise to deliver versatile, cost-effective and environmentally friendly solutions.

Engineering a Better Solution

With over 60 years' experience in rockfall protection systems and natural hazard mitigation, Maccaferri offers a wide range of systems to stabilize rock faces, soil slopes and snow masses, reducing risks to people, buildings, and critical infrastructure. Maccaferri's wide variety of systems offer the highest level of performance in the industry, allowing designers to select the optimum solution for their specific application. Our wide range of engineered systems are certified and tested by leading institutes, in accordance with the latest standards, and are designed using state-of-the-art modeling software and techniques.

Nector Sp. z o.o.
ul. Szlak 65/502
Kraków, Poland 31-153
+48 12 631 85 50
https://nector.biz

NECTOR is a first Polish manufacturer of a double plated machine-made hexagonal mesh and gabion baskets. NECTOR's offer includes all dimensions of machine-made hexagonal mesh baskets with galvanic thick zinc coating, zinc and aluminum coating (Galfan, Crapal, Bezinal) and an additional UV-resistant PVC coating, as well as stainless steel baskets.NECTOR has developed unique high tensile strength hexagonal mesh Nector Hard HD, which is used for slope protection structures with Ground Anchors. NECTOR products are used for making structures exposed to the harmful impact of external factors, which consequently require solid and functional protection. The highest quality parameters and optimum technical properties of NECTOR products ensure the reliability and durability of each form of protection and structure.

Silver Level Sponsors

Access Limited Construction
1102 Pike Lane
Oceano, CA 93445
540-42-02678
www.accesslimitedconstruction.com

Access Limited Construction is a Specialty Contractor based in San Luis Obispo, California. An industry leader, we provide rockfall and debris flow mitigation, slope stabilization, and difficult drilling services for transportation, energy, mining and private sector clients. With our fleet of Spyder Excavators, we can access steep terrain and hard to reach projects throughout the United States from the East Coast to Hawaii.

Gannett Fleming
207 Senate Avenue
Camp Hill, PA 17011
916-532-0658
www.gannettfleming.com

Gannett Fleming is an international planning, design, technology, and construction management firm. Geotechnical and geological services are a cornerstone of Gannett Fleming's long history. Our experience includes dams and earth structures, groundwater resources, building sites, and transportation corridors—including ports and harbors. Whatever the terrain, our experienced team provides resilient stabilization and protection systems that minimize risk and advance project goals.

HDR
15 South Main Street, Suite 601
Greenville, SC 29601
(919) 985-8942
www.hdrinc.com

We specialize in engineering, architecture, environmental and construction services. While we are most well-known for adding beauty and structure to communities through high-performance buildings and smart infrastructure, we provide much more than that. We create an unshakable foundation for progress because our multidisciplinary teams also include scientists, economists, builders, analysts and artists. Our employees, working in more than 200 locations around the world, push open the doors to what's possible each and every day.

Landslide Technology
10250 SW Greenburg Road, Suite 111
Portland, OR 97223
503-452-1200
www.landslidetechnology.com

Landslide Technology is a small-business, geotechnical engineering firm headquartered in Portland, Oregon. The majority of our work is performed on projects in the Pacific Northwest, Mountain West and Alaska, but we regularly work across the nation and internationally when the problem demands our expertise. Founded in 1983, we specialize in complex geologic assignments involving landslides and rockfall that impact critical infrastructure. Our team is highly adapted to rapid response services, and brings the contracting agility to meet tight deadlines. Our full-time staffing resources include fifteen geotechnical engineers, six engineering geologists, two dually-licensed engineer/geologists and two CADD designers. Six of our professional staff are certified by the Society of Professional Rope Access Technicians (SPRAT) to complete geologic reconnaissance, instrumentation, and construction inspection using rope-access techniques for rock slope projects.

Bronze Level Sponsors

Aero Aggregates of North America LLC
1500 Chester Pike
Eddystone, PA 19022
717-574-5614
www.aerofga.com

Aero Aggregates of North America is a Manufacturer of Foamed Glass Aggregate- An Ultra-Lightweight fill material that is durable, sustainable, insulating and free-draining, with a low unit weight (<15 pcf) and a high friction angle.

BGC Engineering, Inc.
701 12th Street, Suite 211
Golden, CO 80401
720-289-9430
www.bgcengineering.ca/

BCG Engineering is an international consulting firm that provides professional services in applied earth sciences. We focus on pioneering responsible solutions to complex challenges.

Boulderscape, Inc.
5253 Old Dowd Road, Unit #1
Charlotte, NC 28208
949-370-8952
www.boulderscape.com

Boulderscape, Inc. is an installer of both structural and architectural shotcrete wall finishes nationwide. BSI specializes in over 126 styles of shotcrete wall finishes from geology, masonry, Class A flat wall finishes to artistic imprints. BSI has installed more than 11.4 million square feet of wall finishes over a variety of retaining wall systems such as soil nail walls, soldier pile walls, sheet pile, lagging, secant, caisson and cast in place walls.

CATLIN Engineers and Scientists
220 Old Dairy Road
Wilmington, NC 28405
910-452-5861
www.CatlinUSA.com

CATLIN provides Geotechnical, Environmental and Civil Engineering services.

Foothills Drilling Equipment Inc
111 Locust Street
Columbus, NC 28722
828-802-1015
www.foothillsequipment.com

East Coast distributor of TEI Rock Drills equipment as well as sales and distribution of mining and construction materials and supplies.

GeoStabilization International
4475 E 74th Avenue, Suite A
Commerce City, CO 80222
720-758-8713
www.geostabilization.com

Our passion is to develop and install innovative solutions that protect people and infrastructure from the dangers of geohazards. We specialize in emergency landslide repairs, rockfall mitigation, and grouting using design/build and design/build/warranty contracting. GeoStabilization's team includes some of the brightest and most dedicated professionals in the geohazard mitigation industry. Our expertise, proprietary tools, and worldwide partnerships allow us to repair virtually any slope stability or foundation problem in any geologic setting.

Hager-Richter Geoscience, Inc.
8 Industrial Way D10
Salem, NH 03079
603-370-7518
www.hager-richter.com

HAGER-RICHTER GEOSCIENCE, INC. is a well-established small business that specializes in Surface and Borehole Geophysics for Engineering applications. The firm has been in business since 1984, has earned a national reputation, and has a nationwide practice

IDS GeoRadar
14818 W. 6th Avenue, Unit A1
Golden, CO 80401
303-232-3047
www.idsgeoradar.com

IDS GeoRadar is a world leading developer of slope monitoring radars designed for real-time evaluation and characterization of slopes and structures as well as ground penetrating radars designed for locating buried utilities and concrete mapping. Based on microwave interferometry, submillimeter displacement can be measured up to four kilometers distance to identify areas of risk and hazard. What can be measured can be managed with IDS GeoRadar.

Signage Sponsor

Voss Signs
Po Box 553, 112 Fairgrounds Drive
Manlius, NY 13104
315-682-6418
www.vosssigns.com

Since 1965, Voss Signs, LLC has produced custom and stock signs for various customers that include: Forestry Professionals, Land Owners, State and Federal Government Agencies.

NECTOR
NATURAL HAZARD PROTECTION SYSTEMS
First and world's only high tensile strength hexagonal mesh
Nector HDMesh 3.65
Mesh size: 2,56 x 4,72 in DxH
Wire diameter: 0,118 in
Tensile strength of wire: ≥256 ksi
Anti-corrosion coating: 95%Zn5%Al eutectic
Anti-corrosion coating: ≥0,0435 lb/ft²
Tensile strength of mesh: ≥12,24 kips/ft
Punching resistance: ≥53,87 kips
Shearing-off resistance: ≥24,69 kips
Breaking strength of the mesh parallel to the slope surface: ≥ 13,4 kips
Mesh elongation: < 6%
Roll width: 9,84 ft
Roll length: up to 114,83 ft
Weight of mesh: 0,403 lbs/ft²
DOUBLE PLAITED PROTECTION
www.nector.biz

71st ANNUAL HIGHWAY GEOLOGY SYMPOSIUM
Exhibitors

Thank you to all participating exhibitors.

Access Limited Construction
1102 Pike Lane
Oceano, CA 93445
540-42-02678
www.accesslimitedconstruction.com

Acker Drill Co., Inc.
710 Shady Lane Road
S. Abington Township, PA 18411
570-586-2061
www.ackerdrill.com

Aero Aggregates of North America LLC
1500 Chester Pike
Eddystone, PA 19022
717-574-5614
www.aerofga.com

Ameritech Slope Constructors, Inc.
P.O. Box 2702
Asheville, NC 28802
828-633-6352
www.ameritech.pro

AMS
3803 Grahams Port Lane
Snellville, GA 30039
706-680-9015
www.ams-samplers.com

BGC Engineering, Inc.
701 12th Street, Suite 211
Golden, CO 80401
720-289-9430
www.bgcengineering.ca/

Boulderscape, Inc.
5253 Old Dowd Road, Unit #1
Charlotte, NC 28208
949-370-8952
www.boulderscape.com

CATLIN Engineers and Scientists
220 Old Dairy Road
Wilmington, NC 28405
910-452-5861
www.CatlinUSA.com

Central Mine Equipment Company
4215 Rider Trail North
Earth City, MO 63045
800-325-8827
www.cmeco.com

ESP Associates, Inc.
P.O. Box 7030
Charlotte, NC 28241
803-627-6756
www.espassociates.com

Foothills Drilling Equipment Inc
111 Locust Street
Columbus, NC 28722
828-802-1015
www.foothillsequipment.com

Gannett Fleming
207 Senate Avenue
Camp Hill, PA 17011
916-532-0658
www.gannettfleming.com

Geobrugg
8004 Windspray Drive
Summerfield, NC 27358
336-337-0945
www.geobrugg.com

GeoStabilization International
4475 E 74th Avenue, Suite A
Commerce City, CO 80222
720-758-8713
www.geostabilization.com

GEOKON
48 Spencer Street
Lebanon, NH 03766
603-448-1562
www.geokon.com

Gilson Company Inc
PO Box 200
Lewis Center, OH 43035-0200
800-444-1508
www.globalgilson.com

Hager-Richter Geoscience, Inc.
8 Industrial Way D10
Salem, NH 03079
603-370-7518
www.hager-richter.com

HDR
15 South Main Street, Suite 601
Greenville, SC 29601
(919) 985-8942
www.hdrinc.com

Hi-Tech Rockfall Construction, Inc.
PO Box 674
Forest Grove, OR 97116
503-357-6508
www.hitechrockfall.com

IDS GeoRadar
14818 W. 6th Avenue, Unit A1
Golden, CO 80401
303-232-3047
www.idsgeoradar.com

Landslide Technology
10250 SW Greenburg Road, Suite 111
Portland, OR 97223
503-452-1200
www.landslidetechnology.com

Maccaferri Inc.
10303 Governor Lane Blvd. 220
Williamsport, MD 21795-3115
301-641-8072
www.maccaferri.com

Nector Sp. z o.o.
ul. Szlak 65/502
Kraków, Poland 31-153
+48 12 631 85 50
https://nector.biz

Pyramid Geophysical Services
503 Industrial Avenue
Greensboro, NC 27406
336-335-3174
www.PyramidGeophysics.com

Rocscience
54 St. Patrick Street
Toronto, ON M5T 1V1
416-698-8217
www.rocscience.com

Williams Form Engineering Corp.
8165 Graphic Dr NE
Belmont, MI 49306
616-866-0815
www.williamsform.com

71st ANNUAL HIGHWAY GEOLOGY SYMPOSIUM

Abstracts & Papers

Monday, May 23, 2022

Monday, May 23, 2022 (Continued)

Wednesday, May 25, 2022

Wednesday, May 25, 2022 (Continued)

Wednesday, May 25, 2022 (Continued)

Using Geophysics to Evaluate the Results of a Grouting Program in Karstic Geology

Christopher Michael Mayer
Schnabel Engineering
3 Dickinson Drive, Suite 200, Chadds Ford, PA 19317
484-524-2968
cmayer@schnabel-eng.com

Jacob Sheehan, PGp
Schnabel Engineering
3 Dickinson Drive, Suite 200, Chadds Ford, PA 19317
865-255-5800
jsheehan@schnabel-eng.com

Mia Ann Painter, PG
Schnabel Engineering
3 Dickinson Drive, Suite 200, Chadds Ford, PA 19317
610-656-5536
mpainter@schnabel-eng.com

Jeremy J. Brown, PE
Schnabel Engineering
3 Dickinson Drive, Suite 200, Chadds Ford, PA 19317
484-467-3603
jbrown@schnabel-eng.com

Sarah McInnes, PE
PennDOT Engineering District 6-0
7000 Geerdes Boulevard, King of Prussia, PA 19406
610-205-6544
smcinnes@pa.gov

Prepared for the 71st Highway Geology Symposium, May 2022

Acknowledgements

The authors would like to thank the individuals/entities for their contributions in the work described:
Pennsylvania Department of Transportation, Engineering District 6-0
Joseph Thomas Coe - Temple University
Atsuhiro Muto – Temple University
Pourya Alidoust – Temple University
Katherine Kubiak – Temple University

Disclaimer

Statements and views presented in this paper are strictly those of the author(s), and do not necessarily reflect positions held by their affiliations, the Highway Geology Symposium (HGS), or others acknowledged above. The mention of trade names for commercial products does not imply the approval or endorsement by HGS.

ABSTRACT

In December 2021, Pennsylvania Department of Transportation (PennDOT) contractors completed karst treatment construction of about a 300 to 400 linear foot section of SR 3015 (Chemical Road), a four-lane road in Montgomery County, Pennsylvania. The project was prompted by over 6 months of recurring subsidence, sinkholes, and settlement on one side of the roadway, and then escalated to emergency status in March 2021 when a sinkhole developed on the opposite side of the roadway. As part of the evaluation and design phase of the project, multiple geophysical methods and test borings were conducted to characterize the karst conditions and aid in the design of the grouting program. Schnabel oversaw the geotechnical investigations and performed geophysical surveys; Temple University, partnering with Schnabel in a collaborative effort, conducted several additional geophysical research studies. A grouting program was then performed in the roadway to treat the sinkhole-prone soil/rock conditions. This included injecting about 22,000 cubic feet of grout into about 400 grout holes that were drilled through the soils and at least 2 ft into rock. Following the grouting program, some of the geophysical survey methods were repeated and compared.

This paper focuses on the results from one of the geophysical methods used: Multi-channel Analysis of Surface Waves (MASW). We present the comparisons between the pre- and post-grouting MASW results, as well as ground-truthing of the geophysics data using the test borings and grout holes. Geophysics is already commonly used to characterize the extent of karst features in the subsurface for roadway projects. This effort expands that knowledge base by following the project through initial site evaluation, ground improvement via a grouting program, and a follow-up geophysical survey to evaluate the results of the grouting program. Our overall goal is to use non-invasive geophysical methods to help develop and then evaluate the results of grouting in karstic geology.

INTRODUCTION

There is always a risk of hazards such as sinkhole and subsidence activity when infrastructure is constructed in karst areas. Sinkholes can form when carbonate rocks naturally dissolve from the process of groundwater circulating through them, causing the rock to breakdown and allowing open space, or voids, to develop. These voids can then collapse, causing the overlying soil to fill the void, which in turn causes the ground surface to subside.

A section of SR 3015 (Chemical Road) and the adjacent streambed of Plymouth Creek in Plymouth Township, Montgomery County, Pennsylvania, experienced subsidence and sinkhole activity. The project area is about 1,000 ft long, generally runs in the east-west direction, and is located between I-476 to the west of West Germantown Pike. Figure 1 shows an eastern portion of the United States compilation of geological formations, with the location of Chemical Road identified.

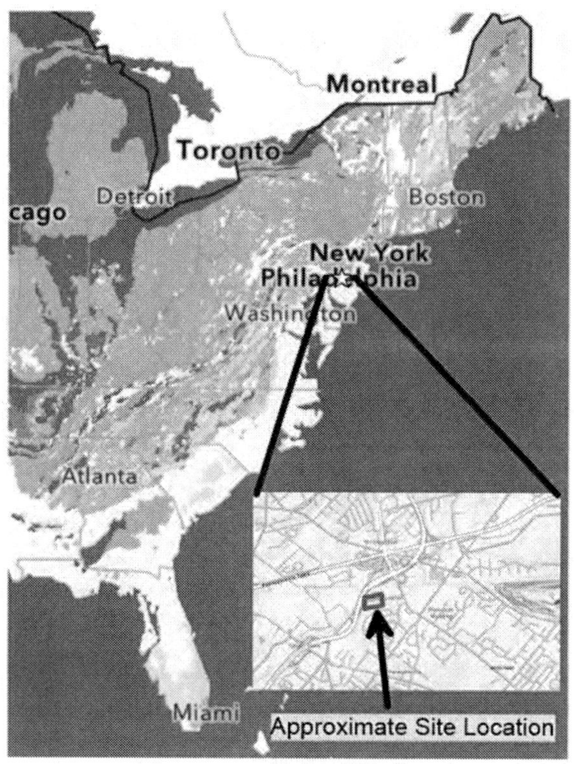

Figure 1 – Location Plan

At this location, the roadway is 5 lanes wide, with 2 southbound lanes (vehicle movement toward the west at the project site) and 3 northbound lanes (vehicle movement toward the east at the project site); the outside northbound lane is a dedicated off-ramp from NB I-476. The Average Daily Traffic (ADT) at this segment of road is nearly 27,000. The southbound lanes of Chemical Road are supported by a 15 to 20 ft tall embankment with a slope that varies from approximately 1.5H:1V to 2H:1V within the project area. At the base of the embankment is Plymouth Creek that is typically dry until after significant precipitation.

There are a considerable number of subsurface and overhead utilities running along Chemical Road. The subsurface utilities include a PECO gas line, a Plymouth Township sewer line, PECO electric conduits, active and abandoned water lines, communication lines, drainage pipes, and potential laterals of these utilities. There are also overhead power lines and poles located behind the existing guiderail at the top of the embankment. Two parallel gas transmission lines, owned by Texas Eastern Gas Pipeline, cross under Chemical Road diagonally near the intersection of the I-476 off-ramp.

TIMELINE OF EVENTS

The site has a history of karst activity, with several documented sinkholes and surface depressions identified on or near the site. Repairs to the outermost southbound lane were made by PennDOT in August 2020 due to a sinkhole at the base of the embankment and subsidence of the roadbed, curb, and guiderail. Following this treatment, subsidence continued, and the outside southbound lane was eventually closed.

During a site visit on December 3, 2020, Schnabel Engineering and PennDOT Engineering District 6-0 personnel observed a sinkhole within Plymouth Creek at the toe of the embankment. A geosynthetic liner in the creek was damaged and undermined in the area of the observed sinkhole. The recently repaired section of asphalt and concrete curb showed signs of additional subsidence, with cracking observed over a wide area of roadway surrounding the repaired pavement. Additionally, two overhead utility poles spaced about 300 ft apart appeared to have tilted toward Plymouth Creek, causing their guywires to become loose. Figure 2 is a picture taken during backfill of a sinkhole.

Figure 2 – Geologic Map of the Project Area

On February 28, 2021, a new sinkhole event in the outside northbound lane (in the vicinity of the subsided area in the southbound lane) caused the NB I-476 off-ramp lane to be closed. Due to continued observed subsidence on the roadway, PennDOT initiated the closure of Chemical Road on March 25, 2021, and classified the remediation design as an "emergency" project. PennDOT initiated an emergency geotechnical and geophysical investigation to be conducted, led by Schnabel, in order to develop sinkhole treatment recommendations.

Schnabel began the pre-grout geophysical investigation on March 8, 2021. In early April 2021, a test boring program was initiated based on the data from the geophysical investigation. After the geotechnical and geophysical investigation, a Limited Mobility Grout (LMG) plan was developed. Bid documents were developed; the project was advertised and awarded to Road-Con, Inc. Road-Con sub-contracted Keller – North American to perform LMG. Verification borings were drilled during construction. Schnabel then conducted a post-grouting geophysical investigation between December 12 and 15, 2021, before the roadway officially reopened to the public on December 21, 2021.

SITE GEOLOGY

The site is located within the Piedmont Lowland section of the Piedmont Physiographic Province and is underlain by the Cambrian Age rock of the Ledger Formation (€l) (Kochanov 2016). In the surrounding area, the Chickies (€ch), Stockton(₸ s), and Elbrook Formations (€e) are mapped and consist of mudstone and siltstone, crystalline quartzite, and dolomite, respectively. Figure 2 includes the approximate site location overlain on a bedrock geologic map.

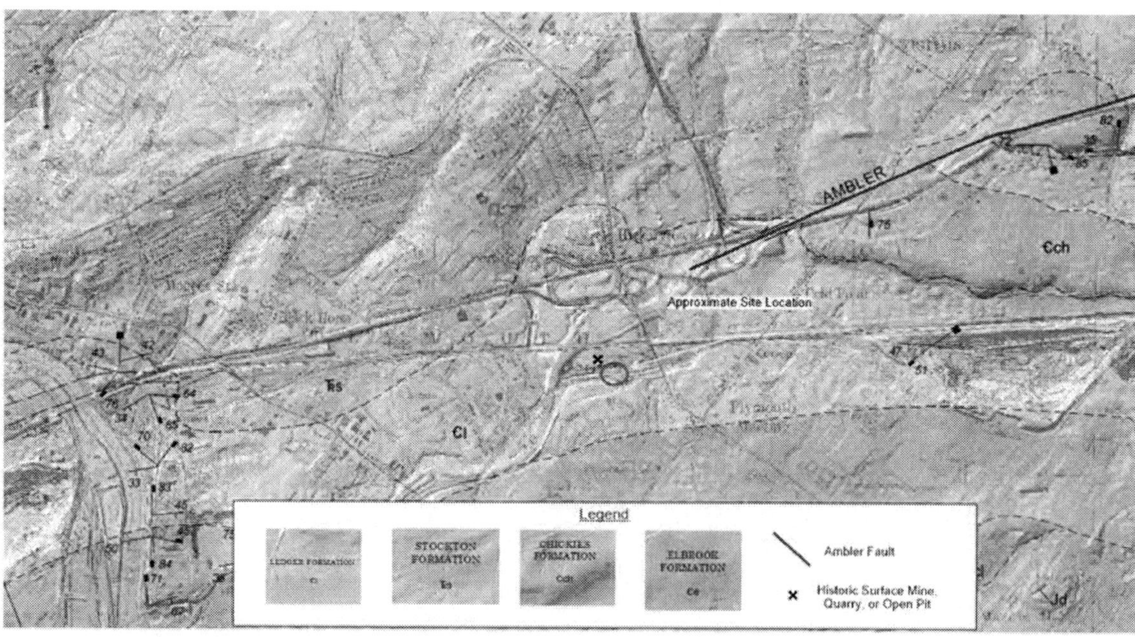

Figure 3 – Geologic Map of the Project Area

The Ledger Formation consists of dolomite, which is a carbonate rock and is commonly susceptible to chemical weathering and karst feature development such as deeply weathered fracture zones, pinnacled bedrock surface, soft soil adjacent to the bedrock, and sinkholes. According to Karst Features in Pennsylvania, provided by the Pennsylvania Department of Conservation and Natural Resources (PADCNR), approximately 160 karst features (surface depressions and sinkholes) are mapped within about a 1.5-mile radius in this formation.

Based on our observations, the Plymouth Creek streambed is typically dry between storm events (known as a losing stream); this indicates that groundwater is deeper than the bottom of the stream bed. During storm events, water was observed flowing from the creek into sinkholes located in the creek bed. Groundwater is likely flowing along the regional trend, and fluctuations in groundwater levels can cause bedrock solutioning and soil voids that can contribute to the development of sinkholes below and adjacent to the stream.

PRE-GROUT GEOPHYSICAL AND GEOTECHNICAL INVESTIGATIONS

Schnabel developed and oversaw a subsurface exploration and field testing program to identify the subsurface stratigraphy underlying the site and to evaluate the geotechnical properties of the materials encountered. As part of this program, Schnabel conducted a geophysical investigation to characterize the karst conditions before geotechnical drilling explorations were started.

Pre-Grout Geophysical Investigation

The pre-grouting geophysical investigation included three methods: electrical resistivity imaging (ERI), multi-channel analysis of surface waves (MASW), and ground-penetrating radar (GPR). Schnabel personnel collected ERI data in the adjacent Plymouth Creek, in the outside southbound lane, and in the northbound shoulder of the off-ramp from I-476. MASW data was collected in the outside northbound lane and in the southbound lanes. GPR data was collected in all lanes.

This paper focuses on the MASW data and interpretations. MASW was used to estimate the presence of, and the lateral and vertical extent of, soft soil zones and voids, and to get a general sense of the depth to massive rock. Shear wave velocity is generally correlated to soil stiffness; however, there is no direct correlation between particular shear wave velocities and N-values. The descriptions of soft and stiff soil based on shear wave velocity are relative comparisons, not an indication of the actual density or consistency of the soil.

Schnabel personnel collected MASW data using a Geometrics, Inc., Geode, 24-channel seismograph and twenty-four 4.5-Hz geophones spaced 5 ft apart. Data was collected using a common-midpoint arrangement with the energy source offset from the end of the geophone array and using a slide-along method with a towed landstreamer. We conducted trials on site to determine the optimal offset and determined that a 15-ft offset provided good waveform development and high-quality results. The energy source was the PEG-40, which is a 100-lb accelerated weighted hammer that strikes a steel plate on the ground surface. The seismic data was recorded on the laptop computer that controlled the seismograph. We collected about 2,200 linear feet of MASW along four lines during the pre-grout phase.

Data analysis was conducted using SurfSeis version 6 by the Kansas Geological Survey. The processing flow consisted of generating plots of energy amplitude as a function of frequency and velocity (known as overtone records) for each shot location. These overtone records were then used to pick dispersion curves that represent the dependence of velocity on frequency. Each dispersion curve was then used to generate a one-dimensional (1D) velocity sounding that best matches the curve. Finally, the 1D velocity soundings from each source/receiver array location were combined to form a 2D cross-section model of the subsurface shear wave velocity for each MASW line to a depth of about 55 ft.

Geotechnical Investigation

Test borings were drilled in targeted locations based on the results of the geophysical surveys in order to better correlate the geophysical data and investigate potential karst conditions. Figure 3 is a plan view location of the pre-grout geophysical survey and geotechnical borings.

Standard Penetration Testing (SPT) and split-spoon sampling were performed continuously in the borings in accordance with ASTM D1586. NQ-size rock coring was performed to the termination depth of the borings.

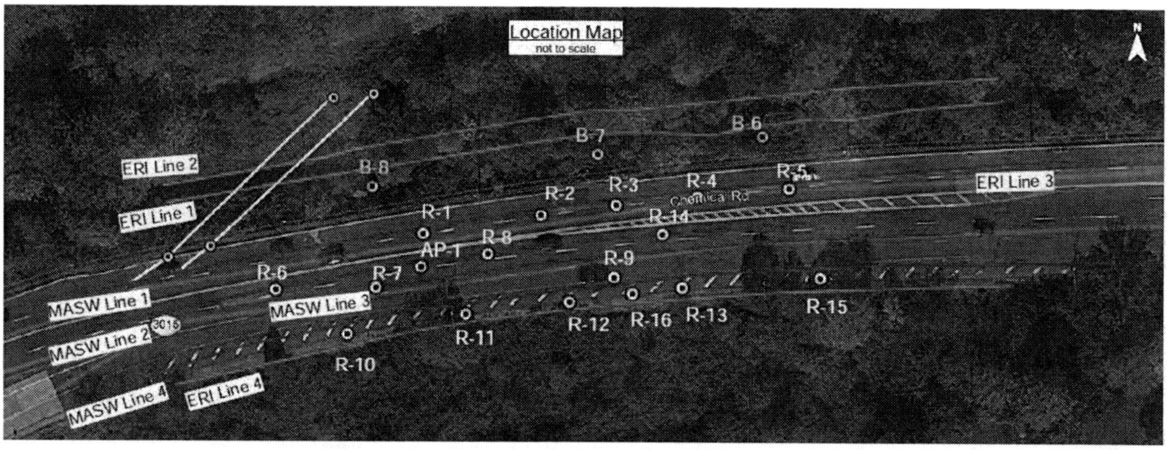

Figure 4 – Plan View of the Pre-Grout Geophysical and Test Boring Locations

The pre-grout MASW results and test boring data both indicated that the depth to rock was variable across the area investigated and ranged from about 10 to 55 ft deep or greater. The geotechnical test boring investigation was conducted after initial MASW data interpretation was completed, and borings were targeted to areas that were interpreted as possible zones of karst, potential sinkhole development, and potential shallow rock. Figure 4 shows the initial pre-grout MASW results with simplified logs from the test borings overlaid.

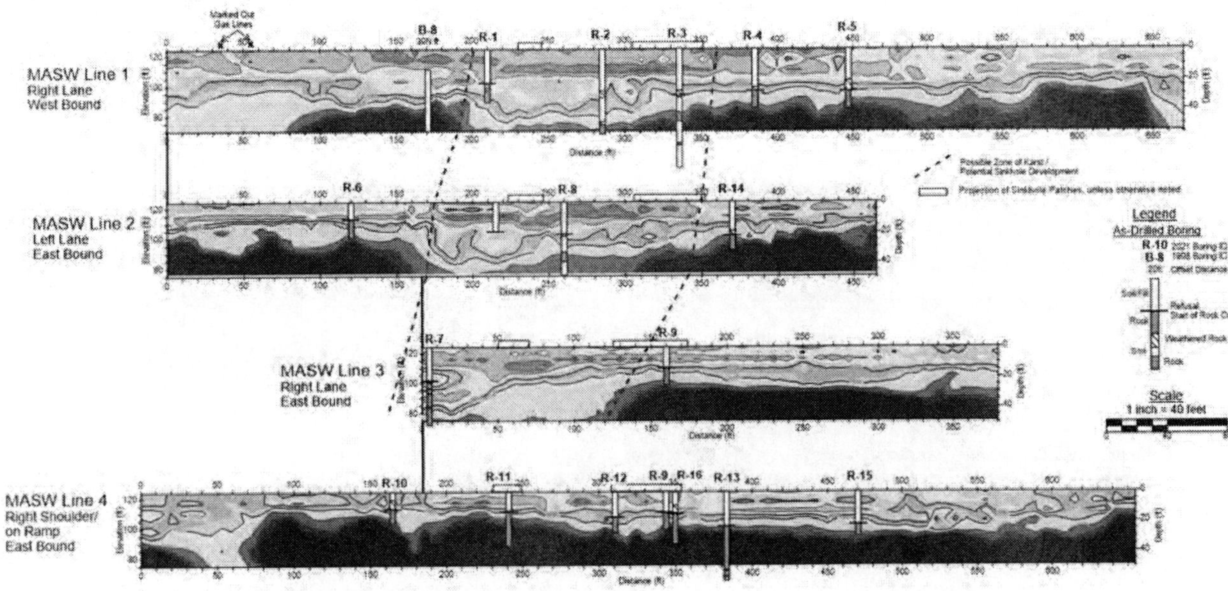

Figure 5 – Pre-Grout MASW Results, Profile View

The initial pre-grout MASW results generally indicated a highly variable subsurface profile typical of the active karst region within the areas where surficial karst features have been observed, with more uniform subsurface conditions located outside this zone. We interpreted the top of rock to be generally between the 1,400 to 1,800 ft/s shear wave velocity contours based on correlation with the drilling. The results from a portion of the MASW Line 1 are included in Figure 5 and show the variations in velocity that are likely from the karst beneath the road. We overlaid the geotechnical borings and used symbols of the soils or rock that was encountered. White colored portions of the boring stick represent residual soils, gray represents dolomite that was cored and a thin black line over the dolomite represents where rock was first encountered. A diagonal line polygon represents areas of no recovery in soils (see key in Figure 4).

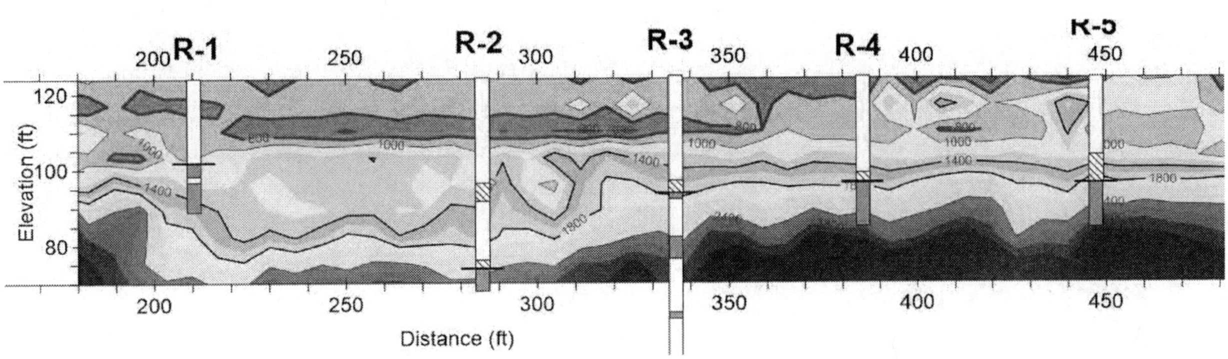

Figure 6 – MASW Line 1 Pre-Grout Velocity Contours (ft/s) with Geotechnical Borings

Another way to look at the pre-grout velocity structure is to examine the full-depth average velocity models gridded into a plan view map, as shown in Figure 6. This shows a zone of lower velocity values that extend over much of the area. This zone is outlined in a black hatched line and is the low velocity zone boundary from the pre-grout MASW; this will be referred to herein as the low velocity zone. For visualization purposes, we have included a dotted gray line that accounts for the locations of observed sinkholes along the creek bed; however, the boundary is an estimate only based on the trend of sinkholes in the road and stream and on our ERI results.

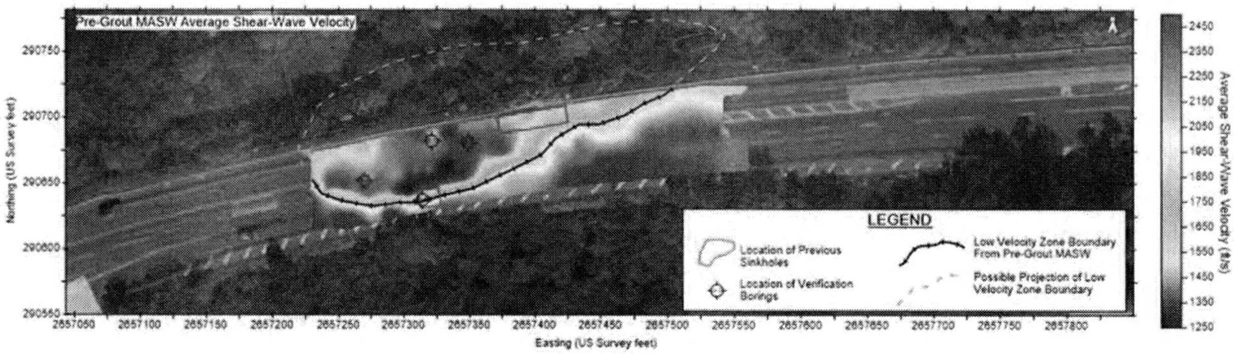

Figure 7 – Pre-grout Full-Depth Average Velocity

KARST TREATMENT PLAN

Based on data from the pre-grout geophysical and geotechnical investigation, Schnabel recommended a LMG program. The intent of the LMG program was to treat the sinkhole-prone soil/rock conditions underlying the roadway and stabilize the northern roadway embankment in order to reduce the likelihood of future sinkhole activity and subsidence impacting Chemical Road at this location. The LMG treatment could be performed by locating grout holes around the dense pattern of utilities at the site with utility locating and monitoring provisions. Battered LMG holes were used to assist with stabilization of the embankment and threading under utilities. Additionally, spot sinkhole plug repairs were recommended at observed sinkhole and soft-spot locations identified within the streambed and on the roadway.

LMG PROGRAM

The LMG program consisted of 273 primary grout holes, 83 secondary grout holes, and 42 tertiary grout holes. Generally, the primary grout holes were situated in a grid pattern with an approximate 10-ft spacing. The spacing was modified to fit the road curvature and locations were adjusted to provide adequate clearance from utilities. A summary of the LMG operations follows:

- A Gill Beetle rig was used with a 4-inch diameter down-hole hammer and drilled holes to depths ranging from 10 to 127 ft. The holes were generally drilled "open-hole" and cased at the time of grouting. Where the top of rock was less than 50 ft, the holes were generally terminated at least 5 ft into rock; where the top of rock was greater than 50 ft, the holes generally terminated in 2 ft of rock.
- A Maxim Link-Belt LS-138H II crane, Comacchio MC 28 rig, and Klemm Bohrtechnik KR 801-3GS rig was used for grouting operations. The grout was pumped through hoses

and risers connected to the crane or rigs and down a 3.38-inch inner diameter flush-joint threaded casing for the two rigs, and a 3.5-inch inner diameter for the crane stinger.

- In general, grout was injected under pressure as the casing was extracted in 2-ft stages. The grout injection rates were limited to 2 cubic feet per minute (cfm). Each 2-ft stage was terminated based on the grout volumes, pressures, and/or grout and heaving.
- Secondary and tertiary holes were added in areas where the adjacent primary holes were observed to have relatively higher grout take volumes per stage.
- Battered grout holes, with batters of 1H:3V to 1H:4V, were used along the northern edge of the embankment and to thread under utilities.

Schnabel provided full-time on-site construction inspection and observation of the drilling and LMG operations to establish necessary drilling depths; verify casing installation; observe the slump testing of the grout; and observe the grout pressures, volumes, and surface movement to assess when a 2-ft stage was completed.

Grout volumes per hole varied substantially across the site, ranging from 4.0 to 758.5 cf. The site contained areas of shallow rock, where relatively lower grout-takes per hole were observed. Other areas contained deeper rock and karst features (rock pinnacles, open voids, soil-filled voids, etc.) where relatively higher grout-takes per hole were recorded.

Post-Grout Verification Test Borings

The verification test boring program included 4 borings to investigate the presence of grout, and to identify lateral migration of the grout, particularly at depths with high grout takes. The presence of grout in the rock core samples retrieved during drilling helped to evaluate if voids or soil-filled zones identified within the rock mass were improved.

Pre-Grout MASW vs. Grouting Program

We compared the pre-grout average shear-wave velocity to total grout volumes; this can be seen in the plan view on . Most of the higher grout volume is located within the low velocity boundary zone.

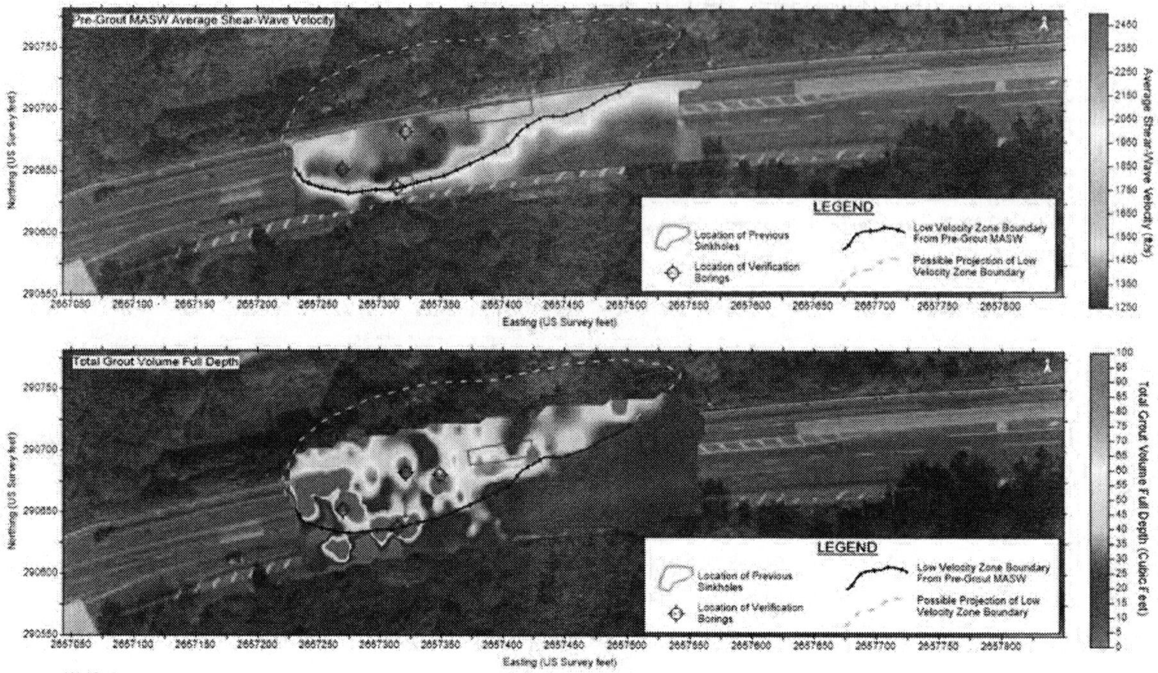

Figure 8 – Pre-Grout Velocity Compared to Grout Volumes

There is good correlation between the pre-grout low velocity zone boundary to grout volumes in most of the site. Outside this low velocity zone boundary area, the average pre-grout velocity is higher and the corresponding grout volumes are lower, which we interpret as less grout being injected due to higher initial densities in the soil and rock.

POST-GROUT GEOPHYSICAL INVESTIGATION

Schnabel conducted a post-grout MASW survey to evaluate the effect of the grouting program on the karstic subsurface conditions under the roadway. It is expected that grout injected under pressure filled void spaces within the soil/rock and densified the loose/soft soils beneath the roadway. This should have increased the bulk density of the soils/rock by adding both mass and strength to the loose/soft soils and void spaces. An increase in bulk density and strength of the subsurface materials would result in a higher shear-wave velocity compared to the pre-grout shear-wave velocity. MASW was used for this comparison.

Schnabel and Temple University personnel partnered to collect data. Temple collected geophysical data for their own pre- and post-grout comparisons, including microgravity and horizontal to vertical spectral ratio (HVSR) data. The analysis of these datasets is ongoing and the results are not included in this paper.

Figure 8 shows locations of the pre- and post-grout MASW lines, grouting holes, and observed sinkhole/subsidence locations. During post-grouting data collection, we attempted to re-occupy the same locations of our pre-grout MASW survey as closely as possible. However, small shifts of a few feet occurred due to various factors. The inherit nature of the MASW method is to measure bulk properties within a zone beneath and to the sides of the actual line location, making the small variations in location less critical.

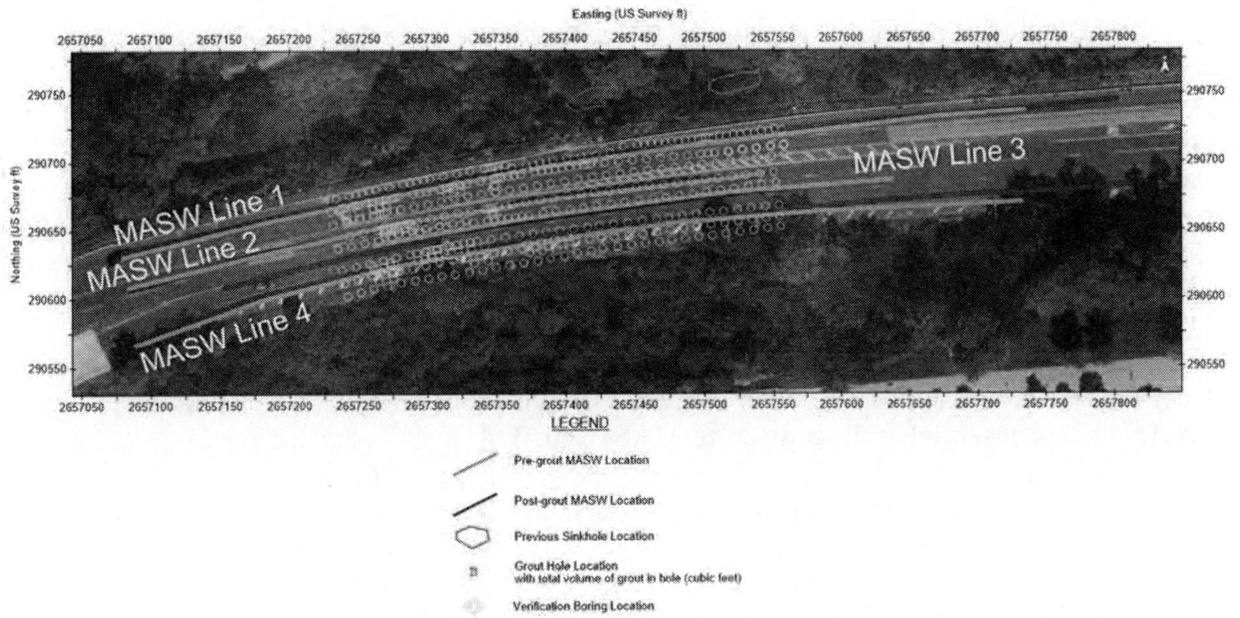

Figure 9 – Post- and Pre- Grout MASW Location Plan

Schnabel collected the post-grout MASW data in a similar fashion to the pre-grout investigation with three differences: (1) The lines were located along the same alignments, but some of the post-grout lines were extended due to differing access restrictions at the time of pre-grout data collection. (2) We added a second 24-channel Geode, so data was collected using a 48-channel array, but still with 4.5-Hz geophones in a landstreamer configuration. (3) For MASW Lines 1 and 4, data was collected using 48 geophones spaced 1 meter apart with an offset of 5 meters. For the MASW method, this essentially the same as the 15-ft offset used in the pre-grout survey. The different arrangement and spacing of the geophones were chosen to match data that was collected by Temple during their research efforts so that data sets could be shared and used for both their research activities and Schnabel's evaluations. During processing of the MASW data along Lines 1 and 4, only 36 geophones were used in order to match the array length used in the pre-grout survey. Approximately 2,380 linear feet of MASW was collected along 4 lines during the post-grout phase.

GEOPHYSICAL COMPARATIVE RESULTS

Following the post-grout MASW, the pre-grout data was reprocessed by the same data processer and parameters as the post-grout in order to ensure as much consistency as possible between the two datasets. The initial and reprocessed pre-grout MASW were very similar to each other with only minor variations. While the data processing and modeling were conducted using Surfseis, much of the analysis and visualization of the results were conducted using Geosoft Oasis montaj version 2021.2 (Geosoft). This process includes importing the modeled velocity results from both the pre- and post-grout MASW survey. These results were combined with GPS information and the creation of 3D velocity models for both phases of the survey. The average velocity over the full-depth range that was observed in both the pre- and post-grout MASW was calculated and gridded using the minimum curvature gridding method.

The 3D velocity models were sampled based on common x, y, and z locations. A point-by-point difference in velocity was calculated by subtracting the pre-grout velocity value from the post-grout velocity value. These difference values were used to generate a 3D percent difference in velocity model, along with an average difference over the full-depth range.

Along with the results from the MASW survey, the recorded grout takes for each segment of each grout hole were compiled using Geosoft. This allowed for the generation of a 3D grout take model and 2D plan view maps showing both the total grout take over the full-depth range and an average grout take per linear foot stage. This grout information was combined with the velocity and velocity difference information from the MASW surveys to gain an understand of how grout take compared to both the pre-grout MASW survey and the change in velocity values observed in the post-grout MASW survey.

Figure 9 shows the pre- and post-grout MASW average shear-wave velocity results. In general, within the full area covered by the grouting program, the average velocity increased from 1,970 ft/sec to 2,042 ft/sec, a change of 70 ft/s which is about a 4% increase. Most of the areas with similar velocities correspond with the injection of shallow and gravity-fed grout and are generally to the south and east sides of the grouted area. We interpret the results of this data as showing the grout injected in these areas was not enough to significantly change the velocity.

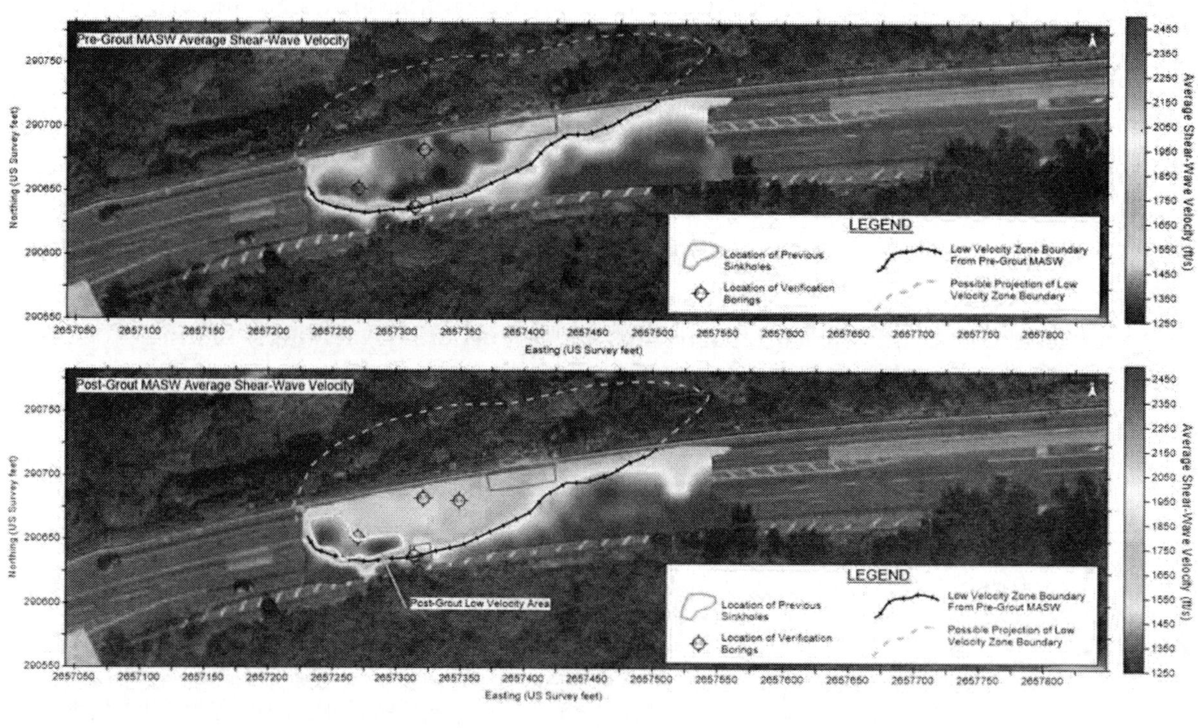

Figure 10 – Shear-Wave Velocity Comparison: Top is Pre-Grout; Bottom is Post-Grout.

The MASW results do show a more significant increase in velocity in the area referred to as the "low velocity zone boundary from pre-grout MASW." This area is also where the greatest amount of grout volumes were injected. Table 1 shows average velocity values for the full grout area, the low velocity zone within the grout area, and the zone outside of the low velocity zone.

Table 1 – Comparison of Velocity Values Before and After Grouting				
Area	Average Pre-grout Velocity (ft/s)	Average Post-grout Velocity (ft/s)	Change in Velocity (ft/s)	% Increase
Grouted Area Average	1,972	2,042	70	4%
Low Velocity Zone	1,479	1,634	155	10%
Outside of Low Velocity Zone	2,179	2,187	8	0%

The table clearly shows the effect the grouting program had on the subsurface velocity values was focused on the low velocity zone, where the average velocity increased by 10% compared to essentially no change in velocity outside this zone.

Within the low velocity zone, there is a smaller area identified as "Post-Grout Low Velocity Area" in Figure 9, outlined in white, where the velocity did not increase after grouting. This low velocity area is observable in the pre- and post-grout MASW results for Lines 2 and 3 at a depth of about 25 to 40 ft. Figure 10 presents the Line 3 pre-grout and post-grout MASW results with B-3, a verification boring, overlaid. The profiles are aligned with each other and with B-3.

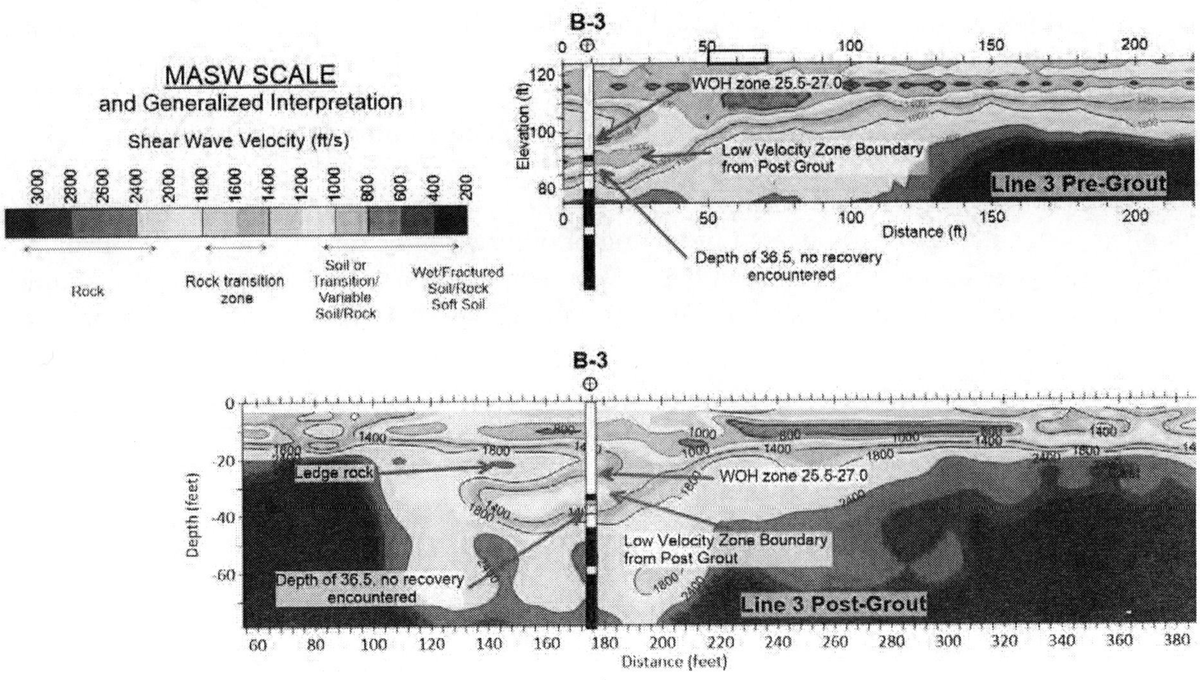

Figure 11 – MASW Compared to Verification Boring B-3: Top is Pre-Grout; Bottom is Post-Grout

We see that within the post-grout low velocity zone the velocity has not changed significantly. Verification Boring B-3 is located just to the outside of the "Post-Grout Low Velocity Area." The log of B-3 shows that from a 25 to 39 ft depth there are intermittent soft soils and zones of no recovery. From 25.5 to 27 ft, there is a sand layer where weight-of-hammer (WOH) material noted, followed by N-values of 3 or less between 27 ft and 30 ft. Continuing in depth, a thin dolomite layer is observed from 32 ft to 34.5 ft, followed by grout from 34.5 ft to 36.5 ft, and then a zone of no recovery between 36.5 ft and 39.5 ft. Below this, there is a sand layer from 39.5 to 44.5 ft, and dolomite is encountered again at 44.5 ft. While the location and specific depths from B-3 do not line up exactly with the post-grout low velocity zone, this is expected because of variations in resolution between test borings and MASW, and the offset of B-3 from the low velocity zone in highly variable subsurface conditions. In this general area, grout drill holes encountered rock at approximate depths of 9 to 16 ft below ground surface. These grout holes were generally terminated 5 ft into rock in accordance with the grouting plan. Based on the grout drill hole data, the "Post-Grout Low Velocity Area" may be situated below a rock ledge; therefore, this low velocity area was likely not grouted since the drilling refusal criteria was achieved.

SUMMARY

There was very good correlation between the pre-grout MASW and the areas that had high grout takes. The high grout takes were in the low velocity zones. MASW was an effective tool for identifying the low velocity zones and for planning the extent of the grouting program.

The areas with the highest velocity differences between pre- and post-grouting MASW correlate well with the areas of highest grout takes. The MASW velocities increased by about 10% between the pre- and post-grout surveys in the areas of high grout takes, indicating a generalized densification/strengthening of the subsurface in the grouted areas. The region outside the area with higher grout takes showed no significant change in the average velocity.

The MASW shows some localized high and low anomalies that are not easily correlated with other data and may be artifacts of modeling or otherwise unexplained results in the data. However, the generalized trends seen in the comparison of the pre- and post MASW with the grouting show good general correlations of improvement of soils in low velocity areas measured prior to grouting.

Comparison of the results from the verification borings with the post-grout MASW profiles generally show that grout was encountered where expected, which supports the interpretation that the grout improved the soils.

Collecting detailed grout take data, verification borings, and a post-grout MASW survey provide more data about the effect of the grouting program on subsurface conditions than any of these elements would alone. Where the grout take data and verification borings give detailed discrete location data, the use of geophysics helped demonstrate the broader effects of the grouting and data on the subsurface conditions after grouting. While shear-wave velocity is not a direct measurement of density or strength of the subsurface, it does give a good general sense of both in order to compare pre- and post-grout conditions.

Additionally, the post-grout MASW survey helped identify localized zones where the grout holes may have terminated in a rock ledge and did not encounter soft zones or voids beneath the rock ledge. This could help focus ongoing surveillance of the roadway and allow for earlier detection and more targeted repairs, if necessary.

REFERENCES

Jones, W. K. "Physical Structure of the Epikarst." *Acta Carsologica,* Vol. 42 (2-3), Carlsbad, NM, 2013. (https://doi.org/10.3986/ac.v42i2-3.672)

Kochanov, W.E. Geology of part of the Chester Valley area, Chester, Delaware, Montgomery, and Philadelphia Counties, Pennsylvania: Pennsylvania Geological Survey, 4th ser., Open File Report OFGA 16-01.0 (2016).

Kochanov, W.E., Lichtinger, J.F., and Becker, M. Sinkholes and karst-related features of Montgomery County, Pennsylvania: Pennsylvania Geological Survey, 4th ser., Open File Report 93-02 (1993).

Efficient Rock Slope Design during Construction of a State Highway Safety Enhancement Project

State Highway 55, Idaho

Luke Ferguson, PE
McMillen Jacobs Associates
2000 SW First Avenue, Suite 410
Portland, OR 97201
(503)-446-2962
ferguson@mcmjac.com

Ethan Guzek, GIT
McMillen Jacobs Associates
1011 Western Ave, Suite 706
Seattle, WA 98104
(206)-209-1394
guzek@mcmjac.com

Prepared for the 71st Highway Geology Symposium, May 2022

Acknowledgments

The author would like to thank the following individuals for their contributions in the work presented in this paper:

Bill Gates – McMillen Jacobs Associates
Jim Struthers – McMillen Jacobs Associates
Alex Deduck – Idaho Transportation Department

Disclaimer

Statements and views presented in this paper are strictly those of the author(s), and do not necessarily reflect positions held by their affiliations, the Highway Geology Symposium (HGS), or others acknowledged above. The mention of trade names for commercial products does not imply the approval or endorsement by HGS.

Copyright Notice

ABSTRACT

In summer of 2020, the Idaho Transportation Department (ITD) began construction work on a safety-enhancement project of SH-55 between Smiths Ferry and Round Valley along the North Fork of the Payette River approximately 50 miles north of Boise. Work to widen and straighten the road included excavating 9 distinct cut slopes in weathered granodiorite using controlled blasting techniques along the approximately one-mile section of roadway. In the spring of 2021, a rockslide from a cut slope under construction impacted the roadway and closed the highway for over a week. Soon after that rockslide a wedge at a different cut also failed, posing a serious risk to workers. McMillen Jacobs Associates (MJA), which had been contributing to the project as a blasting consultant, was retained by ITD following the slope failures to redesign the rock cuts to reduce the potential for additional failures and maintain a safe working environment. MJA arrived on site in March 2021 and in a condensed time frame conducted geologic assessment and mapping using rope access safety techniques. MJA then performed kinematic stability analyses and slope redesigns at each cut slope based on mapped discontinuity orientations to recommend slope cut angles. As cuts were excavated and final slopes exposed, MJA identified potentially unstable rock planes and wedges and, through a combination of field inspection and limit equilibrium analyses, developed appropriate mitigation strategies. This paper presents the techniques, strategy, and workflow utilized to provide a meaningful slope redesign during active construction and within project constraints.

INTRODUCTION

State Highway 55 (SH-55) is an approximately 150-mile-long highway in western Idaho that connects Marsing, ID with New Meadows, ID, intersecting US-95 at both ends of its alignment. In the summer of 2020, the Idaho Transportation Department (ITD) began construction work on a safety-enhancement project of SH-55 between the community of Smiths Ferry and Round Valley along the North Fork of the Payette River approximately 50 miles north of Boise. This section of roadway is heavily used by recreationists from Boise and its surrounding communities to access fishing, camping, hiking, rafting, and snow sport opportunities along the North Fork of the Payette River and in Valley County. This section of SH-55 is also utilized when traveling between the resort town of McCall and the population center of Boise.

The section of roadway being improved by this safety-enhancement project is approximately 1 mile long. This highway section is tightly constrained by slope cuts on the west side of the road and river on the east side of the road. The combination of a narrow roadway and tight curves in this highway section has proven to be especially dangerous to motorists, and the section has seen a high rate of significant and fatal accidents. The location of the 1-mile highway project corridor is shown in Figure 1.

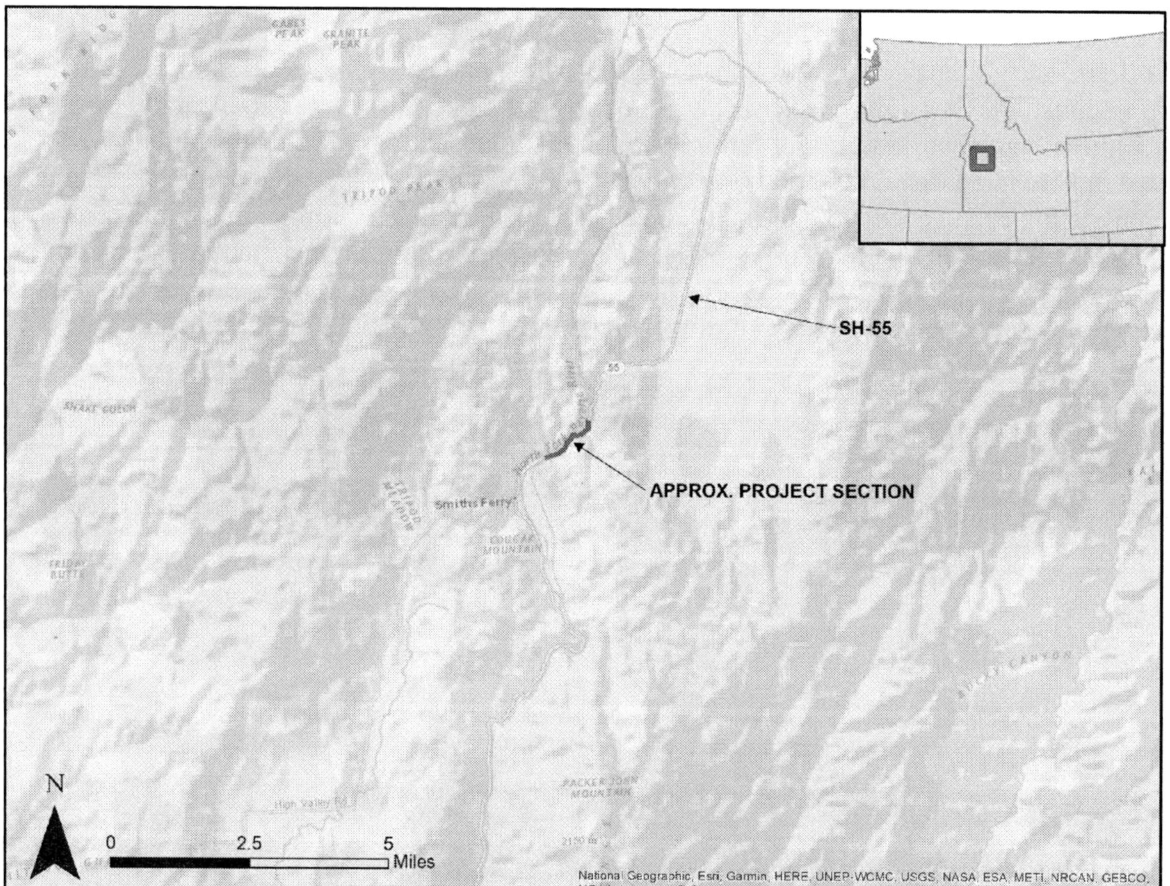

Figure 1 – Project Location

Safety enhancement work at the site consists predominantly of widening and straightening the highway through a combination of slope excavation on the upslope side of the road and construction of retaining walls on the downslope side of the road. This work includes excavating 9 distinct cut slopes (Cut Slope 1 through Cut Slope 9) in granodiorite using controlled blasting techniques. The 9 cuts range in height from approximately 40 feet to 110 feet and in aspect from southeast to southwest. The brows of the cut slopes are generally vegetated with mature conifers, shrubs, and grasses. A representative picture of a cut slope at the project area is provided in Figure 2.

Figure 2 – SH-55 in Project Section

Cut Slope Failures

In the spring of 2021, a rockslide occurred at Cut Slope 9 that was under construction and slide debris impacted the roadway, closing the highway to traffic for over a week while crews cleared the highway of the debris (Figure 3). In a matter of days after this rockslide, another slope under construction, Cut Slope 5, experienced a slope failure that posed a serious risk to workers. The pattern of unintended rockslides prompted ITD to retain McMillen Jacobs Associates (MJA), which was already contributing to the project as a blasting consultant, to redesign the rock cuts and construction sequencing to reduce the potential for additional failures and maintain a safe working environment. MJA mobilized to the site in March 2021, at the beginning of the second construction season, to begin geologic reconnaissance followed quickly by slope redesign.

Figure 3 – Rockslide at Cut 9

Objective

The redesign of the cut slopes included detailed kinematic and limit equilibrium analyses. However, the objective of this paper is not to present comprehensive analytical assumptions, inputs, and results. It is rather to present the techniques, strategy, and workflow utilized to provide a meaningful slope redesign during active construction and within project constraints.

GEOLOGIC SETTING

Regional Geology

The project is located on the western edge of the Atlanta Lobe of the large and silicic intrusive Idaho Batholith, which encompasses much of central Idaho. The Atlanta Lobe exhibits relatively homogenous composition and structure and was emplaced between 83 and 67 million years ago (*1*).

Detailed geologic mapping of the area was completed at a 1:24,000 scale in 2017 by Schmidt, et al (2). The regional geology is composed predominantly of Cretaceous intrusive granitic bedrock and Quaternary surficial deposits of eroded granitic rock deposited by rivers and streams in low-lying areas. The area of the project site is mapped as light gray, fine to medium grained Cretaceous biotite granodiorite. The granodiorite is dated to be on the order of 88 million years old (slightly older than the main lobe of the Idaho batholith) and weathers characteristically into large boulders known as corestones *(2.*

SITE INSPECTIONS AND HISTORY

Slope Failure Inspection

Each of the 9 rock slope cuts was initially designed, bid, and awarded per the contract plans with 0.25H:1V (76°) cut slopes to be achieved by blasting and excavation in order to provide space to widen and straighten SH-55. Construction then began, but as discussed in the "Introduction" above, early attempts at constructing cut slopes according to this design resulted in partial slope failures at multiple locations. This prompted ITD to contact MJA regarding redesigning the cut slopes, without a pause in construction activities. Upon inspection, MJA observed that the rockslides appeared to have failed primarily on adverse dipping joints that had been daylighted by progressive cut slope excavation (an example is provided in Figure 4). After observing exposed fracture planes at multiple cut slope locations, MJA concluded that continuing to excavate the cut slopes at 0.25H:1V would result in additional fractures daylighting, and subsequently additional slope failures.

Figure 4 – Partial Slope Failure During Construction at Cut 5

Geologic Mapping and Rock Mass Characterization

At the time of the initial MJA site inspection, excavation of the cut slopes was at various stages of completeness. In several areas, controlled blasting and excavation had not begun, but in other areas the cut slope was nearly complete. At most of the project cut slopes, 1 to 2 lifts (approximately 15–30 feet vertically) had been blasted and excavated.

General Field Observations

The project site extends along a highway corridor approximately 1 mile in length and consists of 9 rock cuts ranging in height from approximately 40 to 110 feet. The rock type and chemistry are consistent throughout this corridor, but the corridor is atypically variable in its state of weathering, strength, and fracture patterns. Exposed rock in several of the cut slopes consists of intact, excellent quality, strong granodiorite that is only slightly weathered. Exposed rock in other cut slopes consists of extremely weak, poor quality, decomposed granodiorite.

Upon initial site inspection in March, winter snow was still present at the site, though melting rapidly. Groundwater could be seen seeping from fractures and discontinuities at several locations in rock cuts throughout the project corridor. As spring progressed into summer these isolated seepage locations dried up, and by midsummer groundwater seepage was no longer observed in rock cuts throughout the project corridor.

In order to field map the proposed cut slope locations, horizontal scanlines were performed from the ground and vertical scanlines were performed by utilizing rope access techniques (Figure 5). The following data were collected during field mapping:

- Discontinuity characteristics including:
  - Orientations of discontinuities collected with a CLAR® geo-stratigraphic compass
  - Spacing of discontinuities
  - Condition of discontinuities
- Uniaxial compressive strength (UCS) estimates utilizing a geologic hammer, based on published tables by Hoek and Bray, 1981 (*3*)
- Rock Quality Designation (RQD) utilizing Palmström's method (*4*)
- Peak frictional strength estimates utilizing the tilt method
- Extent of weathering
- Groundwater conditions
- Estimates of Rock Mass Rating (RMR) based on tables published by Bieniawski (1989) (*5*)

Figure 5 – Utilizing Rope Access Techniques for Field Mapping

Field Observations

Proposed cut slopes at the site varied from approximately 175 feet to 575 feet in length and approximately 40 feet to 110 feet in height. Exposed rock at the sites varied from slightly weathered to completely weathered granodiorite, with existing slope inclinations ranging from approximately 60° to 80°.

Geomechanical Rock Mass Characteristics

Rock mass characteristics were surprisingly variable between the 9 cut slopes across the approximately 1-mile length of highway. Detailed observations at each distinct cut slope are beyond the scope of this paper, but ranges in rock mass characteristics observed at each cut slope are provided in Table 1.

Table 1: Rock Mass Characteristics

Parameter	Range of Values
Rock Strength	R0 to R4 (extremely weak to strong)
RMR	42 to 79 (Class III fair quality rock to Class II good quality rock)
RQD	23 to 94 (poor quality rock to excellent quality rock)
Joint Spacing	1 foot to 6 feet (closely to widely spaced)
Weathering	Slightly to completely weathered
Structure	Blocky

Peak Friction

Tilt tests were conducted on 36 representative samples to estimate the peak frictional strength of the rock. Results ranged from 32° to 49°, with a mean of 40° and a mode of 33°.

Discontinuities

To assess the orientation of discontinuities in the project area, 640 discontinuity orientation measurements were made on exposed discontinuities both at the ground level and throughout the cut slopes by utilizing rope access techniques. Although each distinct rock cut exhibited smaller and less ubiquitous unique joint sets, three predominant joint sets were observed across all cut slopes in the project area. The orientations of these predominant discontinuities, with dip/dip direction means and ranges, are:

- Joint Set 1: 81° (±10°)/199° (±2°)
- Joint Set 2: 48° (±12°)/173° (±10°)
- Joint Set 3: 66° (±15°)/114° (±20°)

CUT SLOPE REDESIGN

Because of project constraints such as contract requirements, schedule, weather, and mobilization costs, construction could not be put on hold while a redesign of the 9 cut slopes was performed. Therefore, MJA performed a slope redesign at each cut slope while construction was in progress. This required detailed planning and coordination between MJA and both the state transportation department and the contractor. MJA worked with the contractor to prioritize the order in which cut slopes would be redesigned and constructed so that slope redesign efforts could be focused on particular cut slopes to maintain schedule. Other aspects of the highway improvement project, such as culverts, retaining walls, and paving, necessitated certain slopes be excavated sooner than others to avoid schedule delays. Lower priority cut slopes could be excavated at a later date without adversely affecting project operations, and these cut slopes were redesigned last. With this in mind, MJA developed a cut slope redesign strategy consisting generally of:

1. Stabilizing any partially excavated cut slopes that have the possibility of immediate slope failure and therefore pose a hazard to construction crews and the general public. Methods utilized included grouted rock dowels to anchor relatively small unstable rock blocks and trim blasts to remove relatively large unstable rock blocks.

2. Coordinating with the contractor to create a priority list of cut slopes that need to be redesigned immediately and cut slopes that are less time sensitive.

3. Redesigning cut slopes according to priority by utilizing kinematic analyses.

4. Inspecting each lift of each redesigned cut slope as the slope is excavated and stabilizing isolated hazardous features in the slope as necessary. Limit equilibrium analyses were used to analyze stability of isolated rock blocks. Slope stabilization methods utilized included grouted rock dowels, draped mesh, and pinned mesh. Stabilization methods were limited to approaches and materials already in the active project contract.

Kinematic Analysis

A Markland analysis was performed at each slope cut location using joint orientation data collected from field mapping. Where the stability of a rock slope is controlled by the structure of the rock mass, a Markland analysis is a well-documented and widely accepted design tool used to evaluate the rock slope stability relative to a proposed cut inclination (*3, 6*). Collected discontinuity data for each cut slope were plotted on stereonets using the computer program Dips®, developed by RocScience, Inc. Based on results of tilt tests, a friction angle of 33° was assumed as the joint friction. Beginning with 0.25H:1V, and progressing to flatter slopes, cut slope angles were then analyzed for the unique discontinuity orientations at each cut slope to determine the likelihood of planar, wedge, or toppling failure.

Kinematic Analysis Results

Results of the kinematic analysis were unique to each of the 9 individual cut slopes, and overall results and a relative example are provided in this section. In general, results of the Markland analysis indicated that excavating the majority of the cut slopes at 0.5H:1V provides a reasonable compromise between slope stability, additional slope stabilization that would be required after excavation, and additional right-of-way property that would need to be acquired. As an example, stereonets of the Markland analysis at Cut 4 are provided in Figure 6.

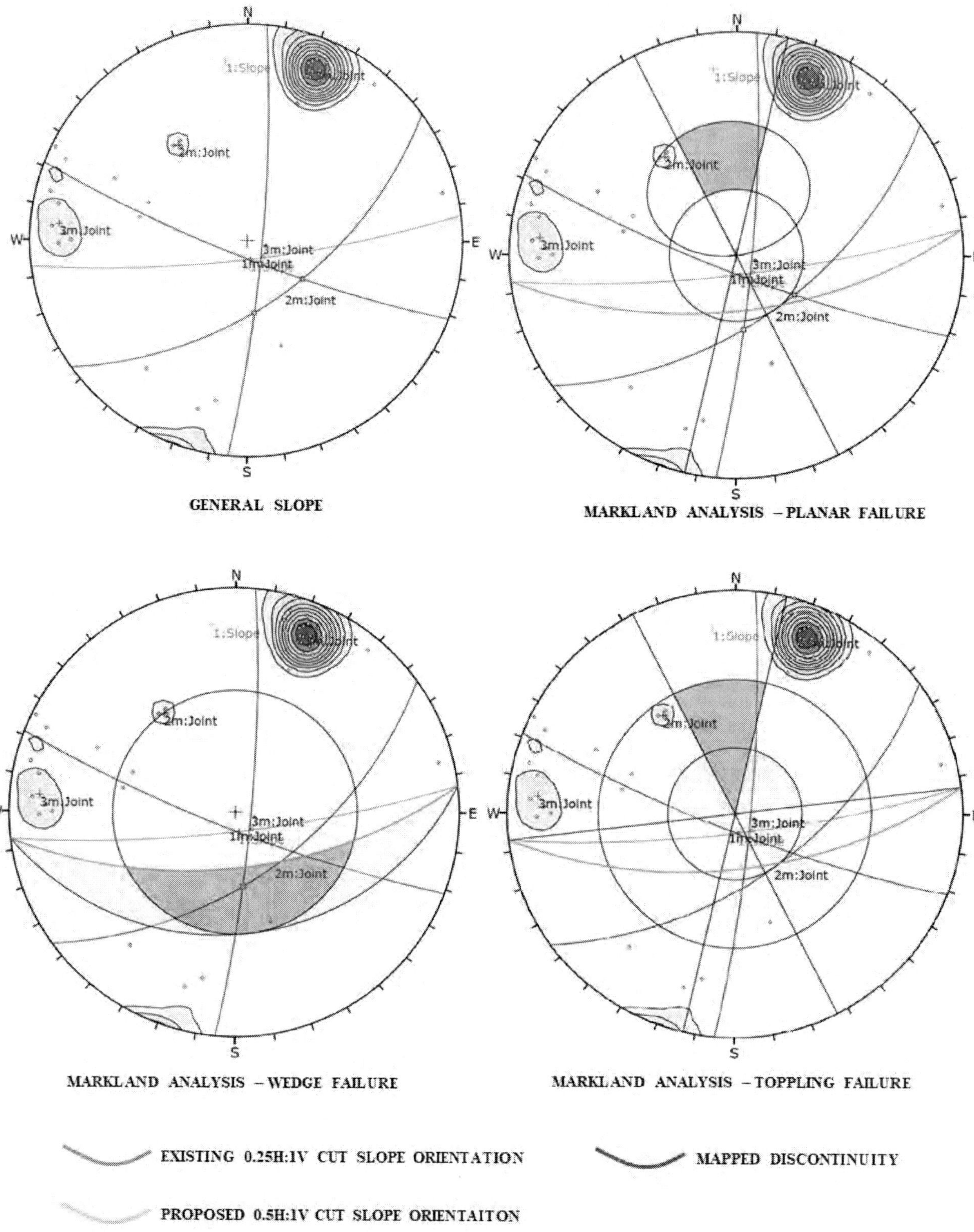

Figure 6 – Markland Analysis Results at Cut 4 with Cut Slope at 0.5H:1V

As can be seen in Figure 6, with the cut slope excavated to 0.5H:1V (orange line) the potential for planar failure and toppling failure at Cut 4 is low. There is a potential for wedge failure at the intersection of Joint 2 and Joint 3, which may require slope stabilization if the wedge is exposed during excavation. If the cut were excavated to 0.25H:1V (green line) the planar failure daylight envelope would increase in size, allowing for potential planar failure on Joint 1. Also, the potential for wedge failure would increase, as the intersection of Joint 1 and Joint 3 would fall in the wedge failure envelope.

One cut slope where right-of-way was available was designed to be cut slightly flatter at 0.6H:1V to remove a persistent potential failure plane. A slope stabilization and draped mesh system was designed for another cut slope that was already nearly fully excavated at 0.25H:1V.

Slope Stabilization

Excavating the cut slopes to 0.5H:1V does not entirely remove the potential for slope failures. This is evident in Figure 6, which shows a potential for wedge failure at Cut 4. To address this hazard MJA utilized slope stabilization techniques, consisting mainly of grouted rock dowels, to anchor potentially unstable blocks to the cut slope as the cut slopes were being excavated.

After each lift (approximately 15–20 feet) of the cut slope was drilled, blasted, and excavated, MJA inspected the exposed portion of the cut slope for any unstable rock blocks with the potential to fail. If no potential wedges, daylighting planes, or unstable blocks were identified, the contractor was given a green light to continue excavation of the next lift at that cut slope. If potentially unstable blocks were identified, MJA collected orientation data for the controlling joints and performed a limit equilibrium stability analysis to calculate a factor of safety of the potentially unstable block and the support force required to increase the factor of safety to an acceptable value.

Limit Equilibrium Analysis

Limit equilibrium analyses were performed on potentially unstable rock blocks using RocScience, Inc. computer software programs; RocPlane® for potential planar failures and SWedge® for potential wedge failures. The objective of the limit equilibrium analysis was to calculate a factor of safety of the potentially unstable block and, if necessary, calculate the required support force to increase the factor of safety to an acceptable value. Figure 7 provides a representative example of a limit equilibrium analysis performed at Cut 5 using RocPlane®. As can be seen in Figure 7, a required support force of 57,386 lb (≈58 kips) is required for every linear foot of the unstable block to increase the calculated factor of safety of the block to 1.30. This support force was multiplied by the length of the block (dimension in and out of the page) and divided by the capacity of an individual dowel to determine the required number of rock dowels to stabilize this block.

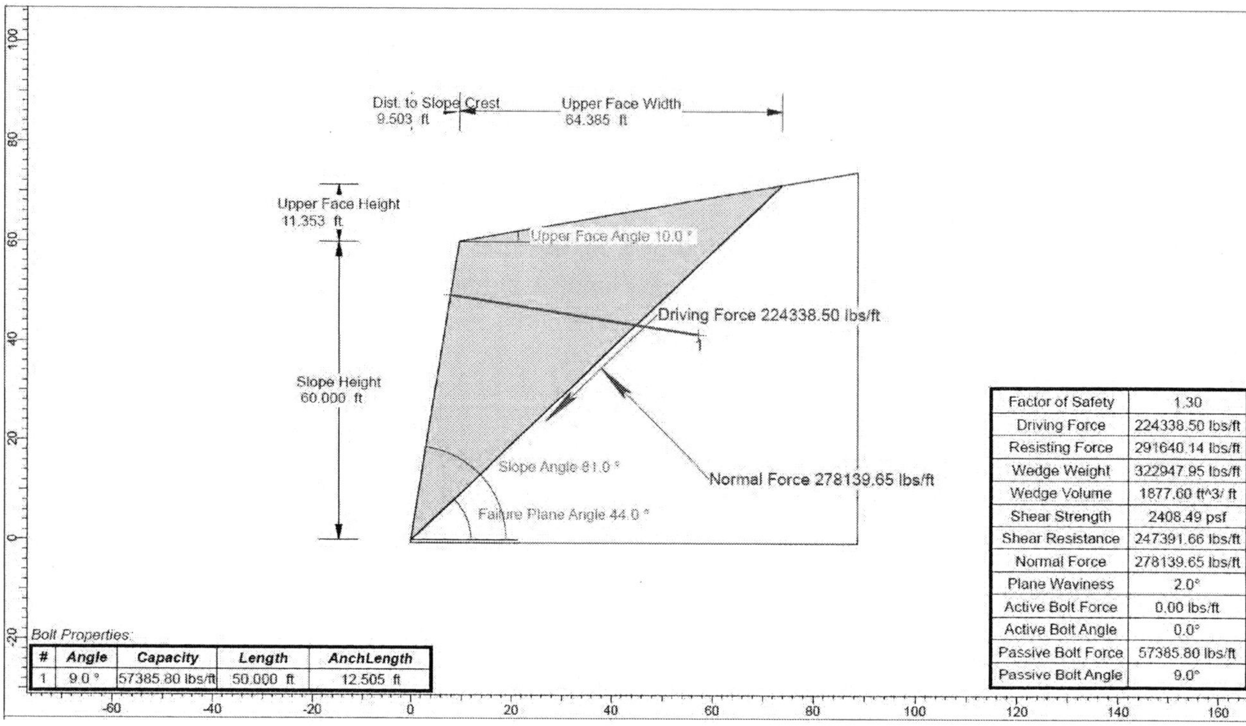

Figure 7 – Limit Equilibrium Analysis for Potentially Unstable Plane at Cut 5

Grouted Rock Dowel Design and Construction

The primary stabilization method utilized on the job was grouted rock dowels, which are passive reinforcing elements consisting of a steel bar grouted in place in a hole drilled into the unstable block to anchor the unstable block to the slope face and prevent slope failure. The capacity of an individual rock dowel is primarily dependent upon the tensile and shear strength of the steel bar, the size of the drilled hole, and the embedment length of the dowel into competent rock. Based on assumptions and analyses not presented in this paper, the project rock dowels were assumed to have an allowable capacity of 75 kips, and a required minimum embedment length of 5 feet. The total required reinforcement load calculated in the limit equilibrium analysis could then be divided by 75 kips to establish the required number of rock dowels to be installed in the unstable block to safely anchor it to the slope and prevent failure. Design rock dowel lengths were established by a combination of field inspection and block modeling in RocPlane® and SWedge®.

After identifying the number, locations, and lengths of required rock dowels at an unstable block location, MJA provided the stabilization design to the contractor. Using rope access techniques, MJA personnel rappelled onto identified unstable rock blocks, and painted design rock dowel locations and lengths on the slope face to facilitate simple installation by the contractor.

Additional Slope Stabilization Techniques

At isolated locations along the project corridor, large, rounded boulders (corestones) are present along the brow of the cut slopes. These corestones pose a rockfall hazard as the brow of the slope softens over time and erosion removes soil material that is supporting the corestones. These boulders are too large to be efficiently scaled off the slope, and too irregular and numerous to be efficiently anchored to the slope with grouted rock dowels. In these locations a pinned mesh system was designed and constructed to restrain the corestones to the slope.

Drainage

Limit equilibrium analyses showed that the accumulation of water and associated increase in hydrostatic pressure in existing fractures in the rock significantly increase the likelihood of unstable blocks failing. The initial project slope failures occurred in the spring, when water from rapid snowmelt filled fractures in the rock mass. To alleviate water pressure and reduce this hazard, the slope redesign included the installation of horizontal drains, both as single drains and as drain arrays.

CONCLUSIONS

Conclusions drawn by the authors consist of the following:

1. Rock in a cut slope is a naturally occurring construction material, and not all rock is created equal. The engineering properties of rock can vary significantly, even within a relatively small project site. This is an important consideration for transportation departments, their engineers and designers, and contractors. A robust and detailed geological or geotechnical investigation program at the outset of a project can provide critical information regarding how a slope will behave when excavated, and two slopes near each other cannot be assumed to behave identically, especially if roadway curves lead to a change in slope orientation.

2. The behavior and stability of a rock slope is largely controlled by existing discontinuities in the rock mass.

3. The importance of clear and direct communication between designers, owners, and contractors cannot be overstated. Because of the fast-paced nature of the project and schedule requirements, formal updated contract drawings of the redesigned slopes could not be created. Therefore, constant communication between all parties was imperative for project success and to maintain efficient and quality construction. In addition, construction work needed to continue as slopes were being redesigned, so designers needed to maintain contact with the contractor to ensure that design work was focused on priority cut slopes.

REFERENCES

1. Byerly, A., Tikoff, B., Kahn, M., Jicha, B., Gaschnig, R., and Fayon, A.K. (2017). Internal fabrics of the Idaho Batholith, USA. *Lithosphere,* 9(2): 283–298.

2. Hoek, E. and Bray, J.W. (1981). *Rockslope Engineering*. London, UK: Institution of Mining and Metallurgy, 357 p.

3. Schmidt, K.L., Stewart, D.E., Lewis, R.S., and Phillips, W.M. (2017). *Geologic Map of the Smiths Ferry Quadrangle, Valley County, Idaho*. Idaho Geological Survey.

4. Palmström, A. (2005). Measurements of and correlations between block size and Rock Quality Designation (RQD). *Tunnels and Underground Space Technology,* 20, 362–377.

5. Bieniawski, Z.T. (1989). *Engineering Rock Mass Classifications: A Complete Manual for Engineers and Geologists in Mining, Civil and Petroleum Engineering*. 251p, New York, NY: John Wiley and Sons.

6. Wyllie, D., Mah, Chris W., and Munfakh, George. (1998). *Rock Slope Reference Manual.* Federal Highway Administration. Report #FHWA-HI-99-007.

Evolution of the Midslope Rockfall Attenuator on Federal Lands Transportation Projects

Nicholas J. Farny, LEG, LG
Federal Highway Administration
Western Federal Lands Division
510 East 6th Street
Vancouver, Washington 98661
(812) 550-0304
Nicholas.Farny@dot.gov

Prepared for the 71st Highway Geology Symposium, May 2022

Acknowledgements

The following people contributed to the midslope rockfall attenuator design advancements presented in this paper:

Douglas Anderson, Federal Highway Administration -Western Federal Lands Division
Todd Butikofer, Federal Highway Administration -Western Federal Lands Division
Boyan Dobrev, Formerly of Washington State Department of Transportation
Brent Black, Cornforth Consultants, Inc.
Lawrence Pierson, Cornforth Consultants, Inc.
Benjamin George, Cornforth Consultants, Inc.

Disclaimer

Statements and views presented in this paper are strictly those of the authors, and do not necessarily reflect positions held by their affiliations, the Highway Geology Symposium (HGS), or others acknowledged above. The mention of trade names for commercial products does not imply the approval or endorsement by HGS.

ABSTRACT

Western Federal Lands Highway Division has employed midslope rockfall attenuators on several projects as a rockfall mitigation or risk reduction measure. The projects are located on federally managed public lands (NPS and FS) or on transportation routes that access federal lands in Idaho, Washington, and Oregon.

During these projects, several improvements were made to midslope attenuator design, specifically in regards to strengthening the system to withstand loads from rockfall impacts, snow creep, and ice, and refining standard plans and special provisions for standard specifications. In addition to functionality improvements to systems constructed during these projects, several challenges were faced regarding aesthetics. All projects on federal lands and most that access federal lands balance providing needed risk reduction improvements and the project partner's desire to maintain aesthetic character of viewsheds. Several adjustments were made to the systems to fit specific needs of each project.

The culmination of all this work is development of a more standardized "base" set of plans and specifications intended for inclusion in the next version of the Standard Specifications for the Construction of Roads and Bridges on Federal Highway Projects, which is currently in development. The intent of this paper is to highlight some of the more significant design improvements, aesthetic challenges, and to provide ideas for potential future research into the midslope rockfall attenuator.

INTRODUCTION

The Western Federal Lands Highway Division (WFLHD) of the Federal Highway Administration (FHWA) has employed the midslope rockfall attenuator on several projects as a rockfall mitigation or risk reduction measure. The projects are located on federally managed public lands (NPS and FS) or on transportation routes that access federal lands in Idaho, Washington, and Oregon.

During these projects, several improvements were made to the midslope attenuator design, specifically in regards to strengthening the system to withstand loads from rockfall impacts, snow creep, and ice, and refining standard plans and special provisions for standard specifications. In addition to functionality improvements to systems constructed during these projects, several challenges were faced regarding aesthetics. All projects on federal lands and most that access federal lands balance providing needed risk reduction improvements and the project partner's desire to maintain aesthetic character of viewsheds. Several adjustments were made to the systems to fit specific needs of each project.

THE MIDSLOPE ROCKFALL ATTENUATOR

The midslope rockfall attenuator is a hybrid system, employing a combination of two rockfall mitigation/risk reduction measures; the flexible rockfall barrier and draped rockfall protection (draped mesh). The flexible barrier commonly consists of a mesh fabric hung from a horizontal wire rope (the support rope) suspended between steel posts. The flexible rockfall barrier mesh fabric is installed without a lower bearing rope, and is instead hung down below the posts and over a portion of the rock slope below. The flexible barrier portion of the system, called the attenuator net, acts to catch and attenuate rockfall debris coming from upslope, dissipating a portion of the kinetic energy. The rockfall debris is then directed down the attenuator net to the ditch line. See Figures 1 to 3.

The system is used by WFLHD primarily as a method of addressing rockfall originating from high areas of the slope that would be cost probative or technically impossible to control with conventional rockfall barriers. The system is typically placed along benches or rockfall chutes occurring in the upper half of a rock slope.

The height of the barrier portion of the system typically ranges from 5 to 12 feet. The design height of the barrier is informed by rockfall modelling and field observations of rockfall activity. The posts are supported by a series of wire rope anchors, which are a length of wire rope inserted and grouted into a hole drilled into the ground surface. The mesh fabric used in the flexible barrier and attenuator net commonly consists of either a double twist wire mesh, a high tensile strength wire mesh, or a cable net with wire mesh backing, depending on the anticipated block size and kinetic energy of the rockfall debris.

The system is, compared to conventional flexible barriers, relatively self-cleaning, as the debris is not captured but is instead funneled down the attenuator net to the ditchline. Along roadways, the attenuator net is terminated a prescribed elevation above the roadway ditch to facilitate the collection of debris, which is removed during periodic ditch cleaning activities.

Figure 1 – Midslope rockfall attenuator installed on a WFLHD project in central Idaho.

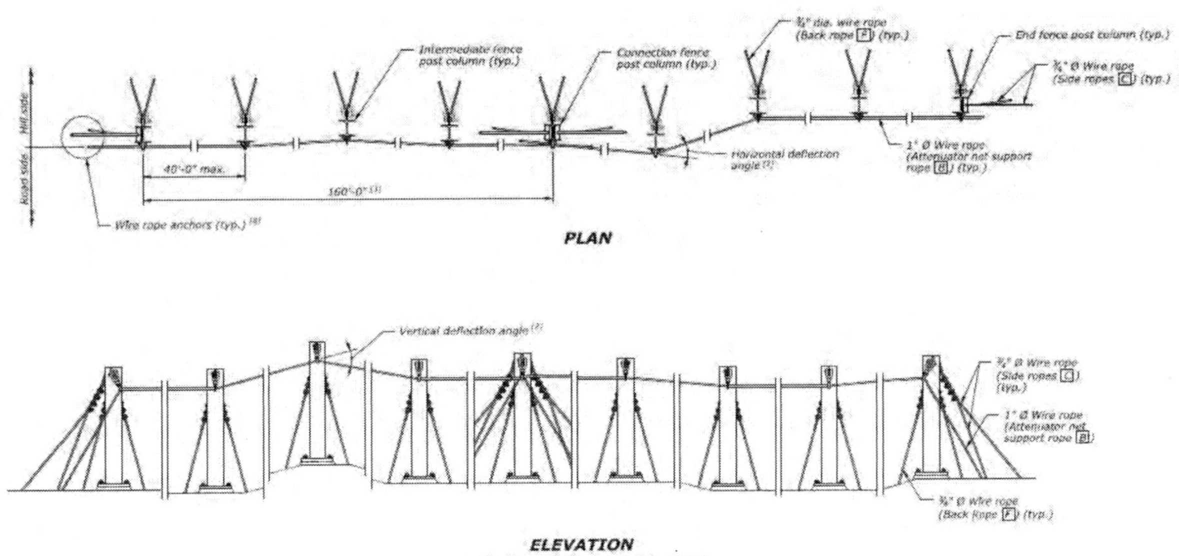

Figure 2 – Plan and elevation view of a midslope rockfall attenuator.

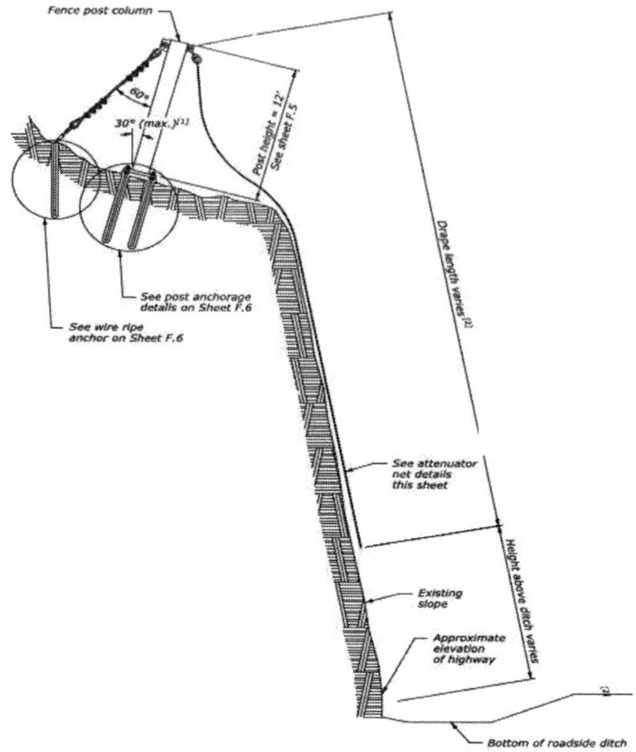

Figure 3 – Typical cross section of a midslope rockfall attenuator.

CASE HISTORIES

The following sections provide a summary of the WFLHD projects that have utilized midslope rockfall attenuators. They also highlight improvements and adjustments made to the systems from previous iterations to address system deficiencies or the aesthetic desires of our partners.

All of these case histories utilize the same midslope rockfall attenuator design (designated as the WsDOT design), which was developed by Boyan Dobrev, formerly a structural engineer with the Washington State Department of Transportation (WsDOT).

Banks-Lowman Highway

The first application of the midslope rockfall attenuator by WFLHD was on the Bank-Lowman Highway project near Garden Valley, Idaho to reduce the rockfall potential from rock slopes along State Highway 17 (Banks-Lowman Road). WFLHD focused on identifying all the rockfall areas along the highway, applying the Rockfall Hazard Rating System to prioritize rockfall sites for mitigation or risk reudction. Cornforth Consultants, Inc., working with David Evans and Associates, was contracted to perform final design fieldwork and develop designs for the six highest rated slopes (FHWA, 2012a).

The rock slopes that were selected for rockfall mitigation or risk reduction consist primarily of massive intrusive igneous rocks associated with the Idaho batholith. The overburden is a mix of talus and weathered rock deposits comprised of unconsolidated angular or subrounded rock fragments in a sandy soil derived primarily from grus.

Midslope attenuators were employed to capture and redirect rockfall on two slopes, designated as Slope 89 and Slope 113, from either overburden talus deposits (in the case of Slope 89) or an established rockfall chute in the exposed rock (in the case of Slope 113) (FHWA, 2012a). The installed systems have a flexible barrier height of 8 feet. See Figures 3 and 4 below. Other rockfall mitigation or risk reduction measures employed include rock reinforcement, rock scaling, draped mesh, and both flexible and rigid rockfall barriers. Work was completed in 2013 and 2014.

Figure 4 – Slope 89 (left) and Slope 113 (right) from the Bank-Lowman Highway (FHWA, 2012a). The red polygons show the approximate location the midslope rockfall attenuator installed at each site.

Aesthetic Considerations

Because this project is inside Boise National Forest, the attenuator systems were stained with a weathering agent called Natina to reduce visual impacts. This product was applied to all exposed steel elements of the systems, which are then allowed to cure prior to being shipped to the project site. During the curing process, the weathering agent reacts to the steel and develops into a rustic, brown color (Natina, 2022). This coloration helps the systems blend into the natural landscapes.

Figure 5 – The midslope attenuator installed at Slope 113 on the Bank-Lowman Highway.

Ketchum-Challis Highway

This project involved rockfall mitigation and risk reduction along an approximately 1.3 mile-long roadway segment of Forest Highway 26 (Idaho State Route 75) in Custer County, Idaho. The roadway is located along the Salmon River and lies within the Sawtooth National Recreation Area (NRA), and the Salmon River in this area is a Federally designated Wild and Scenic River corridor (FHWA, 2012b).

Like the Bank-Lowman Highway project, the site geology is dominated by rock slopes consisting of massive intrusive igneous rocks associated with the Idaho batholith. These igneous deposits are overlain by mix of glacial soils, talus, and areas of weathered rock and grus. These overlying deposits are capable of cobble to boulder sized rockfall events produced via differential weathering (FHWA, 2012b).

Initial Construction

The initial phase of this project was constructed from 2013 to 2015. A total of fourteen midslope rockfall attenuators were employed to capture rockfall occurring in established chutes in the soils and weathered rock overlying the more massive and competent igneous rock that is found in the road cuts along the highway. Cornforth Consultants, Inc., working with David Evans and Associates, was contracted to perform the design. The installed systems were comprised of cable nets with twisted wire mesh backing suspended between posts five feet in height. These were paired with draped rockfall protection, which was installed over the exposed competent igneous rock layers. See Figure 6. Other rockfall mitigation or risk reduction measures employed include rock reinforcement, rock scaling, and an anchored wire mesh system (FHWA, 2012b).

Figure 6 – An example of the rockfall protection scheme utilized for portions along the Ketchum-Challis Highway project. Draped mesh was utilized to capture rockfall originating from exposed competent igneous rock along the road cut, while midslope attenuators were installed at established rockfall chutes above the road cut (FHWA, 2012b).

Aesthetic Considerations

Natina weathering agent was again utilized to aid in reducing the visual impacts by forcing a rusty, brown coloration on the exposed steel potions of the midslope rockfall attenuators. In addition, WFLHD was required to limit the post height for all attenuator systems to 5 feet to reduce the possibility of the systems being spotted on the hillside. The rockfall modeling performed during design indicated that this post height still provides approximately 90% to 99% catchment for the majority of the midslope rockfall attenuator locations. However, this limitation on post height meant that a few of the installations had predicted rockfall catchments ranging from less than 70% to 80% (FHWA, 2012b). The bottoms of the midslope attenuators system were also staggered to break up horizontal lines and reduce visual impacts.

Winter of 2016 and 2017

During the winter of 2016 and 2017, the project area experienced a 30-year snow pack, with approximately 6 to 8 feet of snow on the ground. Early in 2017, a period of rapid warming coupled with increased wildlife traffic on the slopes triggered a series of snow avalanches through the project area. See Figure 7. The attenuator nets from four systems were completely ripped away by snow avalanches. Eight other systems were damaged from either snow avalanches or excessive loads from snow creep.

The area has a history of snow avalanches, and this was known during project development. However, other options for reducing rockfall activity, including realignments or laying back the slopes in and above the road cuts were removed from consideration due to the their larger impact to the environment. Therefore, even after the events of the winter of 2016 and 2017, the use of midslope rockfall attenuators to reduce the rockfall risk was accepted despite the potential for damage from snow creep and snow avalanches.

Figure 7 – Debris from snow avalanches along the Ketchum-Challis Highway project in the winter of 2017.

Forensic Investigation

In the summer of 2017, WFLHD inspected each of the midslope rockfall attenuators to determine the source of the damage and the scope of repairs needed.

In general, damaged attenuators placed below slopes that were sparsely vegetated and oriented at slopes oriented at 45 to 55 degrees from horizontal had a broken attenuator net support rope and at least one post that was bent or deformed at the base where it is attached to its concrete foundation. In all of these cases, the breaking of the support rope resulted in the attenuator net being either partially or completely removed. For these systems, it was assumed that a snow avalanche was the cause of the damage. See Figures 8 and 9.

If the damaged attenuator was placed below slopes that were relatively more vegetated and were oriented at an angle less than 45 degrees from horizontal, the support rope was intact. This means that the attenuator net was still mostly in place. However, it had pulled away from at least one post and slid down the support rope, a damage that which was termed "show curtaining". This is caused by a broken lacing rope, which attaches the top corners of attenuator net to the posts. See Figure 10. Most of these systems also had at least one post that was bent or deformed at the base where it is attached to its concrete foundation. For these systems, it was assumed that a snow avalanche was the cause of the damage.

Repairs

Emergency funding was made available from Idaho Department of Transportation and FHWA for the repairs. The repairs to the attenuator systems included the following work:

- Installing new attenuator nets where the previous net was removed or damaged;
- Replacing or repairing damaged posts;
- Replacing any wire rope anchors on failed support ropes or damaged posts;
- Pulling the attenuator net back to its original position to remove any "shower curtaining";
- Removing any trapped debris from the attenuator net, and;
- Retightening all wire ropes on the wire rope anchors.

Figure 8 – Ketchum-Challis Highway midslope rockfall attenuator with broken attenuator net support rope. The attenuator net has been ripped away.

Figure 9 – Bent base plate on midslope rockfall attenuator post on the Ketchum-Challis Highway project.

Figure 10 – Attenuator net "shower curtaining" on the Ketchum-Challis Highway project.

In addition, repairs were made to several draped rockfall protection systems, including the removal of the trapped rockfall debris, additional areas were scaled, and a new attenuator was installed to cover a previously unaddressed rockfall chute. All work was completed in 2020.

Improvements

To enhance the resiliency of the WsDOT design to snow avalanches and snow loads, a couple of designs improvements were implemented at Ketchum-Challis Highway by WFLHD with the assistance of Boyan Dobrev, former WsDOT Structural Engineer.

As stated above, the primary damage attributed to snow avalanches was the breaking of the attenuator net support rope, which is strung between the posts and holds the attenuator net in place. During the repairs to the Ketchum-Challis attenuators, this support rope (also called rope B on the plan set) was upsized from a 3/4th inch diameter wire rope to a 1 inch diameter wire rope. This means an increase in the breaking strength from to approximately 60,000 to 100,000 pounds.

In addition, several updates were made to address the "shower curtaining" issues, which was interpreted to be caused by excessive snow loads and snow creep. The first of which was an upsizing of the lacing rope, which attaches the corners of the attenuator net to the posts via the swivel, from a 5/16th inch diameter wire rope to a 9/16th inch diameter wire rope. This increases the breaking strength of the lacing rope from approximately 11,000 to 34,000 pounds. The second is the addition of a "corner cable", also called rope K on the plan set, which connects the swivel on the end posts directly to the attenuator net. The "corner cable" not only provides a redundancy in case the lacing rope breaks, but will help to keep the attenuator net in place on the slope if the support rope breaks. See Figure 11.

On top of the upgrades to the system components, a refinement of the structural design was performed. The lead to various adjustments to the angles between posts and the wire rope anchors that support them.

Guidance was added to improve the constructability of the system in regards to the installation of wire rope anchors. Before, it was specified that the wire rope anchors must be "taut", but that language is vague and would often lead to disagreements between the owner and the contractor about what is taut enough. The new standard specifications for the system have a specified tension value that the wire rope anchor must have at installation. These values are checked by the contractor using a calibrated cable tension meter.

Despite the observed damage to the system posts, no effort was made to improve the strength of these parts of the midslope attenuator system. This was an decision made by WFLHD to avoid overbuilding the post foundations. It is our intent to make the post the weak link in the attenuator system, because it is relatively easier and less expensive to repair or replace the posts compared to replacing the attenuator net or the wire rope anchors. In addition, research has shown that more rigid the attenuator post system is, the more damage is received by the structural elements (Ardnt, Ortiz, & Group, 2014).

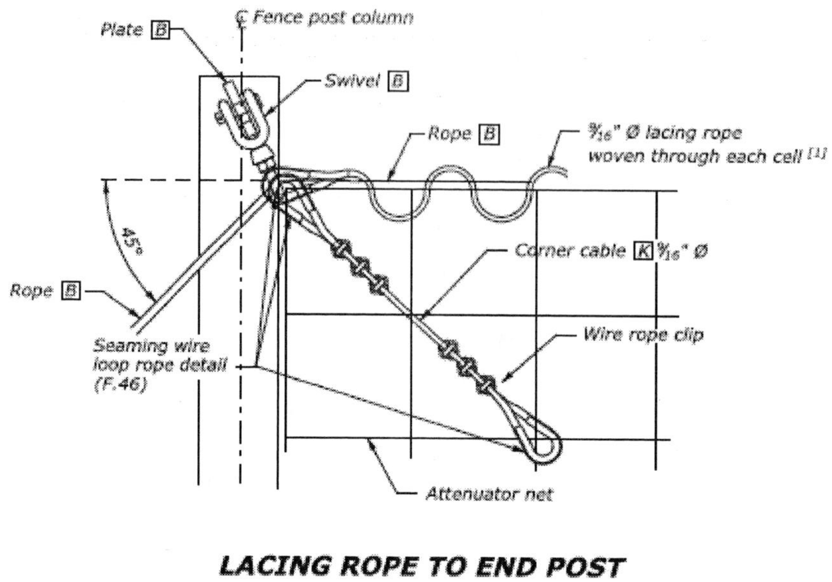

Figure 11 – Some of the improvements made to the attenuator systems during the repairs of the along the Ketchum-Challis Highway, including the 9/16th inch diameter lacing rope which was upsized from a 5/16th inch diameter rope and the new "corner cable" or K rope which ties the attenuator net directly to the end post via the swivel.

Figure 12 – Repaired and improved midslope rockfall attenuator on the Ketchum-Challis Highway project. The inset picture shows the new "corner cable" improvement.

Spruce Railroad Trial, Segment B

The next WFLHD project to utilize the midslope rockfall attenuator was Segment B of the Spruce Railroad Trail in Olympic National Park (OLYM). This project involved the paving of an existing trail on the north side of Lake Crescent which is built on an old railroad bed. Additional improvements to the trial alignment include trail widening, construction of retaining walls and a pedestrian bridge, the rehabilitation of an existing rock tunnel, and the installation of rockfall mitigation or risk reduction measures (FHWA, 2018). WFLHD performed the design of the rockfall mitigation or risk reduction measures, and Shannon & Wilson was contracted to design the tunnel rehabilitation, pedestrian bridge, and retaining structures.

The surface deposits along the Spruce Railroad Trail alignment are mapped as the Crescent Formation, specifically marine pillow basalts (Schasse, 2003). A midslope rockfall attenuator was installed on an existing natural rock bench north of the new pedestrian bridge. Field observations and rockfall modeling indicated that the bench served as a launch feature for rockfall occurring from the basalt outcrops upslope, and that, if left unaddressed rockfall from this feature could impact the bridge. The midslope rockfall attenuator addresses this rockfall hazard by intercepting the rockfall and funneling it down into Lake Crescent below. See Figure 13.

Figure 13 – Midslope rockfall attenuator installed above a pedestrian bridge along Spruce Railroad Trial in Olympic National Park (FHWA, 2018).

This installation features an attenuator net comprised of high tensile strength steel mesh suspended between posts 12 feet high. All system improvements developed during the Ketchum -Challis Highway project were also installed. Natina weathering agent was again utilized to aid in reducing the visual impacts by forced a rusty, brown coloration on the exposed steel potions of the midslope rockfall attenuator (FHWA, 2018a).

In addition to the midslope rockfall attenuator, other rockfall mitigation measures including rock scaling, rock reinforcement, and draped mesh was installed on exposed rock outcrops along the trail (FHWA 2018a). All work was completed in 2020.

Historic Columbia River Highway State Trail, Segment E

The WsDOT design for the midslope rockfall attenuator will be utilized on Segment E of the Historic Columbia River Highway (HRCH) State Trail project in the Columbia River Gorge, Oregon. The overall goal of the HRCH State Trial project is to connect all of the portions of the Historic Columbia River Highway (U.S. Route 30) abandoned during the construction of Interstate 84 into one paved pedestrian and cycling trail that stretches from Troudale to The Dalles (Cornforth, 2018). Rockfall risk reduction measures will be constructed along the HRCH State Trial to meet Oregon Department of Transportation's (ODOT) goal of retaining 90% of rocks that roll onto the trail alignment and 99% of rocks that impact the trail (Cornforth, 2018).

Segment E of the HCRH State Trail project will create several new trail segments that pass below existing rock slopes (comprised of basalt of the Columbia River Basalt Group) in road cuts along Interstate 84. Due to space constraints, these new trail segments will be placed in the existing rockfall catchment areas for these slope. This includes the use of midslope rockfall attenuators at two rocks slopes, designated as the Stepped Cut and Hackly Cut, see Figure 15 (Cornforth, 2018). Cornforth Consultants, Inc., working with David Evans and Associates, was contracted to perform the design. The construction for this project kicked off in late winter of 2022.

Aesthetic Considerations

Natina weathering agent was again utilized to aid in reducing the visual impacts by forced a rusty, brown coloration on the exposed steel potions of the midslope rockfall attenuators.

Stakeholders questioned if the midslope rockfall attenuators could be contoured, which refers to the practice of installing pins in a draped mesh to hold the mesh close to the slope to reduce visual impacts (FHWA, 2012b). Contouring of draped rockfall protection mesh was required by the partnering agencies on the Ketchum-Challis project.

However, the addition of contour anchors traps rock blocks in both the draped mesh and midslope rockfall attenuator system, hindering the self-cleaning ability. This problem was observed at the contoured draped mesh installed at the Ketchum Challis Highway project. The contouring elements, which in the case of the Ketchum Challis Highway project was rigid steel pins, acted as barriers to the migration of rockfall debris beneath the mesh down to the ditch below. See Figure 15. This trapped material, if left unaddressed, will lead tearing and breaking of the draped mesh.

Figure 14 – Proposed midslope rockfall attenuator locations that will be installed along Segment E of the Historic Columbia River Highway State Trail project (Cornforth, 2018).

Figure 15 – Trapped rockfall debris behind contoured draped mesh at the Ketchum-Challis Highway project. Notice that the contoured pins are holding up rock blocks.

As part of the repairs along the Ketchum-Challis Highway project, the draped mesh systems were envaulted and select contour pins were removed to allow free movement of rockfall debris behind the mesh down to the ditch.

In addition, the midslope rockfall attenuator relies on the attenuator net to disperse kinetic energy of rock blocks, and having the attenuator net pinned to the slope via contouring elements would severely hinder the attenuation of rock blocks and would likely cause damage to the net as it is ripped free of the pins. **Therefore, WFLHD does not consider the contouring of midslope rockfall attenuators an acceptable practice.**

Improvements

Previous iterations of the WFLHD design required the contractor to conduct test wire rope anchor pull out tests to loads up to 80% of the ultimate design load for the anchor. For the HRCH State Trial Segment E project, this was changed to a maximum of 60% of the ultimate design load. This change is meant to ensure that the wire ropes are not damaged during the testing of the wire rope anchors. Based on information from testing done by Geobrugg (Shevlin, 2022), testing above 60% of the ultimate design load can permanently deform wire ropes, damaging them and lowering the ultimate capacity.

FUTURE IMPROVEMENTS

WFLHD is developing of a standardized “base” set of plans and specifications for the midslope rockfall attenuator, intended for inclusion in the next version of the *Standard Specifications for the Construction of Roads and Bridges on Federal Highway Projects (FP)*, which is currently in development.

WFLHD is currently looking for opportunities to install a midslope rockfall attenuator that utilizes flexible “floating” posts. These are steel posts that have a metal base plate, similar to rigid posts. However, unlike rigid posts were the metal base plate is secured either to the ground surface or a concrete foundation via grouted anchors (See Figure 3), the metal base plate for “floating” posts sits on the ground and is free to move within the constraints of retaining ropes, which connect the bottom of the post to uphill and downhill ground anchors. Studies have shown that these floating posts are can absorb more that 3 times the impact energy than rigid posts, and are more resilient to damage (Ardnt, Ortiz, & Group, 2014).

REFERENCES:

1. Ardnt, B.M., Ortiz, T., and Group, B. Full Scale Testing of Rockfall Barrier and Post Foundation Systems, In *Proceedings of the 2014 Rocky Mountain GEO-Conference*, TRB, ASCE, Lakewood, CO, 2014. pp. 148-180.
2. Ardnt, B.M., Ortiz, T., and Turner, K.A. *Colorado's Full-Scale Field Testing of Rockfall Attenuator Systems* , Transportation Research Circular E-C141, Transportation Research Board, National Academies of Sciences, Engineering, and Medicine, 2009.
3. Cornforth Consultants, Inc. *Preliminary Rockfall Evaluation Report – Historic Columbia River Highway State Trail Segment E,* Hood River County, Oregon, Report prepared for David Evans and Associates, Inc., Federal Highway Administration, U.S. Department of Transportation, 2018.
4. Federal Highway Administration (FHWA). *Banks-Lowman Highway, Phase 1 Rockfall Mitigations, Final Design (100%)*, Boise National Forest, Boise County, Idaho, WFLHD Geotechnical Report No. 15-11, Prepared by Cornforth Consultants, Inc., U.S. Department of Transportation, 2012.
5. Federal Highway Administration (FHWA). *Ketchum-Challis Highway, Rockfall Mitigation Design,* Sawtooth National Recreation Area, Custer County, Idaho, WFLHD Geotechnical Report No. 04-12, Prepared by Cornforth Consultants, Inc., U.S. Department of Transportation, 2012.
6. Federal Highway Administration (FHWA). *Spruce Railroad Trial Segment B Rockfall Mitigation Project, Unstable Slope Corridor Assessment Report,* WA NPS OYLM 2017(1), Olympic National Park, Washington, WFLHD Geotechnical Report No. 10-18, Prepared by WFLHD Geotechnical Section, U.S. Department of Transportation, 2018.
7. Natina. *Steel Color Solution.* Natina Products LLC, https://www.natina.com/services/steel/, 2022. Accessed 3/8/2022.
8. Schasse, H.W. *Geologic map of the Washington portion of the Port Angeles 1:100,000 quadrangle*, Washington Division of Geology and Earth Resources, Open File Report 2003-6, scale 1:100,000.
9. Shevlin, T. Personal Communication, 3/11/2022.

Utilizing Cellular Concrete in Geohazard Mitigation Solutions

José LuQuin, P.E.
GeoStabilization International®
4475 E 74th Ave, Suite A
Commerce City, CO 80022
970.773.6320
jose.luquin@gsi.us

Prepared for the 71st Highway Geology Symposium, May 2022

Acknowledgments

The author would like to thank the individuals/entities for their contributions to the work described:

Scott Embry, P.E. – GeoStabilization International®

Disclaimer

Statements and views presented in this paper are strictly those of the author(s), and do not necessarily reflect positions held by their affiliations, the Highway Geology Symposium (HGS), or others acknowledged above. The mention of trade names for commercial products does not imply the approval or endorsement by HGS.

ABSTRACT

Cellular concrete is defined as concrete made with hydraulic cement, water, and preformed foam to form a hardened material having an oven-dry density of 50 lbs/ft3 or less (ACI 523.1R-06) and has been an industry-wide technology readily available in both building and geotechnical applications. In the building industry, cellular concrete can be used to make materials such as precast blocks or panels. The residential sector commonly refers to the material as "aircrete". Geotechnical applications include backfill operations, mine shaft or tunnel grouting, culvert abandonment, and annular space grouting.

In geohazard mitigation, the use of cellular concrete as a lightweight backfill has provided tremendous results. One common approach is to remove driving forces by replacing heavier material with lighter material. Another is using soil nail walls, shotcrete reinforced retaining walls, and sheet pile walls along with cellular concrete to restore travel ways and shoulders. A third approach is using this material to fill voids. Case studies will illustrate how cellular concrete was successfully used to stabilize landslides without compromising stability requirements such as bond strengths.

With a widely used technology for other applications, GeoStabilization has proven that cellular concrete is suitable for geohazard mitigation. The engineering properties of cellular grout allow for innovative repairs and should always be considered for projects restoring infrastructure. The material and the construction techniques utilized in these case studies have shown to be cost-effective, fast to construct, and appropriate for numerous distinct scenarios.

INTRODUCTION

Cellular concrete is known by a few terms in the construction industry, including cellular grout, aerated concrete, foam concrete, lightweight concrete, and more. Regardless of semantics, cellular concrete is a material with low-density made with hydraulic cement and water having a homogenous void or air cell structure created with the addition of preformed foam or by the generation of gas.

Used in the marketplace for a time now, the benefits for geohazard and other geotechnical applications are just being realized. These characteristics allow cellular concrete to be the go-to material for geohazard mitigation and other geotechnical applications:

- easy pumping or placement with gravity
- self-compaction
- lightweights
- freeze-thaw resistance
- insulation
- impact absorption
- low water absorption and permeability
- self-leveling slump
- high bearing capacities
- permanent stability without exerting lateral forces

Cellular concrete has been applied in several different markets. The building, residential and commercial industries use it to make precast elements and roof deck fills. The material can also provide storm-resistant, well-insulated, and energy-efficient structures. In highways and roads, cellular concrete is used to stabilize banks, enhance berm design, and as a base or subbase material. Other uses include but are not limited to erosion control, sound dampening, mines and tunnels, annular filling, fire protection, and more.

A brief discussion on physical properties, materials, and mixing of cellular concrete will be presented, along with a comparison of potential alternative solutions. In addition, case studies will be given for void filling, lightweight backfill, and roadway shoulder restoration applications.

CELLULAR CONCRETE

This material is defined as concrete made with hydraulic cement, water, and preformed foam to form a hardened material having an oven-dry density of 50 lbs/ft^3 or less *(1)*. The physical properties of this material are incredibly unique and have endless possibilities. The material components are readily available and inexpensive, making this an excellent alternative to traditional industry-standard materials such as Portland cement concrete.

Physical Properties

Density

The key to controlling the cellular concrete's desired characteristics of starts with mix density. Oven-dry densities typically range from 20 to 50 (lbs/ft^3) with compressive strengths at 28 days ranging from 100 to 1000 (lbs/in^2) *(1)*. Lower densities come with lower strengths but higher insulating ability. The range of compressive strengths is directly related to the density, with oven-dry densities of 20 to 25 (lbs/ft^3) yielding strengths of 70 to 125 (lbs/in^2) while oven-dry densities of 40 to 50 (lbs/ft^3) have strengths of 450 to 750 (lbs/in^2). The modulus of elasticity is also related to the density; the higher the unit weight, the higher the modulus will be. For such a lightweight material, bearing capacities are surprisingly high with a maximum cast density of 50 (lbs/ft^3) possible with a bearing capacity of 11.5 (ton/ft^2) *(1)*, again with higher densities having higher capacity.

Workability

The flowability characteristics of cellular concrete give the user flexibility for choosing to use and place the material. The slump is so high that the material is self-leveling and self-compacting with no shrinkage. Although the workability is high, durability is not sacrificed for this trait, and throughout its design life, the material is essentially permanent and stable. Being so workable, it is naturally pumpable and easily placed by gravity (directly from concrete truck chute).

Additional properties and benefits

Water absorption and permeability are low, allowing designs to neglect the negative impacts of water on projects. Impact absorption capabilities are high due to the air cell structure allowing resistance to distortion. The resistance to freeze-thaw is high for harsher climates.

Materials

Proportions aside, simplifying the make-up of cellular concrete would be replacing the aggregates of concrete with preformed foam. Three essential components are required to create a functional mix of cellular concrete: 1) water, 2) hydraulic cement, 3) preformed foam*(3)*. Other materials have been added to mixes like fine and lightweight coarse aggregates and admixtures to alter physical properties. The availability of these materials makes cellular concrete an invaluable resource.

Water

The water used in a cellular concrete mix must be clean and potable, as with any water used to make concrete. Organics, improper pH levels, etc., shall not be present as they will adversely affect the final product.

Cement

Cement will act as the binder in the cellular concrete material. Portland, blended, and hydraulic cement can be incorporated in the mix designs of cellular concretes, and choices will alter the physical properties. Guidance should come from ASTM Standard Specification for Portland Cement (C 150), ASTM Standard Specification for Blended Hydraulic Cements (C 1157), and ASTM Standard Performance Specification for Hydraulic Cement (C 1157). Depending on desired physical properties (i.e., improved compressive strength), additional cementitious materials can be added to the design, such as fly ash, pozzolans, or slag cement.

Preformed Foam

The preformed foam inside of a cellular concrete mix is the component that provides the homogenous air cell structure. In addition, this ingredient will increase the yield of a neat grout mixture by at least three times. The foam is produced by mixing a foam concentrate with water in predetermined proportions in a foam generator *(2)*. The key for the foaming agent is creating the air cell structure that will stay unbroken during field operations. The foam concentrates are mostly protein hydroxylates or synthetic surfactants *(1)*. The reference manuals, including ASTM Standard Method for Testing Foaming Agents for Use in Producing Cellular Concrete Using Preformed Foam (C 796) and ASTM Standard Specification for Foaming Agents Used in Making Preformed Foam for Cellular Concrete (C 869), provide guidance for densities and other specifications.

Figure 1: Preformed Foam prepared by GSI

Atypical Materials

Depending on the application of cellular concrete, it is certainly possible to add additional elements to the mix design beyond water, cement, and preformed foam. Aggregates are included to modify qualities such as densities and strengths. Admixtures and accelerators can be utilized for similar purposes and to decrease set time. Polymers and fibers can improve mix integrity and strength and help the final product resist shrinkage, cracking, permeability, and absorptivity.

Standard Equipment, Batching, and Mixing

The equipment needed to make the material is a foam machine and, depending on how the cellular concrete will be used and placed, a grout plant, concrete truck, or a specialized mixer.

Figure 2: Goodcell Foam Pump

Mixers capable of high speeds are desirable to appropriately combine the concrete and water. The foam concentrate and water are combined for the desired ratio, typically 1-part foam concentrate with 40 to 100-parts water. The resultant foam is then added to the cement/water mix through means typical of grouting operations with a grout plant or other mechanical mixer. The cellular concrete mixture is ready for pumping with the foam added to the mix. It can be added directly to concrete trucks allowing for placement through gravity directly from the chute, or transferred to a machine for pumping with standard grouting hoses. Although self-leveling lift thicknesses of around three feet should be used when applied as a lightweight backfill.

Figure 3: Cellular Concrete Placed Directly into Grout Plant

SHOULDER RESTORATION CASE STUDY

An active landslide area created a scarp in the pavement and shoulder loss for 275 feet along KY 338, MP 14.30 in Boone County, Kentucky. This site is in an area of Garrard Siltstone, and Kope and Clays Ferry Formations *(4)* consisting of silty clay derived from a clayey residuum weathered from calcareous siltstone and/or clayey residuum weathered from limestone and shale *(5)*. For the entire length of the repair, an in-place railroad steel retaining wall was not capable of holding back the movement of the slide mass as you could see that most of them were out of plum. Powerful rain events and sloping conditions are the likely culprits that activated this slope failure. The saturated soils on the embankment lost shear strength and could not remain in place. The movement began de-stabilizing the downslope.

Figure 4: KY 338, MP 14.30 Before Landslide Repair

Repair Plan and Construction

To stabilize this moving slope, the failing railroad steel system had to be removed, the existing slope excavated and shaped top-down near the edge of the pavement. Next multiple rows of soil nails were installed, along with horizontal drains. Finally, a rigid reinforced shotcrete facing was installed, forming a void for the shoulder restoration.

Figure 5: KY 338, MP 14.30 Construction Progress

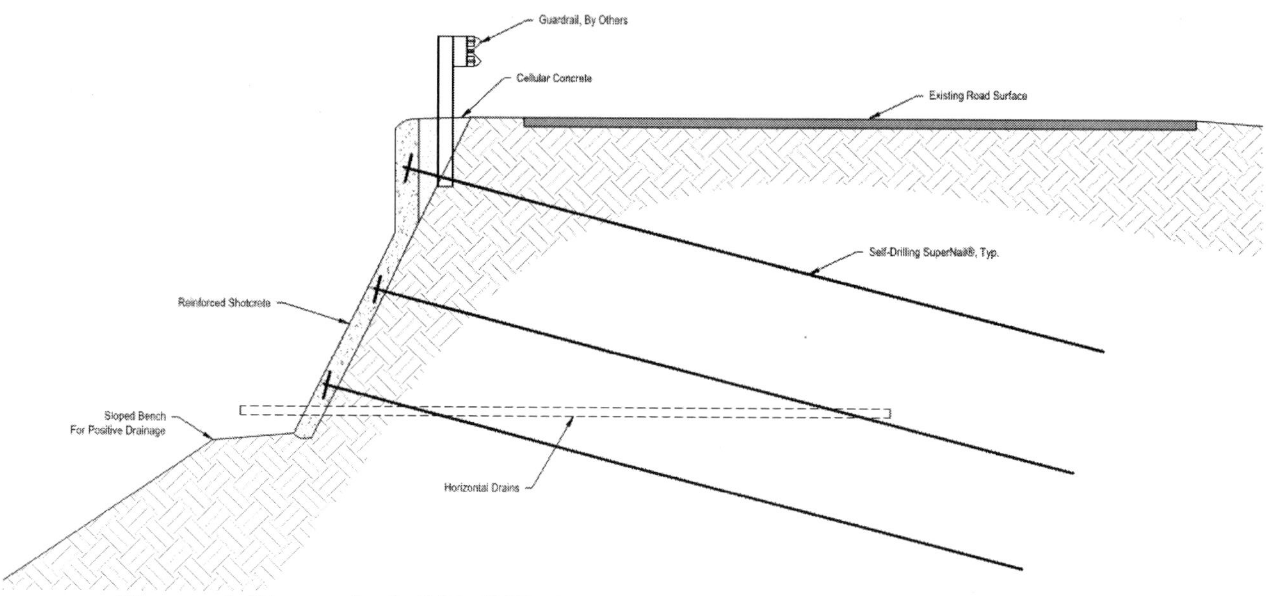

Figure 6: Example Soil Nail Wall with Shoulder Restoration Cross-Section

Cellular Concrete as Shoulder Build-Up

Several materials used to restore the shoulder of a roadway include, but are not limited to, select backfill, crushed stone, AASHTO No. 57 stone, flowable fill, etc. Some of these options come with negative aspects from an engineering perspective. Stones and backfills allow water to pond in the area behind the shotcrete and need drainage holes for daylighting this hydrostatic pressure. Granular materials also exert lateral forces, which is a design consideration when reinforcing the shotcrete. Since these materials are not self-compacting, the small area between the pavement structure and shotcrete wall face is unsuitable for many industry-standard compaction equipment as they may damage the in-place repair facing.

Flowable fill is a good option, being a self-compacting impermeable material and not creating additional lateral forces behind the shotcrete facing. A downside is flowable fills generally have strengths of 1,200 lbs/in^2 and may cause future issues if the repair area needs to be excavated or if guardrail posts need to be driven *(3)*. Cellular concrete has the positive attributes of flowable fills, but the air cell structure allows for easy excavating, cutting, and driving operations, making it ideal for this scenario. The impact absorbing properties will enable this material to hold guardrails, maintaining the design considerations set forth by AASHTO. A Kentucky Transportation Cabinet employee described installing the guardrail posts as easy and like puncturing Styrofoam.

Figure 7: Shoulder Restoration Achieved with Cellular Concrete Placed by Gravity

LIGHTWEIGHT BACKFILL CASE STUDY

On State Route 933 in Mishawaka, Indiana, GeoStabilization responded to a slide undermining the roadway. The material loss under the pavement spanned approximately 111 feet. This road was constructed over top of soils from Ellsworth Shale *(6),* consisting of sandy material with trace clay and gravel. At the time of our response to the geohazard, water was actively flowing from the bottom of the slope. The owner's subsurface investigation showed groundwater present at an approximate depth of 16 feet. The actively flowing water is likely to cause material loss due to accelerated erosion rates, leaving the roadway without any material underneath it, as shown in Figure 8 below.

Figure 8: SR 933 undermining of roadway

Repair Plan and Construction

Our forces cleared, excavated, and reshaped the slope for 11 feet down to install the repair elements. The nature of the available work area, with not much material available for a workbench and the significant annular space, were factored into the chosen repair type. Stabilizing the roadway was achieved by driving sheet piles at the top of the slope a few feet off the back of the guardrail, and multiple rows of self-drilled SuperNails® were installed, creating a composite and unique repair. Challenges in this project included avoiding utilities, which were overcome by angling the soil nail elements away from them.

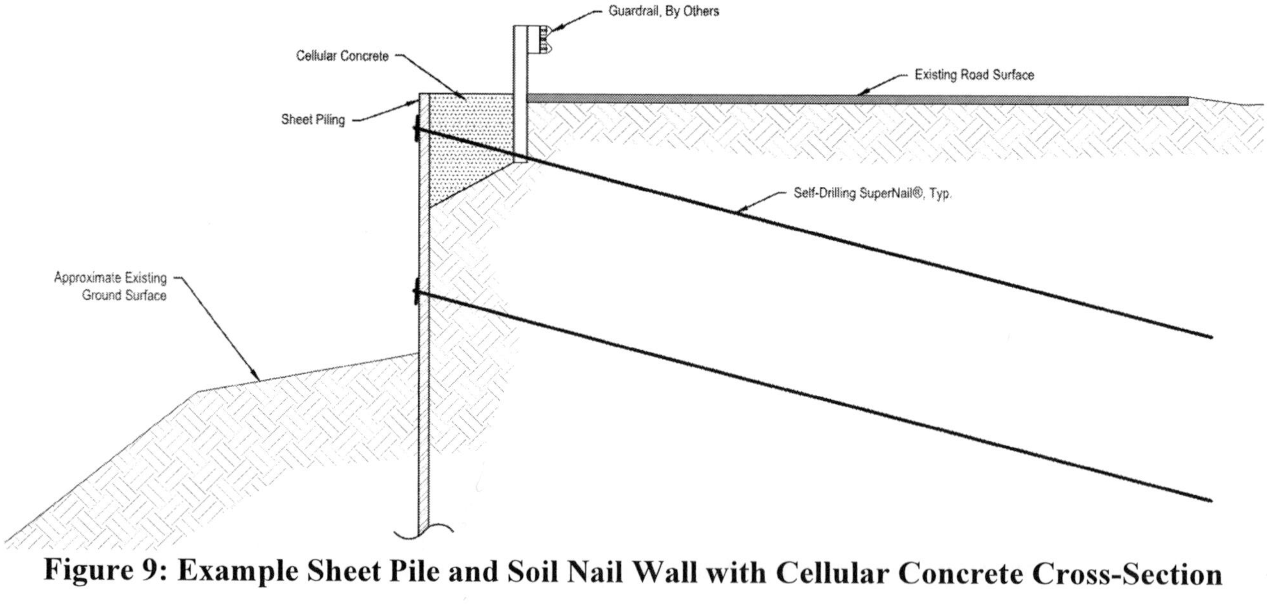

Figure 9: Example Sheet Pile and Soil Nail Wall with Cellular Concrete Cross-Section

During the landslide repair's construction, continued flowing water in the repair area coupled with rain events and erosion of material under the roadway promoted pavement breakage as the weight of the pavement structure had nothing to bear on and failed under its own weight. There was no visible scarp or cracking in the pavement during our initial site visit, and its later presence required some sudden engineering decision-making.

Figure 10: Pavement Damage and Material Loss

Cellular Concrete as a Lightweight Backfill

Due to the pavement structure's undermining, a large volume of material loss needed to be replaced to achieve roadway reclamation and shoulder rebuilding. With the water being aggressive and damaging on this challenging site, an impermeable material was an ideal choice. The empty space needing to be filled was large in volume, and as this was not initially expected at the project's commencement, an economic choice needed to be made. Cellular concrete once again proved to be a great choice. With its impenetrable nature, water will not be able to build up behind the sheets or under the pavement structure anymore. When creating the cellular concrete on-site, yields of typically around three times the original volume of neat grout is reached when adding preformed foam to the mix. This allows costs to remain low when purchasing material to fill that void space. Additional benefits include:

- Negligible lateral pressure on the sheet piles.
- High bearing capacities for live traffic and other loading conditions.
- The shock absorbing nature for potential guardrail impacts.

Figure 11: Stabilized Roadway with Cellular Concrete Build Up

VOID FILLING CASE STUDY

State Route 008 in Hamilton County, Tennessee, experienced pavement cracking and settlement extending to the middle of the roadway, linear cracking in the shoulder area, and loss of shoulder and support of the guardrail posts. With the project limits are on the Pennington formation *(7)* with cobbly and stony colluvium *(5)*, the material underneath the roadway contained a lot of rip rap. A solid rock face is present on the inboard side, draining water toward the road and the outboard slope. With the steep sloping conditions and the rocky material under the roadway, flowing water could damage the material propping up the street, resulting in the activated landslide in this area. With the pavement cracking and dropping, more and more water would infiltrate and lead to more damage. Quickly repairing the slope and repaving was crucial to the project's success and saved State Route 008 before extensive reconstruction and complete road closure would be required on this highly traveled roadway.

Figure 12: SR 8, LM 15.97 Prior to Construction

Repair Plan and Construction

Preserving 265 linear feet of road platform along State Route 008 was accomplished with a soil nail wall, and shoulder build-up, similar to KY 338 mentioned earlier in this paper, although taller with more rows of soil nails. Depending on how far into the roadway the scarp line was, our crews could optimize soil nail lengths. While drilling and grouting the soil nails during construction, the construction crew noted that several holes took much more grout than expected. Increased grout uptake became an issue, as the soil nail elements require a set bond strength to provide the industry standard factor of safety of 1.3. As mentioned previously, this roadway was initially constructed with rip rap underneath the pavement structure, encouraging grout to permeate from the borehole column. The area's geology, having the presence of abundant rhombohedral voids indicative of the removal of calcite or dolomite crystals *(8),* caused additional issues during grouting operations.

Figure 13: SR 8, LM 15.97 During Construction

Cellular Concrete for Void Filling

After understanding that the boreholes drilled from the self-drilling SuperNails® were not providing proper grout coverage and adequate bond strength, alternative operations needed to be considered. Cellular concrete once again became the best available option to this project. What was needed was the soil nail borehole columns to fill up with neat grout and provide enough bond strength to stabilize the landslide properly. Cellular concrete was able to fill the large voids through injection into the landslide mass with self-drilling hollow bar soil nails rather than drilling with air, neat grout, or water. After the cellular concrete set, a switch to neat grout was made to provide higher bond strength than a cellular concrete column would provide. Filling these voids with a granular compacted fill or some other material is impossible. Pullout testing was performed to verify the bond strength and confirmed this void filling method and grouting provided the bond strength needed to stabilize the landslide.

Figure 14: Rocky Grouting Conditions

CONCLUSION

Cellular concrete is an excellent material to utilize for geohazard mitigation. There are several advantages for its use compared to other materials or means and methods, including availability, uncomplicated placement, quick installation, low cost, simplicity, flexible utilization, and superior physical properties. Cellular concrete has become somewhat commonplace in other industries, and geotechnical contractors should consider using it more often in their applications. Geo-structural construction is never as exact in the field as on paper, and cellular concrete provides flexibility when dealing with issues that come with native soils and slip planes. This material has proven itself a worthy alternative when restoring roadway and shoulder elevations, filling voids, and as a lightweight backfill material as described earlier. Cellular concrete will not solve every problem, particularly if compressive strengths must be high, but this material is a tool that should be considered for these non-traditional uses.

REFERENCES

1. ACI Committee 523. *Guide for Cast-in-Place Low-Density Cellular Concrete.* ACI 523.1R-06. American Concrete Institute, Farmington Hills, MI, August 2006.

2. F. Fouad. "Chapter 47: Cellular Concrete". *Significance of Tests and Properties of Concrete and Concrete-Making Materials*, ed. J. Lamond and J. Pielert (West Conshohocken, PA: ASTM International, 2006), 561-569.

3. American Concrete Institute. *Controlled Low Strength Materials (CLSM)*. Report No. 229R-94, ACI Committee 229, Detroit, Michigan, July 1994.

4. Noger, M.C., compiler, 1988, Geologic map of Kentucky: sesquicentennial edition of the Kentucky Geological Survey: U.S. Geological Survey and the Kentucky Geological Survey, scale 1:500,000.

5. Soil Survey Staff, Natural Resources Conservation Service, United States Department of Agriculture. Web Soil Survey. Available online at the following link: http://websoilsurvey.sc.egov.usda.gov/. Accessed June 20, 2020.

6. Gray, Henry H., Ault, Curtis, H., and Keller, Stanley, J., 1987, Bedrock geologic map of Indiana: Dept. of Natural Resources, Indiana Geological Survey, Miscellaneous Map 48, scale 1:500,000.

7. Hardeman, W.D., Miller, R.A., and Swingle, G.D., 1966, Geologic Map of Tennessee: Division of Geology, Tennessee Department of Environment and Conservation, 4 sheets, scale 1:250,000.

8. Chattanooga shale and related rocks of central Tennessee and nearby areas, by Louis C. Conant and Yernon E. Swanson. Washington, U.S. Govt. Print. Off., 1961.

Use of Smart Rocks to Improve Rock Slope Design

Bruma Souza
University of New Hampshire, Department of Civil Engineering
33 Academic Way
Durham, NH 03824
(603)-862-1428
bruma.souza@unh.edu

Jean Benoît
University of New Hampshire, Department of Civil Engineering
jean.benoit@unh.edu

Prepared for the 71st Highway Geology Symposium, May, 2022

Acknowledgements

The authors would like to thank the New Hampshire Department of Transportation Bureau of Materials and Research, in special Krystle Pelham and Neil Olson, for funding and providing all necessary support to conduct this experimental work. Acknowledgments also to Artur Apostolov for his extensive work improving the Smart Rock sensors used in these tests. Thank you also to the Vermont Agency of Transportation and Ameritech for their significant collaboration and interest in this experimental work.

Disclaimer

Statements and views presented in this paper are strictly those of the author(s), and do not necessarily reflect positions held by their affiliations, the Highway Geology Symposium (HGS), or others acknowledged above. The mention of trade names for commercial products does not imply the approval or endorsement by HGS.

Copyright Notice

ABSTRACT

For many states, rockfalls of any size present serious risks to motorists on highways and roads across the country. Assessing these hazards is difficult as it relies on highly empirical methods based on assumed and/or measured slope and terrain surfaces and rock rebound parameters, which can predict unrealistic trajectories due to inaccurate inputs. Research undertaken at the University of New Hampshire over the last two decades includes the development of Smart Rocks (SR), which have been used to instrument field rockfall experiments. The fourth-generation SR sensors are small capsules about 2 inches in length and 1 inch in diameter, equipped with a ±400 g and a ±16 g 3-axis accelerometer and a ±4000 dps high-rate gyroscope, embedded in test rocks and dropped from medium to high hazard rock slopes. This paper summarizes the work performed at a high-hazard rock cut in Vermont during ongoing scaling work. SRs were inserted in the native rocks previously drilled in the laboratory, as well as in two in-place rocks prior to being scaled down. Small- and large-scale acceleration and rotational velocity measurements were obtained and used to characterize rock movement over time. These field experiments have shown that acceleration and rotational velocity data from scaled blocks are significantly less than for smaller blocks released at the same site. This experimental campaign has demonstrated that different block sizes can experience substantially distinct behaviors in rockfall motion, and measurements from the rock perspective are promising in improving our rockfall understanding. A broader description of rockfall movements can be used to enhance input parameters in computer rockfall modeling, which often disregards rotational data in kinetic energy estimates.

INTRODUCTION

Rockfall trajectories are typically simulated through computational modeling to assist in the design of protective structures. This topic is increasingly relevant as climatic changes lead to further erosion of slopes, cliffs, and rocky terrains. Physical and chemical weathering processes dislodge portions of slopes, which lead to rockfall and pose a safety hazard to motorists, infrastructure, and buildings nearby.

The uncertainty related to rockfall behavior and model input parameters is still significantly high. The present-day protective structure design is based on kinetic energy estimates, which typically disregard or inaccurately predict essential aspects of rockfall modeling such as rotational energy and rock rebound (Turner and Duffy, 2012). In addition to overly conservative simulation models, current methods of rockfall analysis typically rely on field/laboratory measurements, high-frame video recording systems, and detailed event back-analyses. However, these techniques often do not provide detailed information about rock-surface interaction and translational and rotational rock kinematics (Caviezel and Gerber, 2018). To address this issue, researchers have started to instrument test rocks with high-rate sampling acceleration and rotational velocity sensors in field rockfall experiments (Caviezel et al., 2018; Disenhof, 2018).

Research conducted at the University of New Hampshire (Durham, NH, USA) over the last two decades developed and improved four generations of Smart Rock (SR) sensors, capable of instrumenting field and laboratory rockfall experiments from the perspective of the falling rock (Harding, 2011; Gullison, 2013; Harding et al., 2014; Apostolov, 2016; Apostolov and Benoît, 2017; Disenhof, 2018; Souza, 2021). Recent research conducted by Disenhof (2018) and Souza (2021) demonstrated the functionality of a Smart Rock for rockfall applications. The measured acceleration and rotational velocity outputs can be used to validate and improve rockfall computational models and help with mitigation methods, as rotational kinetic energy and impact forces can be assessed more accurately.

SMART ROCK SENSOR

Smart Rock sensors have been used extensively at the University of New Hampshire to characterize rock movement over time (free-fall, bouncing, rolling, sliding). The fourth-generation Smart Rocks consist of 3D printed capsules 2 inches in length and 1 inch in diameter (Figure 1), equipped with a ±400 g and a ±16 g 3-axis accelerometer, a ±4000 dps high-rate gyroscope, an altimeter, and a temperature sensor. The Smart Rock records acceleration, rotational velocity, altitude, and temperature data at a sampling frequency of 100 Hz while embedded in field-collected rocks. Sampling frequency can be increased to 500 Hz if the altimeter is not used. The recorded data is automatically saved to a micro-SD card as a .csv file to be analyzed using MATLAB or spreadsheets such as Excel.

The dual accelerometers allow the SR to capture the full range of accelerations the test rock may experience during a rockfall. While the ±400 g accelerometer captures larger magnitude accelerations produced by higher impacts from a fall or a bounce, the ±16 g accelerometer captures smaller magnitude accelerations not gathered from the high-g accelerometer since accelerations within ±2 g are typically obscured by noise in the high-g accelerometer. The low-g accelerometer was limited purposely to ±8 g to decrease signal noise and presents a significant advantage in evaluating the rock behavior as it allows users to identify whether the rock is in free fall or at rest.

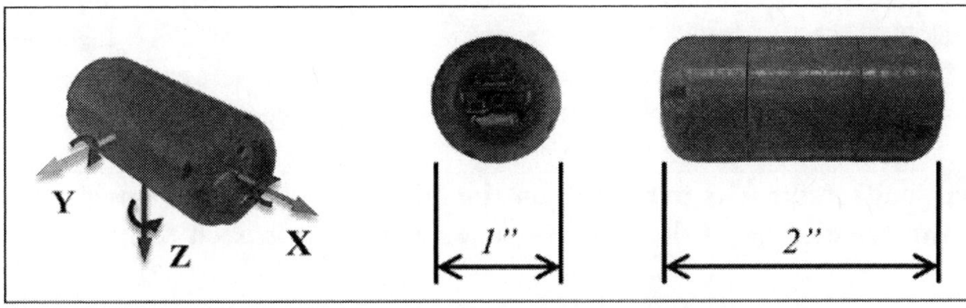

Figure 1 – Fourth-generation Smart Rock sensor.

METHODOLOGY

Site location and characteristics

Eight experimental rockfalls were conducted in two sections of a two-lane high-hazard rock cut in Townshend, Vermont, with heights ranging from 35 to 65 ft. These tests were performed during scaling work conducted for the Vermont Agency of Transportation (VTrans) by Ameritech. During ongoing work, the high rockfall risk required one lane to be temporarily closed, and a concrete barrier was placed between both lanes in the middle of the road.

Due to ongoing scaling work, the catchment ditch was covered with boulders and rock talus. The toe of the slope is inclined towards the road and located 8.2 ft away from the road shoulder. In addition, the slope angles during the scaling work varied between 30° and 80°.

Test rocks

In order to match the slope composition, the test rocks used in the field experiments were retrieved from the site location. Five local amphibolite and greenstone metamorphic rocks (Figure 2) ranging between 12 and 26 lbs were previously prepared in the laboratory and drilled in their centers of gravity to avoid eccentricity from SR measurements during the tests. An additional 12-lbs New Hampshire metamorphic block (referred to as "reference" rock) used in previous research at UNH was also assessed in this site.

Since the test rocks needed to be manually hoisted or hand-carried to the top of the test slopes, the tested block sizes and weights were limiting factors in this experimental campaign. To address this issue, two experimental rockfalls were performed with larger blocks in-place during scaling work (Figure 3). The characteristics of the test rocks used are presented in Table 1. The shape of each rock was classified according to the particle shape classification diagram developed by Sneed and Folk (1958), based on the length, width, and thickness of the block.

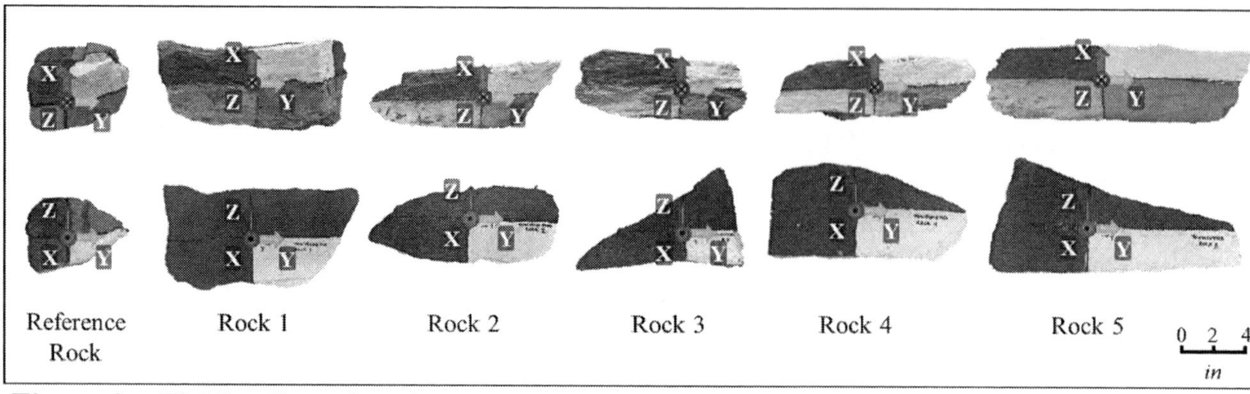

Figure 2 – Field-collected rocks prepared on the laboratory. The axes orientations indicate the orientation of the Smart Rock sensor inside each test rock.

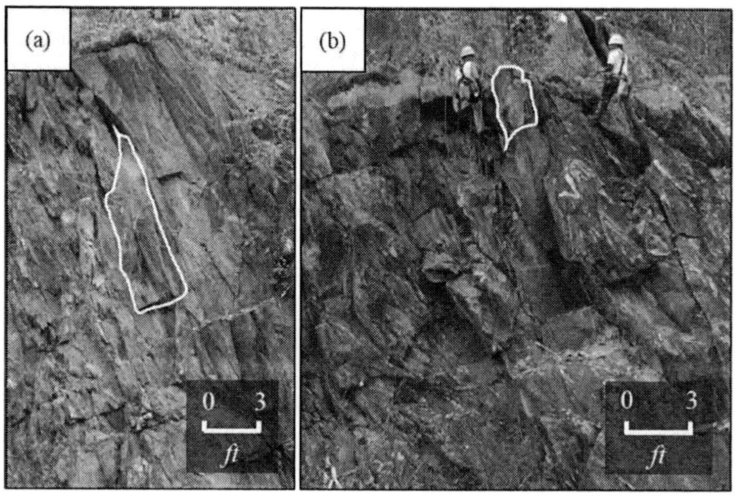

Figure 3 – (a) Second and (b) first scaled rocks (the pink dots mark the SR location).

Table 1 – Test rock characteristics: Townshend, VT

Rock ID	Mass (lbs)	Dimensions (in.)			Shape	Mass moment of inertia lbs·ft²		
		Length Y	Width X	Height Z		I_{XX}	I_{YY}	I_{ZZ}
Reference	11.5	7.9	4.7	4.7	Compact Elongated	0.57	0.57	0.31
1	25.5	10.6	5.1	5.5	Compact Elongated	2.11	0.74	2.04
2	12.7	11.4	3.9	4.7	Elongated	0.76	0.21	0.71
3	13.8	7.9	4.3	4.7	Compact Elongated	0.93	3.32	0.83
4	15.1	11.8	3.5	5.1	Elongated	1.07	0.26	1.00
5	25.4	15.4	4.7	5.5	Elongated	2.80	0.69	2.73
Scaled 1	5,000	45	25	45	Compact	13,000	8,300	8,300
Scaled 2	21,200	120	40	45	Elongated	200,000	45,000	190,000

Test preparation

Before starting each test, the Smart Rock was activated and self-calibrated. The SR was placed inside the drilled holes with known axes orientations (as shown in Figure 2), and a 1-inch diameter expandable rubber plug with a through-hole screw was used to confine the SR securely. The opening in the screw and the SR window hole allow the altimeter to record data through exposure to atmospheric pressure.

After each rock was prepared, a pulley, rope, and bucket were used to hoist them to the top of the slope. The test operator tapped the rock onto the slope surface three times to indicate the start of each test in the data signal; then, the rock was released from the slope with minimal initial velocity possible (preferably zero). After rockfall, the runout distance (perpendicular and parallel) from the slope toe was measured, and the SR was removed from the rock. The sensor data was immediately available for post-processing after data recording. The test data can be easily identified through peaks in acceleration during the initiation taps as well as during the test.

The drop heights were measured in the field with a total station for comparisons with the sensor altimeter data. All field experiments were recorded at 30 fps perpendicularly to the slope face. The rock movement could be tracked using the application Tracker 5.1.5 by Physlets, which assumes that the camera is stationary and perpendicular to the object in motion. The application allows the user to obtain vertical and horizontal displacement and velocity data over time by tracking the rock CG position at each frame. A 2D reference axis and a calibration stick for dimension scaling are defined, and the center of gravity position of the block is tracked at each video frame. The tracking software output was used to evaluate rockfall motion in conjunction with the sensor retrieved data.

The rocks in place were drilled prior to scaling, and the Smart Rock sensors were inserted for instrumentation of large-scale rockfalls. Due to the significant size of the scaled blocks, the holes could not be drilled at the center of gravity of these blocks. The SRs were placed by the rock scalers in holes that they drilled with the portable hand drill used in the laboratory, and the sensor orientations inside the scaled blocks were not known. The locations of the SRs were spray painted for visual tracking since video tracking was not possible in these experiments due to the difficulty in accurately estimating the SR position.

Data processing

The raw data for each rockfall test were processed and plotted using MATLAB. After selecting the time intervals of interest for data analysis, the script calculates relevant aspects from the sensor data, such as resultant acceleration (Equation 1) and rotation (Equation 2). The resultant acceleration vector is composed of both low- and high-g accelerometers, in which low-g acceleration resultants higher than 8 g were replaced by the high-g resultant acceleration.

$$Acceleration_{RES} = \sqrt{A_X^2 + A_Y^2 + A_Z^2} \qquad \text{(Equation 1)}$$

$$Rotational\ velocity_{RES} = \sqrt{R_X^2 + R_Y^2 + R_Z^2} \qquad \text{(Equation 2)}$$

where: $Acceleration_{RES}$ = resultant acceleration,
$Rotational\ velocity_{RES}$ = resultant rotational velocity,
A_X, A_Y, and A_Z = acceleration in X, Y, and Z, respectively, and
G_X, G_Y, and G_Z = rotational velocities about X, Y, and Z, respectively.

The resultant acceleration data also provides information to estimate impact forces to a surface or barrier, which are relevant for protective design against rockfall. These respective resulting g-forces can be converted to force intensities using the rock mass and gravity acceleration (g = 32.17 ft/s²) in Equation 3. Estimating impact forces is fundamental in the design of protective structures, especially at less inclined slopes where higher horizontal motion is likely to be developed. For more details on the retrieved sensor and video test data analysis, the reader is referred to Chapter 4 of Souza (2021).

$$Impact\ force = (Resultant\ g_{force}) * g * (rock\ mass) \qquad \text{(Equation 3)}$$

RESULTS

Test rocks prepared in the laboratory

All rockfall tests were successfully recorded with the fourth-generation Smart Rock. The rockfall trajectories for the six tests with the smaller rocks are presented in Figure 4. The angle reduction from 80° to 30° in the mid-slope cross-section (approximately 30 ft above the ground level) led the block trajectories to bounce and increase their horizontal dispersion. Bounce heights in this launch feature were as high as 3.3 ft for the reference rock.

Figure 4 – Rockfall trajectories: Townshend VT. Please note some horizontal distortion in the trajectories due to the camera position and wide lens to capture the entire slope.

Each test video was analyzed individually and compared to the SR data. An example of video and sensor data compatibility verification is shown in Figures 5 and 6. The letters A through D in both figures indicate the different rockfall stages, matched through both SR and video recording times.

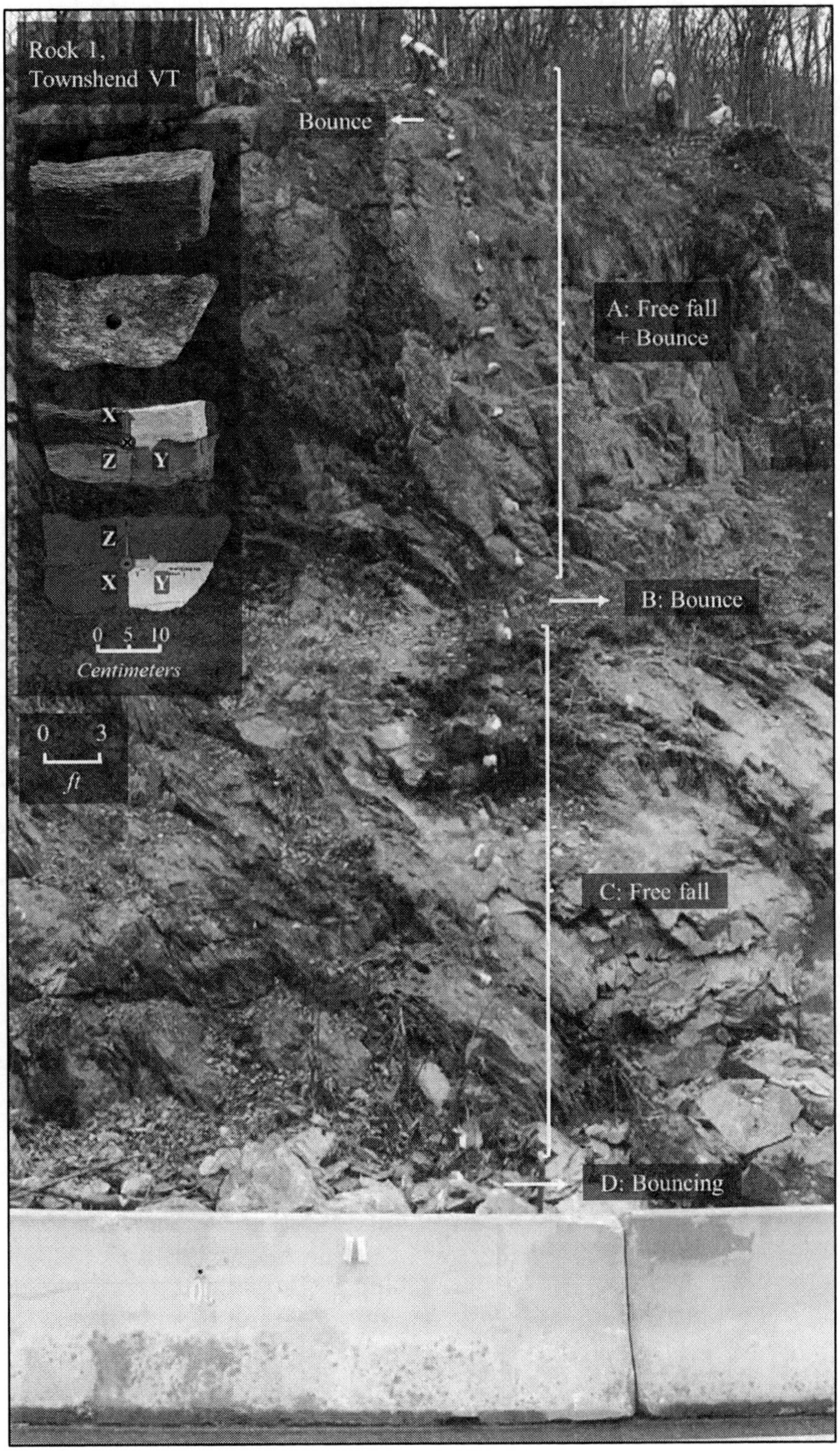

Figure 5 – Rockfall trajectory: rock 1, Townshend, VT.

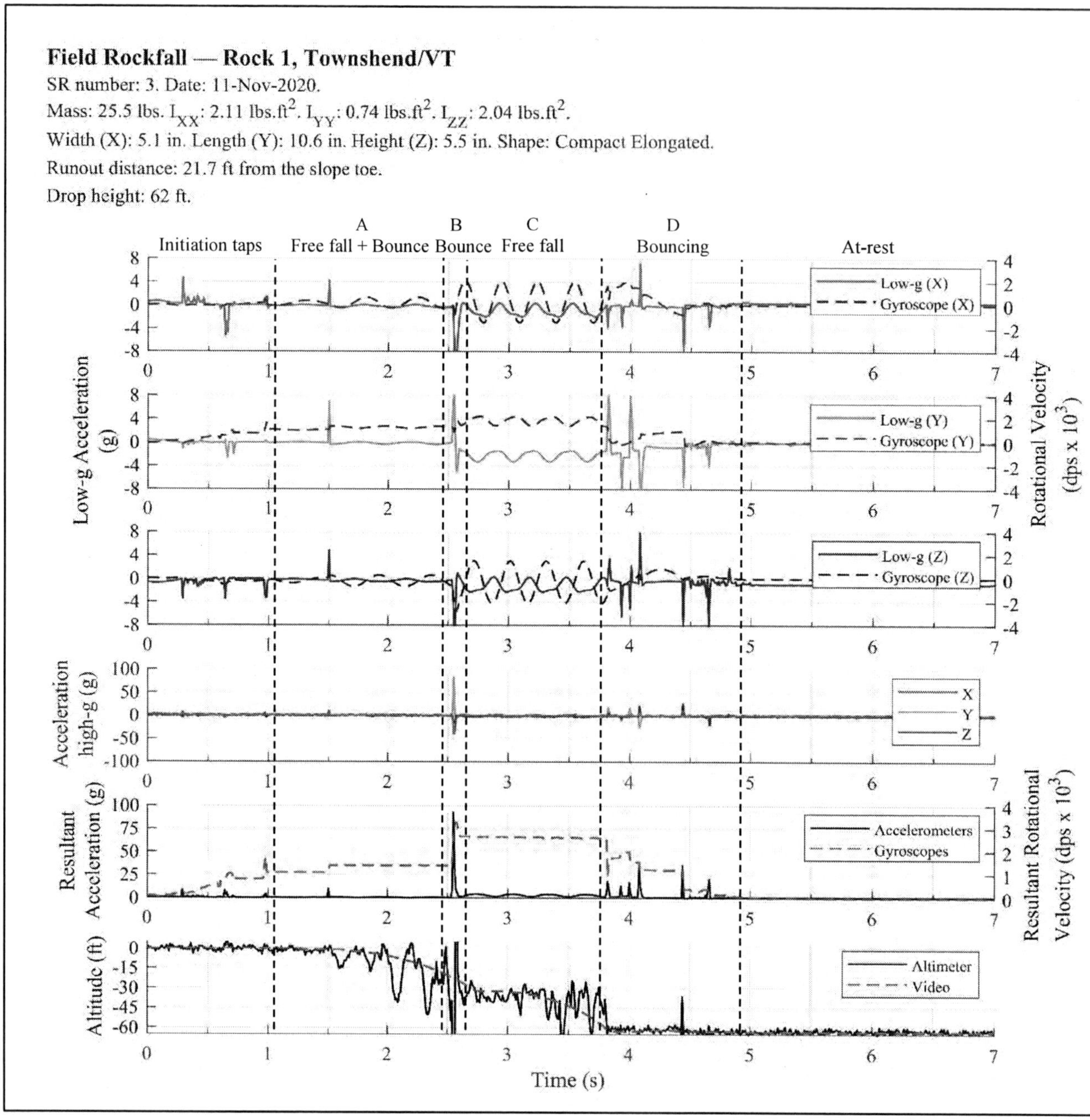

Figure 6 – Smart Rock data: rock 1, Townshend VT.

Rock 1, a 25.5 lbs compact elongated block, was released from a 62 ft drop height. Rock 1 rotated at an approximate rate of 1200 dps (A) until a peak acceleration of 93 g (2.5-kip force) at mid-slope (B). The block rotation increased to 2640 dps at a second free fall (C) before bouncing against the talus catchment ditch and reaching the road (D). Due to the barrier positioned for rockfall protection, video measurements could not be obtained at the lower portion of the trajectory that reached the road. Rock 1 rotated about all three principal axes, but predominant rotation about its shortest axis of inertia (Y, Figure 7) was observed during the entire trajectory.

Figure 7 – Rock 1: rotation about the Y axis (axis of smallest inertia)

The altimeter measurements could be verified with video analysis and are a promising tool for rockfall analyses when video tracking is not feasible. The recorded altimeter data shows a significant noise level which increases during rapid movements and upon impacts exceeding the low-g accelerometer limit of 8 g. The altimeter noise does not allow clear visualization of rock position but allowed to easily identify the test in the sensor data and measure the total block displacement during rockfall.

Table 2 summarizes the test results from the blocks previously prepared in the laboratory. All test blocks experienced similar modes of motion, with one or two impacts at mid-slope separating two major free-falls.

Table 2 – Field rockfall summary (smaller blocks): Townshend, VT

Rock ID	Slope angle	Drop height (ft)	Displacements			Smart Rock Resultant Data			Maximum impact force (kips)
			Lateral (ft)	Lateral dispersion (%)	Runout from toe (ft)	Maximum acceleration (g)	Maximum rotation (dps)	Average rotation (dps)	
Ref	75° / 55°	62	0.7	1%	2.7	206	3172	869	2.5
1	75° / 55°	62	2.9	4%	21.7	93	3304	1424	2.5
2	75° / 55°	62	1.3	2%	10.5	182	3825	1448	2.2
3	80° / 45°	55	-13.3	16%	0.0	295	2901	1209	4.0
4	80° / 45°	55	-6.7	8%	5.2	147	3929	1342	2.2
5	80° / 45°	55	-6.7	8%	1.0	66	3063	690	1.6
Average			4.5	6%	9.2	165	3366	1164	2.5
Standard deviation			6.3	6%	9.5	83	419	314	0.9

Lateral dispersion in rockfall is defined as the ratio of the horizontal distance and the slope length, measured along with the slope profile (Azzoni and de Freitas, 1995). Along with the runout distance measured from the slope toe, lateral displacement estimates are helpful to characterize rockfall dispersion and design compatible protective structures.

The maximum resultant acceleration was equal to 165 g, and the test blocks produced an average maximum impact force of 2.5 kips. Except for rock 5, which experienced the lowest peak acceleration, all remaining rocks exerted peak impact forces above 2 kips. The location of the maximum impact force varied between the experimental tests. Three tests experienced their peak g-forces during bouncing at mid-slope (1, 3, reference rock), while the remaining blocks had their peak accelerations measured upon impact on the catchment ditch (2, 4, 5).

All test blocks had an increase in rotational velocity after bouncing in the middle of their trajectories and had predominant rotation about their shortest axis of inertia, Y, except for the reference rock. This difference in behavior probably occurs because the local rocks from Townshend are more elongated than the 12-lbs metamorphic reference block. All tests except rock 3 had maximum rotation rates higher than 3000 dps (8.3 rotations/s). The remaining test trajectories and detailed sensor data at this site location can be found in Souza (2021).

Test rocks drilled in-place

The first test was conducted with a single SR on a roughly 5,000 lbs "compact" block (Figure 3a), and data were recorded at a sampling frequency of 100 Hz. The scaled block trajectory and SR data are presented in Figures 8 and 9.

After the block was manually dislodged by the scalers (A), it went into free fall (B, D) with an intermediate bounce at mid-slope (C) and a second bounce upon ground contact (E). The peak acceleration of 42 g occurred at C, and an impact force of approximately 200 kips was experienced. The maximum resultant rotation of 425 dps was developed during the second free fall (D).

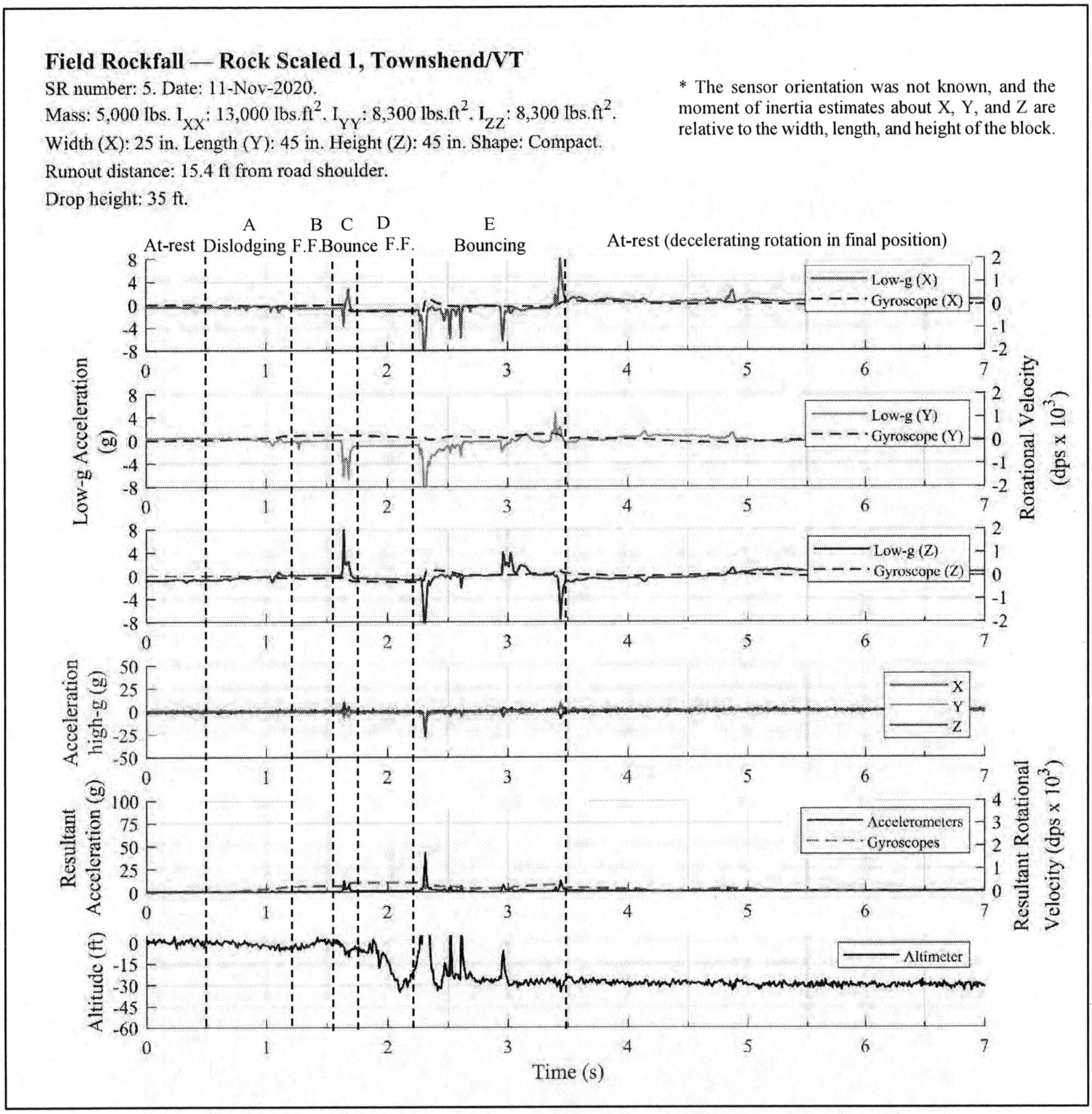

Figure 8 – Smart Rock test data: first scaled rock, Townshend VT. "F.F.": free-fall.

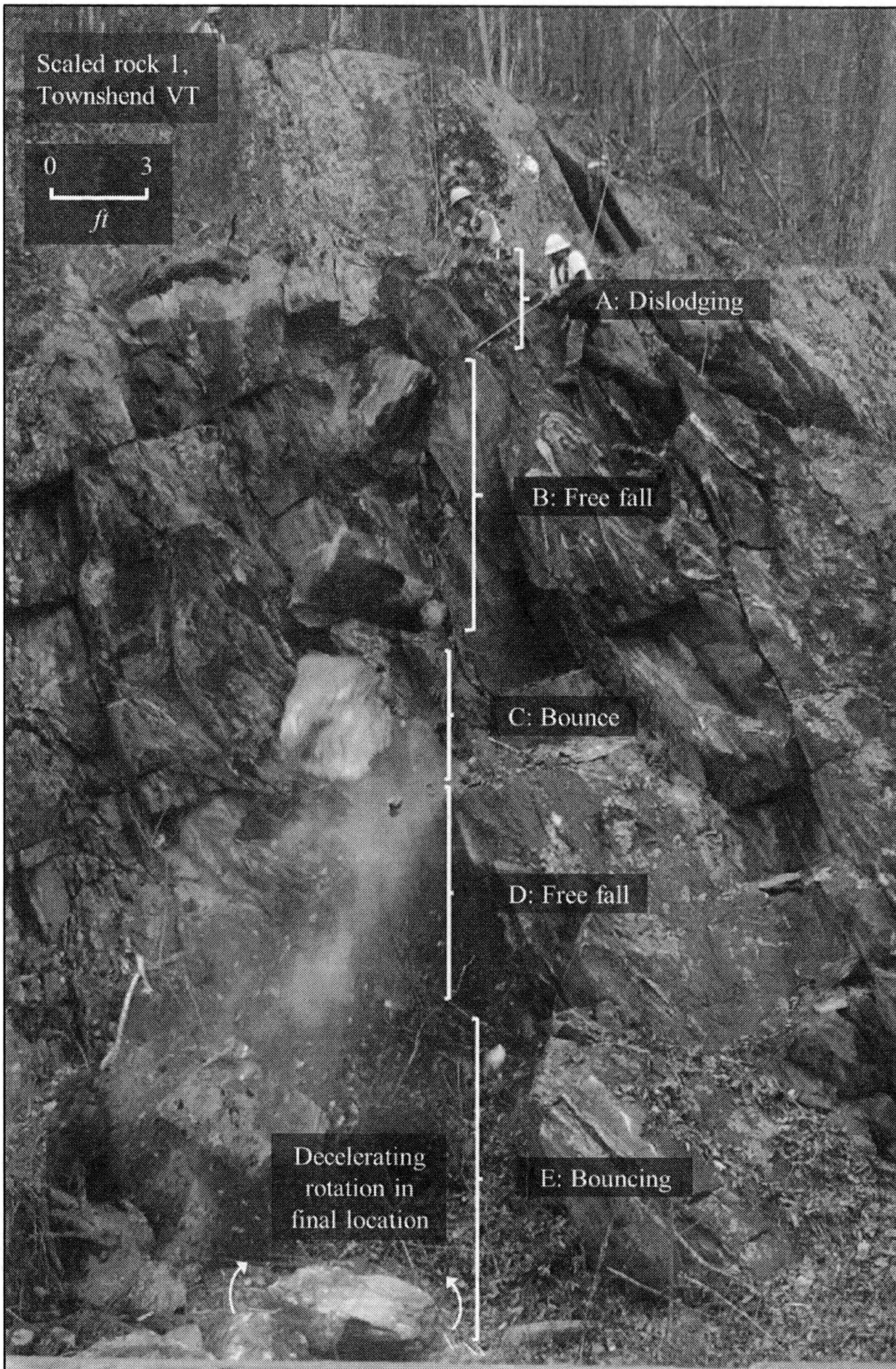

Figure 9 – Rockfall trajectory: first scaled block, Townshend VT.

A second test was conducted with an elongated block of a minimum dimension equal to 3.3 ft. Due to the significant length of the scaled rock, three SRs were positioned inside the block (Figure 10). The top and bottom sensors had the altimeter enabled and recorded data at 100 Hz. The middle SR had the altimeter disabled and recorded data at 500 Hz. The rock was scaled using air pillows placed inside the discontinuity on the upper left side of the block and pry bars.

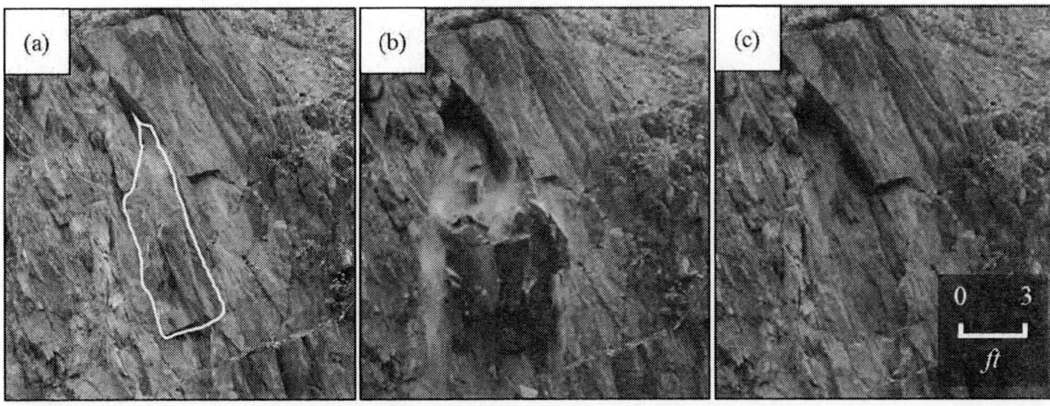

Figure 10 – Second scaled rock (a) prior, (b) during, and (c) after rockfall.

From frontal and lateral video recordings, although position tracking was not possible, it was observed that the block starts dislodging from the top and goes into free fall. The top of the block then impacts the ground surface, and the scaled rock bounces while rotating about the point of impact on the ground (near the top SR) until completely stopping.

A comparison between the experimental data measured from three Smart Rocks positioned in three distinct positions of a 10 ft long scaled block is presented in Figure 11. Since the sensor rotation was not known, only the resultant data were compared. The graph demonstrates how the resultant rotation rates during rock dislodging were similar, and how the acceleration peak for the top sensor stands out compared to the other two SRs. As expected, higher rotational motion was measured about the top Smart Rock, where ground contact initially occurred.

Upon its first impact on the ground, the upper SR recorded a peak acceleration of 148 g and rotational velocity of 100 dps. The maximum impact force estimated for this sensor was equal to approximately 3000 kips. The altimeter noise did not allow clear visualization of rock position but allowed to easily identify the start of the test in the sensor data and the moment of ground impact, as the three initiation taps before the test could not be performed. Block rotation was significantly lower than 1000 dps until ground impacts and showed a clear peak when the block rotates about the top SR.

As seen in the top SR, the mid-SR at 500 Hz also described a resultant rotational velocity of 100 dps during free fall. A smaller peak acceleration of 27 g was recorded upon impact, implying an impact force of approximately 450 kips. The rotation rate measured during rock bouncing was smaller than recorded with the top SR, and a resultant peak rotation of 190 dps was observed.

Finally, for the lower SR, a lower acceleration of 17 g was recorded during ground impact, exerting an impact force of approximately 350 kips. The block rotation during free fall was also equal to 100 dps, and block rotation during bouncing behavior was very similar to the measured data with the middle sensor.

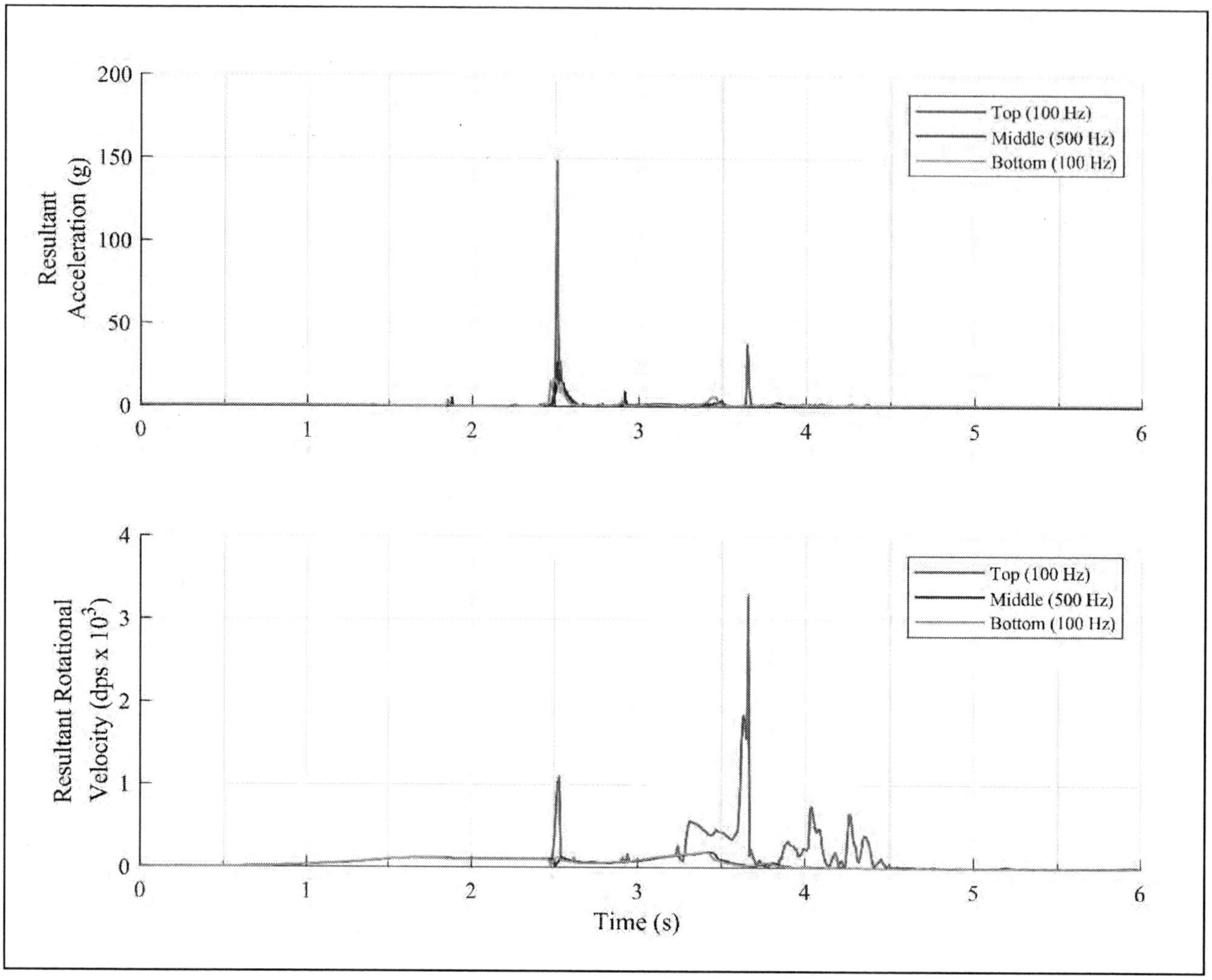

Figure 11 – Combination of the resultant data for the three SRs in the second scaled block, Townshend VT.

The plotted accelerations and rotation for the bottom (100 Hz sampling frequency) and middle (500 Hz sampling frequency) were similar and indicate that a sampling frequency of 100 Hz is sufficient to capture rockfall motion. Smart Rock measurements at 100 Hz are advantageous due to the aid of the altimeter measurements to help identify rock position. Although modes of motion are also readily identified in the 500 Hz data, it is easier to relate rockfall motion with visual observations and video measurements if the altimeter is enabled.

A summary of the SR test data for the scaled blocks is presented in Table 3. The instrumented rockfalls performed at the Townshend site demonstrated that larger blocks tend to experience lower peak accelerations and lower rotational velocities. The lower rotational rates can be related to the significantly higher inertia of large-scale rockfalls, representing a greater difficulty in rotating the block about their principal axes. Although these rotation rates are less than in small-scale events, the rotational KE component is still expected to be significant due to the naturally higher moments of inertia. Besides, although lower accelerations are observed, the impact forces and potential risk of damage produced are significantly greater than in small-scale rockfalls.

Table 3 – Field rockfall summary (scaled blocks): Townshend, VT				
Rock ID	Smart Rock Resultant Data			Maximum impact force (kips)
	Maximum acceleration (g)	Maximum rotation (dps)	Average rotation (dps)	
Scaled 1	42	429	171	200
Scaled 2 (bottom)	17	189	85	350
Scaled 2 (middle)	27	189	60	450
Scaled 2 (top)	148	3292	200	3000

Table 3 also displays how the peak accelerations gradually decrease according to the block position, demonstrating that sensor eccentricity is a crucial factor that can strongly bias rockfall results if the drilling position is unknown.

DISCUSSION

The data recorded by the fourth-generation Smart Rock was successful in obtaining rockfall motion for field-collected and in-place blocks prior to scaling. The findings of this preliminary work demonstrated that acceleration and rotational velocity data from the rock perspective present a high potential to expand rockfall understanding and modeling.

The maximum impact force on a rockfall typically occurs upon impact against the rock face or stiffer material at the ground level (asphalt and rock talus). The acceleration measurements can be described using physics principles. The high-g accelerometer data verified how objects dropped onto rigid and less deformable surfaces can achieve remarkably high levels of acceleration. According to Leonhardt (2001), the acceleration experienced by a dropped object can be estimated using Equation 4.

$$a = \sqrt{\frac{E\,A\,g\,d_1}{h\,m}} \qquad \text{(Equation 4)}$$

Where:
a = acceleration,
A = area of the object being compressed,
E = modulus of elasticity of the dropped object,
g = acceleration of gravity (9.81 m/s^2),
d_1 = drop height,
h = compressed height of the object, and
m = mass of the object.

It was observed that rocks of lower mass generally experienced higher acceleration magnitudes, especially if comparing the field-collected and scaled block data. In turn, consequently, although the sensor has generally recorded higher accelerations inside lighter blocks, heavier blocks typically exert higher impact forces.

Coupled with the accelerometer data, the measured rotational velocities in a rockfall experiment can be used to readily identify changes in rock motion, especially during bouncing and free-falling periods, through constant resultant rotation or abrupt changes in rotational motion, respectively. Blocks of smaller mass were more easily subjected to changes in rotation. This behavior can be associated with the difficulty in rotating blocks with higher mass (higher moments of inertia) for shorter slopes normally encountered in New England.

After rockfall, the test blocks predominantly bounced and rolled after the initial impact with the catchment ditch. A small number of tests completely stopped immediately after impact, demonstrating a complete dissipation of the kinetic energy.

Azzoni and de Freitas (1995) estimate that lateral dispersion of rockfalls typically varies between 10% and 20%. In this test program, an average lateral dispersion of 6% was measured, near the expected range. Two of the three tests (except for the reference rock) released from the 62 ft tall cross-section reached the road, and all three tests dropped from the 55 ft tall cross-section stopped within the ditch limits.

Rock bouncing against the 30° launch feature at mid-slope was a determinant factor to increase runout distances, especially at higher rotation rates when released from 62 ft. Pierson et al. (2001) associate increases of runout distances upon impacts on launch features along the slope length. In addition, less inclined surfaces near 45° are more concerning in rockfall risk mitigation, as they create higher lateral and rotational motion conditions, which are more challenging to dissipate energy (Ritchie, 1963). The measured endpoint locations demonstrate the need for the scaling work performed at the Townshend site.

CONCLUSION

The fourth-generation Smart Rock accurately recorded acceleration, rotational velocity, and altitude from the perspective of the falling rock. In addition, the video tracking measurements were compatible with the added altitude sensor, whose measurements were useful for precisely identifying the time intervals of the rockfall experiments.

The sensor is a promising tool to broaden rock bouncing behavior understanding, whose rotational energy is often disregarded by most studies. When combined with translational velocity data, the rotation data from the falling rock perspective allows accurate kinetic energy calculations, which can be used to estimate more realistic restitution parameters that truly reproduce rockfall motion.

The findings of this study suggest that rockfall events are unpredictable and require further investigation and kinetic energy estimates from the perspective of the falling rock for a safer and in some cases less conservative protective design. Furthermore, the physical motions described by bouncing and rolling phenomena are the least comprehended by rockfall studies, given the significant number of variables regarding impact conditions and rock characteristics. Therefore, the increasing demand for more realistic modeling input parameters is associated with public safety as a primary factor and saves time and resources, redirecting to a higher number of medium-to-high hazard rock cuts.

REFERENCES:

Apostolov, A. (2016). Development and testing of motion tracking "Smart Rock" devices for geotechnical applications. (Master's thesis). University of New Hampshire, Durham, NH.

Apostolov, A. and Benoît, J. (2017). Motion Tracking "Smart Rock" Device for the Study of Landslide and Debris Flow Mechanisms. North American Symposium on Landslides. Roanoke, VA, June 4-8.

Azzoni, A., and de Freitas, M. H. (1995). Experimentally gained parameters, decisive for rock fall analysis. Rock mechanics and rock engineering, 28(2), 111-124.

Caviezel, A., and Gerber, W. (2018). Brief Communication: Measuring rock decelerations and rotation changes during short-duration ground impacts. Natural Hazards and Earth System Sciences, 18(11), 3145-3151.

Caviezel, A., Schaffner, M., Cavigelli, L., Niklaus, P., Bühler, Y., Bartelt, P., and Magno, M. (2018b). Design and evaluation of a low-power sensor device for induced rockfall experiments. ISEE Transactions on Instrumentation and Measurement. Vol. 67 No. 4.

Disenhof, C. R. (2018). Investigation of Surface Models and the Use of a Smart Rock for Rockfall Modeling. (Master's thesis). University of New Hampshire, Durham, NH.

Gullison, M. (2013). Analysis of Smart Rock data from debris flow experimentation. (Master's thesis). University of New Hampshire, Durham, NH.

Harding, M. (2011). Design and development of a debris flow tracking "Smart Rock". (Master's thesis). University of New Hampshire, Durham, NH.

Harding, M. J., Fussell, B. K., Gullison, M. A., Benoît, J., and de Alba, P. A. (2014). Design and testing of a debris flow 'smart rock'. Geotechnical Testing Journal, 37(5), 769-785.

Leonhardt, P. M. (2001). Acceleration levels of dropped objects. Endevco Corporation.

Pierson, L.A., Gullison, C.F., and Chassie, R.G. (2001). Rockfall Catchment Area Design Guide. Report FHWA-OR-RD-02-04m, Oregon Department of Transportation, Dec. 2001.

Ritchie, A. (1963). Evaluation of Rockfall and its Control. Highway Research Board, N.17, 13-28.

Souza, B. M. M. 2021. Use of Smart Rocks to improve rock slope design. (Master's thesis). University of New Hampshire, Durham, NH.

Turner, A.K., & Duffy, J.D. 2012. Evaluation of Rockfall Mechanics. In Turner, A.K. and Schuster, R.L. (Eds). Rockfall Characterization and Control, 285-333. Washington, D.C.: Transportation Research Board.

Geosynthetic Reinforced Soil (GRS) vs. Mechanically Stabilized Earth (MSE); An Overview of Practical Applications of GRS

Jeffrey Stallings, E.I.T.
Field Engineer | GeoStabilization International
4475 E 74th Ave, Suite 100
Commerce City, CO 80022
(855) 579-0536
jeffrey.stallings@gsi.us

Prepared for the 71st Highway Geology Symposium, May, 2022

Acknowledgments

The author would like to thank the individuals/entities for their contributions in the work described:

Michael Laney – Deputy Chief Engineer (Geostabilization International)
Bob Barrett – Founder (Geostabilization International)
Al Ruckman – Founder (Geostabilization International)

Disclaimer

Statements and views presented in this paper are strictly those of the author(s), and do not necessarily reflect positions held by their affiliations, the Highway Geology Symposium (HGS), or others acknowledged above. The mention of trade names for commercial products does not imply the approval or endorsement by HGS.

ABSTRACT

Mechanically Stabilized Earth (MSE) walls have been utilized for years as earth-retention solutions in highway applications. However, Geosynthetic Reinforced Soil (GRS) walls have emerged in more recent years as an alternative approach to ground-up earth retention. Closely spaced layers (typically less than 12 inches) and internal reinforcement that is frictionally (rather than mechanically) attached to the facing material are two unique features that distinguish GRS structures from traditional MSE walls.

MSE technology utilizes a tied-back design approach using uniaxial reinforcement; relatively wide spacing results in localized areas within the reinforced backfill that can be prone to failure. Conversely, closely spaced reinforcement and compacted fill material utilized in GRS construction result in a true composite material, such as concrete, asphalt pavement, fiberglass, and more.

GRS walls can be built in weeks instead of months due to ease of construction and the use of readily available materials and equipment. A reduced construction schedule translates into less exposure around work zones, improving safety. GRS also provides environmental advantages because less steel and concrete are needed. Additionally, MSE systems are prone to construction errors, and comparatively, GRS is less complicated to build.

This paper discusses the advantages of utilizing GRS instead of MSE in many applications and environments. The Federal Highway Administration's LRFD approach for designing GRS walls is included in this paper.

INTRODUCTION

Mechanically Stabilized Earth (MSE) walls are internally stable structures that have been utilized as retaining walls, bridge abutments, and seawalls for years. Tensile reinforcement is placed between layers of soil to prevent failure. The interaction between the reinforcement and the soil as a unit gives the mass greater strength than unreinforced soil. The earliest use of reinforced soil was the ziggurats near modern-day Iraq and the Great Wall of China; woven mats of reeds and tree branches were embedded in gravelly soil layers (*1*). Typically, MSE construction utilizes uniaxial (one-directional strength) geotextile reinforcement placed in widely spaced (greater than 12 inches) inclusions within a backfill. Using a higher strength material at a wider spacing can result in localized "weak" areas of the backfill prone to failure. A similar reinforcement technology called geosynthetic reinforced soil (GRS) utilizes closely spaced layers of geosynthetic material to reinforce a backfill. A composite mass built with GRS creates a freestanding internally supported structure with reduced lateral earth pressures with considerable strength. Therefore, a GRS composite is not rigid and is tolerant to differential foundation settlement (*2*).

GRS structures behave as unique composites and exceed the sum of their components. For example, one cannot predict the behavior of concrete pavement with only tests of the cement, water, and aggregate. Likewise, the behavior of a layered system of aggregate and geosynthetic fabric in closely spaced inclusions cannot be predicted based on the individual properties of each of the elements. Inclusions provide measurable confining effects in granular backfill up to four inches from each sheet. Researchers at the University of Colorado, Denver, have demonstrated that matrix/inclusion interaction rarely extends beyond 4 inches from a planar reinforcement. For this reason, the typical spacing for a GRS wall is nominally 8 inches, which results in complete interaction between the constituent elements (*3*). Proximal confinement prevents particle dilation and induces intra-particle failure modes (as with concrete and bedrock).

MSE, on the other hand, is a simple composite and assumes that performance is predictable through element contribution. With wide reinforcement spacing and negligible confinement, backfill particles in MSE structures can dilate more readily; thus, mainly through interparticle shear, maintaining stability. MSE has a failure rate, and with the certainty that many standing MSE walls are just marginally stable. This phenomenon results from the early assumption that stronger, stiffer inclusions on wider spacing were equal to lighter inclusions on close spacing and that wider spacing was less expensive to construct.

MECHANICALLY STABILIZED EARTH

Since the early 1980's, MSE walls have gained wide acceptance as the go-to solution in bottom-up earth retention applications. The Federal Highway Administration (FHWA), the American Association of State Highway and Transportation Officials (AASHTO), and the National Concrete Masonry Association (NCMA) have each developed design guidelines to facilitate and promote the construction of these walls. As a result, the MSE wall industry has evolved into a wide variety of proprietary systems with various combinations of facing types and connection methods for different reinforcements (*4*).

A MSE wall has three significant components: reinforcement, soil backfill, and facing elements. Reinforcement is typically made from geosynthetic or metallic material; this can be in the form of strips, grids, and sheets. Backfill should consist of granular material, having low plasticity and a high internal friction angle. Additionally, it should be free of fine soils and deleterious material. Facing elements typically consist of concrete panels or wire mesh baskets that are mechanically attached to the reinforcement.

Issues with MSE

Even with safeguards and design redundancies in place, there is a significant failure rate of MSE structures, reported to be around 5% (*5*). While MSE walls are robust with redundancy in terms of connection, reinforcement strength and length requirements, and external stability requirements, a host of performance issues can occur when not designed or built correctly (*4*). A 2013 failure analysis of 171 failed geosynthetic mechanically stabilized earth (GMSE) walls reported that 98% of the failures were determined to result from improper design or construction. Furthermore, about 70% of the failed walls were built with concrete modular blocks; 65% of the walls were between 13 feet and 39 feet high; more than half were built with fine-grained backfill, and 72% of the walls were identified to have been built with poor to moderate compaction.

Valentine reports similar findings regarding failed MSE walls (*6*). Additionally, Wendland stated that 90% of wall failures result from either poor communication or water (*7*). The typical project life cycle of an MSE wall could contribute to this failure rate. The conception of many MSE wall projects takes place in a low-bid contractor market. Improper design is also at the root of many MSE wall problems: the cookbook fashion of plugging and chugging numbers into design software often makes the wall design process deceivingly simple (*4*). The simplicity of construction is another source of performance issues when design details are either omitted or incorrectly installed. Additionally, the multitude of parties involved in an MSE wall project contributes to poor communication and a universal lack of understanding among the team; a wall construction process can involve a civil engineer, geotechnical engineer, wall vendor, wall designer, contractor, subcontractor, surveyor, architect, inspector, and owner (*7*). Lu et al. (2019) identified the following ten problems which indicate possible distress in MSE walls: geometry and wall layout, obstructions, wall embedment, surface drainage, contractor experience, claims, backfill placement and compaction, panel joints, leveling pad, and durability of facing (*8*).

Case Histories of Failures

Soda Springs, Idaho

Mahmood (2009) presented a case history of the failure and rehabilitation of an MSE bridge abutment constructed in Soda Springs, Idaho in 1978 (*9*). 24 years after construction, six of the precast concrete facing panels "popped out" in a localized area of the walls. Corrosion of the galvanized steel soil reinforcing strips was determined to be at fault; lateral earth pressures exceeded the connection's remaining capacity. Horizontal drilled and grouted crosstie ground anchors were installed in the approach walls, anchored soldier piles at the abutments, and a reinforced shotcrete facing was installed to the existing MSE facing panels. Each drilled anchor was subjected to a class one corrosion protection system. Strands were coated with a corrosion inhibitor and encapsulated in plastic shells. The corrosive nature of the fill material, coupled with the use of metallic strip reinforcement, contributed to this MSE failure.

Figure 1. Localized failure within a mechanically stabilized earth mass (*8*).

Southeastern Pennsylvania

Paxson et al. (2004) detail the failure of a geogrid-reinforced segmental retaining wall (SRW) constructed in southeastern Pennsylvania (*10*). 5 months after construction, a failure occurred; prior to this failure, no signs of distress were reported. This failure occurred after several significant rain events, as well as testing of a fire protection system that drained into the parking lot above the wall. The failure was relatively shallow, and most of the reinforced zone remained intact. However, the wall was dismantled in the presence of several geotechnical engineers. Laboratory testing indicated that the material was not adequately compacted and was wet of optimum. While observations during wall removal suggest that the geogrid reinforcement was placed in the general location and length as specified on design drawings, the drainage stone at the face did not appear to have been placed as specified. Removal of a stormwater pipe that flowed from a stormwater inlet in the parking lot supported by the wall revealed that the joints were not sealed; both the pipe and inlet were bedded on stone that was likely connected to this facing drainage layer. Two months after the first failure was repaired, tension cracks and settlement of the pavement above a separate section of the SRW were observed. Over the following months, the cracks opened wider, and settlement continued to nearly 8 inches of vertical displacement. Shortly after this was observed, the wall completely collapsed. Repair of the wall was valued at roughly $150,000. A post-failure analysis indicated that hydrostatic pressure, coupled with poor compaction of reinforcement material was to blame for both failures.

Figure 2. First failure of SRW constructed in southeastern Pennsylvania (Paxson et al. 2004).

Review of Failures

Corrosion of steel reinforcement resulted in the localized failure in Soda Springs, Idaho. Elton details the criterion of MSE backfill, stating that the selected aggregate should meet the specified electrochemical criteria of the governing body (*1*). However, corrosion of metallic reinforcement is not problematic in GRS construction, as the geosynthetic fabric is used exclusively for reinforcement. Additionally, the six panels "popped out" due to lateral earth pressure exceeding the strength of the connection and facing. GRS reinforcement is frictionally, rather than mechanically, attached to its facing elements. Additionally, GRS design does not rely on facing strength in design; due to its unique composite nature, lateral earth pressure at the face should be effectively zero.

GRS: INCEPTION, IMPLEMENTATION, AND THE CURRENT STATE OF PRACTICE

In reality, GRS is a type of MSE wall. Appearing through the early 2000s, the term MSE was used interchangeably to refer to both traditionally mechanically stabilized earth structures and geosynthetic reinforced soil masses (*1*). While many characteristics of MSE and GRS are similar, there are several key differences in design and construction.

Background

GRS facing typically consists of concrete masonry unit (CMU) or SRW blocks; other facing elements such as welded wire mesh, gabion baskets, or natural rock have been used successfully. While facing elements serve as a façade and protect against loss of backfill from erosion, the primary purpose of facing elements is to serve as a form of compaction. Additionally, the facing elements of a GRS structure are frictionally connected, rather than mechanically connected, to the soil reinforcement.

Woven biaxial geosynthetic fabric is typically used as GRS reinforcement rather than uniaxial geogrid or metallic strips utilized in MSE construction. Biaxial support means that the geosynthetic has the same strength properties in both directions, while uniaxial carries its strength in only one direction. The use of biaxial reinforcement lessens the likelihood of constructability errors resulting from laying the fabric in the wrong direction. The critical difference between GRS and MSE is in the reinforcement spacing. Closely spaced layers (nominally 8 inches, or the height of one CMU block) used in GRS mass construction adequately reinforce the soil mass and lessen the likelihood of localized unreinforced areas of the structural backfill. In the case of a GRS-IBS, this reinforcement inclusion is "doubled up" in the area of the GRS mass that directly supports the bridge superstructure.

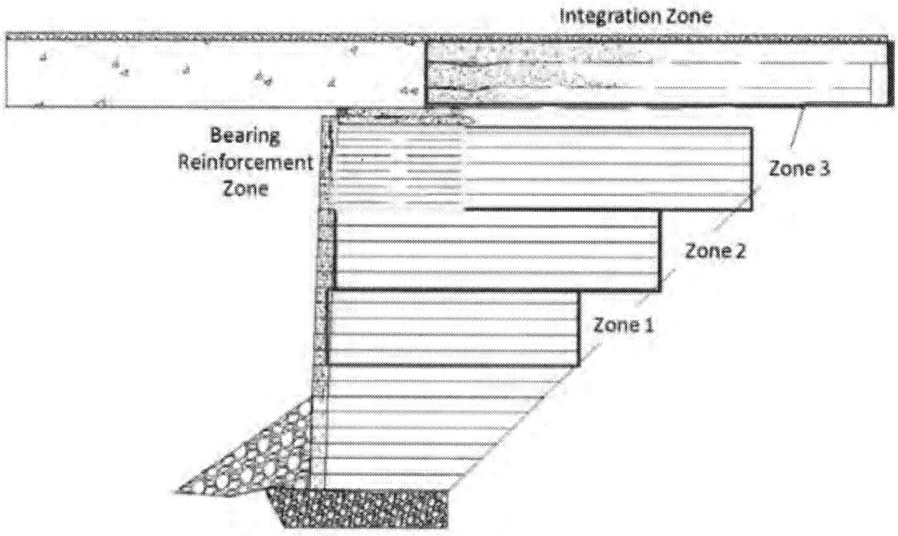

Figure 3. Reinforcement truncated in zones for a GRS bridge abutment (*11*).

State-of-Practice

During the past 30 years, GRS technology has been used to build walls, shallow foundations, culverts, bridge abutments, and rockfall barriers. The technology has also been used to stabilize slopes and repair roadways (*11*). Most recently, many bridges atop GRS masses, dubbed Geosynthetic Reinforced Soil – Integrated Bridge System (GRS-IBS), have been successfully utilized to replace single-span bridges on county and state roads throughout the country.

The inclusion of GRS in bridgework has prompted the Federal Highway Administration to publish multiple reports detailing the success of these bridges and design protocol and construction details for the aspiring GRS-builder. Many of the early walls, particularly those used in government-sponsored load tests, were "cowboy engineered," with little thought given to the material properties of the reinforcement and in-situ stress that it was facing. However, beginning in 2011, the preferred design method was an Allowable Stress Design (ASD) procedure that carried FHWA endorsement. Recently, a Load and Resistance Factored Design (LRFD) process was released by FHWA officials. This change is a crucial step toward the ongoing implementation of GRS, as the legitimacy of a statistically calibrated design method instills confidence in any overlooking agency that might choose to construct a GRS wall.

LRFD FOR GRS APPLICATIONS

An ASD approach was taken throughout most of history when designing GRS structures. An external stability analysis that evaluated direct sliding, bearing capacity, and global stability of the structure was followed by an internal stability analysis that evaluated internal bearing resistance, tolerable deformation limits, and required strength of the geosynthetic reinforcement. These potential failure modes are still assessed; however, the Federal Highway Administration has developed a LRFD approach for designing GRS structures. Note that this approach is intended for designing a GRS-IBS (geosynthetic reinforced soil – integrated bridge system). However, this approach is valid for any GRS structure; the absence of any superstructure bearing on the GRS mass can be accounted for in the corresponding equations.

Calculate Applicable Loads and Pressures

An estimate of loading imposed onto a GRS mass should be calculated for design. These loads include lateral earth pressures (due to both reinforced backfill and retained fill), dead loads (DL) (e.g. road base, additional fill, and overhead superstructures), and live loads (LL) imposed by traffic.

Lateral Pressures

Lateral earth pressure can be calculated according to classical soil mechanics for active earth pressure. For vertical walls, the active earth pressure coefficient (K_a) is calculated according to equation 1.

$$K_a = \frac{1-sin\emptyset}{1+sin\emptyset} = tan^2 * \left(45° - \frac{\emptyset}{2}\right) \quad \text{(Eqn. 1)}$$

Where:
K_{ab} = Coefficient of active earth pressure for the retained backfill
ϕ_b = Friction angle of interest

$\sigma_{h,W}$ is found using Rankine's active stress condition shown in equation 2.
Lateral stress distribution due to weight of reinforced backfill in GRS:

$$\sigma_{h,W} = \gamma_r * z * K_{ar} \quad \text{(Eqn. 2)}$$

Where:
K_{ar} = Coefficient of active earth pressure for the reinforced backfill
z = depth from the top of the wall
γ_r = unit weight of the reinforced backfill

$\phi_{h,t}$ and $\phi_{h,rb}$ (lateral pressure due to traffic LL surcharge, and equivalent lateral stress distribution due to the retained soil behind the GRS soil mass) are found using equations outlined below.

$$\sigma_{h,t} = q_t * K_{ab} \quad \text{(Eqn. 3)}$$

Where:
q_t= roadway LL surcharge due to traffic

$$\sigma_{h,rb} = q_{rb} * K_{ab} \quad \text{(Eqn. 4)}$$

Where:
q_{rb}= surcharge due to the structural backfill of the road base

Note that both equations assume that the loading is continuous across the retained soil. When loads are not continuous across the GRS mass or retained soil (e.g., loads from bridge superstructure), additional steps must be taken to determine the stress distribution using Boussinesq theory. Adams et al (2018) provides a further discussion of this topic (*2*).

Dead Loads and Live Loads

The unfactored and factored DL and LL from any superstructure should be provided by the bridge designer based on *AASHTO LRFD Bridge Design Specifications.*
Permanent dead loads can result from the bridge superstructure, the road base behind the superstructure, and, when considering the stability of the RSF, the weight of the facing.
The weight of facing elements (W_{face}) per unit length adds pressure on the RSF and underlying foundation soil, but it also helps resist the applied lateral pressures. For modular block facing, the weight can be calculated according to equation 5

$$W_{face} = N_{block} * \frac{W_{block}}{L_{block}} \quad \text{(Eqn. 5)}$$

Where:
N_{block} = number of blocks in a single column along the cross-sectional height of the abutment
W_{block} = weight of an individual facing block
L_{block} = length of a facing block (e.g., 15.625 inches for a CMU)

Conduct an External Stability Analysis

External stability is evaluated by looking at three potential external failure mechanisms: direct sliding, bearing capacity, and global stability. It should be noted that because a GRS mass is relatively ductile and free of tensile strength, overturning about the toe, in a strict sense, is not a possible response to earth pressures at the back of the mass or loading on its top (*11*). Other factors, such as the existing superstructure atop the GRS mass in the case of a GRS-IBS, contribute to combatting the possibility of an overturning failure mode.

Direct Sliding

GCS mass must resist translation, or direct sliding. Direct sliding should be evaluated at both the interface between the GRS mass and RSF and Between the RSF and foundation soils.

Thrust forces behind GCS mass are calculated as shown:

$$F_b = \frac{1}{2} * \gamma_b * K_{ab} * {H_b}^2 \qquad \text{(Eqn. 6)}$$

$$F_{rb} = q_{rb} * K_{ab} * H \qquad \text{(Eqn. 7)}$$

Where:
q_{rb}= surcharge due to structural backfill of integrated approach
$F_t = q_t K_{ab} H$
q_t= roadway LL surcharge

Total factored driving force for direct sliding calculations at the base of GRS mass calculated by summing each factored thrust force. Load factors for max horizontal earth pressure ($\gamma_{EH\ MAX}$) and traffic LL surcharge (γ_{LS}), are utilized for retained backfill, road base, and traffic surcharges.:

$$F_n = \gamma_{EH\ MAX} * (F_b + F_{rb}) + \gamma_{LS} * F_t \qquad \text{(Eqn. 8)}$$

Factored resisting force at base of GRS mass is calculated as such:

$$R_R = \emptyset_\tau * (W_{T,R} * \mu) \qquad \text{(Eqn. 9)}$$

Where:
$\emptyset_\tau$= sliding resistance factor (equal to 1.0)
μ = friction factor between the wall and RSF, taken as $\frac{2}{3}\tan(\emptyset_r)$
$W_{T,R}$ = total factored resisting weight

$$W_{T,R} = \gamma_{EV\ MIN} * W + \gamma_{DC\ MIN} * (q_{DL} * b) + \gamma_{DC\ MIN} * (W_{face}) + \gamma_{EH\ MIN} * (q_{rb} * b_{rb,t}) \qquad \text{(Eqn. 10)}$$

Where:
$\gamma_{EV\ MIN}$= minimum vertical earth pressure load factor
W= weight of the GRS abutment backfill
$\gamma_{DC\ MIN}$= minimum DL load factor
q_{DL}=superstructure DL pressure
b = bearing width of the bridge
W_{face} = weight of the facing elements
$\gamma_{EH\ MIN}$ = minimum horizontal earth pressure load factor
q_{rb}= surcharge due to structural backfill (road base) DL
$b_{rb,t}$ = width of the traffic and road base surcharges over the GRS abutment

$$W = \gamma_r * H_r * B \qquad \text{(Eqn. 11)}$$

Where:
γ_r = unit weight of the reinforced backfill

For LRFD, the ratio of the factored resistance and the factored driving force must be greater than or equal to 1.0. If not, lengthening the reinforcement at the base should be considered.

$$\frac{R_R}{F_R} \geq 1.0 \qquad \text{(Eqn. 12)}$$

The nominal lateral force behind GRS and RSF due to retained backfill the road base surcharge, and the roadway LL surcharge are determined along the height of GRS mass and depth of the RSF.

$$F_{b,RSF} = \frac{1}{2} * \gamma_b * K_{ab} * (H + D_{RSF})^2 \qquad \text{(Eqn. 13)}$$

$$F_{rb,RSF} = q_{rb} * K_{ab} * (H + D_{RSF})^2 \qquad \text{(Eqn. 14)}$$

$$F_{t,RSF} = q_t * K_{ab} * (H + D_{RSF})^2 \qquad \text{(Eqn. 15)}$$

$F_{R,RSF}$ is calculated by summing each thrust force. Maximum horizontal earth pressure load factor and LL surcharge load factor, which are determined using tables from Adams et al. (*2*), are utilized for the retained backfill, road base, and traffic surcharges.

$$F_{R,RSF} = \gamma_{EH\ MAX} * \left(F_{b,RSF} + F_{rb,RSF}\right) + \gamma_{LS} * F_{t,RSF} \qquad \text{(Eqn. 16)}$$

Factored resisting force for direct sliding at base of RSF calculated according to:

$$R_{R,RSF} = \phi_\tau * (W_{T,RSF} * \mu_{RSF}) \qquad \text{(Eqn. 17)}$$

Where:
ϕ_τ= sliding resistance factor (equal to 1.0)
$W_{T,RSF}$= total factored resisting weight including the RSF
μ_{RSF}= friction factor between base of RSF and foundation soils

$$W_{T,R,RSF} = W_{T,R,} + \gamma_{EV\ MIN} * W_{RSF} \qquad \text{(Eqn. 18)}$$

Where:
$W_{T,R}$= total factored resisting weight
$\gamma_{EV\ MIN}$= minimum vertical earth pressure load factor
W_{RSF}= weight of the RSF (Eqn. 19)

$$W_{RSF} = \gamma'_{RSF} * B_{RSF} * D_{RSF} \qquad \text{(Eqn. 19)}$$

Where:
γ'_{RSF}= effective unit weight of the RSF backfill
B_{RSF}= base width of the RSF
D_{RSF}= depth of the RSF

In LRFD, the ratio of the factored resistance and the factored driving force must be greater than or equal to 1.0. If not, consideration should be given to widening RSF. Alternatively, a more complex analysis, including the full weight of grs mass up to the cut slope, can be performed. Note that passive pressures due to any material in front of RSF are not included as a conservative measure; however, the designer may elect to calculate this resistance, assuming the material will remain in place throughout the life of GRS.

$$\frac{R_{RSF,R}}{F_{RSF,R}} \geq 1.0 \qquad \text{(Eqn. 20)}$$

Bearing Capacity

Vertical pressure at the base of RSF must not exceed the allowable bearing capacity of underlying geologic materials. In an IBS, the vertical pressure is a result of the weight of the GRS mass, the weight of RSF, the bridge DL, the road baseload from the integrated approach, the LL on the superstructure, the LL on the approach pavement

The factored vertical pressure at the base of GRS is:

$$\sigma_{v,base,R} = \frac{\Sigma V_R}{B_{RSF} - 2e_{B,R}} \qquad \text{(Eqn. 21)}$$

This is calculated according to a Meyerhof-type distribution.

Where:
ΣV_R = total factored vertical load
B_{RSF} = base width of the RSF
$e_{B,R}$ = factored eccentricity for bearing resistance

$$\Sigma V_R = \gamma_{EV\,MAX} * (W) + \gamma_{EV\,MAX} * (W_{RSF}) + \gamma_{DC\,MAX} * (W_{face}) + \gamma_{LS} * (q_t * b_{rb,t}) + \gamma_{EH\,MAX} * (q_{rb} * b_{rb,t}) + \gamma_{DC\,MAX} * (q_{DL} * b) + \gamma_{LS} * (q_{RLL} * b) \qquad \text{(Eqn.22)}$$

Where:
W_{RSF} = weight of the RSF
W_{face} = weight of the facing element
γ_{LS} = the traffic LL surcharge load factor
q_t = roadway LL surcharge due to traffic
$b_{rb,t}$ = width of the traffic and road base surcharges over the GRS mass
$\gamma_{EH\,MAX}$ = maximum horizontal earth pressure load factor
q_{rb} = surcharge due to the structural backfill of the integrated approach (i.e., road base)
q_{DL} = superstructure DL pressure
b = bearing width of the bridge seat
q_{LL} = bridge LL pressure

$$e_{B,R} = \frac{\Sigma M_{D,R} - \Sigma M_{R,R}}{\Sigma V_R} \qquad \text{(Eqn. 23)}$$

Where:
$\Sigma M_{D,R}$ = total factored driving moment

$\Sigma M_{R,R}$ = total factored resisting moment

Equations 24 and 25 for moments are calculated about bottom center of the width of RSF; however, moments can be calculated about any point (e.g., the toe of the RSF, etc.) as long as the designer is consistent. Note that if $e_{B,R}$ is negative, $e_{B,r}$ equal to zero should be taken.

$$\Sigma M_{D,R} = \gamma_{EH\,MAX} * F_{b,RSF} * \left(\frac{H + D_{RSF}}{3}\right) + \gamma_{LS} * F_{t,RSF} * \left(\frac{H + D_{RSF}}{2}\right) + \gamma_{EH\,MAX} * F_{rb,RSF} * \left(\frac{H + D_{RSF}}{2}\right)$$

(Eqn. 24)

$$\Sigma M_{R,R} = (\gamma_{DC\,MAX} * q_{DL} * b + \gamma_{LS} * Q_{LL} * b)\left[\left(\frac{b}{2} + a_b\right) - \left(\frac{B_{RSF}}{2} - x_{RSF} - b_{block}\right)\right] + (\gamma_{LS} * q_t b_{rb,t} + \gamma_{EV\,MAX} * q_{rb} * b_{rb,t})\left(\frac{B_{RSF}}{2} - \frac{b_{rb}}{2}\right) + \gamma_{EV\,MAX} * W\left(\frac{B_{RSF}}{2} - \frac{B}{2}\right) + \gamma_{DC\,MAX} * W_{face} * \left(B + \frac{b_{block}}{2} - \frac{B_{RSF}}{2}\right)$$

(Eqn. 25)

Where b_{block} is the width of the facing block.

The factored bearing resistance (q_R) of the foundation can be found using the equation below. Based on AASHTO, the bearing resistance factor (ϕ_{bc}) is equal to 0.65.

$$q_R = \phi_{bc} * (c_f^{*'} N_c + \frac{1}{2} * B * \gamma_f' * N_\gamma + \gamma_f' * D_f * N_q \qquad \text{(Eqn. 26)}$$

Where:
C'_f = cohesion of the foundation soil
N_c, N_γ, and N_q = dimensionless bearing capacity coefficients (*2*).
γ_f' = effective unit weight of the foundation soil.

The friction angle should be taken as the foundation's effective friction angle (ϕ_f').

Ratio of the factored bearing resistance and factored applied pressure must be greater than or equal to 1.0. If not, options include increasing the width of the GRS abutment and RSF by increasing the length of the reinforcement layers, replacing the foundation soil with a more competent soil, or adding embedment depth.

$$\frac{q_R}{\sigma_{v,base,R}} \geq 1.0 \qquad \text{(Eqn. 27)}$$

Global Stability

A global stability analysis should be performed in accordance with a classical slope stability theory; either a rotational or wedge analysis is recommended. Global failure modes should be protected by a safety factor of at least 1.5 (*11*). These analyses are generally performed using modern software such as SLIDE (limit equilibrium analysis), as large numbers of iterations are carried out in a limit equilibrium analysis. It is imperative to gather quality soil property information for this analysis; otherwise, the critical failure surface may go unnoticed.

Conduct an Internal Stability Analysis

Internal stability for GRS includes ensuring adequate internal bearing resistance, tolerable deformations, and required reinforcement strength. Connection strength is not checked, as with traditional mechanically stabilized structures, as the reinforcement is frictionally, not mechanically, connected to the facing elements. Additionally, pullout failure is not evaluated in this design approach. The design of GRS structures assumes a relatively constant earth pressure with depth at the wall face; this method considers the tensile forces in the reinforcement, which counteract the classical lateral earth pressure distribution. This occurs because the reinforcement, not the wall face, acts to restrain lateral deformation of the soil (*11*).

Internal Bearing Resistance

The nominal bearing resistance of a GRS mass is determined either empirically through a GRS performance test or analytically through a semi-empirical equation. It is recommended that the ultimate capacity be found empirically, as testing will provide the most accurate results for the design. If using the applicable GRS performance test results, special care should be taken to ensure that the test used the same geosynthetic reinforcement and compacted granular backfill having identical soil properties. The nominal bearing resistance ($q_{n,emp}$) is defined as the stress at which the GRS composite fails at the strength limit (i.e., cannot sustain any additional loading). The factored applied stress on top of the GRS mass ($V_{applied,f}$) is equal to the sum of vertical pressures on the bridge bearing area multiplied by their respective load factors. Live loads and dead loads should be accounted for in this calculation; resulting surcharges due to q_{rb} and q_t due to the approach pavement are located behind the bearing area and are therefore not included in the bearing resistance related to the bridge superstructure (*2*).

$$V_{applied,f} = \gamma_{DC\,MAX} * q_{DL} + \gamma_{LL} \quad \text{(Eqn. 28)}$$

The factored applied pressure must be less than or equal to the factored vertical resistance (Eqn. 29). The resistance nominal factor ($\emptyset_{cap}$) is equal to 0.45.

$$\frac{\emptyset_{cap} * (q_{n,emp})}{V_{applied,f}} \geq 1.0 \quad \text{(Eqn. 29)}$$

Alternatively, Adams et al. (2018) details the process for determining the nominal bearing resistance of a GRS mass by using a semi-empirical formula (*2*).

$$q_{n,an} = \left[0.7^{\left(\frac{S_v}{6d_{max}}\right)} * \frac{T_f}{S_v}\right] * K_{pr} \quad \text{(Eqn. 30)}$$

Where:
$q_{n,an}$ = nominal bearing resistance of the GRS mass using the analytical method

S_v = reinforcement spacing
D_{max} = maximum grain size
T_f = ultimate reinforcement strength
K_{pr} = coefficient of passive earth pressure for the reinforced fill (calculated in Eqn. 31)

$$K_{pr} = \frac{1+sin\emptyset_r}{1-\emptyset_r} = tan^2(45° + \frac{\emptyset_r}{2}) \quad \text{(Eqn. 31)}$$

The factored applied pressure must be less than the factored bearing resistance. $\emptyset_{cap}$is equal to 0.45.

$$\frac{\emptyset_{cap}(q_{n,an})}{V_{applied,f}} \geq 1.0 \quad \text{(Eqn. 32)}$$

Deformations

Horizontal and vertical displacements of the GRS mass are estimated assuming zero volume change (*11*). Vertical displacements can be estimated using a classical settlement analysis. Anticipated settlement should be considered at all locations across a wall face; if an overlying superstructure is present, differential settlement must be accounted for in the design and monitored post-construction. Horizontal displacements are more difficult to estimate and are often approximated in the design phase. It is assumed that the applied factors of safety for external and internal stability will ensure lateral deformations are within limits.

Required Reinforcement Strength

The properties of the geosynthetic reinforcement must meet both strength and serviceability requirements. Selecting a geosynthetic material with adequate ultimate strength and stiffness properties will prevent failure of the GRS composite and limit reinforcement strains under service conditions. The required reinforcement strength must be less than the allowable reinforcement strength and must be less than the strength at 2% reinforcement strain in the direction perpendicular to the wall face. The factored required reinforcement strength ($T_{req,f}$) can be determined analytically. This should be calculated at each layer of reinforcement to ensure adequate strength throughout the GRS mass.

$$T_{req,f} = \left[\frac{\sigma_{h,f}}{0.7^{\left(\frac{S_v}{6d_{max}}\right)}}\right] * S_v \quad \text{(Eqn. 33)}$$

The factored total lateral pressure within the GRS mass ($\sigma_{h,f}$) takes into account lateral pressure due to the following: weight of the GRS mass, equivalent bridge load (if applicable), road base surcharge, and traffic surcharge. Adams et al (2018) provides a detailed explanation of calculating these loads and selecting their corresponding load factors (*2*).

Typically, a default wide width tensile strength of 4,800 lb/ft is often selected; however, the required strength may be more or less depending on the project requirements. To account for long-term strength losses of the geosynthetic, a global reduction factor (RF_{global}) of 2.25 is recommended; this factor accounts for creep, durability, and installation damage.

CONCLUSION

MSE walls are internally stable structures that have been utilized as retaining walls in highway applications since the early 1980s. Familiarity with the design process by state DOTs and the federal government has led to this solution being utilized in numerous infrastructure projects throughout the years. However, GRS technology provides an alternative solution in ground-up earth retention applications that could result in project cost reduction if utilized correctly. Additionally, the failure rate of MSE structures far exceeds any documented GRS failures. The simplicity of construction, availability of materials and labor required for GRS, and a streamlined design process (recently endorsed by the FHWA) suggest that GRS could be a cost-effective alternative to traditional MSE walls.

The benefits of GRS have been well-documented since implementation in the 1980's. However, the lack of LRFD design guidelines have resulted in reluctancy among local, state, and federal oversight bodies to utilize these solutions. While ASD calculations have been presented in numerous GRS engineering submittals, state DOTs and similar organizations tend to prefer pre-approved wall systems or engineered structures that follow LRFD protocol. When the FHWA published the LRFD manual for GRS-IBS in 2018, widespread implementation of GRS wall systems became a reality.

This document should serve the user several purposes. When evaluating potential ground-up earth retention solutions, the feasibility of GRS versus MSE should be taken into account. Adams et al. provides further discussion pertaining to situations in which GRS would not be advantageous over MSE (*2*). If it is deemed that GRS could be a potential solution for any given project, a cost-analysis should be performed comparing GRS to MSE. The user should follow the LRFD process outlined in this paper when designing a GRS structure, ensuring that all factors of safety are suitable. The benefits of GRS that have been outlined within this paper, coupled with advancement in research sponsored by governing organizations, make this technology a sustainable solution for the future of earth retention.

REFERENCES

1. Elton, D.J., and Barrato P., M.A. (2005). *Mechanically Stabilized Earth (MSE) Reinforcement Tensile Strength from Tests of Geotextile Reinforced Soil*. Alabama Highway Research Center, June 28.
2. Adams, M., and Nicks, J. (2018). *Design and Construction Guidelines for Geosynthetic Reinforced Soil Abutments and Integrated Bridge Systems*. Publication No. FHWA-HRT-17-080, Federal Highway Administration, Washington, DC.
3. Barrett, R.K. (2010). *GRS/GCS/GeoMonolith Theory, Design, and Construction.*
4. Nicks, J.E., and Adams, M.T. (2018). "A risk assessment for MSE wall projects". Geosynthetics Magazine, Feb. 1, https://geosyntheticsmagazine.com/2018/02/01/development-of-a-risk-assessment-for-mse-wall-projects/.
5. Berg, R.R. (2010). "Fill walls: Recent advances and future trends." Proc., 2010 Earth Retention Conf., American Society of Civil Engineers, Reston, VA., 19-36.
6. Valentine, R.J. (2013). "An assessment of the factors that contribute to the poor performance of geosynthetic-reinforced earth retaining walls." Proc., Int. Symp. On Design and Practice of Geosynthetic Reinforced Soil Structures, DEStech Publications, Lancaster, Pa.
7. Wendland, S. (2011). "When Retaining Walls Fail: The Lessons Learned." PowerPoint presentation, March 17, https://vdocuments.mx/when-retaining-walls-fail-the-lessons-retaining-walls-fail-the-lessons-learned.html?page=1.
8. Lu, Y., Ibrahim, A., Mahar, J., Mashal, M., and Sharma, S. (2019). "Development of an Inventory and Inspection Database Framework for Asset Management of MSE Walls." Idaho Transportation Department Research Report, August, https://www.researchgate.net/publication/337870386_Development_of_an_Inventory_and_Inspection_Database_Framework_for_Asset_Management_of_MSE_Walls.
9. Mahmood, T. (2009). "Failure Analysis of a Mechanically Stabilized Earth (MSE) Wall Using Finite Element Program PLAXIS". Master's Thesis Defense, Arlington, TX., May.
10. Paxson, G., Cadden, A., Wargo, R., and Gomez, J. (2004). "MSE Walls in Distress: Repair Them or Rebuild Them?". Proc., Int. Conf. on Case Histories in Geotechnical Engineering, New York, NY., 2-3.
11. Adams, M., Nicks, J., Stabile, T., Wu, J., Schelatter, W. and Hartmann, J. (2011). *Geosynthetic Reinforced Soil Integrated Bridge System Interim Implementation Guide*. Publication No. FHWA-GRT-11-027, Federal Highway Administration, Washington, DC.

FLOOD REPAIRS ALONG THE SR 187 CORRIDOR

Jason M. Gardner, P.E.
Gannett Fleming, Inc.
202 Senate Avenue
Camp Hill, PA 17011
(717)-886-5429
jgardner@gfnet.com

Prepared for the 71st Highway Geology Symposium, May 2022

Acknowledgements

The author would like to thank the following individuals/entities for their contributions in the work described:

Robert E. Johnson, P.E. – PENNDOT 3-0, District Geotechnical Engineer
Isaac R. Bragunier, P.E. – PENNDOT 3-0, Assistant Geotechnical Engineer

Disclaimer

Statements and views presented in this paper are strictly those of the author(s), and do not necessarily reflect positions held by their affiliations, the Highway Geology Symposium (HGS), or others acknowledged above. The mention of trade names for commercial products does not imply the approval or endorsement by HGS.

ABSTRACT

The summer of 2018 was the wettest on record for Pennsylvania. In mid-August, a 2-day storm system dumped approximately 6-8 inches of rain on the northern tier of Pennsylvania that resulted in extreme flooding in Bradford County. The flooding caused erosion of roadway slopes resulting in many landslides that affected roadways owned and maintained by PennDOT, District 3-0. The SR 187 corridor in southeastern Bradford County was one of the hardest hit areas of the region. Within a distance of approximately 2.5-miles, four distinct sections of the SR 187 roadway were affected by the erosion/landslides. In this area, the slope movement lead to three sections of SR 187 being reduced to one lane, and another section experienced surficial slope failures that if left untreated, had the potential to adversely affect the SR 187 roadway in the future. A subsurface exploration program was performed to determine the subsurface conditions at each of the four sites. In addition, laboratory testing was performed on soil samples collected in the borings to estimate engineering properties of the site soils. Multiple remediation alternatives were considered to repair each site and the selected alternatives included a rock buttress at one site, rock veneer at one site, and cantilever sheet pile walls at two sites. Unique aspects of the project include accelerating the design schedule and bundling three of the repairs into one construction contract. The paper will also contain lessons learned from installation of driven sheet piles within an active landslide.

INTRODUCTION

SR 187 is a two-lane roadway that is a significant north/south corridor through the Endless Mountains Region of Bradford County in northeast Pennsylvania. The SR 187 corridor is situated in the eastern portion of Bradford County and carries traffic between SR 87 at the south end of the corridor to the New York border at the north end of the corridor.

A massive storm event dumped approximately 6-8 inches of rain on Bradford County, Pennsylvania between August 14-15, 2018. The excessive rain resulted in flooding along many local waterways. The erosion that resulted from the flooding triggered a significant number of landslides in the region that impacted many roadways owned and operated by the Pennsylvania Department of Transportation (PennDOT). The SR 187 corridor in southeast Bradford County was one of the hardest hit areas of the region, as 4 distinct areas of the roadway were impacted by landslides within an approximately 2.5 mile stretch of SR 187 to the south of the Borough of Wyalusing, Pennsylvania. The landslide projects were individually designated by PennDOT, from south to north along the SR 187 corridor, as follows:

- SR 187, Section 079
- SR 187, Section 080
- SR 187, Section 088
- SR 187, Section 081

A map showing the general location of the projects is provided in Figure 1 and each project site is provided in the site location map presented as Figure 2.

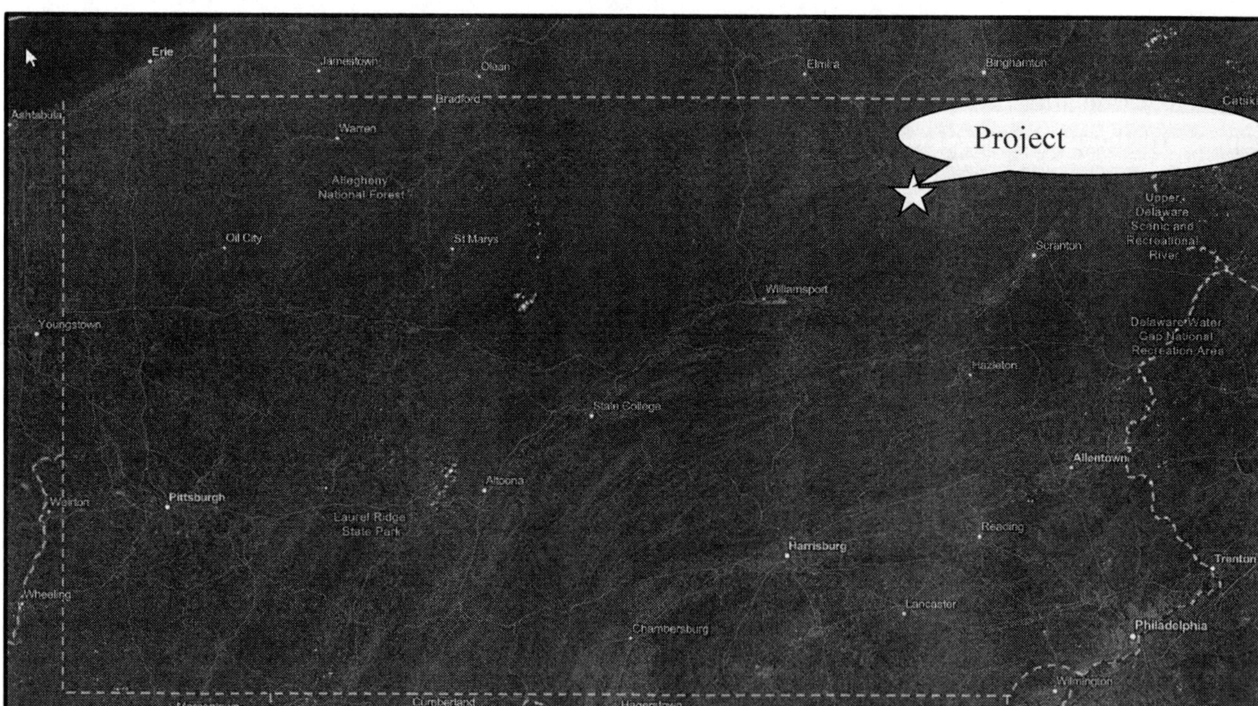

Figure 1: Project Location Map

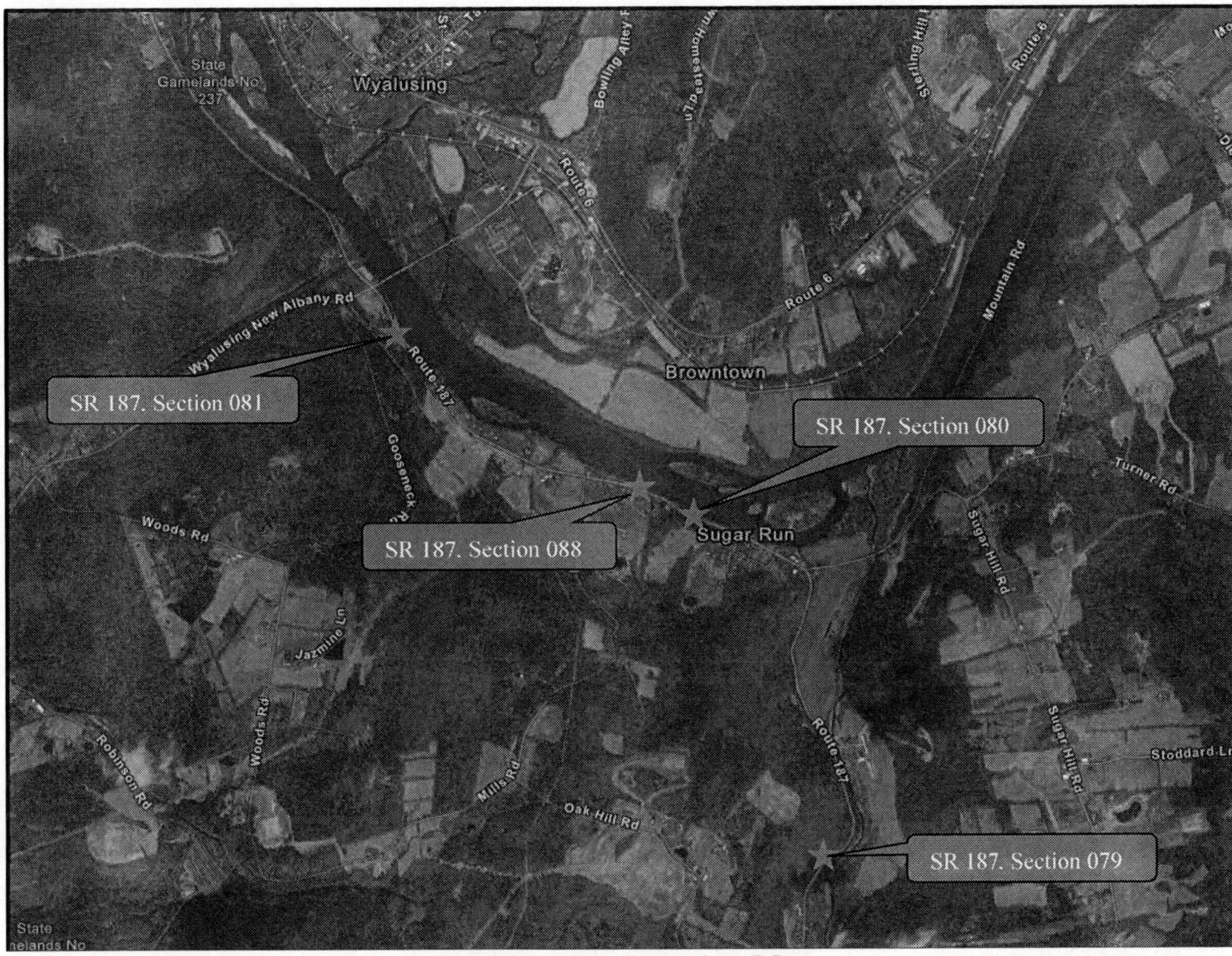

Figure 2: Site Location Map

The SR 187, Section 079 landslide was located along Sugar Run Creek, which is a tributary to the Susquehanna River and the SR 187, Sections 080, 081 and 088 landslides were located along the Susquehanna River. PennDOT engaged Gannett Fleming in September 2018 and the landslide remediations were advertised in early 2019 and were completed by October 2019.

REVIEW OF PUBLISHED LITERATURE

Surficial Geology

Based on the Pennsylvania Bureau of Topographic and Geologic Survey, the surficial geology at each landslide site consists of Valley-bottom Sand and Gravel (VSG) along the Susquehanna River and Sugar Run Creek, with Ice-contact Sand and Gravel (ISG), and Glacial Till (T) mapped along the slopes flanking the waterways. Glaciolacustrine deposits, which are typically associated with landslide activity in this area of Pennsylvania, were not mapped at any of the landslide locations. The VSG consists of a heterogeneous mixture of stratified sand and gravel with some beds of silt and clay. Clasts are dominantly sandstone. Deposits underlie valley bottoms. Thickness is variable and is typically more than 100 feet in the Susquehanna River valley. The ISG is composed of a heterogeneous mixture of cobbles, gravel, sand, silt, some clay, and some boulders. Materials are rounded and occur in stratified beds of variable thickness and bedding dip. Thickness is generally unknown but may be several 10's of feet. The Glacial Till is an unsorted mixture of clay, silt, sand, pebbles, cobbles, and boulders. Dominant clast composition is controlled by underlying bedrock. Matrix (silt, clay, and sand) varies from very silty to very sandy. Deposits occur as fill in small valleys, as an apron on the lower parts of slopes, and as a cover of variable thickness on higher slopes and uplands. Thickness may be more than 100 feet in places, but probably averages between 10 and 25 feet (*1*).

Geologic Setting

Based on the Pennsylvania Department of Conservation and Natural Resources, each landslide site is underlain by the Devonian aged Catskill (Dck) Formation (*2*). The Catskill Formation consists of a succession of graying-red sandstone, siltstone, shale and some conglomerate and mudstone, generally in fining-upward cycles (*3*).

FIELD RECONNAISSANCE

SR 187, Section 079

Field reconnaissance of the SR 187, Section 079 project area was performed on September 6, 2018 by Gannett Fleming personnel. The following observations were made during the site visit.

- Sugar Run Creek is located at the base of the hillside. Recent heavy rainfall has caused Sugar Run Creek to erode the toe of the slope on the east side of SR 187 as shown in Photo 1.
- Both lanes remain open, however the toe erosion has resulted in the loss of a portion of the northbound shoulder and guiderail along the east side of SR 187 (see Photo 1).
- The impacted portion of the roadway is approximately 400 to 450 feet in length.
- The slope height was estimated to be approximately 30 feet in height and the estimated slope angle is approximately 0.5H:1.0V or steeper (see Photo 1).
- Durable rockfill has been placed in the area of the 48-inch pipe where it outlets to the slope as shown in Photo 2. This rockfill appears to not have been affected by the recent flooding.
- Subsequent to the field view, the northbound lane of SR 187 was closed to traffic for safety reasons. A temporary traffic light was utilized for traffic control.

Photo 1: SR 187, Section 079 Landslide – Erosion of Existing Slope

Photo 2: SR 187, Section 079 Landslide – Durable Rock at Pipe Outlet

SR 187, Section 080

Field reconnaissance of the SR 187, Section 080 project area was performed on September 6, 2018 by Gannett Fleming personnel. The following observations were made during the site visit.

- The landslide has impacted approximately 40 feet of the northbound shoulder of SR 187, and has moved the guiderail toward the Susquehanna River, resulting in a single lane closure as shown in Photo 3. The total length of the landslide is approximately 150 feet in length.
- Approximately 4.0 to 4.5 feet of displacement was measured at the crown. The pavement section consists of about 1.5 feet of asphalt underlain by 3.5 feet of tan clayey sand with some rounded to subrounded gravel as shown in Photo 3.
- A toe bulge and overturned tree was observed within the slide mass. The toe bulge was on the riverbank, just above the water level of the Susquehanna River.

Photo 3: SR 187, Section 080 Landslide – Site During Field View

SR 187, Section 088

Field reconnaissance of the SR 187, Section 088 project area was performed on September 27, 2018 by Gannett Fleming personnel. The following observations were made during the site visit.

- The limits of the landslide area span approximately 65 feet from left flank to right flank along the northbound shoulder of SR 187 (See Photo 4).

- The landslide consists of a series of shallow, generally less than 2 feet deep slumps or shallow soil slips.
- The roadway and guiderail directly above the slide area appear to be unaffected by the soil sloughage.

Photo 4: SR 187, Section 088 Landslide – Slumps Observed at Site

SR 187, Section 081

Field reconnaissance of the SR 187, Section 081 project area was performed on September 6, 2018 by Gannett Fleming personnel. The following observations were made during the site visit.

- The landslide is approximately 230 feet in length and impacts the roadway and shoulder of the northbound lane of SR 187 resulting in closure of the northbound lane as shown in Photo 5.
- Approximately two to three feet of vertical displacement along the headscarp was measured as shown in Photo 5. The headscarp is primarily located within the shoulder and the material observed is comprised of asphalt millings, possibly indicating past movement was observed in this area based on the fill placement.

Photo 5: SR 187, Section 081 Landslide – Scarp Along NB Lanes

SUBSURFACE EXPLORATION

The subsurface exploration program conducted at the four (4) project areas took place between September and October 2018. The borings were performed to determine the subsurface conditions at each project area and collect soil and rock samples for laboratory testing to substantiate the geotechnical design of each landslide remediation. A brief summary of the subsurface exploration program performed at each site is summarized below.

SR 187, Section 079

Three (3) borings were drilled a few feet behind the head scarp of the landslide, in the northbound lane of SR 187 because access to the landslide area was not practical due to the steep slopes. The subsurface profile encountered at the site consisted of glacial soils (i.e., till, outwash, and ice contact), alluvial, and residual soils overlying bedrock. The overburden soils, regardless of origin identified by the on-site inspection staff, were typically identified as medium dense to very dense sands and gravels, which is consistent with the exposed slope observed during site reconnaissance. The bedrock was described as interbedded siltstone, sandstone, and limestone, and was encountered at depths ranging from 37.0 feet to 53.4 feet below roadway grade.

SR 187, Section 080

Two (2) borings were drilled a few feet behind the head scarp of the landslide, in the northbound lane of SR 187 because access to the landslide area was not practical due to the steep slopes. The subsurface profile encountered at the site consisted of glacial till. The glacial till was typically identified as medium dense to very dense sands and gravels with varying amounts of silt and clay. No bedrock was encountered to a depth of 40 feet below roadway grade.

SR 187, Section 088

One (1) boring was drilled in the northbound lane of SR 187, directly above the soil sloughs. The subsurface profile encountered at the site consisted of glacial till overlying bedrock. The glacial till was typically identified as medium dense to very dense gravel with silt. Bedrock was encountered at a depth of 16.5 feet below roadway grade and was described as sandstone.

SR 187, Section 081

Four (4) borings were drilled a few feet behind the head scarp of the landslide, in the northbound lane of SR 187 because access to the landslide area was not practical due to the steep slopes. The subsurface profile encountered at the site consisted of glacial till. The glacial till was typically identified as either stiff to hard silt or medium dense to very dense gravel. No bedrock was encountered in the borings, which ranged in depth from 40 feet to 50 feet below roadway grade.

LABORATORY TESTING

Soil samples collected during the subsurface exploration were tested in the laboratory. Tests performed included sieve and hydrometer analyses, Atterberg limits, natural moisture content, and direct shear. No laboratory testing was performed for the SR 187, Section 088 project. A summary of laboratory test results for each of the project areas are shown in Table 1.

Boring	Sample	Depth (ft)	Material Description	USCS	LL	PL	PI	Moisture Content (%)	Shear Strength
SR 187, Section 079									
RB-01	ST-1	18.0-20.0	Silty Sand	SM	NP	NP	NP	26.0	34.5°
RB-02	S-2 to S-3	3.0-6.0	Sandy Silt	ML	23	20	3	16.6	-
RB-02	S-4 to S-6	6.0-10.5	Silty Gravel	GM	NP	NP	NP	10.1	-
RB-02	S-9 to S-10	16.0-19.0	Silty Sand	SM	NP	NP	NP	14.5	-
RB-04	S-2 to S-4	3.0-7.5	Silty Sand	SM	28	24	4	10.8	-
RB-04	S-8 to S-11	12.0-16.9	Silty Gravel	GM	22	19	3	7.0	-
RB-04	S-14 to S-16	21.0-25.5	Sandy Silt	ML	NP	NP	NP	17.6	-
SR 187, Section 080									
RB-01	S-1 to S-2	1.5-4.5	Silty Sand	SM	NP	NP	NP	11.7	-
RB-03	S-4 to S-6	6.0-10.5	Silt w/ Sand	ML	NP	NP	NP	22.3	-
RB-03	S-7 to S-9	10.5-15.0	Silty Gravel	GM	NP	NP	NP	13.0	-
RB-03	S-14 to S-16	21.0-25.5	Silty, Clayey Gravel	GC-GM	27	21	6	9.6	-
SR 187, Section 081									
RB-01	S-2 to S-5	3.0-9.0	Silt	ML	NP	NP	NP	22.5	-
RB-01	S-6 to S-9	9.0-15.0	Silty Gravel	GM	NP	NP	NP	11.7	-
RB-01	S-15 to S-17	22.5-27.0	Silt	ML	NP	NP	NP	34.8	-
RB-02	S-11 to S-13	16.5-21.0	Silty Gravel	GW-GM	NP	NP	NP	9.7	-
RB-03	S-5 to S-7	7.5-12.0	Silt	ML	NP	NP	NP	23.9	-

RB-03	S-19 to S-21	28.5-33.0	Silt	ML	NP	NP	NP	33.9	-
RB-04	S-2 to S-4	3.0-7.5	Silt	ML	NP	NP	NP	22.4	-
RB-04	S-18 to S-21	27.0-33.0	Silt	ML	NP	NP	NP	34.1	-

Table 1: Summary of Laboratory Test Results

LANDSLIDE TRIGGER MECHANISMS

Several factors are believed to have contributed to triggering the landslides. The main cause of the landslides can be attributed to the excessive precipitation over a short duration. The excessive rain initiated flooding and high stream/river velocities that exacerbated erosion. In addition, the rain saturated the surficial soil resulting in a reduction in shear strength of the soil mass. Specific trigger mechanisms for each of the project areas are provided below.

SR 187, Section 079

The main trigger that contributed to the landslide at this location was erosion of the hillside toe during the flood events in 2018. Based on review of aerial photographs between 1957 and 2018, the alignment of Sugar Run Creek has migrated approximately 100 to 130 feet across the valley floor toward the toe of hillside supporting SR 187. This creek migration exacerbated the erosion of the toe to a point where a combination of the slope saturation and steepness of the slope resulted in the observed landslide. The 1957 aerial photograph is presented in Figure 3.

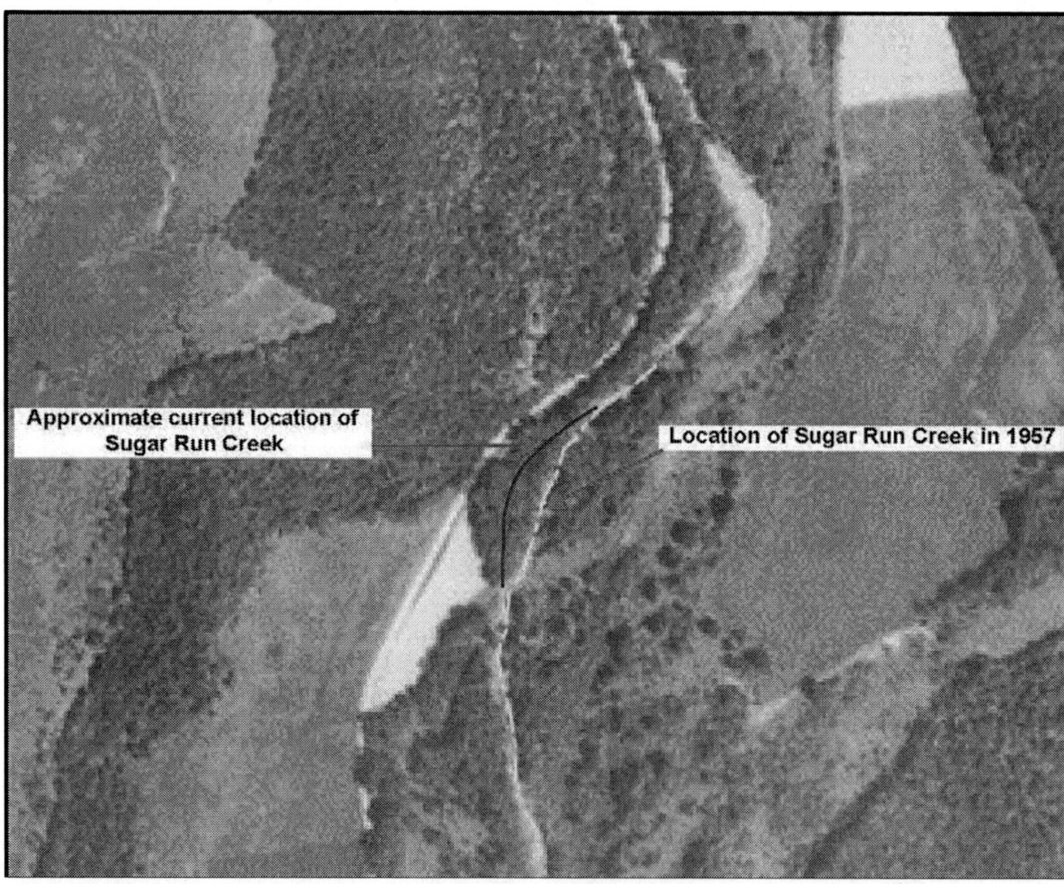

Figure 3: 1957 Aerial Photograph of SR 187, Section 079 Landslide Area

SR 187, Sections 080, 088 and 081

The main trigger that contributed to the landslides at these project locations is believed to be saturation of the slopes during the flood event. The saturated slopes resulted in a reduced shear strength of the soil mass, and as the Susquehanna River level rapidly decreased, the conditions at these project sites were ideal for landslide activity to occur.

LANDSLIDE REMEDIATION ALTERNATIVES

SR 187, Section 079

Based on field observations, it was believed that the failure plane of the landslide was located at the current ground surface along the hillside. A deep-seated failure plane that extends up slope of SR 187 was not expected to be an issue/concern. Based on the height of the hillside, two feasible alternatives were considered for remediating the landslide: a tangent drilled shaft wall and restoration of the hillside slope using durable rock embankment. Both alternatives required a detour to construct, but detouring this portion of SR 187 was permitted per PennDOT. The alternatives and associated approximate costs were presented to PennDOT. Based on the estimated cost to construct the drilled shafts being approximately double the cost to restore the slope using rock, and the fact that the portion of the slope that was constructed of rock at approximately 1.5H:1V slope did not fail during the flood event, it was recommended to restore the hillside slope using a 1.5H:1V durable rock embankment. In addition, since the 1.5H:1V rock slope will encroach into the existing stream channel, it was required to relocate the stream as part of this project.

SR 187, Sections 080 & 081

During final design of these projects, PennDOT indicated that the SR 187 Sections 080 and 081 landslide repairs would be bundled together into one construction contract. Therefore, it was determined that utilizing the same remediation for the Section 080 and 081 landslides would be most cost effective for PennDOT. Several alternatives were considered to remediate these landslides, including overexcavation and replacement with durable rock embankment and structural solutions, such as drilled shaft tangent walls and sheet pile walls. Design calculations showed that the required limits of durable rock embankment would require a road closure of SR 187. Since PennDOT committed to the local school district that SR 187 in the area of these two landslides would remain open for school bus traffic, the durable rock embankment option was dismissed. It was determined that the sheet pile alternative was quicker to install and substantially more economical than the tangent walls; therefore, it was determined that a sheet pile wall was the preferred landslide remediation alternative for both Sections 080 and 081.

SR 187, Section 088

During final design, PennDOT also indicated that SR 187, Section 088 would be bundled together with the SR 187, Sections 080 and 081 landslide repairs. For consistency with the Section 080 and 081 projects, a sheet pile wall was considered for the Section 088 landslide. However, the sheet pile wall alternative was not considered feasible at this location because of the shallow bedrock encountered in the borings, which would prohibit sheet pile installation to the design depth. Additionally, the sheet pile alternative was not considered the most economical solution to repair the shallow slumps that occurred at mid slope (i.e., the slumps did not impact the SR 187 roadway in this area). An alternative consisting of excavation of the shallow slumps and replacement with a rock veneer was considered and was determined to be feasible and most cost-effective landslide remediation at this location. Therefore, the rock veneer alternative was recommended for remediation of the slumps at this location.

LANDSLIDE REMEDIATION DESIGN

SR 187, Section 079

The existing rock slope that was not impacted by the flood was an approximately 1.5H:1V slope. Therefore, it was determined that the rock slope should be designed for a 1.5H:1V slope and the total length of repair was 600 feet. RocScience's SLIDE (*4*) computer program was used to design the rock embankment. Subsurface conditions modeled in the analyses were based on information obtained from the borings, laboratory testing, and visual observations. The soil parameters utilized in the landslide remediation design are provided in Table 2.

Material	Unit Weight, γ (pcf)	Saturated Unit Weight, γ_{sat} (pcf)	Friction Angle, ϕ (degrees)	Cohesion (psf)
In-Situ Soil	120	125	34	0
Proposed Rock Fill	115	120	40	0
Bedrock	140	145	40	1,000

Table 2: Summary of Soil Parameters Used in Remediation Design

Toe key configurations with varying depths and widths were analyzed in SLIDE (*4*) to determine the preferred toe key configuration for the 1.5H:1V rock slope. The analyses indicated that the toe key should be a minimum of 4 feet deep and 15 feet wide to provide a global stability factor of safety of at least 1.3. In order to provide erosion protection of the rock embankment during future flood events, each lift of the rock embankment was grouted up to the 100-year flood elevation. A typical section of the rock embankment remediation is shown in Figure 4.

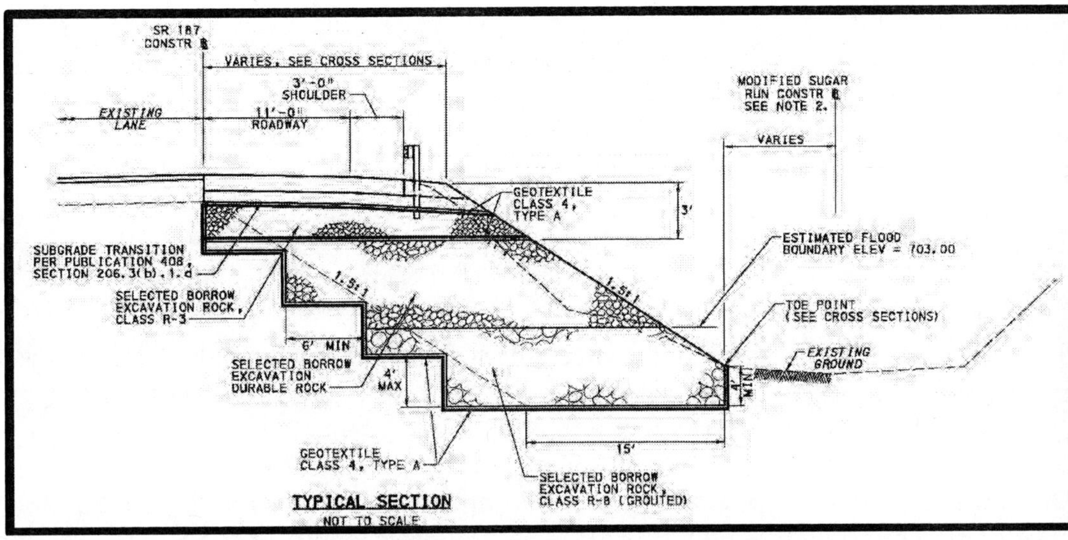

FIGURE 4: Typical Section of SR 187, Section 079 Remediation

SR 187, Sections 080 & 081

For constructability purposes, it was determined that a single sheet pile design (i.e., sheet size and length) for both sites would be preferred. The existing slope geometry and subsurface conditions at both sites were evaluated to determine the worst-case scenario to use as the design case. Based on review of the data, the conditions at SR 187, Section 080 controlled the design because the slope in front of the wall was steeper, the exposed wall height was greater, and the water level was higher than the SR 187, Section 081 condition. The subsurface conditions at Section 080 were slightly denser than the soil conditions encountered at Section 081; however, the soil properties used to represent the subsurface conditions at Section 080 were considered reasonable because subsurface conditions encountered at the Section 081 project were similar. Therefore, the sheet pile design developed for Section 080 was recommended for the sheet pile wall at the Section 081 location.

The actual scarp height observed at Section 080 was around 5 feet, but the sheet pile design was conservatively performed for an exposed wall height of 8 feet. Additionally, the design was performed for a 2H:1V slope in front of the wall and groundwater was modeled at a depth of 7 below the top of the wall.

The subsurface conditions used in the design were based on information obtained from the borings. The soil strength parameters used in the analyses were based on SPT N_{60} values and PennDOT's DM-4 Design Manual (*5*). A summary of soil parameters utilized in the analyses are provided below in the Table 3.

Material	Depth (ft)	Unit Weight, γ (pcf)	Saturated Unit Weight, γ_{sat} (pcf)	Friction Angle, ϕ (degrees)	Cohesion (psf)
Sand and Silt	0 to 10.5	120	125	30	0
Sand and Gravel	10.5 to 75	125	130	34	0

Table 3: Summary of Soil Parameters Used in Remediation Design

Based on the calculations for the 8-foot exposed height, the required embedment to satisfy stability per LRFD design methodology (*5*) was approximately 28 feet, resulting in a total sheet pile length of 36 feet. The calculations indicated that the minimum section modulus of the sheet pile must be 30 cubic inches (in^3). Published sheet pile data suggests that the commonly used PZ27 sheet meets the requirements for the minimum section modulus (i.e., 30.2 in^3). Deflection of the wall was estimated to be 1.2 inches, which was considered reasonable to support the SR 187 roadway.

Global stability of the slope with the sheet pile wall installed was analyzed using the SLIDE (*4*) computer program. Based on the slope stability analyses, the 36-foot-long sheet pile wall satisfied global stability (i.e., FS≥1.3).

The limits of the sheet pile wall were determined in the field as a collaborative effort between Gannett Fleming and PennDOT staff. The proposed length of the SR 187, Section 080 sheet pile wall was 165 linear feet, and the proposed length of the SR 187, Section 081 wall was 290 linear feet, resulting in 455 linear feet of sheet pile wall to remediate these two landslides. A typical section of the sheet pile wall remediation is shown in Figure 5.

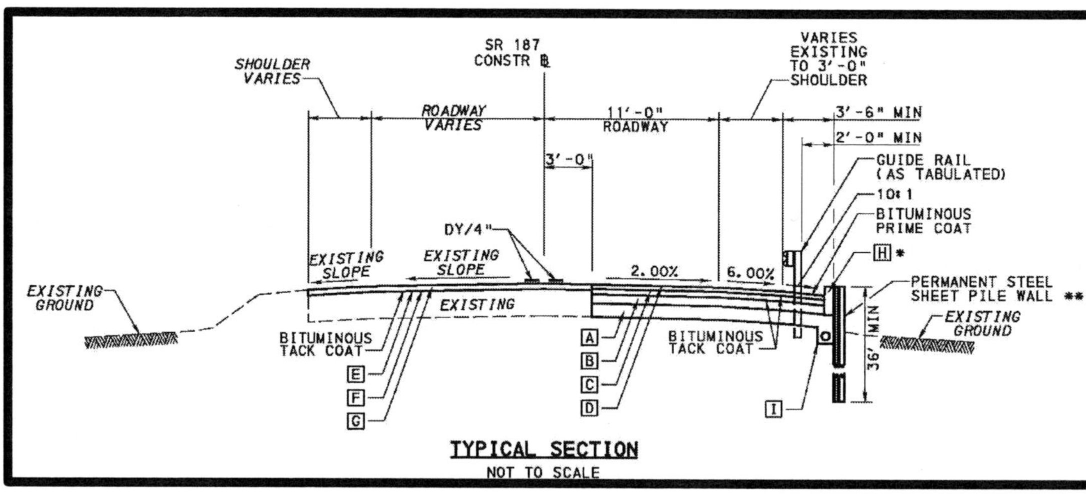

FIGURE 5: Typical Section of SR 187, Sections 080 and 081 Remediation

SR 187, Section 088

Based on the geometry of the slope and the location of the shallow slumps, it was determined that providing a 3-foot-thick rock veneer would result in complete removal of the soil slumps while also limiting excavation operations to the existing slope and therefore minimizing impacts to the SR 187 roadway and shoulder. Therefore, a 3-foot-thick rock veneer was recommended to remediate the landslide.

The rock veneer remediation was analyzed using the SLIDE (*4*) computer program. Subsurface conditions modeled in the analyses were based on information obtained from the boring and visual observations.

The soil strength parameters used in the design were based on SPN N_{60} values and PennDOT's DM-4 Design Manual (*5*), as well as PennDOT Publication 293 (*6*) guidance for the rock fill. The bedrock parameters were estimated based on engineering judgement. A summary of soil parameters utilized in the SLIDE computer program are provided below in Table 4:

Material	Unit Weight, γ (pcf)	Saturated Unit Weight, γ_{sat} (pcf)	Friction Angle, ϕ (degrees)	Cohesion (psf)
In-Situ Soil	120	125	36	0
Proposed Rock Fill	115	120	40	0
Bedrock	130	130	40	1,000

Table 4: Summary of Soil Parameters Used in SR 187, Section 088 Remediation Design

Veneer configurations with varying bottom elevations were analyzed in SLIDE (*4*) to determine the preferred veneer configuration. The analyses indicated that a 3-foot-thick veneer extending to Elevation 650 was required to satisfy global stability (i.e., FS>1.3). The rock veneer treatment was recommended to extend approximately 100 feet to remediate the slumps at this location. A typical section of the rock veneer slump remediation is shown in Figure 6.

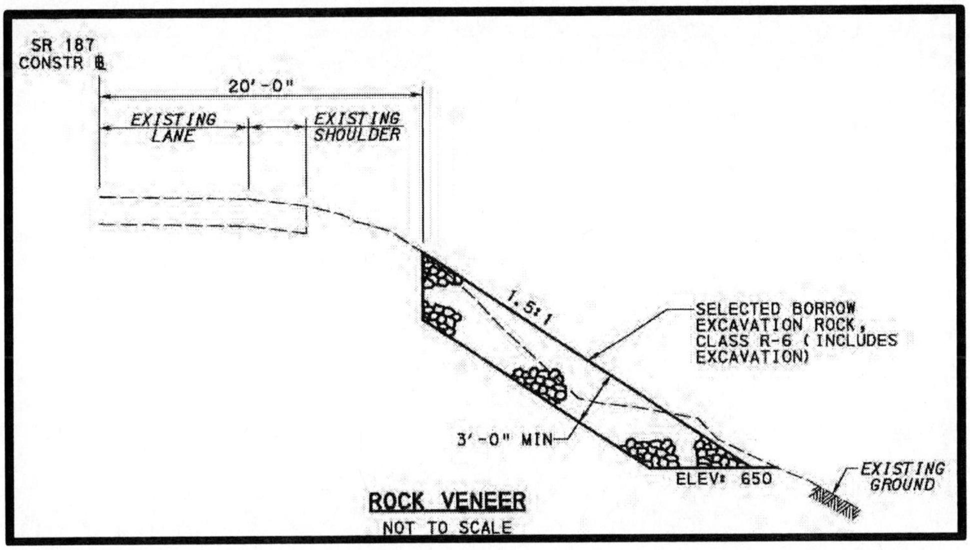

FIGURE 6: Typical Section of SR 187, Sections 088 Remediation

LANDSLIDE REMEDIATION CONSTRUCTION

SR 187, Section 079

The construction documents were prepared and were expected to be advertised in January 2019, but the advertisement was delayed due to permitting required for the stream relocation. The project was eventually advertised in March 2019. Glenn O. Hawbaker, Inc. submitted the low bid of approximately $2.0 million and was awarded the landslide remediation contract in May 2019.

Construction of the remediation was completed by October 2019. Photos 6 and 7 were taken during construction of the landslide remediation.

Photo 6: SR 187, Section 079 – Rock Embankment Construction

Photo 7: SR 187, Section 079 – Rock Embankment Construction

SR 187, Sections 080, 081 & 088

The project was advertised in January 2019 and Clearwater Construction, Inc. submitted the low bid of approximately $977,000, and was awarded the contract in February 2019 to remediate these three landslide areas along SR 187. Construction of the three project areas was completed by June 2019.

Sheet pile installation for Section 080 and 081 was required directly adjacent to residential housing. Vibration monitoring, as well as pre- and post-construction surveys were performed on structures located in close proximity to the sheet pile walls to ensure construction activities did not impact these residences. The monitoring indicated that construction activities did not impact these residences.

During construction of the Section 080 sheet piling, instability issues were observed to the west of the wall station limits identified in the Contract Documents. It is believed that this area was near equilibrium during the design phase and the vibration associated with sheet pile installation caused additional landslides. The sheet pile wall in this area was lengthened by approximately 100 feet during construction to mitigate this additional ground movement. Photos 8 and 9 were taken during construction of the Section 080 project.

Photo 8: SR 187, Section 080 – Sheet Pile Installation

Photo 9: SR 187, Section 080 – Finished Sheet Pile Wall

REFERENCES

(1) Sevon, William D. and Braun, Duane D., Pennsylvania Bureau of Topographic and Geologic Survey, *Surficial Geology of the Wellsboro and Towanda 30x60-Minute Quadrangles, Pennsylvania.* Open File Reports 97-02 and 97-03, 1997.

(2) Pennsylvania Department of Conservation and Natural Resources, Bureau of Topographic and Geologic Survey, *PAGEODE,* September 2018.

(3) Geyer, S.R. and Wilshusen, J.P., Pennsylvania Bureau of Topographic and Geologic Survey, *Engineering Characteristics of the Rock of Pennsylvania,* Revised 1982.

(4) Rocscience, Inc., *SLIDE 2D Limit Equilibrium Slope Stability for Soil and Rock Slopes,* 2018.

(5) Pennsylvania Department of Transportation, Publication 15M, *Design Manual Part 4,* 2015.

(6) Pennsylvania Department of Transportation, Publication 293, *Geotechnical Engineering Manual 4,* 2016.

Evaluation of Mine Subsidence Conditions using Borings and Downhole Investigation Techniques

David L. Knott, Principal Consultant
DiGioia Gray & Associates
570 Beatty Road, Monroeville, PA 15146
412-491-7659
dknott@digioiagray.com,

Richard E. Gray, Principal Consultant
DiGioia Gray & Associates
570 Beatty Road, Monroeville, PA 15146
724-787-5518
dick@digioiagray.com

John Lea, FAusIMM, Director,
Groundsearch Australia Pty. Limited
178 Racecourse Road Rutherford, NSW 2320 Australia
+61 427 494 234
john.lea@groundsearch.com.au

Hayden Streater
Newcastle Geotechnical Group Manager
WSP Australia Pty Limited
51-55 Bolton Street, Newcastle, NSW, 2300 Australia
+61 414 515 532
hayden.streater@wsp.com

Prepared for the 71st Highway Geology Symposium, May 2022

Acknowledgements

The authors would like to thank Wendy Sherer for their work on formatting the document.

Disclaimer

Statements and views presented in this paper are strictly those of the author(s), and do not necessarily reflect positions held by their affiliations, the Highway Geology Symposium (HGS), or others acknowledged above. The mention of trade names for commercial products does not imply the approval or endorsement by HGS.

ABSTRACT

A properly planned and executed mine subsidence investigation is critical to understanding subsidence issues and mitigation. Typically, it includes:

- Desktop assessment of potential subsidence types, such as if sinkholes from roof falls or trough subsidence from pillar failure, or both could occur.

- Developing an investigation program to assess subsidence varies with the anticipated subsidence type(s) as follows:

  - Sinkholes – Borings typically target open rooms and conditions where sinkholes are more likely to develop.

  - Troughs – Separate borings typically target pillars to assess if crushing has occurred and an adjacent room to assess mined conditions and caving.

- Drilling borings using coring or air rotary, or in combination with each other. In addition to obtaining samples of the subsurface materials, valuable information can be obtained during drilling, such as the presence of voids being indicated by tool drops and fractures and voids indicated by the loss of water or air return. All borings should be cased in the soil zone to allow for further investigation with downhole techniques and mitigation. Borings should also extend into the mine floor and into harder rock units if pillar punching is an issue.

Downhole techniques to supplement borings include:

- Downhole geophysical techniques
- Borehole camera
- Cavity scanning
- Borehole sonar
- Borehole imagery
- In-Seam

The information obtained from the investigation can then be used to assess if subsidence has occurred or not, future subsidence deformations, and mitigation options and quantities.

In summary, a mine subsidence investigation needs to consider expected mine subsidence types, mine conditions, and information needed to assess subsidence and mitigation.

1. Introduction

A properly planned and executed mine subsidence investigation is critical to understanding subsidence issues and mitigation.

2. Mine subsidence background

"Mine subsidence is the downward movement of the ground surface due to gravity in response to a loss of support at mine level. The ground surface and whatever is constructed upon it is supported by a structural system that comprises the overburden (the soil-mantled sequence of rock strata situated between ground surface and mine level), the coal pillars, and mine floor. Excessive deformation or failure of one or more of these components over time can result in mine subsidence." (Bruhn et al., 1978). Subsidence can occur as sinkholes or troughs, as shown on Figure 1. Ground cracks can sometimes form around troughs.

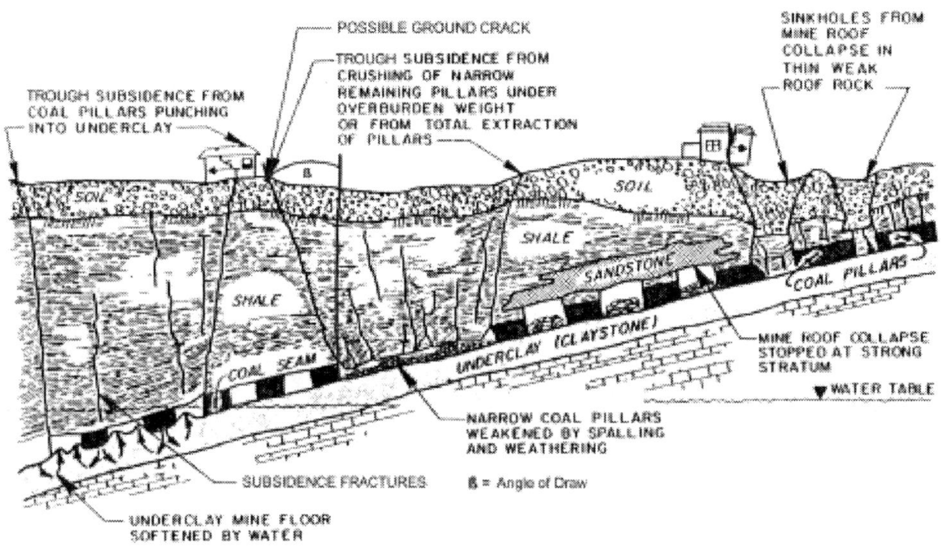

Figure 1 Types of subsidence (modified from Bruhn et al, 1978)

3. Desktop Assessment

Desktop assessment should include review of potential subsidence types, sinkholes from roof falls or trough subsidence from pillar failure, or both may occur. Obtaining information on over - burden thickness, rock types, geologic structure, mining conditions, and previous subsidence events will help with this assessment. Tying the mine map to the surface is a key task. If coordinates are available, they can be used to tie the mine map to the surface. If they are not available, surface features, such as roads, streams, oil and gas wells, and mining infrastructure can be used.

4. Investigation Planning

Developing an investigation program to assess subsidence varies with the anticipated subsidence type(s) as follows:

- Sinkholes – Borings typically target open rooms and conditions where sinkholes are more likely to develop.

- Troughs – Separate borings typically target pillars to assess if crushing has occurred and an adjacent room to assess mined conditions and caving.

In addition, a variety of conditions can be encountered at mine level as shown in Figure 2.

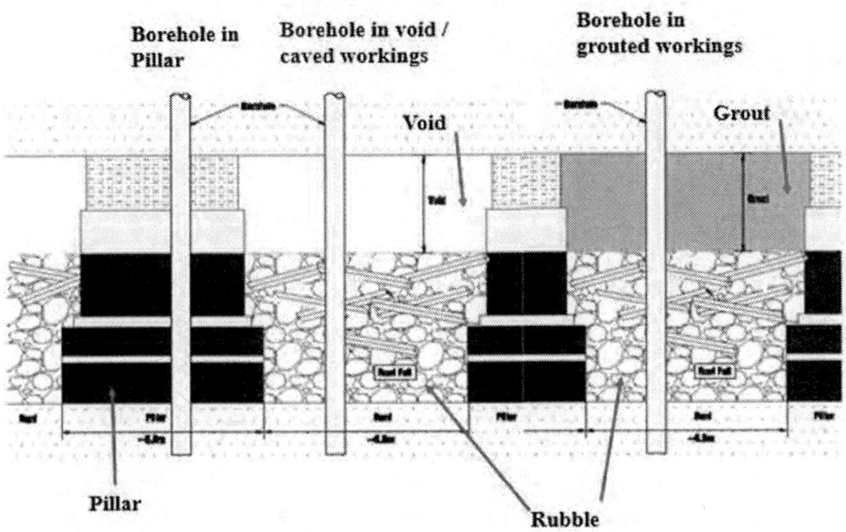

Figure 2 Typical mine level conditions encountered in drilling (Knott et al, 2016)

Some safety considerations also need to be considered at this time, such as:

- Gases that are potentially explosive and / or dangerous may emanate from the borehole;
- Artesian water from the mine workings may be encountered; and
- Sinkholes can occur from soil flowing into a mine void in an uncased borehole.

5. Investigation Methods

5.1.1 Borings

Borings are typically drilled using coring or air rotary, or in combination with each other on larger projects. In addition to obtaining samples of the subsurface materials, valuable information can be obtained during drilling, such as the presence of voids as indicated by tool drops and fractures and voids indicated by the loss of water or air return. All borings should be cased in the soil zone to allow for further investigation with downhole techniques and mitigation. Borings should also extend into the mine floor and below soft rock units if pillar punching is an issue.

5.1.1.1 Cored rock borings

In cored borings, rock is generally recovered, allowing an assessment of the rock types, discontinuities, and subsidence fractures. Some downhole techniques can also be used to obtain this information as indicated below. Figure 3 illustrates an example of rock cored where a trough subsidence event has occurred. The boring encountered fracturing above the coal due to pillar crushing at mine level.

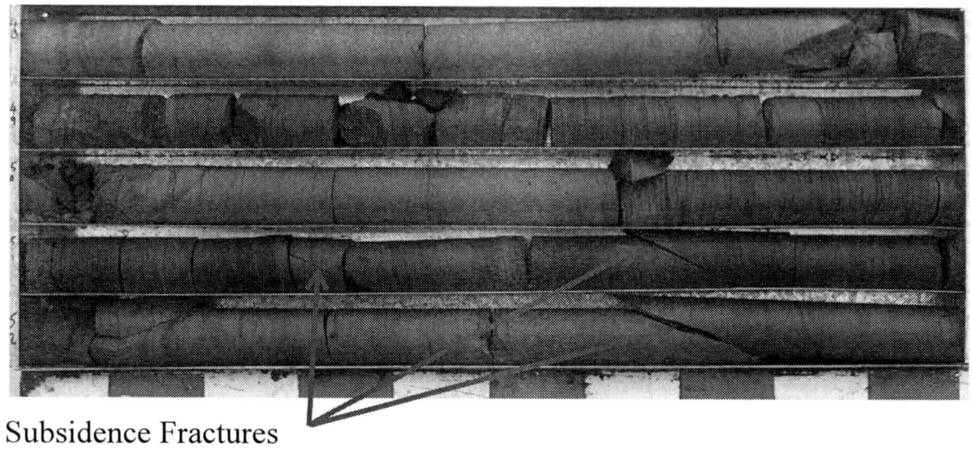

Figure 3 Typical trough subsidence fractures above Borehole Coal Seam, Newcastle, Aus where a trough subsidence event occurred in 1896, shortly after mining, Core depth is 157.5 ft to 173.9 ft (48 to 53m), with the top of the seam at 212.8 ft (64.87 m) (Knott et al, 2012)

5.1.1.2 Air Rotary Borings

As the drill bit grinds up the rock with air rotary drilling, only chips of rock or dust may be recovered; which is why they typically have a lower cost than cored borings. However, they are beneficial in helping to provide data on coal depth, voids, and overburden conditions. An example of air rotary drilling is provided in Figure 4.

Figure 4 Air rotary drilling Note, in many cases a water well drilling rig is used (note dust) Aqua earth website

5.2 Downhole techniques

5.2.1 Downhole geophysical techniques

Downhole geophysical logging is commonly used in resource exploration. It can also be used in mine subsidence assessment / mitigation to:

- Assess seam thickness and pillar crushing by determining the top and bottom of the coal seam in areas of poor recovery;
- Pick up voids and material properties in zones of "no return";
- Assess the effectiveness of subsidence mitigation work, such as the presence of cement fly ash grout in verification holes; and
- Assess if a "void" is open or filled with "soft" material which can impact grout volumes and effectiveness.

Tools that measure density, velocity, borehole deviation, and natural gamma are used in mine subsidence assessments, but due to space constraints, we will focus on density and deviation.

5.2.1.1 Density

Density measurement is the most common and valuable method. It picks up variations in rock density by measuring average density of the material using high energy gamma rays emitted from a source that pass through the rock surrounding the boring following Short and Long spaced travel paths to be measured at two receptors as shown in Figure 5. The tool is useful for distinguishing between voids and coal as they have a lower density than the other rock types as shown in Figure 6.

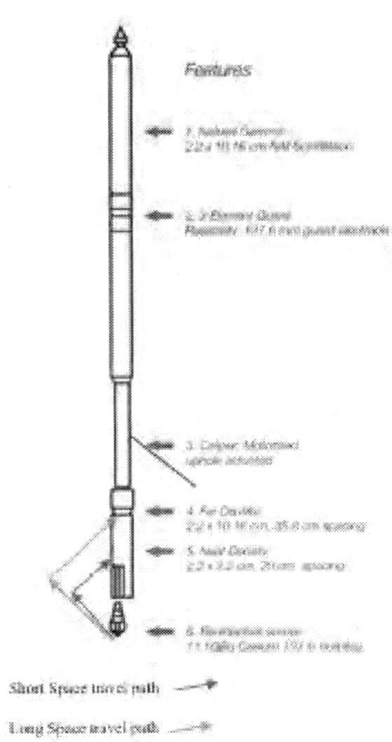

Figure 5 Density Tool

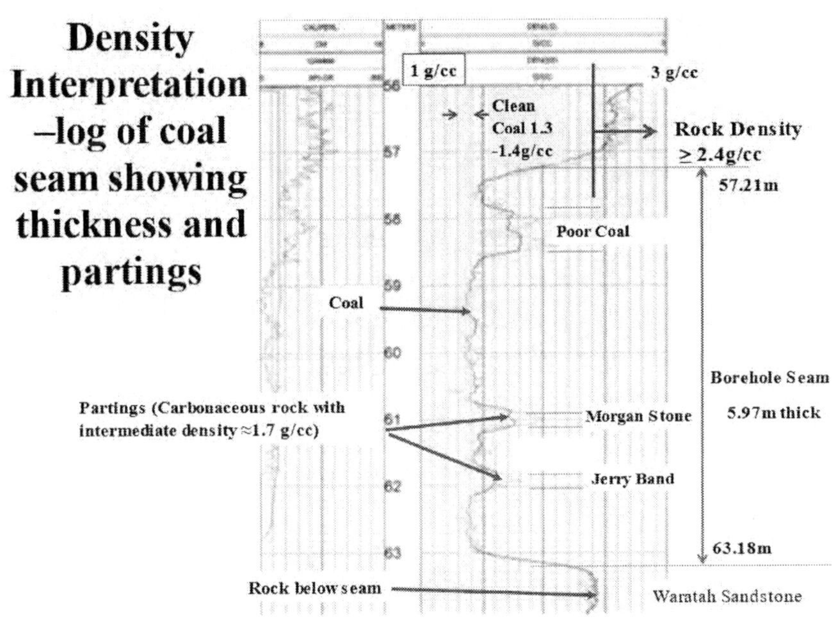

Figure 6 Density Interpretation –log of coal seam showing thickness and partings

Borehole sidewall stability is a key issue in the use of the device as getting a radioactive source lost in a boring is a major issue. This results in the two following cases:

- Unstable Boring – Where the boring penetrates unstable ground, such as caved material from subsidence, the tool is lowered down the casing with the drill rig over the hole to reduce the potential for the tool being stuck in the ground as shown in Figure 7.
- Stable Boring – Where the ground is stable, the device can be used after the boring is completed, provided the soil zone is cased as shown in Figure 8.

If the density is measured through steel casing, the impact of the steel density on the readings must be accounted for in data processing.

Figure 7 Unstable borehole conditions - Lower device through drill rods with rig on the borehole

Figure 8 Stable borehole conditions - Lower device through casing in soil zone after drilling

5.2.1.2 Deviation

Assessing deviation is important as borings can veer from their intended straight path during drilling due to subsurface conditions such as boulders and / or fractured zones. Also, an accurate location aids in assessing the position of the mine level target with respect to the surface. The device is lowered down the hole and provides measurement of hole position with depth to an accuracy of ± 2° for the bearing and ± 0.5° for the slant angle. The type of device used depends on if the boring is open or has steel casing as follows:

- Open Hole – Magnetic deviation tool

This tool contains a magnetometer and inclinometer package that records the tools inclination and bearing at specific depths. From this data, an azimuth with corresponding inclination which relates to the starting and end-point are calculated.

- Cased Hole - Gyroscope Tool

This tool produces the same basic data as the magnetic deviation package and is processed in a very similar manner except that a gyroscope is used due to the steel casing impacting the readings. An example of the output is provided in Figure 9.

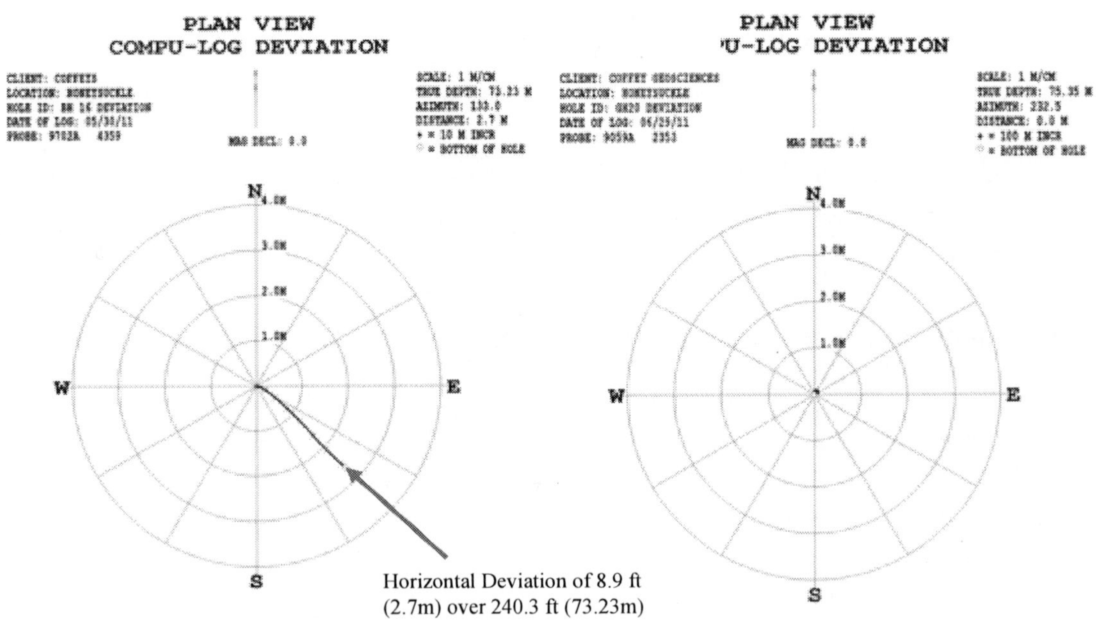

Planned vertical grout hole that missed target due to deviation of 8.9 ft (2.7m at 73.23m) depth during drilling (driller had to redo hole at his own expense)

Grout hole "right on the money" at 240.6 ft (73.35m)

Figure 9 Typical Deviation Plots

5.2.2 Borehole camera

The first author has used borehole cameras on projects since 1987 and found them extremely beneficial in interpreting subsidence and mine level conditions. Conditions in the rock overburden and at mine level can be viewed above and below the groundwater level. For the first author, the real need for using a camera extensively was identified on a mine grouting project in West Virginia in the early 1990s when a 16ft (4.9m) high "void" was reported based on air rotary drilling. It was thought the grout hole would be a "big taker"; however, it took very little grout. Apparently, the hole contained soft material, possibly claystone roof fall and gob (poor material in the coal left in the mine). A camera would have picked up that the "void" was not open, but filled. Borehole cameras are used extensively in Australia. Papers of interest are provided in Pells et al (1988), Rouvray and Davies (2005), Kingsland et al. (2004), Fennell (1997), and Millar and Holz (2011).

The use of an appropriate camera is important. At times, sewer inspection cameras have been used for mine subsidence work due to availability or low cost. However, sometimes the results were not good, as in one case where poor lighting and shadows resulted in images that were so bad that it appeared that more voids were present than encountered during the drilling.

Features of importance for a camera include:

- Hole Size – It should be able to be used in an HQ (3.78 in, 96mm) OD or smaller hole to avoid having to ream out the hole.
- Have a tilting head to allow side and downhole viewing as well as the ability to rotate upwards and view the roof in voids. If a tilting head camera is not available, attachments for simultaneous downhole and side-hole viewing with a mirror, compass and side view lens for void viewing are beneficial.
- Adequate light, as mine voids tend to "soak" up light and many features are lost in the dark. This may require adding better lighting to the camera.
- Ability to focus near (i.e. side of borehole to see rock types and discontinuities) and far (to assess voids and pillar conditions).
- Camera orientation with a compass is useful to map the direction of workings and pillar ribs to tie the workings to the surface.

Current cameras provide color images, such as the GeoVisionTM, which has a rotating head that allows 360° viewing and 170° of tilt as shown in Figure 10 and Figure 11. It can fit in a 1.75 in (44.5mm) diameter hole and has a minimum focus distance of 1.5 in (38mm) and a maximum focus distance of 5 ft (1500mm).

Figure 10 View of camera equipment

Figure 11 View of camera

The camera is useful during the investigation phase to assess caving and mine level conditions, such as the orientation and openness of the workings, and pillar integrity as shown in Figure 12 through Figure 16. The camera also allows the true height of open voids to be assessed, as the roof rock may be pushed down as a result of drilling pressure. Borehole cameras are also of use to assess the effectiveness of grouting as illustrated in Figure 17. Millar and Holz, (2011) also have images of mine level grout placement.

The camera can also be used to assess groundwater conditions. Groundwater inflows can be" friend" or "foe", as small flows may help to clean the sides of the hole, while heavy inflows generally make mine level viewing difficult, as it is like looking through a waterfall.

Several factors that help with viewing are as follows (Knott and Streater, 2017):

1. Case the hole in the soil zone – This helps to keep "mud" from migrating down the sides of the hole in the period between drilling and viewing and keep the borehole open. Note the borehole should also be capped to reduce the potential for material falling into the borehole and reduce air flow in and mine gas flow out of the borehole for safety reasons.

2. Flush the hole with water for flooded and non-flooded conditions, as this helps to remove cuttings from the sides of the hole and flush sediment from the hole. This may lead to quicker viewing time below the water level as there are less particles to settle. Also, if too many suspended solids remain in the borehole, when they settle it will "fill" part of the hole so that the bottom of the hole may not be able to be viewed.

3. For below water viewing, unless good flushing is performed, two days to several weeks may be needed to allow suspended particles to settle. Flocculants have also been used to help settle suspended solids quicker, but environmental impacts need to be assessed. Flowing water in the workings also helps to clear the water as sediments from drilling are flushed from the area of interest.

4. Suspended particles can be easily stirred up and it is better to look at features of interest on the way down rather than waiting to check on the way back up as particles may become resuspended once the camera passes thought them.

5. Adjust lighting as needed to improve viewing.

6. Pan slowly when viewing sideways and pause at features of interest.

Some disadvantages associated with using borehole cameras include:

1. Waiting time for suspended solids to settle.
2. Difficulty judging distance and the size of objects.
3. Some camera operators will not lower device into a void due to a fear of getting it stuck.
4. Debris at mine level, such as rubble, blocking sideways view.
5. Insufficient light, particularly underwater to illuminate features of interest in the distance.
6. Lowering the camera too fast and missing features of interest.

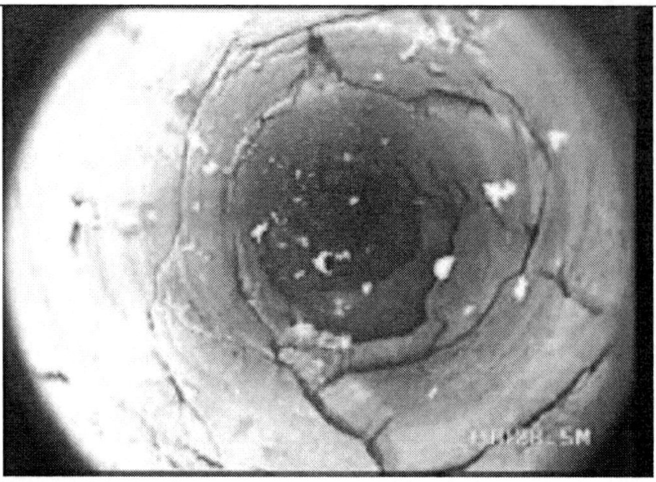

Figure 12 Underwater image of broken rock due to caving (Note suspended particles)

Figure 13 Side view of roof joint intersection in unflooded workings

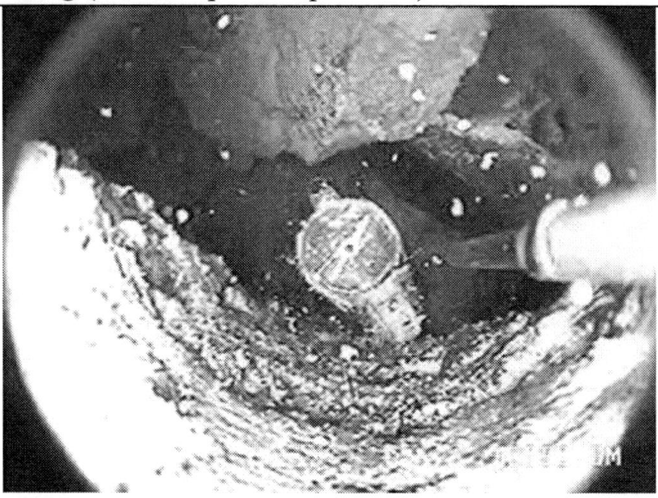

Figure 14 Borehole encountering edge of pillar and room (underwater)

Figure 15 Downward looking underwater view of in place coal in Yard Seam, Newcastle, Aus at 84.3 ft (25.7 m) depth (borehole encountered

Figure 16 View of light lowered into another borehole about 100 ft (30m) away indicating open haulageway

Figure 17 Grout enveloping conveyor in haulageway (Knott et al, 2013)

5.2.3 Void scanning

Laser surveys are generally conducted in air-filled voids / cavities and sonar surveys in water-filled voids (see next section). Modern 3D scanner technology provides superior qualitative and quantitative information than other cavity survey methods with deployment at any level in boreholes which penetrate cavities, including abandoned mines. The complete tool length does not need to be deployed into most mining cavities; thereby mitigating the risk of getting stuck inside the void. The scanning devices rotate 360 degrees in the horizontal plane and tilt in the vertical plane to produce 2D vertical and horizontal sections, 3D point cloud models and volume estimations. Typically, rotating scans record horizontal sections data in 2° azimuth increments and tilting scans of vertical sections data in 3° increments. The data are viewed in real time. For both systems, the clear "line of sight" survey distance range is 6 inches (150 mm) to a maximum of 196.9 ft (60m) for the laser, and > 656 ft (200 m) for the sonar. Accuracy is 1/1000 of object distance; e.g., ¾ inch (2 cm) for a 65.6 ft (20 m) distant target. The volume precision is typically +/- 1.5%. However, both reduce where the incidence angle on the void wall is small and there are remnant items present, such as pit props, etc.

This survey example is of an abandoned 1930s coal mine slope entry (inclined access) located in an Australian urban area. It was surveyed to establish the physical conditions and dimensions for remediation grouting.

A Flodim SARL high-definition, color video camera and 3D laser tool was used in a 3-3/8 in (96 mm) diameter borehole drilled into the cavity, with the setup of the tool prior to deployment in the cased borehole as shown in Figure 18 and a diagram of features in Figure 19. A sinker bar is attached to the top of the tool to prevent rotation during horizontal section surveys. The data were acquired using a truck-mounted, Century Geophysical LLC-equipped, slimline logging unit.

Video and still images were recorded concurrently with the 3D laser survey which provided valuable information on the physical condition of the slope in real time. Figure 20 indicates physical deterioration with spalling of the slope roof and walls and fallen material on the floor.

The 3D laser survey results indicated that the slope is backfilled to a depth of 17.1 ft (5.2 m) below ground level (mbgl) and it has a volume of 97.8 cy (74.8 m3) (Figure 21). It dips to the east at a grade of 3H:1V or 18° and had a maximum void height of 6.6 ft (2.0 m) (Figure 22) and is oriented east / west (Magnetic North) as shown on Figure 23.

Oriented, superposed horizontal sections shown in the plan diagram (Figure 23) show the areal extent of the slope entry. The width was between 5.9 ft (1.8 m) and 8.2 ft (2.5 m) with widening to 11.5 ft (3.5 m) in one area in the NE quadrant. The inclined length was 79 ft (24 m).

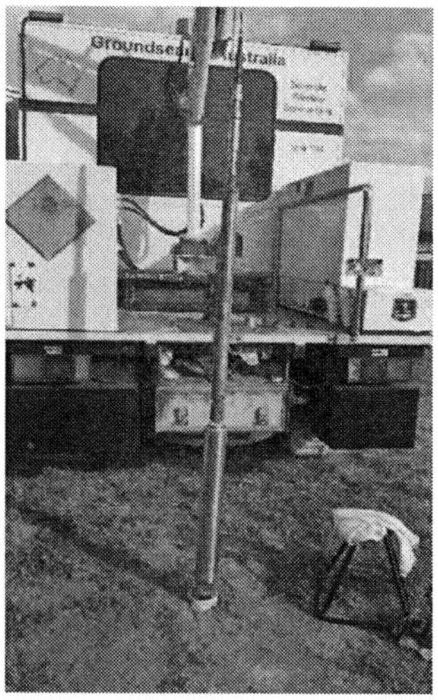

Figure 18 Logging unit setup with laser / video

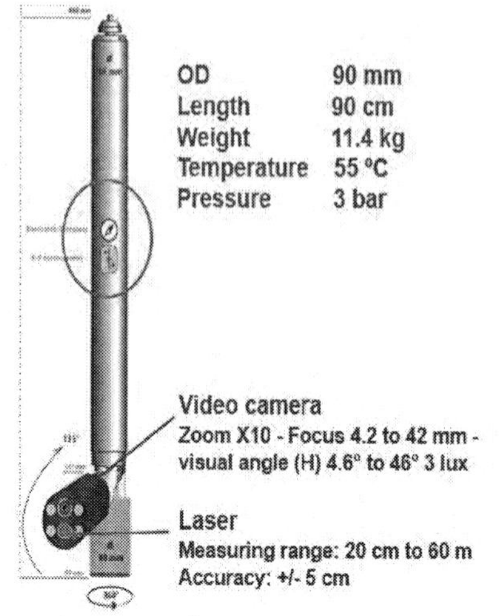

Figure 19 Laser tool diagram

Figure 20 Image from laser / video looking down-gradient from the west.

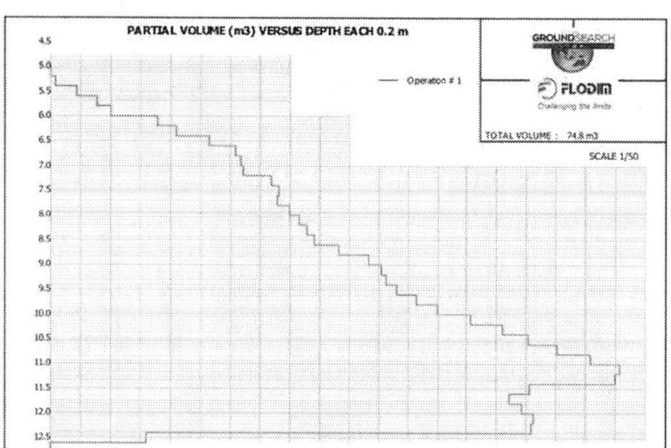

Figure 21 Partial volume (X axis) versus depth (Y axis) at 7.8 in (0.2 m) intervals.

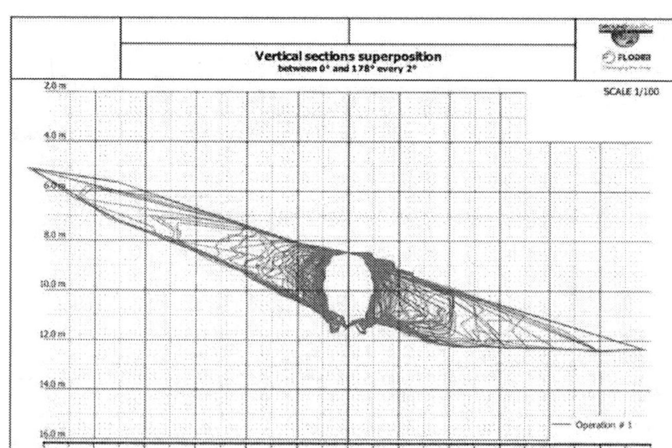

Figure 22 Superposed vertical sections showing the cavity height, distance from survey borehole (X axis) and depth (Y axis).

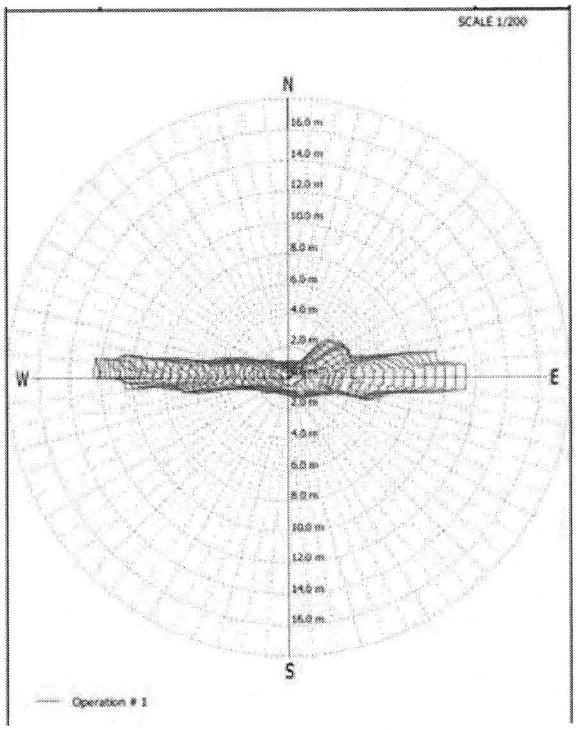

Figure 23 Superposed horizontal sections showing the areal extent and orientation of the cavity.

Models of the cavity were created from digital horizontal and vertical point data cloud slices. Figure 24 represents cardinal point viewpoints. The distance from the survey point is represented in separate coloured zones.

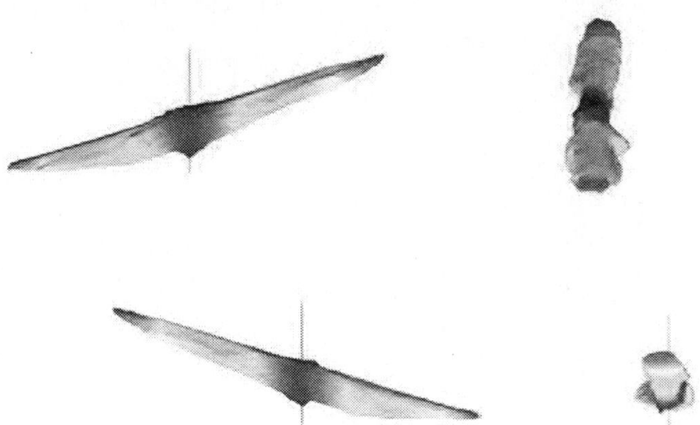

Figure 24 Cavity models – Views in clockwise direction from upper left showing view from North, East, West, and South

5.2.4 Borehole sonar

5.2.4.1 2D Sonar

The sonar device is typically lowered down a vertical hole into a flooded mine void and will scan a horizonal cross-section of the void surfaces in 360° at depths of interest. Voids less than 1 ft

(300mm) high are difficult to image. It should be noted that the imaged void may be in the roof overlying the mined workings and not the mined interval due to roof fall; therefore, it may not give the actual mined width, but the smaller caved width of the roof void. A view of the device is provided in Figure 25 with a view of the output showing the configuration of the mine workings in Figure 26, and a view of the mine map at the corresponding location of the boring indicating a "match" in Figure 27.

Figure 25 Downhole sonar setup with 10 ft (3m) rod attachment

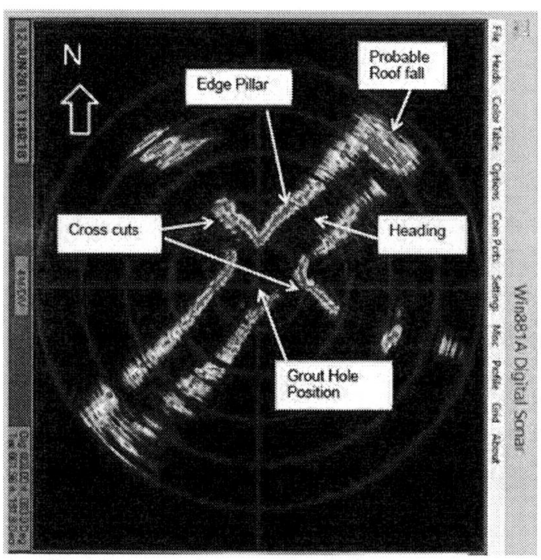

Figure 26 Sample sonar output

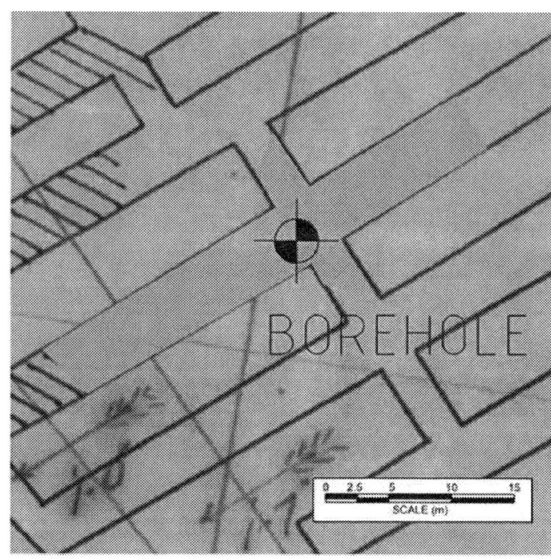

Figure 27 View of mine map corresponding to sonar output

5.2.4.2 3D Sonar

As indicated in a previous section, 3D sonar systems use a scanning to develop a 3D model of the void. They are deployable in >H-size (3-3/8 in (96 mm)) boreholes.

As an example, the device was used in the assessment of a void in abandoned mine workings in the about 20 ft (6 m) thick Borehole Seam, in Newcastle, Australia (Figure 28). The mine workings were completed prior to 1908 and are below sea level and therefore flooded, as mining ended prior to about 1916 (Hawkins and Harvey, 2001). The 3D sonar survey was performed using Flodim SARL 3D sonar technology since the workings were underwater and it could provide an image in areas with poor water clarity. The results indicate that the cavity roof was at a depth of 249.7 ft (75.8 m) and had a maximum void height of 6.6 ft (2.0 m) (Figure 29), the volume of the cavity was 123 cy (94.1 m^3) (Figure 30), and is oriented southwest / northeast (Magnetic North) as shown in Figure 31. The mine workings were flat-lying, as would be expected based on geologic conditions, with all surfaces uneven. The survey took 3.5 hrs.

Figure 28 Sonar survey equipment before borehole deployment.

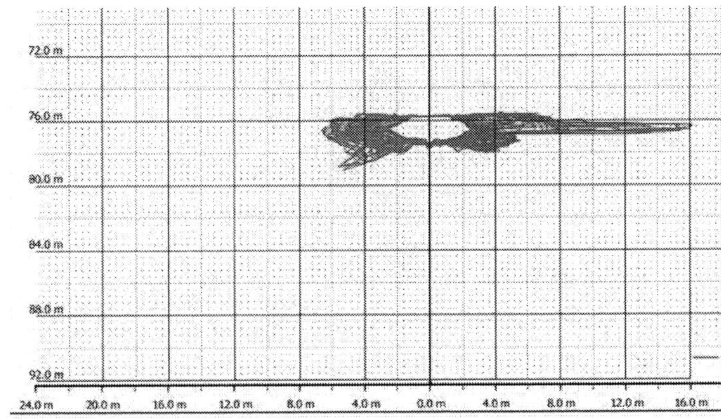

Figure 29 Superposed vertical sections showing the cavity height, distance from survey borehole (X axis) and depth (Y axis).

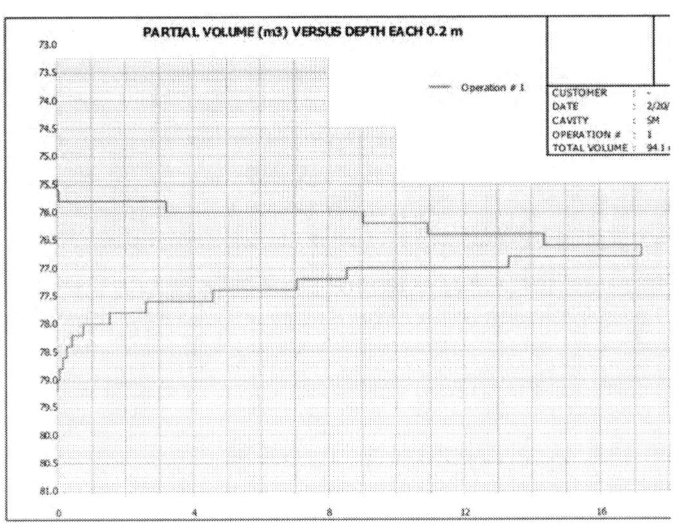

Figure 30 Partial volume (X axis) versus depth (Y axis) at 7.8 inch (0.2 m) intervals.

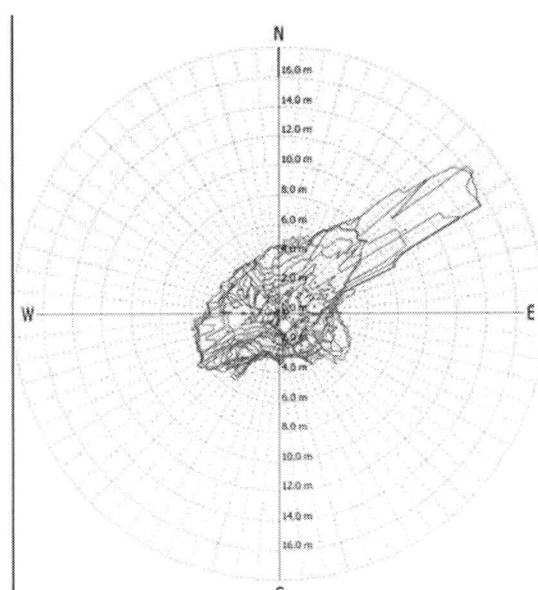

Figure 31 Superposed horizontal sections showing the areal extent and orientation of the mine void between 248 ft (75.6 m) and 258,5 ft (78.8 m) depth.

Models of the void can also be created from digital horizontal and vertical point data cloud slices similar to those previously provided in Figure 24.

Figure 32 shows the sonar data overlaid on the mine map. It indicates that the mine map is accurate in this area. The data provide the detail required to optimize the stabilization of the mine workings, thus resulting in savings to the client.

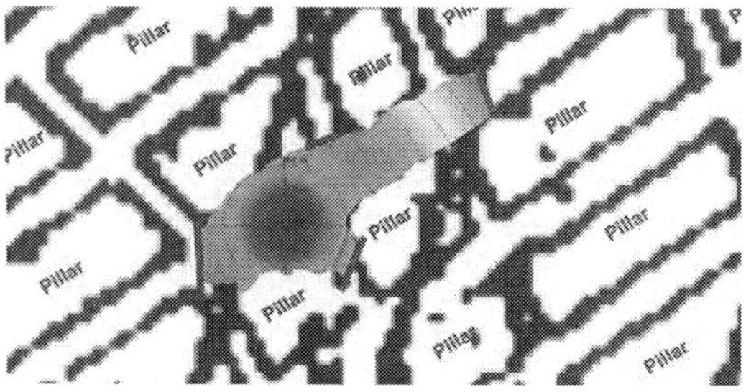

Figure 32 The overhead solid model shows the areal extent and orientation of the void with respect to the mine workings. Mine plan (RC, 1908).

5.2.5 Borehole Imagery

Acoustic Televiewer (ATV) and Optical Televiewer (OTV) scans of a borehole wall are centralized, depth-based, continuous, fully oriented 360° images enabling identification and analysis of planar features such as:

- Lithology characterization;
- Bedding planes (including separations and dip and strike);
- Fractures / joints / cleats (including frequency and orientation);
- Aperture;
- Veins and mineralization; and
- Borehole breakout and other borehole anomalies.

Typical applications include:

- Borehole core orientation / provide information in core loss zones;
- Geotechnical site investigations (including cuts and tunneling);
- Open cut and underground mines;
- Hydrogeology (secondary permeability / casing inspection);
- Structural geology (hydrocarbons and mineral exploration);
- Mine subsidence investigations (overburden characteristics);
- Increased understanding and confidence in computer-generated models.

Acoustic scanners use high-resolution sound waves and operate only in water-filled boreholes without the need for clear water. Logging speeds are 3.3 ft/min (1 m/min) for 2.5/64 in (1 mm) sample interval and 14.8 ft/min (4.5 m/min) for 3/16-inch (5 mm) sample interval. Boreholes with diameters from 3 inch (75 mm) to 9 inches (230 mm) are logged generally. Data are viewed in real time with processing in commercial software.

Optical scanners use a precision, wide-angle lens and a camera to capture a high-definition video image and operate in both air and water-filled boreholes with clear water only. Logging speeds are from 3.3 ft/min (1 m/min) to 19.6 ft/min (6 m/min) depending on required vertical resolution. Boreholes with diameters from 1.9 inch (48 mm) to > 19.6 in (500 mm) are generally logged. The image is oriented to Magnetic North (or to the high side of the borehole) using a 3-axis magnetometer and accelerometer in the tool as shown in Figure 33. The scanner data interpretation procedure is based on the on-screen, manual superposition of sine curves onto features. The height of the sine curve determines the dip and the trough indicates the dip direction. Using automatic picking software to assess discontinuities can miss critical discontinuities. Figure 34 and Figure 35 represent the output from the devices. Data analyses and graphical representations such as contoured plots can be produced.

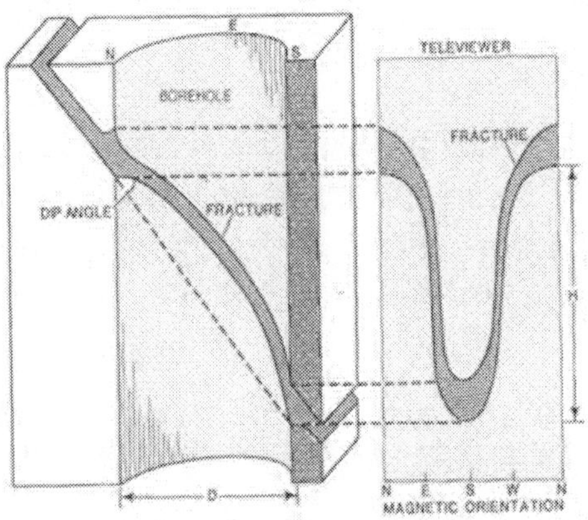

Figure 33 Diagram of borehole feature (left) as represented in flattened, 360° scanner view.

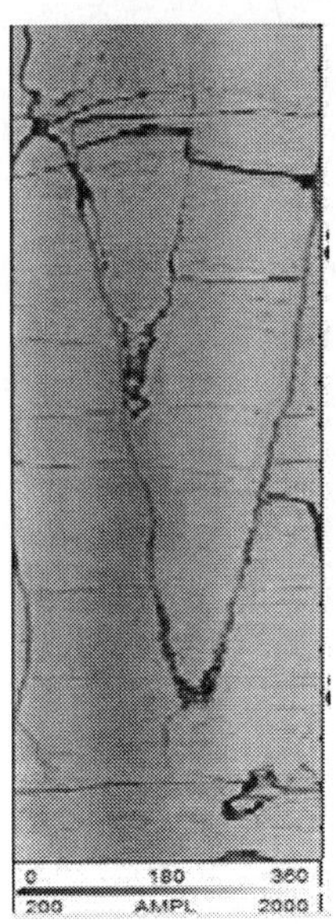

Figure 34 Flattened, 360° ATV image showing fractures in coal measures interburden.

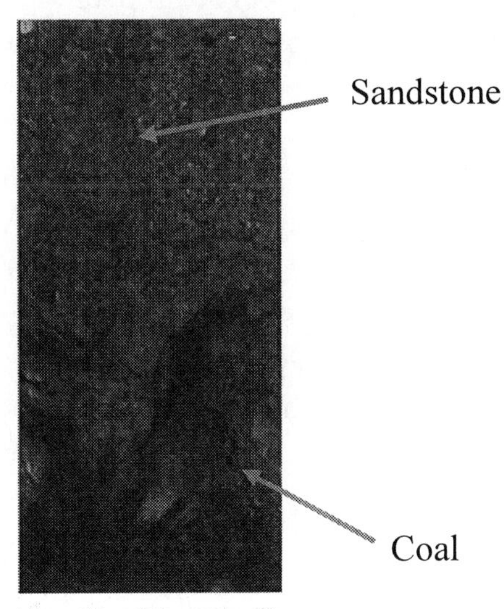

Figure 35 Flattened, 360° OTV image showing overburden and coal seam contact with the top of the coal dipping at 47° in the dip direction of 132° magnetic north.

The scanners are a cost-effective and accurate tool to measure borehole breakout which can be a reliable indicator of the orientation of the in situ, maximum horizontal stress (SH). They can also be seen with a borehole camera.

ATV and OTV surveys provide accurate and reliable identification of planar features that intersect borehole walls providing valuable in situ data in zones of geological, hydrogeological and geotechnical significance. Ultimately these surveys increase data confidence for project design, development and costings.

5.2.6 In-Seam

Radio Imaging Method (RIM) technology uses EM (radio signal) waves between separate borings, one with a transmitter antenna and the other with a receiver antenna, drilled into a coal seam. The signal strength between borings can be used to assess if mining has occurred or not as indicated in Figure 36.

The antennas are lowered to the middle of the seam in both the transmitter and receiver borings, and the signal propagates through the coal seam waveguide as the signal is bounded by the over and underlying rocks due to their differing electrical conductivities. The receiver unit measures the signal strength. It is important to have available accurate seam depth information to position the antennas in the appropriate part of the coal sequence. However, irrespective of the provided depth information, experimentation in the field by the RIM engineer will confirm the position of the antenna in the seam (moving of the probes out of the coal will result in a noticeable decrease in signal strength).

The detection of voids within a coal seam using RIM is based entirely on the waveguide behavior of the coal seam itself. The RIM EM wave travels in a "trapped" mode in the coal between the conductive roof and floor material. The EM wave travels along a "ray path" or "wave front" from transmitter to a companion receiver, decaying in signal strength as a function of distance. In homogeneous conditions, the rate of this decay is consistent and predictable beyond the near field of the transmitting antenna. In a homogeneous coal seam, an EM wave attenuates (decays) with distance traveled at a fixed rate; this is termed the attenuation rate. If a geological anomaly exists along the ray path, the receiving antenna will measure lower signal strength (increased attenuation rate). Geological anomalies that will affect the RIM signal include faults, dikes, paleochannels, seam thinning, and increased water in the seam. Non-geological anomalies that may affect the RIM signal include abandoned mine workings. If a portion of that seam waveguide is water-filled or air-filled, the rate of decay changes.

The RIM downhole instrumentation consists of a multi-frequency transmitter and receiver units designed for borehole applications. The antennas consist of wound ferrite cores powered by downhole batteries and phase linked by a fiber-optic synchronization cable. The field procedure is to set up transmitter and receiver units in adjacent boreholes and measure the decay of the RIM signal over distance (the "measured signal strength").

In general, RIM equipment should be deployed into vertical boreholes lined with PVC casing, never metal casing. Casing prevents damage or loss to the system resulting from hole collapse or debris. If the geology is exceptionally competent, the probes can be used without PVC casing.

The borehole depths can be a minimum of 20 ft (6 m) and a maximum of 1500 ft (457 m). (Note this section was based on information extracted from Stolarczyk and Peng (2003)).

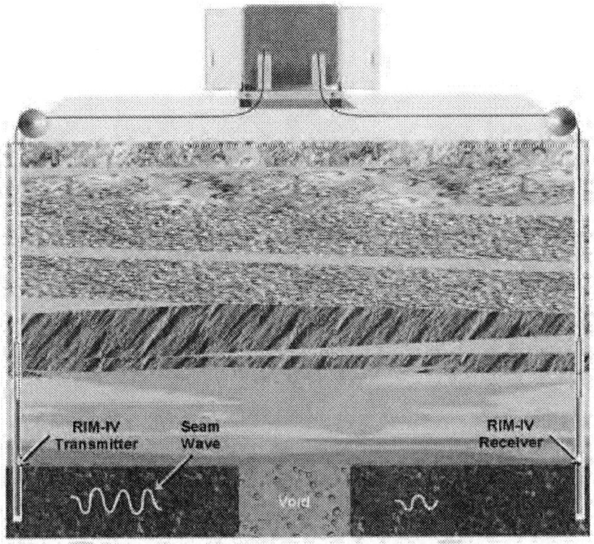

Figure 36 Illustration of the RIM setup and EM wave propagation

6 Assessment of Subsidence

The information obtained from these techniques can then be used to assess if subsidence has occurred or not, and help assess mitigation options and quantities. For example, an accurate measure of coal seam thickness can indicate if a seam has been crushed or not and void height and extent can be obtained.

7 Summary

In summary, a mine subsidence investigation needs to consider expected mine subsidence types, mine conditions, and information needed to assess subsidence and mitigation. The following tools can be used to supplement the information obtained from borings:

- Density - Assess rock types and the presence of voids and coal seams and the presence of grout;
- Deviation – Assess boring drift with depth;
- Borehole Camera – View the strata encountered in the boring, including fractures and mine level conditions;
- Laser surveys - Provide a 3D image of air-filled voids; workings are generally conducted in cavities and: sonar surveys in water-filled cavities. Laser and sonar data can be combined into a single model as can multiple location surveys. In addition, the 3D laser and sonar technologies are important tools for the cost-effective, remote determination of the in-situ void conditions and dimensions thereby enabling a highly accurate void volume determination for subsequent assessments.
- 2D sonar – Used to assess the extent of underwater voids, with the data taken in horizontal planes.

- 3D sonar – Used to assess the extent of underwater voids, with the data taken in all directions.
- Borehole Imagery – Can be used to provide data such as strike, dip, and width of discontinuities encountered in the boring.
- In-Seam – Can assess if mining has occurred between two borings.

References

Bruhn, RW; Knott, DL; Sanger, DB and Kyper; TN. "Effectively Designing for Potential Mine subsidence at a Disposal Facility in Northern Appalachia", Proceedings of Joseph F. Poland Subsidence Symposium, Association of Engineering Geologist – Annual meeting, at Sacramento, California, 1995

Bruhn, Robert W.; Magnuson, Malcolm O.; and Gray, Richard E.; (1978); "Subsidence Over the Mined-Out Pittsburgh Coal"; Preprint 3293 "Coal Mine Subsidence" ASCE Spring Convention and Exhibit; Pittsburgh, Pennsylvania 1978.

Fennell, P. A, (1997) "Downhole camera observations of the Yard Seam, Newcastle", Australian Geomechanics, June 1997, pp 66 – 72

Hawkins, G.C. and Harvey, J.P. (2001) "Stability of abandoned mines – Geotechnical Investigations of the Borehole Seam workings beneath Newcastle CBD", Proceedings of the 5th Triennial Conference - Current Practice and Issues; Mine Subsidence Technological Society, Maitland, NSW Aug 26 to 28

Kingsland, R.; Mills, K.; Stahlhut, O.; Huang, Y.; and Butcher, R. (2011) "Subsidence hazards and mitigation strategies on Minmi to Buchanan Section of the Hunter Expressway" Proceedings of the Mine Subsidence Technological Society 8th Triennial Conference on Management of Subsidence: State of the Art, Pokolbin, NSW pp 121 -129

Knott, D.L. and Streater, H.; (2017); "Downhole Techniques to Assess Mine Subsidence and Mitigation Effectiveness"; Mine Subsidence: Adaptive Innovation for Managing Challenges; 10th Triennial Conference Proceedings, Mine Subsidence Technological Society, Pokolbin, NSW, Aus, 5 – 7 November 2017

Knott, D.L. Baker, S and Solomou, N. (2016); "The use of downhole geophysical logging in assessing subsidence from abandoned coal mines", 35th International Geological Congress, Cape Town, South Africa, August 30, 2016

Knott, DL., (2006) "Assessment of Potential Subsidence Impacts from Coal Mining using Test borings, Mine Maps and Empirical Methods" 2006 Technical Group on Abandoned Underground Mines Meeting; Rochester, New York

Millar, D. and Holz, B. (2011) "Ipswich motorway upgrade – filling of abandoned coal mines", Department of Main Roads and Technology Conference, Brisbane, 2011

Pells, P.J.N.: Openshaw, P.; Love, A.; and Pedersen, I.S. (1988) "Investigation & Backfilling of early workings, Yard Sea, for construction of high rise building, Burwood St. Newcastle",

Proceeding of conference on building and structures subject to mines subsidence. Sponsored by the Institution of Engineers, Australia (Newcastle Division) and the Mine Subsidence Board, N.S.W., Maitland, NSW

Rouvray, B.J. and Davies, W. (2005) "Case study: Mine void investigation and remediation for the West Charlestown Bypass, Newcastle" in Australian Geomechanics Vol 40, No 1 March, pp 91 – 100

Royal Commission (1908) Report of the Royal Commission into Earth Subsidences at Newcastle

Stolarczyk , L.G. and Peng, S. S, (2003) "Advanced Electromagnetic Wave Technologies for the Detection of Abandoned Mine Entries and Delineation of Barrier Pillars" , presented at Mine Safety and Health Administration (MSHA) and Office of Surface Mining Reclamation and Enforcement (OSMRE) Interactive Forum on Geophysical Technologies for Detecting Underground Coal Mine Voids, July 28–30, 2003, Lexington, Kentucky

Unstable Slope Inventory along the Blue Ridge Parkway, NC

Brian Banks, PG

Schnabel Engineering
244 Princess Street, Suite 203
Wilmington, NC 28401
240-832-6272
bbanks@schnabel-eng.com

Jennifer Bauer, PG

Appalachian Landslide Consultants, PLLC
PO Box 5516
Asheville, NC 28813
828-329-3640
jennifer@appalachianlandslide.com

Majed Abdelhadi, PE

FHWA Eastern Federal Lands Highway Division
22001 Loudoun County Parkway Building E-2, Suite 200
Ashburn, VA 20147
571-434-1569
majed.abdelhadi@dot.gov

Timothy Ramey, PE

WSP
13530 Dulles Technology Drive, Suite 300
Herndon, VA 20171
703-742-5827
Timothy.ramey@wsp.com

Prepared for the 71st Highway Geology Symposium, May 2022

Acknowledgements

The authors would like to thank the following contributors for their partnership and support in accomplishing this project:

Mounir Abouzakhm - FHWA Eastern Federal Lands
Stephen Fuemmeler - Appalachian Landslide Consultants
Sue Buchanan - Schnabel Engineering
Kenny Megginson - Schnabel Engineering
Robin Reed - Schnabel Engineering
Jason Holland - Schnabel Engineering
Andrew Bain - WSP
Shuo Zhang - WSP
Craig Yow - National Park Service
Carl Stepp - National Park Service
Eric Bilderback – National Park Service

Disclaimer

Statements and views presented in this paper are strictly those of the author(s), and do not necessarily reflect positions held by their affiliations, the Highway Geology Symposium (HGS), or others acknowledged above. The mention of trade names for commercial products does not imply the approval or endorsement by HGS.

Copyright

ABSTRACT

The Unstable Slope Management Program (USMP), developed in 2019 for Federal Lands Management Agencies, is in its early stages of implementation. The program provides a framework to rank the hazards and risks associated with unstable slopes along roads and trails as part of a proactive geotechnical asset management strategy. In 2021, a consultant team implemented the USMP to inventory unstable slopes along 102 miles of the Blue Ridge Parkway in western North Carolina. The Blue Ridge Parkway was designed in the 1930's and constructed over a 52-year period within extremely rugged terrain. Frequent rockfalls, landslides and debris flows impacted construction and are an ongoing maintenance concern. The project field teams evaluated 1,290 slopes and inventoried 454 unstable slopes within the project corridor. Fifty-seven of these are rated Poor for slope stability hazard and risk.

This project was a first of its kind conducted by the Eastern Federal Lands Highway Division (EFLHD) on behalf of the National Park Service (NPS). The experience gained on this large-scale implementation of the USMP resulted in a number of lessons learned and suggested best practices for future efforts. As a next step, EFLHD will proactively pursue risk mitigation strategies for the highest rated slopes. They will develop design concepts and comparative cost estimates to allow them to prioritize slopes to receive mitigation based on cost-benefit analysis. In this way, the USMP is the first step for EFLHD and NPS to take a proactive approach in managing its slope assets, reduce the maintenance burden, and ultimately increase safety for park visitors.

INTRODUCTION

The Blue Ridge Parkway is a scenic roadway that extends 469 miles along the Appalachian highlands from Shenandoah National Park in Virginia to Great Smoky Mountains National Park in North Carolina. Owned and maintained by the National Park Service (NPS), it is the most visited part of the National Park system.

NPS maintenance crews are routinely forced to deal with unstable slopes along the Blue Ridge Parkway. Unstable slope events, including landslides, embankment failures, rockfalls and debris flows, are common occurrences along the parkway. The high frequency of events necessitates daily monitoring of the roadway for traffic safety, emergency response, road closures, debris removal and roadway repair by NPS maintenance crews. These activities have historically been handled in a reactionary mode on a case-by-case basis. However, with the recent development of the Unstable Slope Management Program (USMP) by Federal Lands Highway Division, NPS is pursuing a proactive approach in managing its slope assets along the Blue Ridge Parkway.

This paper presents the inventory and assessment of slopes along 102 miles of the Blue Ridge Parkway in North Carolina using the January 2019 edition of the USMP. This was a collaborative effort between NPS, Eastern Federal Lands Highway Division (EFLHD), and a consultant team consisting of WSP, Schnabel Engineering, and Appalachian Landslide Consultants. The consultant team applied project-specific selection criteria to identify unstable slopes, and numerically rated the relative hazard and risk of each unstable slope using USMP criteria. The results of this USMP inventory provided valuable information for NPS to start to develop its asset management approach for unstable slopes along the Blue Ridge Parkway and program limited funds for effective risk reduction on a cost-benefit basis.

This project was a first of its kind conducted by EFLHD on behalf of NPS. The experience gained on this large-scale implementation of the USMP resulted in a number of lessons learned and suggested best practices for future efforts, as discussed herein.

HISTORY OF SLOPE INSTABILITY

Construction of a roadway to connect Skyline Drive in Shenandoah National Park in Virginia to Great Smoky Mountains National Park in North Carolina was approved by the federal government in 1933 (*2*). With a budget of $16 million, the route for the Parkway was chosen with the visitor's experience in mind. This involved traversing, crossing, and tunneling through the rugged terrain of the mountains. Construction began in 1935 and was almost completed by 1966, except for the 7.7 mile section at Grandfather Mountain. The Linn Cove Viaduct was constructed to protect a fragile ecosystem around Grandfather Mountain and was completed in 1987.

Frequent rockfalls, landslides and debris flows impacted construction and are an ongoing maintenance concern. According to conversations with Parkway maintenance staff, rockfalls are a weekly occurrence for some slopes, particularly in the winter or rainy season (*3*).

The primary trigger of landslides and debris flows in western North Carolina in general, and specifically along the Parkway, are heavy rain events (*4*). Because the Parkway traverses the tallest ridges in western North Carolina, it is subject to the orographic effect of tropical cyclones and convective thunderstorms passing over the area. Therefore, the Parkway often receives some of the highest rainfall totals recorded for these events. Storms that have triggered instability along the Parkway include:

- Unnamed Tropical Cyclone, August 13-14, 1940, most intense rainfall was 10 inches within 6 hrs. (*4*)
- Storm, August 28-31, 1940, 13 inches of rainfall over 2 days (*4*)
- Thunderstorms, May 26-28, 1973, most intense rainfall was 7.7 inches in 1 hr. (*4*)
- Unnamed Extratropical Cyclone, November 5-7, 6 inches of rainfall in 2 days (*4*)
- Tropical Cyclone Frances and Tropical Cyclone Ivan, September 6-8 and September 16-17, 2004 respectively, 23.5 inches in 2 days followed by 17 inches in 2 days, 8 days later (*4*)
- Tropical Storm Fred, August 16-17, 2021, 13 inches of rain in 2 days (*5*)

The Blue Ridge Parkway Historic Photograph Collection archive has dozens of historic photographs of rockslides, landslides, and debris flows along the parkway dating from the late 1930s through 1979 (*6*). Figures 1-9 are a few of the many historical examples of slope instability along the Blue Ridge Parkway from 1939 through 2021, many of which correspond to regional storm events.

PARK	CLASSIFICATION NO.	NEGATIVE NO.
BLUE RIDGE PARKWAY PHOTO LIBRARY	625	6049 (747b)
SUBJECT	OTHER	NATIONAL ARCHIVES NO.
Rock slide Heavy maintenance		LIBRARY OF CONGRESS NO.

LOCATION

Sec 2C Sta 130+00
Bluff Park MP 239.6

PHOTOGRAPHER & COMPANIONS

KCM

DATE TAKEN

?

REMARKS

747-E

GPO 873-282

NPS 10-30 (8/68) NATIONAL VISUAL INVENTORY CARD

Figure 1 - "Rock slide with maintenance worker" by KCM, unknown date. MP 239.6.

PARK
BLUE RIDGE PARKWAY
PHOTO LIBRARY

CLASSIFICATION NO
625

NEGATIVE NO.
7016 (643-3)

NATIONAL ARCHIVES NO.

OTHER

LIBRARY OF CONGRESS NO.

SUBJECT
Slide on Sec 2K

643-3

LOCATION
Sec 2K Sta 141+00
MP 320.3

PHOTOGRAPHER & COMPANIONS
Liles

DATE TAKEN
8/16/40

REMARKS

GPO 873-282

NPS 10-30 (8/68) NATIONAL VISUAL INVENTORY CARD

Figure 2 - "Landslide near Milepost 320" taken August 16, 1940 by Liles. MP 320.3.

PARK
BLUE RIDGE PARKWAY
PHOTO LIBRARY

CLASSIFICATION NO
551.5

NEGATIVE NO.
6925 (646b)

OTHER

SUBJECT
Flood damage Slide
started above Parkway

646-B

LOCATION
Sec 2E Deep Gap MP 276.4

PHOTOGRAPHER & COMPANIONS
ASB

DATE TAKEN
8/17/40

REMARKS

NPS 10-30 (8/68) NATIONAL VISUAL INVENTORY CARD GPO 902-243

Figure 3 - "Flood damage showing slide above Parkway" by Albert S. Burns. MP 276.4 in Deep Gap, taken August 17, 1940.

Figure 4 - "Cut slide" taken Sept. 1953 by R.E. Howe. MP 376.5.

Figure 5 - "Rock slide covering Parkway near Crabtree Meadows" taken Sept. 1953 by unknown photographer. MP 339.5.

Figure 6 - "Fill slide" taken September 1953 by R.E. Howe. MP 377.

Figure 7 - Rockslide near MP 467 taken November 24, 2015. Photo is from Blue Ridge Parkway Facebook page.

Figure 8 – Embankment failure near MP 128 in May 2020. This section of the Parkway remains closed. NPS Photo.

Figure 9 - Debris flow at MP 421, photo August 20, 2021 by Majed Abdelhadi. Several debris flows and slides were triggered by rains from Tropical Storm Fred, August 17, 2021.

In 2009, the North Carolina Geological Survey completed an evaluation of many of the rock slopes along the Blue Ridge Parkway, including a relative ranking of the potential for future movement (*7*). This evaluation included stereonet analysis of the rock structures identifying potential failure modes for the highest rated slopes. The data were available as GIS layers that were used for historical context and slope failure history during the 2021 USMP project.

Additionally, FHWA Eastern Federal Lands personnel have designed and contracted mitigation efforts for an unspecified number of rockfall and landslide sites along the Blue Ridge Parkway over the years on behalf of the National Park Service. Mitigation efforts have included scaling and debris removal, slope benching, soil nails and rock anchors.

UNSTABLE SLOPE MANAGEMENT PROGRAM (USMP)

The USMP provides a risk-based framework for proactively managing a portfolio of unstable slopes such that the hazards and risks presented by the slopes can be compared against each other and used to prioritize funding and implement mitigation and hazard-reduction techniques before dangers are fully realized. In its totality, the USMP encompasses a spectrum of activities to address unstable slope assets within a broader transportation asset management context, including identifying performance objectives, conducting slope inventory and ratings, applying cost-benefit analysis for risk-reduction measures, and program-level performance monitoring.

The USMP inventory process is a fundamental part of the program. It involves identifying unstable slopes and ranking them in terms of their relative hazards and risks through a systematic approach. USMP tools to facilitate slope inventory include a standardized slope rating system, a mobile software application, and the USMP website that hosts an inventory database with a GIS-based map interface. The rating system allows users to quantitatively assess the relative hazards and risks of unstable slopes along roadway or trail corridors. Field crews use the mobile software application for rapid slope inventory data collection. The inventory database and corresponding GIS map interface allow easy documentation and access of available slope information and rating data.

The USMP slope rating system is detailed in Chapter 4 of the USMP manual (*8*). The manual includes rating forms and instructions on how to download and use the USMP mobile application. Slope hazard and risk ratings are based on slope and roadway geometry, rockfall or landslide characteristics, maintenance history and costs, impact on use of the roadway, and potential impacts outside the right-of-way. Rating categories fall into three groups: preliminary ratings, detailed hazard ratings, and detailed risk ratings. Figure 10 shows an example of the rating form and some of the categories used for data collection.

Once completed, the USMP inventory enables prioritization of unstable slopes in terms of relative hazard and risk exposure so that the owner can more precisely focus its attention and resources on its highest risk slopes. More detailed assessment and engineering analysis of the highest risk slopes are needed to develop mitigation alternatives and cost estimates, which then provides an opportunity for NPS to decide where to spend its limited funds and resources in implementing risk reduction measures on a cost-benefit basis.

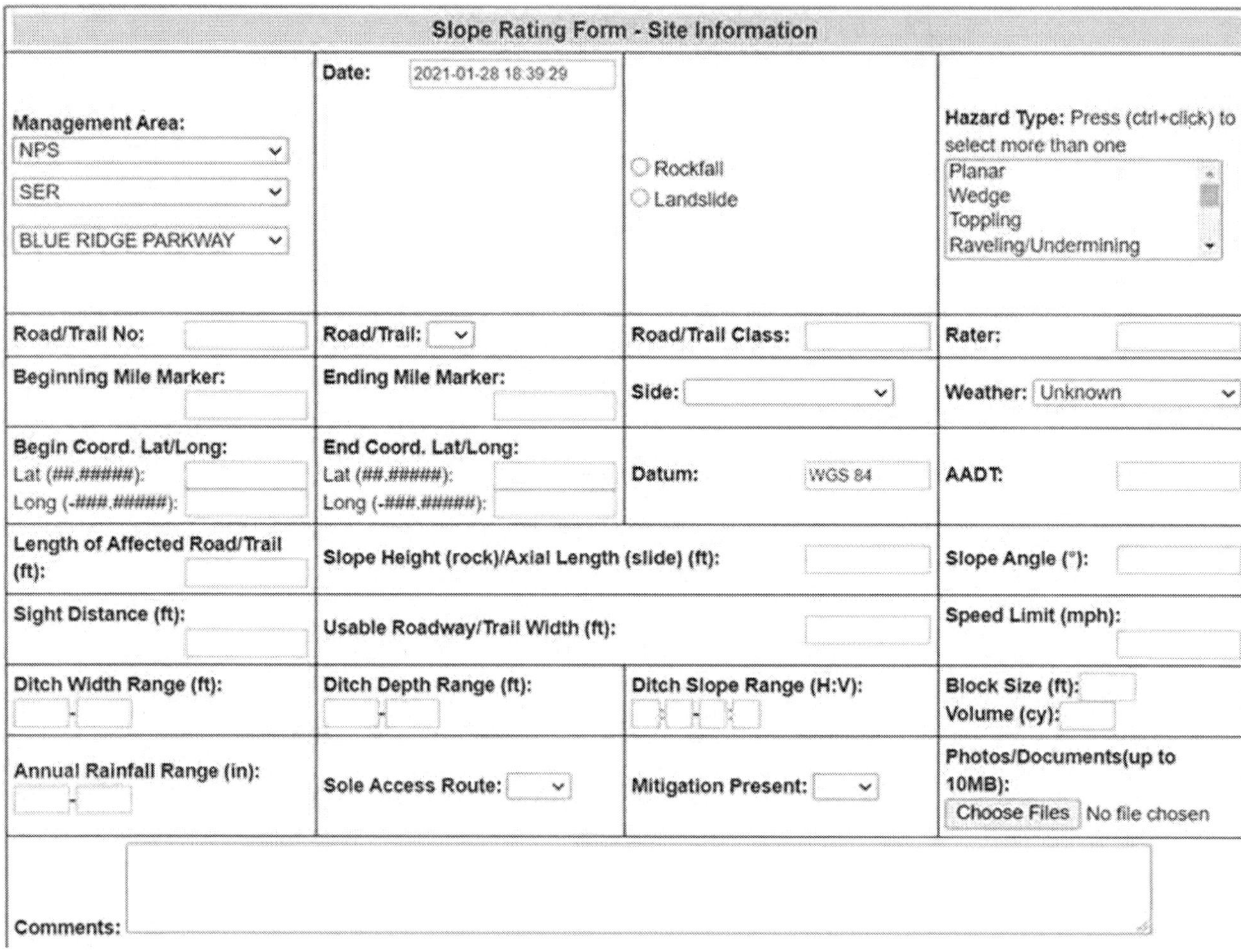

Slope Rating Form - Site Information			
Management Area: NPS / SER / BLUE RIDGE PARKWAY	Date: 2021-01-28 18:39:29	Rockfall / Landslide	Hazard Type: Press (ctrl+click) to select more than one: Planar, Wedge, Toppling, Raveling/Undermining
Road/Trail No:	Road/Trail:	Road/Trail Class:	Rater:
Beginning Mile Marker:	Ending Mile Marker:	Side:	Weather: Unknown
Begin Coord. Lat/Long: Lat (##.#####): Long (-###.#####):	End Coord. Lat/Long: Lat (##.#####): Long (-###.#####):	Datum: WGS 84	AADT:
Length of Affected Road/Trail (ft):	Slope Height (rock)/Axial Length (slide) (ft):		Slope Angle (°):
Sight Distance (ft):	Usable Roadway/Trail Width (ft):		Speed Limit (mph):
Ditch Width Range (ft):	Ditch Depth Range (ft):	Ditch Slope Range (H:V):	Block Size (ft): Volume (cy):
Annual Rainfall Range (in):	Sole Access Route:	Mitigation Present:	Photos/Documents(up to 10MB): Choose Files No file chosen
Comments:			

Figure 10 - Example of the preliminary information captured in the USMP database.

It should be emphasized that the USMP inventory is not intended to be a one-and-done process. The USMP ratings, and therefore the slope priorities, should be updated as unstable slope events occur and as risk mitigation is implemented. If additional unstable slopes are discovered, the USMP has a procedure to add them to the inventory. The USMP also provides guidance to monitor the effectiveness of slope mitigation efforts over time across the entire portfolio of slope assets.

Details of the USMP can be found at https://highways.dot.gov/federal-lands/geotechnial. The resources provided on the USMP website include the USMP Field Manual, links to the USMP mobile applications for Android and iOS, a link to the inventory database and GIS interface, various field forms, and training videos.

USMP INVENTORY FOR THE BLUE RIDGE PARKWAY

In 2021, EFLHD contracted with WSP, Schnabel Engineering and Appalachian Landslide Consultants (ALC) to apply the USMP to inventory and assess unstable slopes along

102 miles of the Blue Ridge Parkway in North Carolina. The work along the roadway was grouped into four sections, Sections A through D as shown in Figure 11. The inventory field work was accomplished in April and November, 2021. The project field teams evaluated a total of 1,290 slopes for signs of instability and inventoried 454 unstable slopes within the project corridor. Due to the unique setting of the parkway, many types of slopes are present along the alignment including soil and rock, natural and constructed, and deep hillside-fill embankments.

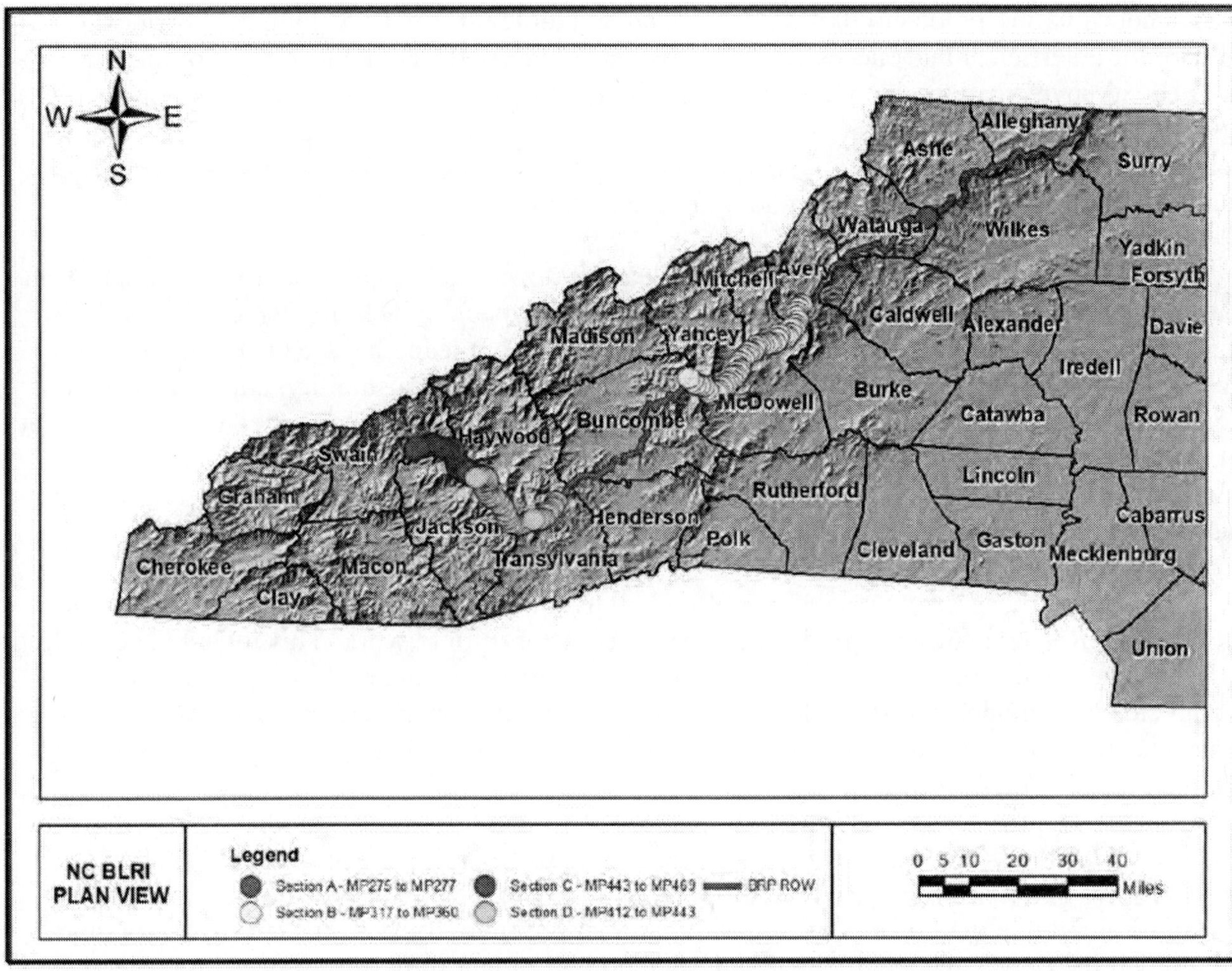

Figure 11 - Map of the NC Portion of the Blue Ridge Parkway. Green dots indicate slopes rated using USMP criteria during this project. Section A: MP 275-277 (near Boone, NC), Section B: MP 317-360, Section D: MP 412-443, Section C: MP 443-469 (ending in Cherokee, NC in Swain County).

Project Team

WSP served as the contract manager. Schnabel Engineering provided task management and technical oversight. Geologists from ALC who had prior training and experience with USMP implementation served in an advisory role, providing USMP orientation and training to the field teams, conducting the GIS-based desktop analysis, and assisting field teams daily during data collection to ensure consistent application of the USMP standards. The two-person teams conducting the USMP inventory in the field were made up of geologists and geotechnical engineers from Schnabel Engineering (two teams) and WSP (one team) selected based on their familiarity with identification of slope instabilities. This prior experience with unstable slopes proved extremely valuable in the successful execution of the project.

Planning and Desktop Study

Prior to initiation of the slope inventory in the field, significant efforts were directed toward coordinating field activities and assessing available information along the corridor to prepare for an efficient and successful field program. These efforts included developing a detailed site investigation plan with quality and safety requirements, communication protocols, equipment needs, and a schedule of activities. Additional emphasis was placed on arming the field teams with the appropriate tools, information and processes to achieve a high-level of data quality, efficiency and consistency among the field teams.

As part of the planning efforts, project leaders developed project-specific slope selection criteria to provide field personnel with a documented approach to deciding which slopes qualified for input into the USMP inventory. Field crew team leaders were instructed to include slopes that displayed evidence of being unstable, had a history of instability, and/or presented a significant potential for instability based on field characteristics, and they relied to a large extent on their experience and professional judgment to determine which slopes to include in the inventory. The slope selection criteria provided guidance to help them make that determination based on geomorphic signatures observed in LiDAR data or in the field.

In order to ensure the database captured all available information about landslides and rockfalls, a GIS-based desktop study was performed prior to field work. This included compiling GIS data such as the 2017 QL1 LiDAR tiles for the project area and processing them into a digital elevation model (DEM) with ~0.5m resolution pixels. From the DEMs, topographic hillshade and slope functions were generated. ALC created a geodatabase of feature classes that provided data on the slopes for the field teams. Prior to field work, ALC used the hillshade and slope data to identify slopes that might meet the selection criteria. These slopes were denoted as "Potential USMP BRP Slopes" as points in the geodatabase and symbolized based on being cut or fill slopes. The field teams used these points as a starting place when deciding if a slope should be entered in the USMP or not. As the project progressed, ALC made a first-pass field call to identify slopes that should be inventoried and eliminate some slopes based on selection criteria.

Prior to fieldwork, ALC reviewed the hillshade figures and identified features that had geomorphic characteristics of landslides. These features were added as polygons to the geodatabase and shared with field teams. As an example, one landslide near MP454 had created two bumps in the road that were repaired multiple times and continued to emerge. When viewed in the hillshade, it was apparent that these two bumps marked the right and left lateral scarps of a large landslide that extends almost to the top of the ridge and down into the neighborhood below the roadway (Figure 12). The LiDAR data helped the project team recognize the extent of the landslide so that it could be communicated effectively in the database and when making decisions about possible mitigation strategies.

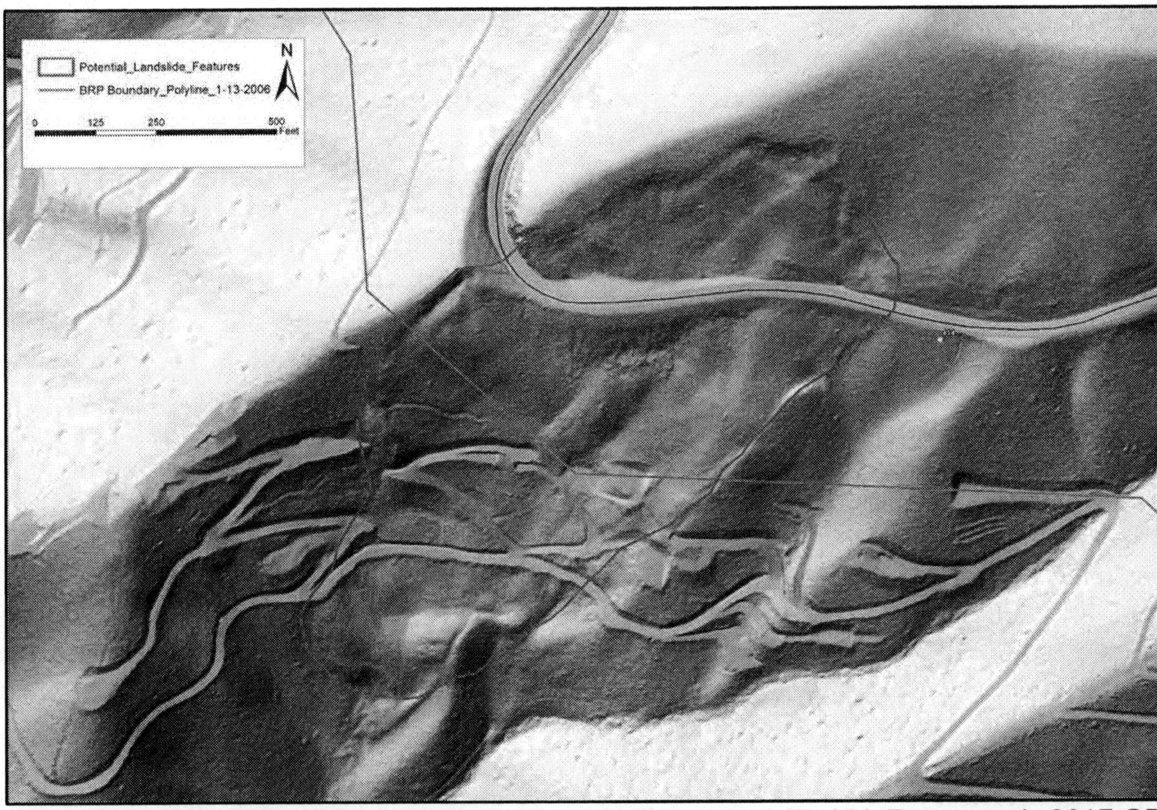

Figure 12 - Map of the "Thunderstruck" landslide near MP 454. Basemap is 2017 QL1 LiDAR hillshade. Red outline defines the extent of the landslide based on LiDAR. Teal line indicates the extent of the Blue Ridge Parkway property.

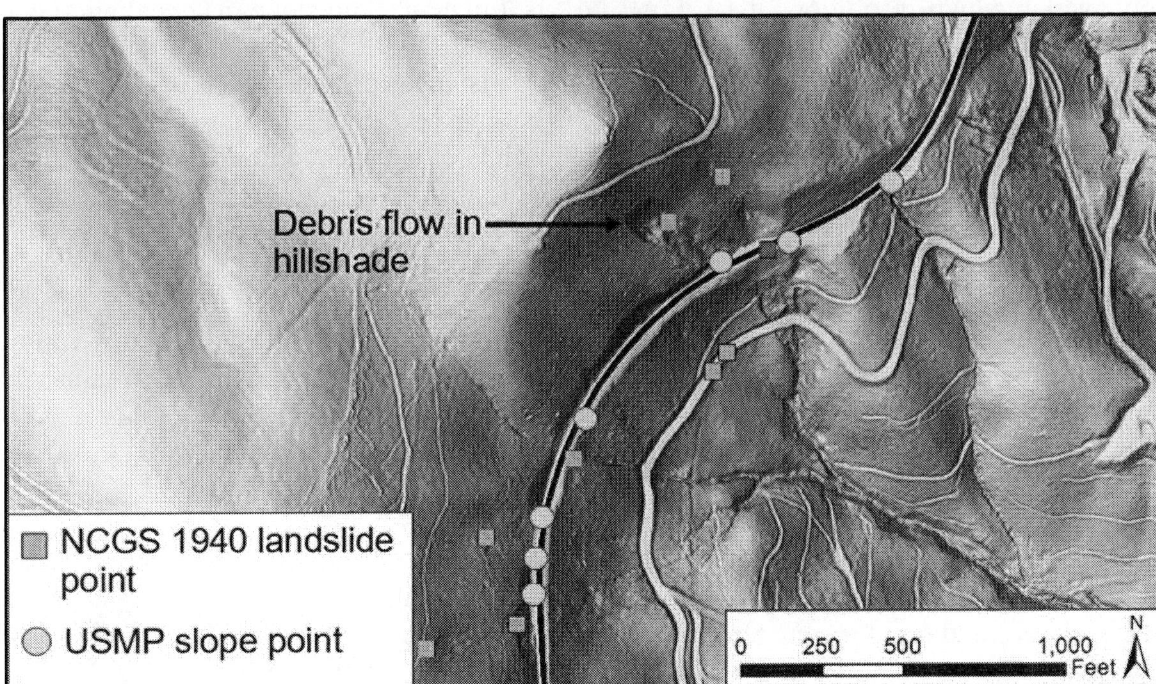

Figure 13 - Map of the Blue Ridge Parkway in Watauga County near MP 277. Basemap is 2017 QL1 LiDAR hillshade. Debris flows from the August 1940 storm are discernable.

During the desktop study, the project team identified locations of past landslides and debris flows that were mapped previously or that were evident in the LiDAR hillshade map. Figure 13 is an example of the hillshade map with the points of past landslides from the NCGS landslide database, many of which were debris flows from the August 13-14, 1940 storm. By having the landslide inventory data, locations of historical debris flows were included in the USMP inventory.

Consistent ratings are very important to the success of the USMP so the ratings can be compared relative to each other for a meaningful ranking of risk prioritization. To achieve consistency among the three field teams, the field staff were oriented in the application of the USMP at the beginning of the project, both virtually and in the field. The virtual training included an introduction to the USMP, description of the rating form fields, discussion of the slope selection criteria, and instruction on how to use the GIS geodatabase and the USMP website and mobile applications for data collection. On the first field day of the project, ALC demonstrated field data collection, then the field teams all collected data on the same slope to compare the results. Throughout the project, ALC provided oversight to the teams and answered questions to help keep the ratings consistent among the teams. At the end of each field day, the field teams would gather to share what they learned, discuss problems encountered and exchange information for incremental improvements.

Field Inventory

The field crews used laptop computers equipped with GIS software to facilitate execution of the field inventory and to increase accuracy and productivity. The GIS was pre-populated with publicly available high-resolution QL1 LiDAR DEMs, hillshade, and slope rasters along the project corridor for use during the slope assessments. The LiDAR data were extremely helpful for identifying evidence of slope instability, measuring distances and elevations at the top and bottom of slopes (to more accurately calculate slope heights and axial lengths), and for location accuracy to confirm coordinates of the start and end points of slopes. Additional layers in the GIS geodatabase were used to communicate other useful information to the field teams, such as geologic mapping, rainfall data, mile markers, property boundaries, historical landslide and debris flow records, maintenance history and other specific points of interest.

Maintenance history is one of the most important factors in the USMP inventory rating. Team members captured information in the GIS geodatabase while riding with NPS maintenance personnel discussing each slope. Information included which slopes were already known to be unstable, the frequency and size of unstable slope events, types of clean-up and mitigation efforts that have been performed in the past, and approximate maintenance/repair costs.

The project team used the USMP mobile software application installed onto mobile phones and tablets to conduct the USMP slope ratings. The mobile application guides the rater through each required input parameter. Rating scores are automatically calculated on the app so that the teams get a sense of the rating while still in the field. Data are stored locally on the handheld device until there is an internet connection, then the data are uploaded into the USMP website. Figure 14 shows a screenshot of the USMP website. Slope ratings are geospatially located in the GIS-based platform. The type of icon indicates if the rated slope is a rock slope or landslide, and each icon is color-coded by the rating (Good, Fair or Poor). Additional details for each slope are available by clicking on the icon, including scoring parameters and supplemental documentation such as site photos. The project team emphasized uploading high-quality photos for the record. Other documents can also be uploaded to the website and associated with individual slopes, such as previously collected data and reports.

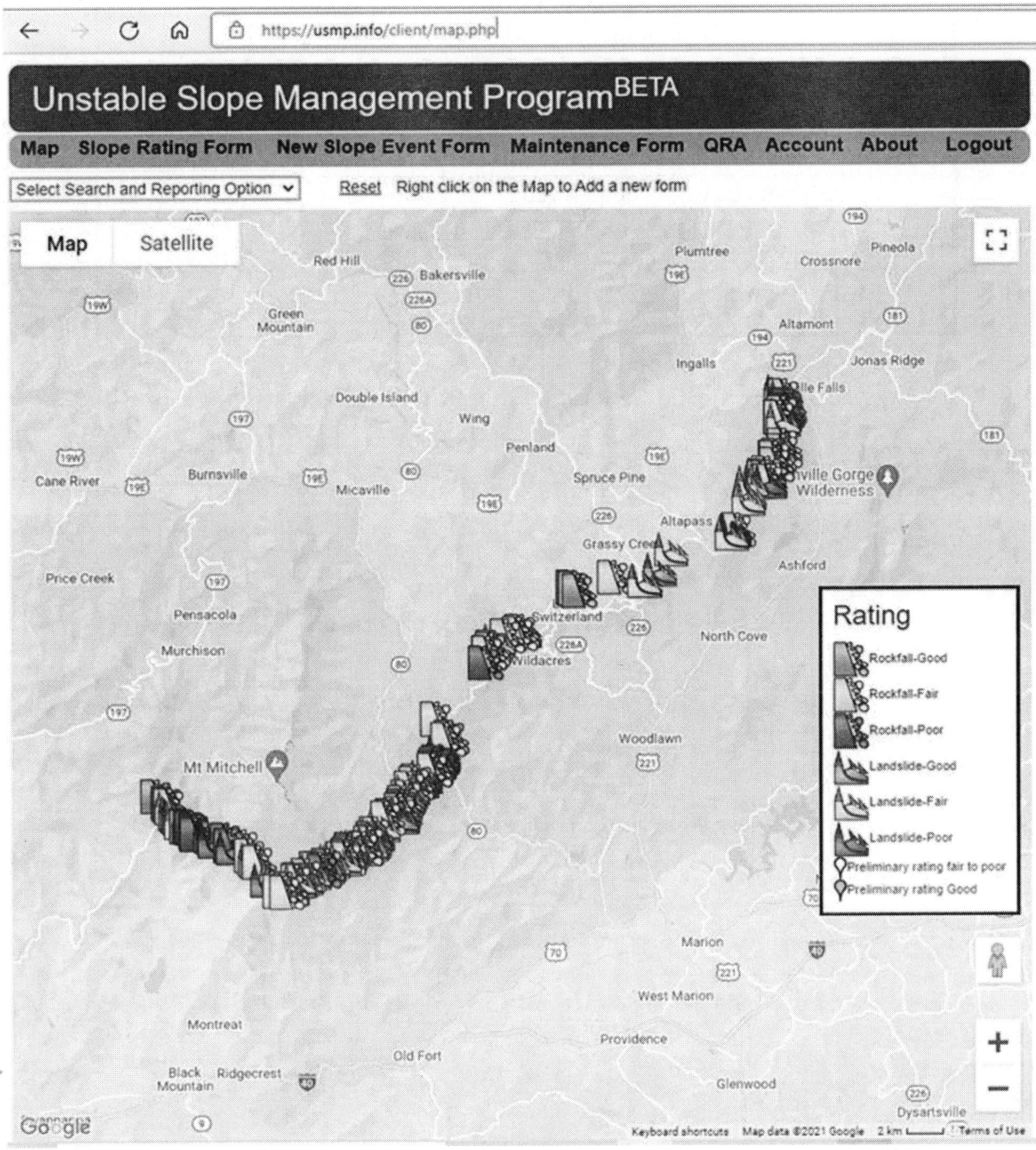

Figure 14 - Screenshot of USMP website for Section B (MP 317-360).

The USMP inventory for all 102 miles was completed in 18 field days with 3 crews working simultaneously. Table 1 sumarizes the rating results. Figure 15 provides a graphical representation of the USMP ratings delineated by rock slopes (orange) and landslides (blue).

Table 1 – Summary of USMP Inventory Results	
Total Slopes Evaluated	1,228
Total Slopes Inventoried in USMP	454
Rock Slopes	277 (61%)
Landslides	177 (39%)
Highest Rating	904
Lowest Rating	113
Average Rating	347
Average Rock Slope Rating	320
Average Landslide Rating	389
Rock Slopes Rated "Poor"	20
Landslides Rated "Poor"	37
Slopes with Rating above 500	57

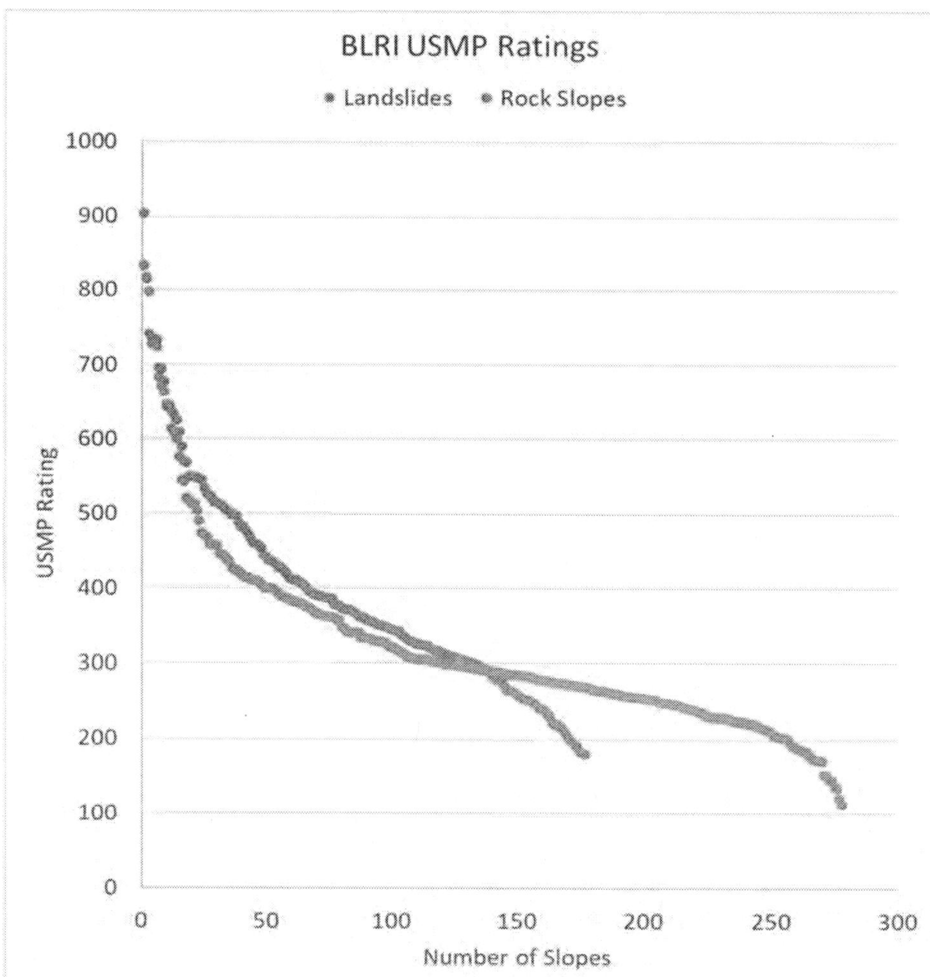

Figure 15 - USMP Inventory Rating Results.

Highest-Rated Slopes

As an example of the types of unstable slope issues that are present along the Blue Ridge Parkway within the project corridor, the top five worst-rated slopes are described below. As indicated in Table 1 and Figure 15, there is a total of 57 rock slopes and landslides categorized as "Poor" in the USMP ranking system, a clear indication that there is no shortage of slope instability issues along the Parkway.

Landslide at MP 454

USMP rating 904. Large active landslide near the "Thunderstruck" overlook. Maintenance described bumps in the road and frequent smoothing of the road and repaving. (Figure 12)

Rock Slope at MP 356.4

USMP rating 833. Rock slope with large blocks and limited catchment (Figure 16). Maintenance personnel did not indicate this as an area of concern, which emphasizes that high-risk slopes don't always catch the attention of maintenance personnel.

Figure 16 - Photo of Rock Slope at MP 356.4

Rock Slope at MP 434.2

USMP rating 817. Tall slope with weathered, loose blocks. Slope wraps around the nose of a ridge, which contributes to instability. Maintenance personnel stated this was one of the most active rockfall slopes (Figure 17).

Figure 17 - Photo of Rock Slope at MP 434.2

Landslide at MP 344.1

USMP rating 815. Active landslide with cracks in the pavement. The landslide is also affecting a barrier wall (Figures 18 and 19). Maintenance said this was one of the slopes of highest concern due to the offset and damage to the barrier wall.

Figure 18 - Photo of Landslide tension cracks in the roadway embankment at MP 344.1

Figure 19 - Photo of offset stone barrier wall at MP 344.1

Rock Slope at MP 429.9

USMP rating 797. Long, tall slope with limited catchment and groundwater seepage. Maintenance personnel reported frequent rockfall up to 2 ft diameter and previous slides that crossed the road and closed the road for over a month (Figure 20).

Figure 20 - Photo of Rock Slope at MP 429.9

BEST PRACTICES AND LESSONS LEARNED

The experience gained on this large-scale implementation of the USMP resulted in a number of lessons learned and suggested best practices for future efforts.

Experienced Staff

The consultant team relied on the expertise of geologists and engineers with experience in recognizing and evaluating slope instability issues. We believe this ultimately led to a comprehensive unstable slope inventory as well as accurate relative ratings among the field teams. These personnel were able to use their experience to apply project-specific slope selection criteria, that were in large part based on field evidence of slope instability.

The use of experienced staff for such a large and fast-paced field inventory was critical to the scope and schedule expectations. The USMP is set up so that "anybody" can fill out the ranking and get a rating. However, it is important that the ratings are accurate, and even more important that they are relatively consistent between the sites because that is how the system is used to prioritize slopes. Using experienced geologists and engineers who already know how to recognize rockfall potential, landslides and geomorphic signatures is hugely valuable to increase accuracy and consistency, and improves confidence in the data as a decision-making tool. It also reduces training requirements. Staff that don't have experience with observing, documenting and evaluating rock slopes and landslides in the field are going to take longer to train and may miss some important details. Application of the slope selection criteria relies on the experience and professional judgment of trained staff.

USMP Advisor

ALC served as advisor to the field team. They kicked off the project by training field staff in how to apply the USMP rating system. ALC also had a person in the field full time during the inventory to address implementation questions promptly and consistently across the field crews. They also completed QC field checks to ensure relative consistency among the rating teams, and an office check to verify that the uploaded slope locations in the USMP webviewer matched the actual coordinates of the slope in GIS. Other advantages of having this full-time advisory role were that they could help coordinate access and sequencing, obtain and disseminate maintenance input, and bring local experience with landslide features. This helped with overall efficiency and let the raters progress faster with the ratings.

USMP Interpretation

USMP provides good guidance, but when it came to application for particular slopes there were numerous questions that needed to be addressed. Even experienced raters have questions about how to apply the USMP rating criteria. Field teams had to talk on a daily basis about what they were seeing and how to apply certain categories. This communication resulted in better consistency among the field teams in applying rating criteria. Here are a few examples of USMP rating criteria that benefited from discussions among the field teams:

- Start/end of rock slopes – It was sometimes difficult to identify the start and end of rock slopes with variable conditions. Field crews were instructed to break out portions of slopes that exhibited a change in conditions that may present a change in the hazard and risk profile.
- Category G: Impact on Use – Clarification was needed to apply the USMP terminology, "probably worst-case scenario".
- Category I: Slope Drainage – Discussion improved consistency in application of surface runoff control criteria (e.g., well, moderately, poorly and not).
- Category K: Axial Length – Field teams ended up calculating axial length measurements by using the available LiDAR data to measure horizontal distance from top of the fill slope to the bottom. They used a clinometer to measure the slope angle in the field, if possible, or the slope overlay generated from the DEM, if not. They then calculated the axial length from these two measurements.
- Category Y: ROW Impacts – Clarification was needed to apply the USMP terminology, "likely to" vs. "actively threatening".
- Category Z: Env./Cultural Impacts – Supplemental information and discussions were needed to clarify potential environmental impacts and historical features.

- Category BB: Event Cost – Information was obtained from NPS maintenance personnel about how they respond to certain events, what equipment they use, etc. to help calibrate event costs.

Maintenance Input

Getting input from maintenance – the people and crews who clean up the site after slope events – is critical. Maintenance personnel deal with slopes on a daily basis in various types of weather in all seasons. They know when past events have happened, the impact to the roadway, and the effort it took to get the road back open. They know which slopes are most active and the changes that have occurred over time. This information goes into the USMP rating system. Rather than rely on phone calls or maintenance reports, the team scheduled a ride along with the maintenance personnel for the entire corridor. They used GIS to take spatially referenced notes to collect specific maintenance input on each slope. This information was transferred to the field teams through the geodatabase and lists, who then entered it into the USMP site. Maintenance information is important for developing and implementing mitigation concepts.

It is important to gather maintenance history early in the process so that field teams can have it prior to rating the slopes. Due to tight time budgets, maintenance ride-alongs took place after the first few days of ratings for the first Section and meant that field teams had to add maintenance comments after the ratings. This process was streamlined in subsequent Sections, and maintenance information was given to the teams prior to their ratings as the project progressed.

Some of the slopes that rated highly were not flagged in the maintenance ride-along as a concern. Perhaps these have not yet risen to the level of becoming a maintenance concern, or perhaps there are other signs of instability that have not triggered maintenance priority. Maintenance personnel mentioned that there were slopes that hadn't moved in years that failed and blocked the road. Identifying unstable slopes prior to failure is a valuable benefit of using a standardized system like USMP.

Weather / Time of Year

Time of year for conducting a large-scale inventory like this one is critical to get the most out of the cost and effort. It is best to conduct it when vegetation does not obscure the slopes, and when there is no snow or ice blocking the road and slopes. The optimal time for field data collection is late fall after leaf drop, but there is also a good window in early spring before leaf out.

Location Accuracy

The USMP process assumes that the accuracy of the GPS of the device that is used for the mobile app is high enough to assign coordinates to the start and end of the slopes in the correct location. However, we found that the GPS accuracy varies significantly by device model, age, and type (phone vs tablet). Even so, there was no device that we felt was as accurate as locating the slope on the GIS maps and entering those latitude and longitude coordinates.

Teams used the lidar data and satellite imagery to identify the correct coordinates for the start of the slopes. Coordinates were updated in the website so that the slope icons on the map in the USMP website accurately reflect the slope locations. If we had just relied on the GPS locations from the handheld devices, they would have been off…in some cases by thousands of feet. This step needs to be done. It takes extra time, but it needs to be done.

Using GIS data

Using GIS-based data, and not just the USMP app, added to the accuracy (as mentioned above) and efficiency of data collection. It also allowed for a more thorough understanding of the slope morphology and areas of repeat slope movement. For example, all four debris flows that occurred during Tropical Storm Fred on August 17, 2021 initiated within landslide scarps that could be seen on the 2017 LiDAR. The photograph in Figure 21 provides evidence of the older and younger landslide scarps. This example indicates the importance of including past areas of activity in the ratings because areas of prior instability that were not mitigated can reactivate.

Figure 21 - MP 413.1 August 2021 debris flow triggered by Tropical Storm Fred outline in yellow. Older landslide outline in red.

Two-Person Field Teams

Two-person field teams were used for safety and to improve efficiency. Data collection was initiated at the start of the tourist season. Sometimes drivers can be distracted by the amazing views, and not see someone standing on the side of the road. While one team member was collecting data using a mobile device, the other team member would be on the lookout and verbally announce oncoming traffic. Prior to field work every day, teams set up traffic-alert signs at the start and ends of the working segments. They also used traffic cones to mark out the work area and wore high-visibility vests and had flashing lights on the vehicles. The teams would start each day with a safety briefing to keep safety on everyone's minds during the day.

Using a two-person field team helped with efficiency as well. One team member entered data into the mobile device or used the GIS database while the other was taking measurements making the work go faster.

NEXT STEPS

As a next step, EFLHD and NPS will work to complete USMP slope ratings for the remainder of the Parkway. Once the inventory of the slopes along the entire length of the Parkway is completed, NPS and EFLHD will proactively pursue risk mitigation strategies for the highest rated slopes. EFLHD will then develop alternative design concepts for various risk-mitigation alternatives, quantify expected levels of risk reduction, and prepare comparative cost estimates including construction and lifecycle costs for feasible alternatives. EFLHD will then be able to develop a prioritized list of slope mitigation projects based on cost-benefit analysis. The list will ultimately be used to program projects as funding becomes available.

The USMP inventory completed by the project team is the first step for EFLHD and NPS to take a proactive approach in managing its slope assets along the Blue Ridge Parkway, reduce the maintenance burden, use limited funds efficiently, and ultimately increase safety for park visitors.

REFERENCES

1. Blue Ridge Parkway Association (BRPA). *Plan Your Trip.* https://www.blueridgeparkway.org/plan-your-parkway-trip/. Accessed Apr. 14, 2022.
2. Blue Ridge Parkway NC, VA. *Construction of the Parkway.* National Park Service. https://www.nps.gov/blri/learn/historyculture/construction.htm. Accessed Apr. 14, 2022.
3. Stepp, C. *Personal Communication.* Maintenance personnel, Blue Ridge Parkway, National Park Service. April 7, 2021.
4. Wooten, R.M., Witt, A.C., Miniat, C.F., Hales, T.C., Aldred, J.L. *Chapter 9 Frequency and Magnitude of Selected Historical Landslide Events in the Southern Appalachian Highlands of North Carolina and Virginia: Relationships to Rainfall, Geological and Ecohydrological Controls, and Effects.* In: Greenberg, C.H., Collins, B.S. (eds.), Natural Disturbances and Historic Range of Variation, Managing Forest Ecosystems 32. Springer International Publishing, Switzerland, 2016, p. 203-262.
5. Moore, P. *Personal Communication.* Lead Meteorologist, National Weather Service Greenville-Spartanburg Office. September 3, 2021.
6. Blue Ridge Parkway Historic Photograph Collection (1933-1979). Various photos. Digital Archive on National Park Gallery. US National Park Service. https://npgallery.nps.gov/blri. Accessed on Apr. 14, 2022.
7. Latham, R. S., Wooten, R. M., Cattanach, B. L., Merschat, C. E., & Bozdog, G. N. Rock slope stability analysis along the North Carolina section of the Blue Ridge Parkway: Using a geographic information system (GIS) to integrate site data and digital geologic maps. In *Conference Proceedings: 43rd US rock mechanics symposium and 4th US-Canadian rock mechanics symposium,* American Rock Mechanics Association, Asheville, NC, 28 June–1 July 2009, 171. p. 12
8. Beckstrand, D., Stanley, D., Thompson, P., Bilderback, E., Wittie, M., Danewala, U., Cuelho, Eli, Anderson, D.A. *Unstable Slope Management Program for Federal Land Management Agencies.* Federal Highway Administration, U.S. Department of Transportation, 2019.

Rock Slope Rockfall Risk Reduction – Little River Road (Forest Highway #69) Douglas County, Oregon

Brent A. Black, CEG, LHG, RG
Landslide Technology (a division of Cornforth Consultants, Inc.)
10250 SW Greenburg Road
Portland, OR 97223
(503)-452-1200
BrentB@landslidetechnology.com

Evan Garich, PE
Federal Highway Administration – Western Federal Lands Highway Division
610 East Fifth Street
Vancouver, WA 98661-3893
(360) 619-7824
evan.garich@dot.gov

Adam Koslofsky, CEG, RG
Landslide Technology (a division of Cornforth Consultants, Inc.)
10250 SW Greenburg Road
Portland, OR 97223
(503)-452-1200
AdamK@landslidetechnology.com

Prepared for the 71st Highway Geology Symposium, May, 2022

Acknowledgements

The authors would like to thank the individuals/entities for their contributions in the work described:

Doug Anderson, LEG, LG – FHWA-WFLHD
Angela Rogge, PE – David Evans and Associates, Inc.

Disclaimer

Statements and views presented in this paper are strictly those of the author(s), and do not necessarily reflect positions held by their affiliations, the Highway Geology Symposium (HGS), or others acknowledged above. The mention of trade names for commercial products does not imply the approval or endorsement by HGS.

ABSTRACT

The Federal Highway Administration - Western Federal Lands Highway Division (WFLHD) retained Landslide Technology (LT) through David Evans and Associates, Inc. (DEA) to provide preliminary and final PS&Es and technical support during construction of rockfall risk reduction measures on a 900-foot long segment of roadway east of Glide, Oregon. The rock slope is adjacent to Little River Road (MP 24.6) in Douglas County, Oregon, which is within the Umpqua National Forest. It is the primary access to the North Umpqua Ranger District.

A 900-foot section of the two-lane road had a history of on-going rockfall activity and increased maintenance efforts from rock cut slopes that are up to 150 feet tall. This section of roadway was blocked by a large rockfall event in 2012 that contained rock blocks 20 feet in-size, damaging the pavement surface and destroying segments of the guardrail. Portions of one travel-lane remained closed for eight years until construction was completed in 2020. The rock outcrops consist of Oligocene-aged lapilli tuffs overlain by volcanic breccia and basaltic andesite. The Unstable Slope Management Program (USMP) rating was as high as 1,082 for this slope.

Rockfall stabilization and protection measures were designed and installed at this site to reduce the risk from rockfall and lessen maintenance efforts following rope-supported investigation and analyses. Mitigation included 1,600 individual scaling hours, 7,800 linear feet of rock bolt and dowel installations (up to 35 feet in length), 59,200 square feet of draped mesh, and 29,700 square feet of 12-foot-tall midslope attenuator fencing. Final ditch improvements completed this successful rockfall risk reduction project.

INTRODUCTION

The Federal Highway Administration Western Federal Lands Highway Division (FHWA-WFLHD) retained Landslide Technology (a division of Cornforth Consultants, Inc.) out of Portland, Oregon to provide geotechnical design to reduce the risk of rockfall on a section of Little River Road (MP 24.6) in Douglas County, Oregon. Landslide Technology performed the work as a subconsultant to David Evans and Associates, Inc. (DEA) out of Portland, Oregon.

Background and Purpose

An approximately 900-foot segment of Little River Road at MP 24.6 (east of Glide, Oregon) has a history of rockfall activity and increased maintenance efforts. In December 2012, this section of roadway was blocked by a large rockfall event that damaged the pavement surface and segments of the guardrail. Portions of the westbound travel lane remain closed due to this event and subsequent rockfall activity. These rockfall events removed basal support for portions of the rock cut slopes resulting in a moderate to high risk for additional rock slope failures.

A subsequent large-scale failure occurred in the same area as the December 2012 event in June of 2017. In September 2017, Landslide Technology provided a Preliminary Geotechnical Design Report (PGDR), 30% level plans, and engineer's estimate to reduce the risk of rockfall entering the roadway. On November 24, 2017, another rockfall event occurred from a rock outcrop above the cut slope. This event generated approximately 10 to 15 cubic yards of debris that landed in the roadway. The largest block observed in the debris was approximately 3½ feet in size. Representatives from the FHWA and Douglas County observed the slope above the cut and identified a shallow slump feature just west of the upper rock outcrop that was contributing to rockfalls. Representatives from Landslide Technology (LT) performed another site reconnaissance in February of 2018. Following this effort, LT provided interim rockfall risk reduction recommendations in March 2018. In June of 2018, LT performed an additional site reconnaissance to finalize design recommendations.

The purpose of this project was to reduce the risk of rockfall entering the roadway using a combination of typical rockfall risk reduction techniques. This included subsequent development and delivery of 30%-, 95%-, and Final – PS&E Contract Documents. LT provided technical assistance and part-time construction observation services for the duration of construction. The contract was awarded to Triptych Construction LLC out of Glide, Oregon. Construction began on July 25, 2019 and was fully completed on July 31, 2020.

Project Description

Little River Road (Forest Highway #69 and County Road #17A & #17) connects OR-138 with FDR-27 in the North Umpqua Ranger District of the Umpqua National Forest, and serves the communities of Glide and Peel, Oregon. Little River Road is one of the primary access routes to the North Umpqua Ranger District. Little River Road also provides access to BLM, private timber, and agricultural lands. The project is located approximately 14.5 miles southeast of Glide, Oregon. The segment of roadway identified in the task order is approximately 900 feet of two-lane road that traverses approximately east-west, along the north bank of the Little River. The road is classified as a minor collector for Douglas County, and is federally classified as a rural major collector. Seasonal average daily traffic (ADT) is estimated to be 200. The rock cut slopes are generally south to southwest facing and are between 50 and 150 feet tall.

GEOTECHNICAL EVALUATION AND DESIGN DEVELOPMENT

The tasks performed for this project include the following:

- Review of rockfall history and regional geology;
- Onsite meeting with FHWA and Douglas County representatives to review rockfall risk reduction goals and design elements;
- Integration of photogrammetry and LiDAR collected at the site by FHWA into the construction documents;
- Field investigations to develop 30% level risk reduction mitigation options;
- Stability analyses to estimate reinforcement requirements for probable modes of failure;
- Return site visits to evaluate the feasibility, effectiveness and constructability of rockfall risk reduction measures;
- Development of a Preliminary Geotechnical Design Report (PGDR);
- Onsite meeting with FHWA and other stake holders to review and discuss risk reduction mitigation concepts; and,
- Develop 95% and Final (100%) PS&E design package and a final GDR.

Regional and Local Geology

The project is located in the Western Cascades physiographic province. The Western Cascades are generally composed of deformed volcanic rocks from the late Eocene to late Miocene. The bedrock at the project site is thought to be of the Little Butte Volcanic Series, Oligocene and early Miocene in age (approximately 34 to 17 million years ago). This unit consists of rhyodacitic welded tuff and very light gray vitric crystal tuff, overlain by andesite tuff flows and beds of volcanic conglomerate, that chiefly are greenish-gray massive vitric lapilli tuff (Peck, 1964). This material experienced a period of tilting and faulting during the middle Miocene (approximately 16 to 12 million years ago) followed by a period of lava eruptions during the development of the Western Cascades volcanic arc. Locally, the rock outcrops observed at the site consist of greenish-gray, welded tuffs and volcanic conglomerates (lapilli tuffs) overlain by mafic volcanic sandstones, agglomerates, breccias, and basaltic andesite.

Unstable Slope Management Program Rating

Prior to the initial field reconnaissance efforts, representatives from LT visited the project site and identified four separate slope sections along the approximately 900-foot rock cut slope segment. The slope sections were delineated based on similar geology, slope geometry, rockfall hazards, fallout (ditch) capacity, and potential failure modes. The four design sections were evaluated and ranked using the rating criteria of the Unstable Slope Management Program (USMP) for Federal Land Management Agencies (FLMAs). This system is designed to evaluate both rock slopes and landslides on low volume roads managed by agencies such as the Bureau of Land Management and Douglas County, rather than for high volume roads and highways managed by state DOTs. Preliminary scores for sections US-01 through US-03, resulted in 'Poor' ratings. The preliminary score for section US-04 resulted in a "Fair" rating. Table 1 provides a summary of the results.

Table 1: USMP Rating Summary

Section (Stationing)	USMP Scores			
	Preliminary	Hazard	Risk	Total Score
US-01 (61+86 to 66+04)	316 (Poor)	605	476	1081
US-02 (66+04 to 67+25)	238 (Poor)	497	304	801
US-03 (67+25 to 69+57)	316 (Poor)	605	477	1082
US-04 (69+57 to 70+97)	105 (Fair)	172	237	409

Structural Mapping and Kinematic Analysis

Structural mapping was conducted at three of the delineated design slope sections using LiDAR and photogrammetric methods with the software programs Cloud Compare® (version 2.8.1) and Photoscan (version 1.3.2). The 3D point clouds used included one developed by FHWA using terrestrial LiDAR that was collected in July, 2018 and one generated by LT based on photogrammetric techniques from photos taken during the initial site reconnaissance. Structural measurements were also collected by hand in the field to verify the computer mapping results. Kinematic analyses using the computer program DIPS (version 6.0) was performed for three of the slope sections. The results for each slope are provided in Table 2.

Table 2: Kinematic Analysis Rating Summary

Section (Stationing)	No. of Joints Mapped	Joint Sets	Primary Failure Mode
US-01 (61+86 to 66+04)	1,300	2 Primary, 1 secondary	Planar, Toppling
US-02 (66+04 to 67+25)	870	2 Primary, 1 secondary	Wedge, Planar
US-03 (67+25 to 69+57)	1,200	3 Primary, 1 secondary	Wedge, Planar

Stability Analysis

Both field observations and kinematic analyses indicate that planar or large sliding block failures are the most prevalent instability concern at Section US-01. Specific block geometries on the rock cut slope were measured to estimate the condition and size of a potential failure block. Existing failed block geometries were also measured from the rock debris resting in the westbound lane. A two-dimensional computer program (Rocplane v3.0) and a sliding block analysis (per Hoek and Bray, 1981) were used to analyze observed and interpreted planar failures. The two-dimensional computer program Swedge v6.0 was used to analysis observed and interpreted wedge failures at Sections US-02 and US-03. Back analyses were performed assuming a Factor of Safety (FOS) of 1 to estimate Mohr-Coulomb strength parameters for each method. These analyses were performed assuming that there was no water pressure acting on the joints (i.e., "dry" condition). Once reasonable Mohr-Coulomb strength parameters were determined, water pressure was added to the models to simulate failure and the amount of reinforcement needed to increase the FOS to 1.25 was calculated. This resulted in a load (in pounds per unit width) needed to reinforce a block to a FOS of 1.25. This load was then scaled to the observed block sizes in the field to determine total load required. Unlined drains were also added to mitigate water pressure acting on the failure planes. The number, location, and capacity of rock bolts (and drains) needed to impart the total load requirements were estimated based on observed conditions.

SECTION US-01 (STATIONS 61+86 to 66+04)

Section US-01 is a south facing slope approximately 419 feet long and 130 feet tall. This slope section received an USMP Rating of 1,081. According to Douglas County, the site requires a relatively high maintenance effort due to its history of large failure events. In December of 2012, this section of roadway was blocked by a large rockfall event (over 3,000 cubic yards) that damaged the pavement surface and destroyed segments of the guardrail. Portions of the westbound travel lane were closed due to this event and subsequent rockfall activity. These rockfall events removed basal support for portions of the rock cut slope resulting in a high risk for additional rock slope failures.

Site Observations and Rockfall Hazards

This site originally had a rockfall catchment area that ranges from 12 to 14 feet wide. The rock slope was excavated at an inclination of ½H:1V to ¼H:1V; however, it appeared that the western portion of the cut slope failed back to a flatter slope inclination of approximately 53° (¾H:1V). What appeared to be a remnant of the 2012 failure was observed at the east end of Section US-01(see Figures 1 and 2). The rock block is approximately 15 ft. tall x 20 ft. wide, x 20 ft. thick. Large planar and sliding block failures associated with the December 2012 event appear to have failed on southerly dipping planes that have left large overhanging and unsupported rock blocks along the top of the cut slope crest. The rock consists of medium hard to hard (R3-R4), green-gray, slightly weathered welded tuff with localized zones of volcanic conglomerate. This rock is moderately jointed to massive (joint spacing 1½ to 20 feet). Numerous seeps and springs were observed throughout the US-01 rock slope section, particularly along the eastern portion of the slope section. The near vertical to overhanging upper portion of the slope is composed of large blocks similar in size to the blocks that failed and are not well supported. The potential for planar failures on the slope and a larger-scale failure from the upper zone was considered high (see Figure 3).

Figure 1: View looking northeast at rockfall debris in roadway from large failure at approximately station 65+61 at section US-01.

Figure 2: View looking northwest at rockfall debris in roadway from large failure at approximately station 65+61.

Figure 3: View looking northwest at overhanging rock slope on eastern end of section US-01.

Rockfall Risk Reduction Measures

The recommended risk reduction measures for Section US-01 were based on rockfall history, past maintenance efforts, geotechnical evaluations, and an assessment of the rockfall hazards. They include both scaling and intensive scaling to remove a large, loose, rock blocks from the cut slope; rock dowels and rock bolts to knit the slope together and reinforce potential sliding blocks; unlined drain holes to reduce the effects of groundwater pressure; and the addition of draped mesh to control rockfall trajectory and energy in order to restrict rockfalls from entering the roadway. This work also included hazard tree removal and boulder removal/ditch reconditioning. A breakdown of the mitigation quantities for this slope section are given in Table 3 in the Construction Section discussed below.

SECTION US-02 (STATIONS 66+04 to 67+25)

Section US-02 is approximately 125 feet long and 105 feet tall. This slope section received an USMP Rating of 801. According to the County, this section requires periodic maintenance effort to clear rockfall from the roadway. On November 24, 2017, another rockfall event occurred from a rock outcrop above the cut slope between Sections US-02 and US-03. This event generated approximately 10 to 15 cubic yards of debris that landed in the roadway. The largest block observed in the debris was approximately 3½ feet in size. This event necessitated that interim rockfall mitigation elements to be installed before construction of final design measures could be implemented.

Site Observations and Rockfall Hazards

Section US-02 has a rockfall catchment area approximately 12 feet wide. The rock slope was excavated at an inclination of ½H:1V to ¼H:1V. The western portion of Section US-02 is dominated by a fault that has sheared and altered the rock mass over an approximately 25-foot-wide area (see Figure 4). The rock in the faulted area is soft to medium hard (R2-R3), red-gray, moderately to highly weathered welded tuff. This rock is highly to moderately jointed (joint spacing 3-inches to 1½ feet). Numerous seeps and springs were observed on the western portion of the fault that forms the flank of the large failure area in the eastern portion of Section US-01. The eastern portion of Section US-02 consists of medium hard to hard (R3-R4), green-gray, slightly weathered welded tuff with localized zones of volcanic conglomerate. This rock is moderately to slightly jointed (joint spacing 1½ to 6 feet) as shown on Figure 5. Seeps and springs were also observed throughout this portion of the rock slope section. Near the crest of the cut slope, the welded tuff is capped by medium hard to hard (R3-R4), red to dark gray, slightly weathered volcanic sandstone/agglomerate. This material appears to be a separate flow overlying the welded tuff.

The interim measures installed in Section US-02 included a 12-foot tall moveable rockfall barrier (MRB) installed in the westbound travel-lane to provide protection from rockfalls. The MRB was located between Stations 66+83 and 67+88. Concrete barrier rails were also placed along the centerline of the roadway to provide additional rockfall catchment area. The County windrowed the remnants of the rockfall debris from past failure events at Section US-01 along the outboard shoulder of the roadway. The westbound travel-lane through Section US-02 was also closed due to the presence of rockfall debris in the road.

Figure 4: View looking north at fault on the west end of section US-02.

Figure 5: View looking northeast at rock cut slope along section US-02.

Rockfall Risk Reduction Measures

The recommended rockfall risk reduction measures for Section US-02 consisted of scaling; rock dowels and rock bolts; unlined drain holes; and draped high-tensile strength wire mesh. This work also included hazard tree removal and boulder removal/ditch reconditioning. A summary of the mitigation quantities for this slope section are provided in Table 3 in the Construction Section discussed below.

SECTION US-03 (STATIONS 67+25 to 69+57)

Section US-03 is approximately 236 feet long and 150 feet tall (see Figure 6). This slope section received an USMP Rating of 1,082. According to Douglas County, the site requires a relatively high maintenance effort due to its history of large failure events. In June of 2017, this section of roadway was blocked by a large wedge failure at approximately Station 67+80 that reportedly deposited over 250-300 cubic yards of material in the westbound travel-lane. Portions of the rock outcrop above this section of the roadway also failed on November 24, 2017. This event generated approximately 10 to 15 cubic yards of rockfall debris, up to 3½-foot in size, that landed in the roadway. Representatives from FHWA and Douglas County observed the slope above the cut after the failure and identified a shallow slump feature just west of the upper rock outcrop that was also contributing to rockfalls. This landslide feature was measured to be roughly 45 feet wide by 50 feet long in slope distance. The western portion of the shallow landslide is in Section US-02.

The interim measures installed in Section US-03 included the 12-foot tall moveable rockfall barrier (MRB) installed in the westbound travel-lane to provide protection from rockfall. Scaling (including hazard tree removal) on the rock outcrop above the cut slope and the shallow landslide area. Installing concrete barrier along the centerline of the roadway between Stations 63+86 and 68+53. Shifting of the outboard lane closer to the river to increase catchment area and repositioning traffic control signs to reduce the risk to traffic stopped at the queues and increase road patrols.

Figure 6: View looking east at rock cut slope along section US-03.

Site Observations and Rockfall Hazards

This site has a rockfall catchment area that ranges from 10 to 12 feet wide. The rock slope appears to have been excavated at an inclination of ½H:1V to ¼H:1V. The rock consists of medium hard to hard (R3-R4), green-gray, slightly weathered welded tuff with localized zones of volcanic conglomerate. This rock is moderately jointed to massive (joint spacing 1½ to 10 feet). Numerous seeps and springs were observed throughout the rock slope. Near the crest of the cut slope, the welded tuff is capped by a medium hard to hard (R3-R4), red to dark gray, slightly weathered volcanic sandstone/agglomerate (see Figure 6). This material appears to be a separate flow overlying the welded tuff. Above this material, an outcrop of more highly jointed basaltic andesite was observed. This is the source area for the rockfall event that occurred in November of 2017.

In February 2018, LT performed a site reconnaissance of the slope above the crest of Sections US-02 and US-03 using rope access techniques. At that time, the County had performed interim rockfall risk reduction measures discussed above. The outcrop had been heavily modified by scaling efforts since our site reconnaissance in July 2017 (see Figure 7). The top and bottom of the outcrop are located at approximate elevations 1,387 feet and 1,350 feet, respectively. It appeared that the main source of the continued rockfalls at the site was the shallow landslide feature to the west of the outcrop. The landslide feature appeared to be a slump failure in a mixture of residual soil and colluvium. Large rock blocks, up to 3½-foot in size were observed in the slide debris. The slump measured approximately 70 feet across (west to east) in February 2018. The top of the headscarp was measured at approximately elevation 1,410 feet. The depth of the slump was estimated to be 10 to 20 feet. The base (or toe) appeared to be located at, or below, the elevation of the base of the adjacent rock outcrop to the east (approximate elevation 1,350 feet). Based on field measurements, the failure had increased in-size since observed by WFLHD, retrogressing upslope and expanding to the west. With this retrogression, existing trees would continue to be undermined and represent a hazard to the roadway. Approximately 50 cubic yards of rockfall debris was observed behind the 12-foot tall MRB that was installed by the County to help reduce the risk associated with falling debris from the upper active slope that produced the rockfall in November of 2017.

Figure 7: View looking northeast at rock outcrop above the cut slope in June 2018 after a failure event and subsequent scaling in the fall of 2017.

Rockfall Modeling Results

Two cross sections were developed to model potential rockfalls from the upper rock outcrop and the shallow landslide located above the crest of the rock cuts at Section US-03. The two cross sections were modeled at stations 66+54 and 66+97 to assess potential locations for a rockfall protection fence (attenuator). Two potential locations were selected for the rockfall protection fence; i) a lower rockfall protection fence alignment located between 75 and 100 feet above the roadway, and ii) an upper rockfall protection fence alignment located between 100 and 110 feet above the roadway. The rockfall protection fence modeled was based on a 12-foot tall design by the FHWA and was battered outboard at angle of 20 degrees from vertical. For both rockfall protection fence alignments, analysis points were placed at the rockfall protection fence to obtain impact energies on the fence, and just behind the fence to assess bounce heights of any rocks that are not intercepted by the fence. Rockfall simulations showed that the rockfall retention for the upper rockfall protection fence location was slightly better and the impact energies were significantly lower than the lower fence location. Based on this, we recommended the upper fence location. The maximum 99th percentile impact energy on the upper rockfall protection fence was 211 ft-tons.

Rockfall Risk Reduction Measures

The rockfall risk reduction measures for Section US-03 included: i) scaling on the lower cut slope; ii) scaling of the outcrop on the upper slope and slope regrading (scaling) to flatten the over-steepened headscarp of the shallow slump; iii) rock dowels and rock bolts; iv) unlined drain holes; v) a rockfall protection fence (attenuator) along the crest of the cut slopes along portions of Sections US-02 and US-03, and vi) draped mesh. This work also includes hazard tree removal and boulder removal/ditch reconditioning. A breakdown of the mitigation quantities for this slope section are given in Table 3 in the Construction Section discussed below.

SECTION US-04 (STATIONS 69+57 to 70+97)

Section US-04 is approximately 140 feet long and 50 feet tall. This slope section received an USMP Rating of 409. According to Douglas County, the maintenance efforts are rare at this site and typically involve occasional removal of rockfalls from the roadside ditch.

Site Observations and Rockfall Hazards

Section US-04 is a southwest facing slope approximately 140 feet long and 50 feet tall. The rock slope appears to have been excavated at an inclination of ¼H:1V. The middle to eastern portion of Section US-04 (approximate Stations 70+40 to 70+95) is dominated by a shallow slough feature or trough that narrows at the road grade. It is unclear if this feature is related to a fault. On either side of this feature, the rock consists of hard (R4), green-gray, slightly to moderately weathered volcanic conglomerate. This rock is highly to moderately jointed (joint spacing 3-inches to 1½ feet). No seeps or springs were observed on the slope.

This site has a rockfall catchment area approximately 11 feet wide. According to Douglas County maintenance personnel, only minor amounts of rockfall debris, generally less than 1-foot in size, periodically reach the roadway. The crest of the cut slope, between approximate Stations 70+40 and 70+95 is over-steepened in the trough area due to shallow sloughing within the slope. This headscarp area is likely supported locally by tree roots and vegetation. Given the rock mass conditions observed in the cut slope and the adequate fallout ditch, the risks posed from rockfall and larger block failures appeared to be relatively low. No structural mapping or kinematic and stability analyses were performed for this site. The stability hazards for this this slope section are likely associated with the over-steepened headscarp of the shallow sloughing area. In time, this area will retrogress (or progressively fail back) to a flatter configuration, which has the potential to undermine and create hazard trees and increase rockfall activity.

Rockfall Risk Reduction Measures

The rockfall risk reduction measures for Section US-04 included scaling on the cut slope and slope regrading (scaling) to flatten the over-steepened headscarp of the shallow slough area to a more stable configuration (1.0H:1.0V inclination) and rock dowels and bolts to provide reinforcement to the rock mass. No large boulders are present in the ditch at this slope sections; however, the inboard ditch should be cleaned and reconditioned. A breakdown of the mitigation quantities for this slope section are given in Table 2 in the Construction Section discussed below.

CONSTRUCTION

The contract was awarded to Triptych Construction LLC out of Glide, Oregon. Construction began on July 25, 2019 and was fully completed on July 31, 2020. Table 3 shows the different rockfall risk reduction elements and quantities installed at the project. Select photographs during the installation of rockfall risk reduction measures are provided on Figures 8 through 11.

Table 3: Rockfall Risk Reduction Construction Quantities

Rockfall Item	Unit	US-01	US-02	US-03	US-04	Total Quantity
Scaling	HR	600	200	740	60	1,600
Rock Bolt (40 kips)	LF	850	750	1,600	100	3,300
Rock Bolt (80 kips)	LF	2,735	0	0	0	2,735
Rock Dowel	LF	465	120	1100	60	1,745
Unlined Drains	LF	1,590	510	900	0	3,000
Attenuator Fence	SF	0	0	29,700	0	29,700
Draped Mesh (DT)	SF	24,500	0	13,200	0	37,700
Draped Mesh (HS)	SF	0	21,555	0	0	21,555
Hazard Tree Removal	EA	15	5	15	5	40
Boulder Removal	CY	1,500	500	500	0	2,500
TRRP	LS	0.25	0.25	0.25	0.25	1
Traffic Control	LS	0.25	0.25	0.25	0.25	1

Figure 8: View of scaling on slope above US-02 and US-03.

Figure 9: Rock bolts being installed with crane-support drill.

A significant number of rock dowels and bolts were installed on this project. Rock dowels were located in estimated key blocks to 'knit' a rock mass together so any subsequent reinforcement load can be distributed over a larger area of the rock mass. Rock dowels consisting of Grade 75, No. 8 all-thread bar, generally 15-feet long were used. Rock bolts consisting of both Grade 75, No. 8 and No. 14 all-thread bar were used to obtain design loads of 40 and 80 kips. Based on rock block dimensions, rock bolt lengths ranged from 20 to over 35. As previously discussed, in order enhance drainage and reduce the effects of porewater/groundwater pressures on stability, a significant number of unlined drain holes were installed in the rock slope. The drain holes were unlined 3-inch diameter holes drilled at an upward inclination of 3° to 5° above horizontal to a length of 30 feet. The drains were drilled in a pattern, nominally spaced on 40-foot centers. However, a tighter pattern (30-foot center to center) was used between stations 64+60 and 66+05 of Section US-01 due to the size of the potential rock blocks needing additional reinforcement using rock bolts. The rock dowels, bolts, and unlined drains were installed using a combination of techniques including drilling by hand and both crane-support and buggy drills.

Figure 10: Rock bolts being drilled with a wagon drill.

The rockfall attenuator fence installed at US-03 between Stations 66+83 and 68+29 was based on a new FHWA design consisting of six, 12-foot-tall posts with a suspended cable net. These systems typically have higher energy absorption capacity than draped mesh but lower than flexible barriers. Attenuators intercept rockfalls similar to flexible barriers and control the rock's movement similar to draped mesh. Attenuators are typically located on the slope, particularly at launch features, and limit the amount of draped mesh required.

Both double-twist and high tensile-strength draped mesh was used for this project. Given the potential for large volume failures, 3mm high tensile-strength mesh was used for rock slope design Section US-02. Draped wire mesh is an effective and economical method of controlling rockfall trajectory and energy. The mesh retards the rate of descent of falling rocks as they work their way down slope behind the mesh. As a result, when the rocks exit the bottom of the mesh, they are moving slowly enough to be controlled by other protection measures or retained in the roadside ditch.

In addition to the rockfall risk reduction measures discussed above, all four sites included hazard tree removal and boulder removal/ditch reconditioning. Temporary roadway rockfall protection (TRRP) was provided by 12-foot-tall MRBs and concrete barrier with 6-foot tall fence extensions. Given the relatively low average daily traffic at the site (less than 200), the County instituted prolonged temporary delays or closures through the rock slope section to facilitate rockfall risk reduction measures.

Figure 11: View looking northwest at upper attenuator fence and draped mesh installed.

FHWA-WFLHD provided a project manager and a full-time, on-site contract construction project inspector. LT provided technical office support during the submittal process and during construction and part-time, on-site support. LT's primary on-site activates consisted of evaluating the thoroughness and quality of scaled areas, confirming rock bolt and dowel locations, identification of rock bolt locations on difficult access locations on the slope using rope access techniques, assisting with the placement of mid-slope attenuator post locations, and the adjustment of planned mitigation elements to accommodate field conditions. In addition, representatives from LT were on-site to assist with the performance testing of rock bolts and to observe the non-destructive testing (NDT) of rock dowels using a Krautkrammer USM 25 ultrasonic flaw detector due to the concern over the length of select installation locations.

REFERENCES

1. *Geology and Mineral Resources of Douglas County, Oregon, 1972, Bulletin 75*, State of Oregon Department of Geology and Mineral Industries.

2. Schmidt, R.G., *The Ore Bin, 1970, Vol. 32, No. 5, May 1970, 1972*, State of Oregon Department of Geology and Mineral Industries.

3. Peck, Dallas, L., et. al., *Geology of the Central and Northern parts of the Western Cascade Range in Oregon*, 1964, Geological Survey Professional Paper 449, Department of the Interior prepared in cooperation with the State of Oregon Department of Geology and Mineral Industries.

4. Hoek and Bray, *Rock Slope Engineering*, The Institution of Mining And Metallurgy, London, Third Edition, 1981

Potential Applications of Steel Fin Piles in Highway Transportation Infrastructure

Sarah McInnes, P.E.
Pennsylvania Department of Transportation, Engineering District 6-0
7000 Geerdes Boulevard
King of Prussia, PA 19406
610-205-6544
smcinnes@pa.gov

Jonathan Hubler, PhD
Villanova University - Department of Civil and Environmental Engineering
800 Lancaster Ave
Villanova, PA 19085
(610) 519-5109
Jonathan.Hubler@villanova.edu

Anthony LaRegina, EIT
AECOM Transportation
30 Knightsbridge Road
Piscataway, NJ 08854
(732) 564-3321
Anthony.LaRegina@aecom.com

Hannah M. Iezzoni, P.E.
Villanova University - Department of Civil and Environmental Engineering
800 Lancaster Ave
Villanova, PA 19085
(720) 443-0728
hannah.iezzoni@villanova.edu

Prepared for the 71st Highway Geology Symposium, May 2022

Acknowledgements

The authors would like to thank The U.S. Federal Highway Administration; PennDOT Engineering District 6-0; Mission Critical Solutions, PA Manufacturing Innovation Program, GRL Engineers, Buckley Construction Company, Inc. and Terry Foundation, Inc for their work on the various aspects of this project.

Disclaimer

Copyright Notice

Potential Applications of Steel Fin Piles in Highway Transportation Infrastructure

Author: Sarah McInnes, P.E., Pennsylvania Department of Transportation, Engineering District 6-0, 7000 Geerdes Boulevard, King of Prussia, PA 19406, phone: 610-205-6544, smcinnes@pa.gov

Coauthor: Jonathan Hubler, PhD, Villanova University – Department of Civil and Environmental Engineering, 800 Lancaster Avenue, Villanova, PA, 19085, phone: 610-519-5109, Jonathan.Hubler@villanova.edu

Coauthor: Anthony LaRegina, EIT, AECOM Transportation, 30 Knightsbridge Road, Piscataway, NJ 08854, phone: 732-564-3321, Anthony.LaRegina@aecom.com

Coauthor: Hannah M. Iezzoni, P.E.,. Villanova University – Department of Civil and Environmental Engineering, 800 Lancaster Avenue, Villanova, PA, 19085, phone: 720-443-0728, Hannah.iezzoni@villanova.edu

Steel fin pile foundations utilize fins on the side of the piles to develop significant frictional resistance between the soil and the finned pile. The fins serve the purpose of increasing lateral and torsional resistance of the pile. Typical scenarios with large lateral and torsional loads can be found in foundations for power transmission lines, roadway signage, solar panels, wind turbines, and marine applications. Many of these loading scenarios are common in highway transportation projects. Steel fin pile foundations are a rather new product to the market and case history data of applications and performance are limited compared to conventional alternatives such as shallow foundations, driven piles, and drilled shafts. The goal of this study is to provide a comparison for steel fin pile foundations with conventional alternatives. Additionally, field load testing of steel fin pile foundations was performed at an existing project site to evaluate engineering performance. This study will focus on ease of construction, applicability for different transportation infrastructure, and cost. The results of the load test data and comparison with conventional design show the viability and economy of steel fin pile foundation use in highway transportation projects.

INTRODUCTION

The introduction of new deep foundation alternatives may provide reliable and cost-effective performance when compared with traditional design choices. One of these new foundations is the steel fin pile. The steel fin piles analyzed for this paper were manufactured by Mission Critical Solutions (MCS). The steel fin piles are installed via a vibratory hammer. Steel fin piles feature additional "fins" that extend out from the pile diameter and along a determined length of the pile shaft. The increased stiffness, surface area, and bearing area added by these fins is not fully studied nor understood.

STEEL FIN PILES

Steel fin piles utilize fins on the side of the piles, as shown in Figure 1 and Figure 2, to increase the circumference in order to develop additional frictional resistance between the soil and pile. The fins also increase the flexural stiffness of the pile, therefore increasing the flexural and torsional capacities. These steel fin pile foundations are installed into the ground in minutes using a vibratory hammer and are immediately weight-bearing. As a result, they are an attractive option when compared to alternatives such as drilled shafts, which need time to cure prior to application of loads. Steel fin piles are relatively new to the industry, therefore the case history and performance data versus conventional alternatives is lacking in the literature which focuses on laboratory models (Dührkop and Grabe, 2008; Bienen et al., 2012; Azzam, 2017) or numerical analyses (Babu and Viswanadham, 2018; Pei et al., 2020). This paper summarizes scenarios where steel fin piles may be applicable in highway transportation infrastructure. Benefits of steel fin piles and comparisons with conventional alternatives is discussed. Additionally, data from proof-of-concept load tests for a typical 35-foot light pole structure in Pennsylvania will be presented.

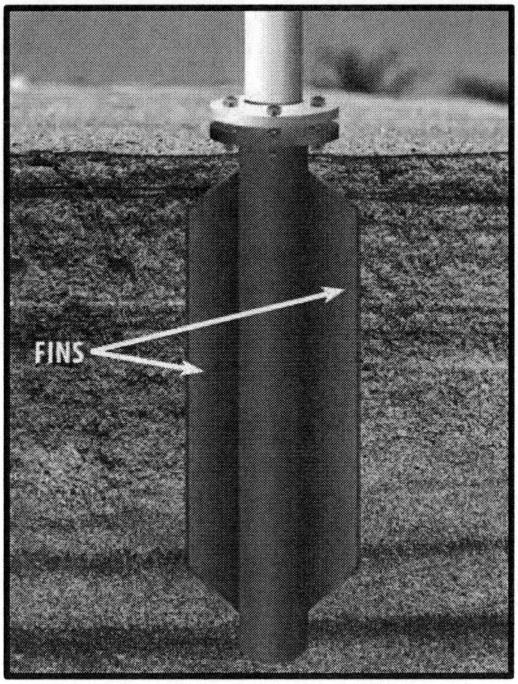

Figure 1. Example of Steel Fin Pile Foundation Design (Schumaker, 2012)

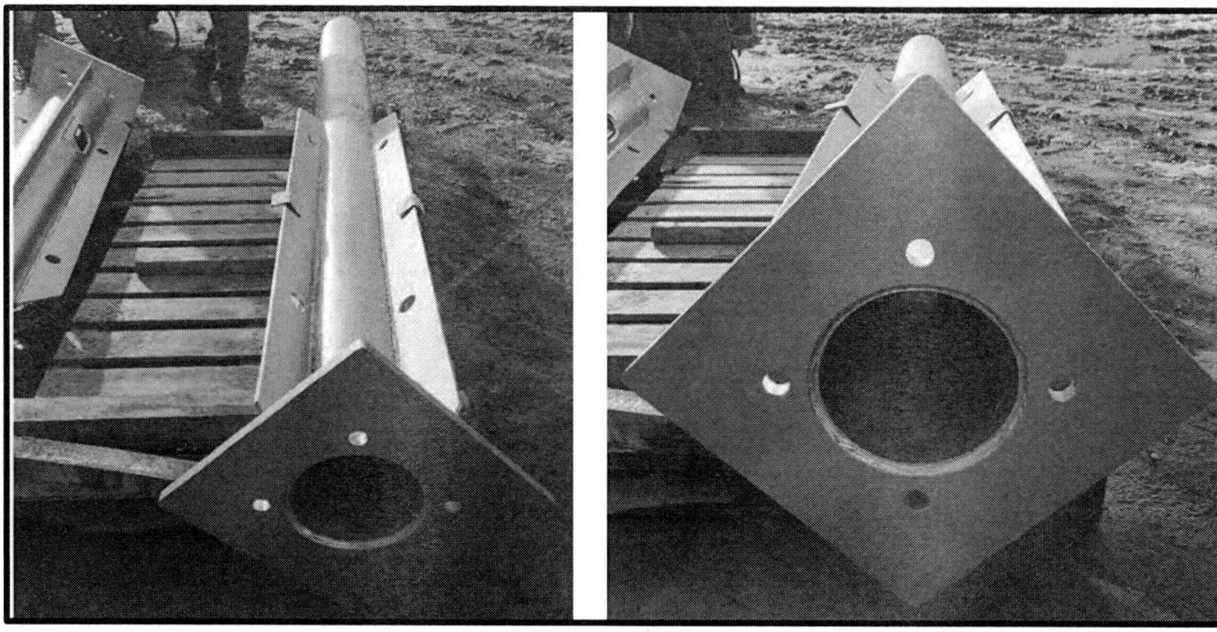

Figure 2. Photographs of Steel Fin Piles prior to Installation

POTENTIAL APPLICATIONS AND BENEFITS

The emergence of steel fin piles provides an opportunity for innovation in lightly loaded highway structures. Steel fin piles' relative ease of installation, higher capacity, and increased flexural stiffness makes them an attractive choice in some project scenarios. Steel fin pile designs have been used in harsh weather conditions and for projects with short timelines (Chernauskas et. al, 2011). Often piles are subject to large lateral loads that must be resisted to maintain stability of the supported structure. Due to the increased stiffness from the affixed fins; the total length of a steel fin pile can be reduced in comparison to that of a conventional circular steel pipe pile. This reduction in material can result in reduced material costs with improved performance due to increased lateral and torsional resistance. Additionally, steel fin piles may offer reduced installation costs compared to conventional alternatives (Chernauskas et. al, 2011) as they are installed with vibratory hammers, which may accelerate project timelines. Potential applications for steel fin piles in highway transportation projects include:

- Lightly loaded roadway signs
- CCTV poles and similar structures
- Highway lighting
- Temporary structures such as working platforms
- Shallow slope stabilizations

Foundation selection is driven by the magnitude of loads applied to the foundations and the quality of the soils supporting the structure. Common foundation types for these structures include shallow (spread) foundations, typical driven piles, and drilled shafts. All types have varying impacts on the total cost, schedule, risk, and performance of the structure. Drilled shafts are often selected due to their high flexural capacity and small footprint, however, the installation can be costly and take more time. The advantages and disadvantages of select foundation systems can be found in Table 1.

Table 1: Pile Alternatives (after FHWA, 2016)

Pile Type	Advantages	Disadvantages
Spread Footings	No specialized installation required	High overturning moments require very large footings
Driven Piles	Easy to vary lengths Capacity estimated during driving	Installation vibrations Low lateral capacities for vertical piles (can batter)
Drilled Shafts	Very high lateral and axial capacities Minimal vibrations	Specialty Construction Very costly
Steel Fin Piles	Higher capacities than traditional driven piles	Fins can lock up during driving in dense soils

CASE STUDY ON FIELD PERFORMANCE

In-situ testing of two MCS steel fin piles was conducted along the Interstate 95 corridor near Philadelphia, PA to evaluate the performance of steel fin piles and provide data to the limited existing literature. The test site was provided by the Pennsylvania Department of Transportation (PennDOT) on a site near the Frankford Creek shown in Figure 3.

Figure 3: Testing Site Location

SOILS AND GEOLOGY

Physiography & Topography

The testing site is located in the Lowland and Intermediate Upland section of the Atlantic Coastal Plain Physiographic Province near the boundary of the Coastal Plain and the Piedmont Physiographic Province, which is known as the Fall Line. The topography is characterized by flat upper terrace surfaces cut by shallow valleys of very low relief and the Delaware River floodplain. The area is underlain by unconsolidated to poorly consolidated sand and gravel deposits over complexly folded and faulted metamorphosed sedimentary and igneous rocks, primarily schist and gneiss. The drainage patterns are dendritic. Consequently, the project site is underlain by mostly unconsolidated to poorly consolidated sand and gravel.

Soil Survey

The Soil Survey Map of Bucks and Philadelphia Counties indicates the predominant soil within the project area is Urban Land (Ub). This designation represents highly variable and disturbed materials, generally including fill, resulting from previous construction and various land uses over time. Urban structures and works cover so much of this land type that identification of the soils is not practical. Most areas have been smoothed and the original soil material has been disturbed, filled over, or otherwise destroyed over time.

Adjacent to the Delaware River, the project area consists of loose man-made fills of various materials overlying native soils deposited by the Delaware River. They consist primarily of granular material intercepted by lenses of clayey and silty soils. The uppermost strata are, for the most part, man-made fills. Sand and silt dominate the stratified deposits.

Regional Geology

Figure 4 presents a portion of the Pennsylvania Geological Map (Philadelphia and Camden Quadrangles) with the project location indicated. As shown, the project site is mapped as being underlain by the Quaternary-aged Trenton Gravel (Qt). According to the Pennsylvania Geologic Survey and described in the *Engineering Characteristics of the Rocks of Pennsylvania*, the Trenton Gravel formation consists of gray to pale reddish-brown, very gravelly sand with interbedded, cross-bedded sand and clay-silt layers. The Trenton Gravel is deeply weathered and composed of outwash and alluvium that consists of weathered gravel of granite, sandstone, gneiss, siltstone, and quartzite. Thickness of the formation is approximately 60 feet at the project site.

Below the Trenton Formation lies the Wissahickon Formation, Oligoclase-Mica Schist Member composed of quartz, feldspar, muscovite, and chlorite. The oligoclase-mica schist variation is more coarsely crystalline than the associated albite-chlorite variation, excessively micaceous, and feldspar is more abundant. The estimated thickness of this formation is 8,000 to 10,000 feet. Bedding is fissile to thin and steeply dipping in most places. Fracturing is well developed and highly abundant. Joints are for the most part irregular, poorly formed, widely spaced, steeply dipping, and open. It is moderately resistant to weathering and often highly weathered to a moderate depth.

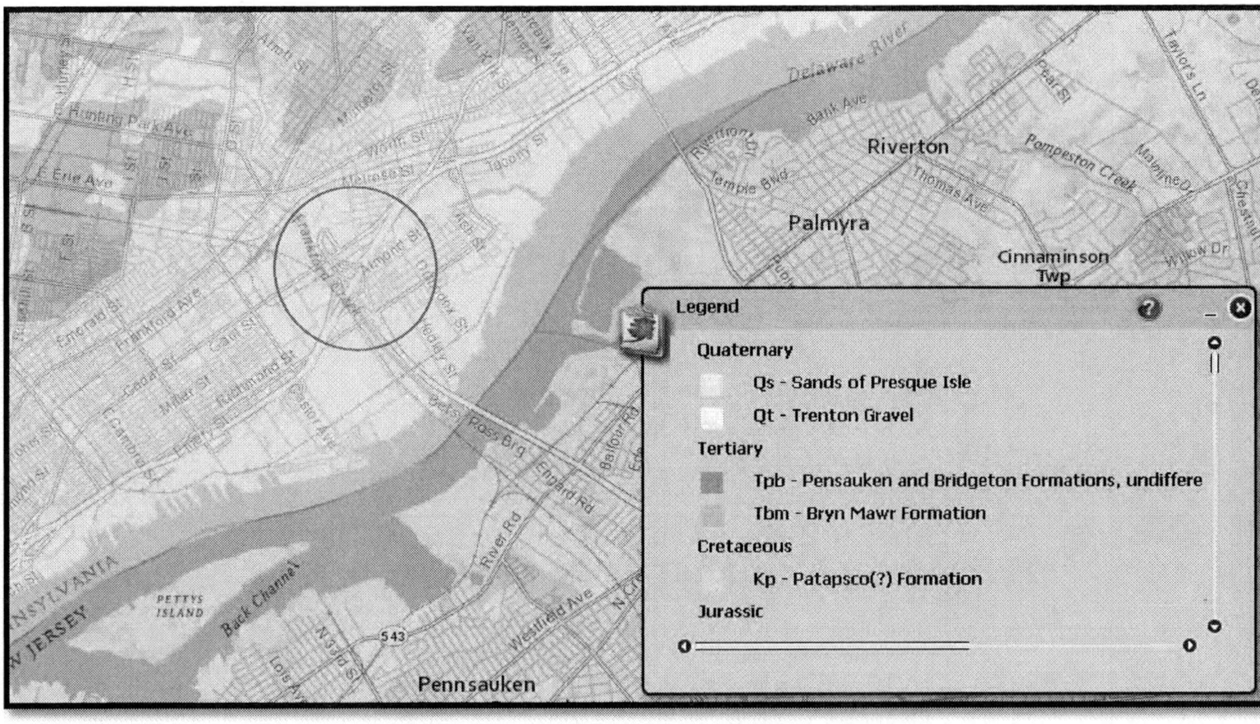

Figure 4: Geology Map of Test Site

SUBSURFACE INVESTIGATION AND CONDITIONS

A subsurface investigation was performed and the data obtained from an adjacent embankment/retaining wall project was able to be assessed prior to the field testing of the steel fin piles. Eleven test borings with continuous standard penetration testing (SPT) were taken in the vicinity of the pile testing site. Additionally, because of the known potential for clay layers, organic silts and running sands encountered on other I-95 sections, five Shelby tube samples were collected and five cone penetrometer tests (CPT) were specified. Two of the CPT borings were drilled adjacent to the SPT test borings. The laboratory testing program for both locations included a series of tests to confirm classification, measure typical index properties, and evaluate compressibility, strength, and corrosion potential.

Overall, the subsurface conditions at the site were generally consistent and can be categorized into five (5) soil layers based on the field-tested blow counts, CPT, soil classification and material properties from the laboratory test results. The soil stratigraphy is presented in Table 2. The average groundwater elevation at the site is approximately Elev. 0.0 feet. Undisturbed Shelby Tube samples were collected and the compressibility of this soil layer was evaluated through one-dimensional consolidation test with consolidation pressure applied to 32 tsf. The tested pre-consolidation pressures were between 5.8 tsf to 6.3 tsf. These pre-consolidation pressures correspond to an Overconsolidation Ratio (OCR) between 3.5 and 4.5.

Table 2: Summary of Subsurface Conditions

Soil Layer	Layer Thickness (ft.)	Soil Descriptions	Average N Value
1	14.0	Loose to medium dense Silty Fine Sand fills. Average grain size D_{50}: 0.2 mm, fine content (passing #200 sieve): 30%-35%.	14
2	12.0	Very dense poorly graded alluvial Sand with Silt and Gravel. Average grain size D_{50}: 2 mm, fine content: 10%-15%. Out of 5 CPT borings, refusal was encountered in 3 borings.	43
3	10.0	Stiff alluvial Lean Clay (plastic index less than 15) or non-plastic Silt. Sand content is usually less than 10%.	6
4	22.0	Medium dense alluvial poorly graded Sand and Silt. Average grain size D_{50}: 0.5 mm, fine content: 15-20%.	19
5	28.0	Very dense completely weathered bedrock (saprolite soil). Soils can be classified as Silty Sand with Gravel. Average grain size D_{50}: 1.0 mm, fine content: 10-15%.	Split spoon refusal

LOAD TESTING OF THE STEEL FIN PILES

Axial and lateral load tests were conducted on two MCS steel fin piles (P1 and P2) with a length of 12 feet and 3 inches to evaluate their performance as a typical 35-foot light pole structure foundation. The pipe portion of the pile is 10.75 inches in diameter with a 0.5 inch wall thickness. The pile fins are 5 inches wide, 0.375 inches thick, and 6 feet long with a spacing of 90° between each fin for a total of 4 fins on the pile. The piles are covered with a top plate to attach structural elements to the pile such as the driving equipment or the light structure. The steel used for the top plate of the piles and the fins have a yield strength of 36 ksi, per ASTM A36. The fins are welded to the pipe portion of the pile with a yield strength of 42 ksi, per ASTM A500. These piles are approved for use by PennDOT Publication 72M.

The test program consisted of installing two piles and performing axial and lateral load tests on each pile. Installation was carried out using a Dawson EMV 450 vibratory hammer. It took approximately 15 minutes to install each pile, highlighting the benefit of fast installation time for these piles. The testing was performed in early March 2021. Figure 5 shows a photograph of the axial load test setup, and Figure 6 shows a photograph of the lateral load test setup. The governing design criteria for the piles is their lateral capacity in this scenario; therefore, axial capacity does not govern pile design. Axial load testing followed ASTM D1143 Method A: Quick Test, and the load was applied in 0.5-kip increments (ASTM, 2013a). These increments were held for 5 minutes before moving onto the next increment. The lateral load testing followed the loading schedule Method A from ASTM D3966 (ASTM 2013b).

Figure 5: Axial Load Test Setup for Fin Pile

Figure 6: Lateral Load Test Setup for Fin Pile

Results from the axial load tests showed that the piles moved 0.030 inches at a load of 20 kip for the P1 pile and 0.032 inches at a load of 24 kips for the P2 pile. The axial capacity was greater than expected based on the design calculations. This increased capacity is attributed to the pile reaching a stiff gravel layer at a depth slightly shallower than expected based on the boring used for design. The lateral tests were conducted with the load applied in different orientations to assess any difference in performance in the fin orientation to the direction of loading. This setup is shown in Figure 7. The maximum test shear load of 24 kips was applied 2 feet above the ground surface for both piles. The resulting deflections showed the orientation of the fins with regards to the direction of the load had some impact on the performance of the piles. The rebound of both piles was 0.1 inches. The maximum displacements were not equal, with the pile loaded between the fins (P1) deflecting less than the pile loaded in-line with the fins (P2). The movement recorded at the light pole design moment of 30 kip-feet (15 kips shear) was less than the design criterion of 0.50 inches. The P1 pile deflected 0.29 inches and the P2 pile deflected 0.36 inches at the design moment. Overall, the piles demonstrated adequate performance at the design loads for a 35-foot light pole structure, while providing ease and quickness of installation.

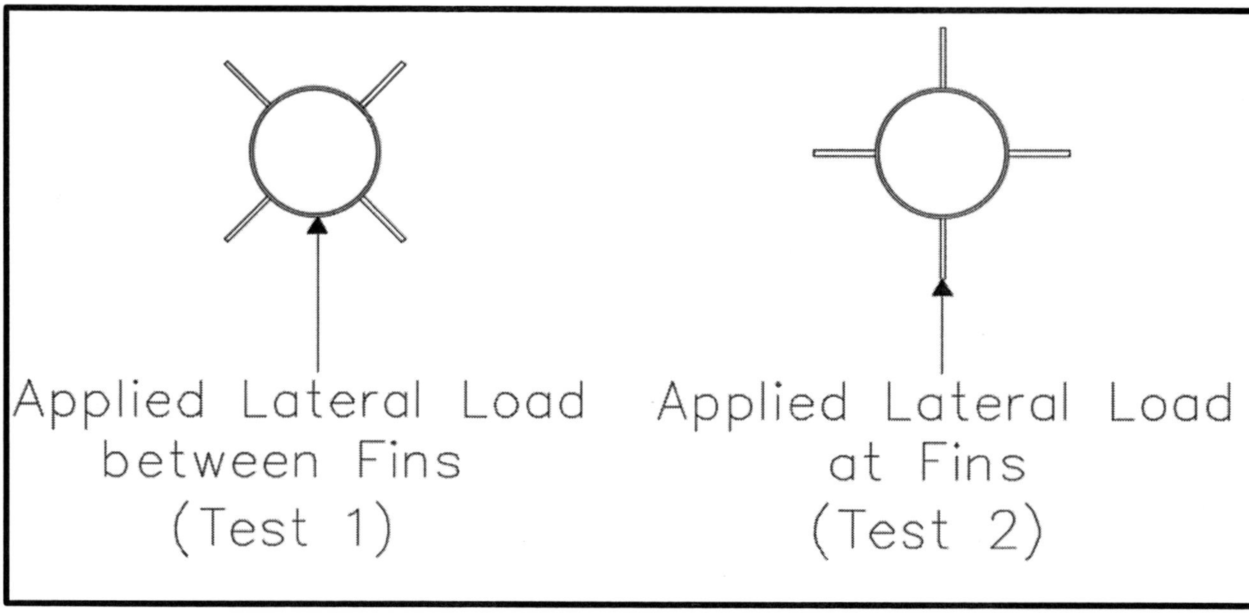

Figure 7: Lateral Load Test Primary Load Application Direction for Test Piles

CONCLUSIONS

Based on the field testing performed and subsequent analysis of a variety of structures the fin piles may be appropriate for, we have concluded that they are a worthwhile foundation type to pursue. Due to the increased capacity provided by the fins, a fin pile can be installed to a shallower depth compared with other foundation types resulting in a reduction of material needed for the foundation. This will result in reduced project costs with improved performance due to increased lateral and torsional resistance. In conjunction with these benefits, steel fin piles can be installed using vibratory hammers, which accelerate project timelines and will further reduce costs related to time of installation, specifically in comparison with the traditional drilled shaft required by some singular smaller structures such as lightly loaded roadway signs, CCTV poles, highway lighting, temporary structures and for shallow slope stabilization.

REFERENCES

1. ASTM D1143, "Test Methods for Deep Foundations Under Static Axial Compressive Load." *ASTM International*, West Conshohocken, PA, 1-15, 2013a.

2. ASTM D3966, "Test Methods for Deep Foundations Under Lateral Load." *ASTM International*, West Conshohocken, PA, 1-18, 2013b.

3. Azzam, W. R., "Model Study on the Performance of Single-Finned Pile in Sand under Tension Loads." *International Journal of Geomechanics*, 17(3), 2017.

4. Babu, K. V., and Viswanadham, B. V., "Numerical studies on lateral load response of fin piles." Geomechanics *and Geoengineering,* 14(2), 85–98, 2018.

5. Bienen, B., Dührkop, J., Grabe, J., Randolph, M. F., and White, D. J., "Response of Piles with Wings to Monotonic and Cyclic Lateral Loading in Sand." *Journal of Geotechnical and Geoenvironmental Engineering*, 138(3), 364–375, 2012.

6. Bureau of Design, "Standards for roadway construction: series RC-1M to 100M," Pennsylvania Dept. of Transportation, Harrisburg, PA, 2010.

7. Chernauskas, L. R. "The use of spin fin® piles in Massachusetts." *Deep Foundations Institute*. 1-6, 2011.

8. Dührkop, J., and Grabe, J., "Laterally Loaded Piles With Bulge." *Journal of Offshore Mechanics and Arctic Engineering,* 130(4), 2008.

9. Pei, T., Qiu, T., and Laman, J. A., "A Numerical Investigation of Laterally Loaded Steel Fin Pile Foundations." ASME/IEEE Joint Rail Conference, 2020.

10. Schumaker, M. "An Introduction to Shaner Industries' Metal Foundation System." Shaner Industries, Ambridge, PA, 2012.

Experience in the Face of Unknowns

Bridge Foundation Alternatives for the Leesport Bridge, Pennsylvania

Bruce Shelly, P.E.
AECOM
625 W. Ridge Pike
Conshohocken, PA, 19428
610-234-5155
bruce.shelly@aecom.com

Sarah McInnes, P.E.
Pennsylvania Department of Transportation, Engineering District 6-0
7000 Geerdes Boulevard
King of Prussia, PA 19406
610-205-6544
smcinnes@pa.gov

Jeff Rai, P.E.
Pennsylvania Department of Transportation, Engineering District 5-0
1002 Hamilton Street
Allentown PA 18101
610-871-4568
jrai@pa.gov

Prepared for the 71st Highway Geology Symposium, May 2022

Acknowledgements

The authors would like to thank PennDOT Engineering Districts 5-0 & 6-0; Michael Baker International and Geo-Explorers, Inc; for their contributions and work on the various aspects of this project.

Disclaimer

Statements and views presented in this paper are strictly those of the author(s), and do not necessarily reflect positions held by their affiliations, the Highway Geology Symposium (HGS), or others acknowledged above. The mention of trade names for commercial products does not imply the approval or endorsement by HGS.

Experience in the Face of Unknowns

Bridge Foundation Alternatives for the Leesport Bridge, Pennsylvania

Author: Bruce Shelly, P.E., AECOM, 625 W. Ridge Pike Conshohocken, PA, 19428, Phone: 610-234-5155, bruce.shelly@aecom.com

Coauthor: Sarah McInnes, P.E., Pennsylvania Department of Transportation, Engineering District 6-0, 7000 Geerdes Boulevard, King of Prussia, PA 19406, phone: 610-205-6544, smcinnes@pa.gov

Coauthor: Jeff Rai, P.E. Pennsylvania Department of Transportation, Engineering District 5-0, 1002 Hamilton Street, Allentown PA 18101, phone: 610-871-4568, jrai@pa.gov

The Leesport Bridge over the Schuylkill River, originally built in 1915, was slated for replacement after 100 years of service. An existing pedestrian sidewalk was especially in need of repair, as the river bisected the small town. A geotechnical reconnaissance of the existing conditions determined the existing bridge was founded on shallow foundations and situated on a geologic contact between the Ontalaunee formation (Dolomite) and Hamburg Sequence (Limestone). There were reports of nearby sinkhole repairs by PennDOT Maintenance crews. During the subsurface exploration, voids at the top of bedrock and soft rock layers of rock were found in most of the borings but rock was consistently shallow. Also found were large layers of concrete unrelated to the existing footings.

Initial recommendations called for grouting of the bedrock and a deep micropile foundation. This foundation would have been accepted as there was considerable evidence to be conservative here. However, an error in the top of pile cap elevation placement at Abutment 1 paused review of the project and alternatives were suggested which started a multi-District, multi-Consultant re-evaluation of the substructures and a foundation risk matrix was developed.

This project is about overcoming fear which resulted in significant conservatism and cost. It's a lesson learned in emphasizing what can be gleaned from test borings vs. field observations vs. the experience of practiced engineers.

INTRODUCTION

The Wall Street (SR 1003) bridge over the Schuylkill River is located in West Leesport, Berks County, just north of Reading in Southeastern Pennsylvania. Wall Street connects the Borough of Leesport on the west to Route 61 on the east (Figure 1). Like Asheville, Leesport is situated in the foothills of the Appalachian Mountains.

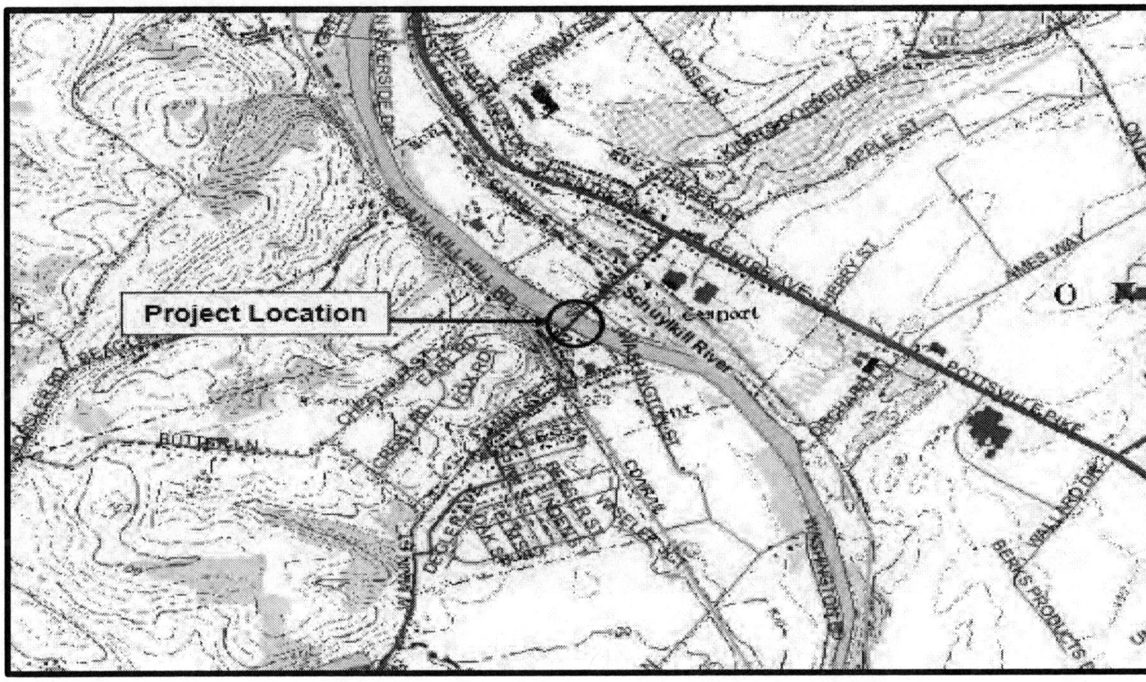

Figure 1: Location Map

This Bridge is owned by the Pennsylvania Department of Transportation (PennDOT) in Engineering District 5 which is on the eastern side of the state between Philadelphia and Scranton. The project design team was led by Michael Baker, International with the subsurface investigation and foundation design performed by the geotechnical subconsultant, Geo-Explorers, Incorporated. The Department used an open-end agreement with AECOM and consultation with the District Geotechnical Engineer from adjacent PennDOT District 6 to review the Foundation Submission and design. The existing bridge was constructed in 1915 as a three-span reinforced concrete closed spandrel arch bridge with a total length of 213' and a total width of 24' (Figure 2) and a sidewalk was cantilevered on the south side of the bridge in 1950. The existing plans of the original structure are unavailable but the structure plans for the addition of the sidewalk in 1950 indicates all substructures are spread footings. There was no known subsurface exploration.

The proposed bridge, on the same alignment, was a 214' long, two-span composite prestressed concrete PA bulb-tee beam bridge with an out-to-out width of approximately 38 ft. The bridge was widened to the north to avoid a WWII Memorial site and post office on the south side and the number of spans was reduced to increase the waterway opening.

Figure 2: Existing Structure

SOILS AND GEOLOGY

Physiography and Topography

The project is located within the Great Valley Section of the Ridge and Valley Province (Figure 3). The Great Valley is a continuous basin spanning the eastern side of the Valley and Ridge province. The Schuylkill River forms from many streams within the Blue Mountains of the Appalachian range and flows through the project site. The width of the Schuylkill River is approximately 200' in Leesport.

Wall Street crosses a contact between the Limestone Section of the Hamburg Sequence (Ohl) and the Ontelaunee (Oo) Formation (Figure 4). The Ohl formation consists of finely crystalline limestone and shaly limestone which is well bedded with a platy pattern and well developed, moderately abundant, and steeply dipping. Foundation stability is good and limestone should be investigated for solution cavities. The Oo formation consists of light to dark gray, very finely to medium-crystalline dolomite, some limestone, and interbedded and nodular chert at its base. It is well bedded, with thick beds and an average thickness of about 750 feet. It is moderately resistant to weathering and slightly weathered to a shallow depth. Both steeply and gently dipping set occur. Foundation stability is good and should be investigated thoroughly for solution cavities. There is a concern for sinkholes forming in these formations but sinkholes at the project location have a low occurrence.

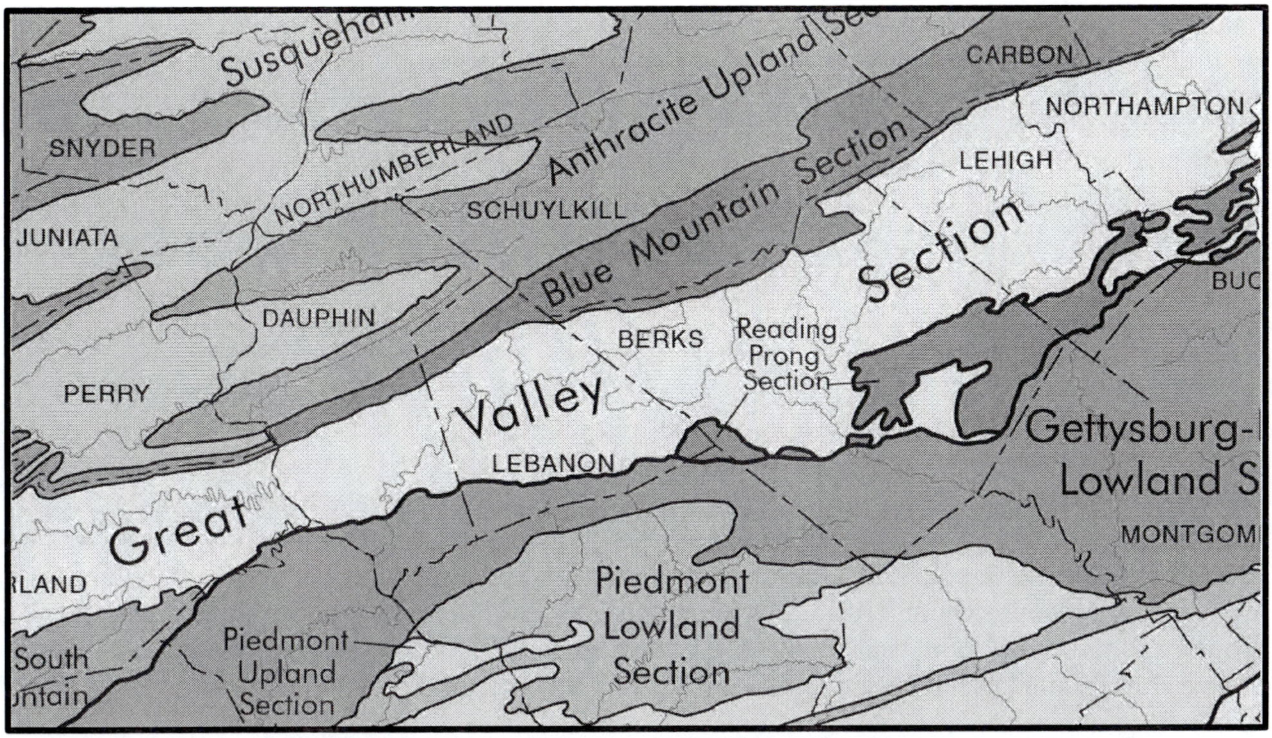

Figure 3: Location of the Great Valley

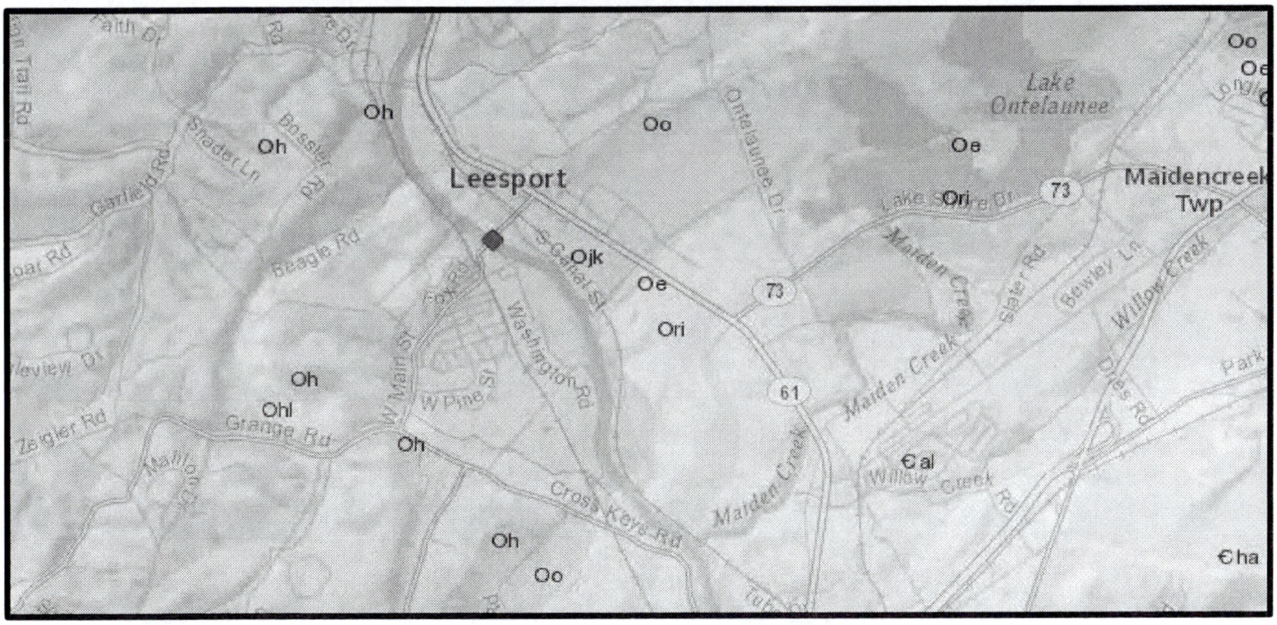

Figure 4: Geology Map, Red Dot Indicates Project Location & Contact

Bridge Inspection Report

The Bridge Inspection Report from 2010 was reviewed as is typical during the Reconnaissance phase of the project. The structural inspection revealed considerable large cracks, section loss, and spalling at the near and far abutments and exposed rebar at locations along the arches. None of the cracks or section loss was determined to be related to the foundations. Pier 1 noted undermining below the footing but also noted rock outcrops along the base of the footing. In fact, a sketch of the bridge identifying scour along each substructure also identified rock outcrops at every substructure. Pier 2 was previously repaired for undermining by surrounding the footing with a concrete apron. So, overall, the foundations were slightly undermined due to scour but in fair condition and were not the reason for the bridge replacement.

Visual Site investigation

With the geologic concerns at the project site and unknowns related to the existing bridge, an extensive site investigation was made. The visual site inspection verified the abutments, wings and piers had large horizontal and vertical cracks, spalling, and exposed rebar however, no horizontal or vertical movement was observed as well as no geotechnical related instability. There was no evidence of surface or subsurface drainage problems. Concrete pours around the existing Pier 2 appeared to be scour/structure related. A large outcrop of dolomite bedrock was found completely around and presumed to be beneath the entire Abutment 1 (Figures 5 & 6). No evidence of closed depressions, ground subsidence or sinkholes were observed at the project location.

Figure 5: Existing Outcrop in Front of Abutment 1

Figure 6: Vertical Bedding Evident in the Outcrop

Based on the known information, concerns about the geology, and the lack of existing subsurface information, a comprehensive test boring program was recommended. A minimum of two test borings were proposed for each substructure (Figure 7). From the existing information, rock was expected to be rather shallow however, as in some carbonate formations, also expected to be variable. All borings were to be drilled at least 20' into bedrock to investigate solutioning extent in accordance with Department protocol. Drilling included two (2) boring on a barge to investigate the new Pier location.

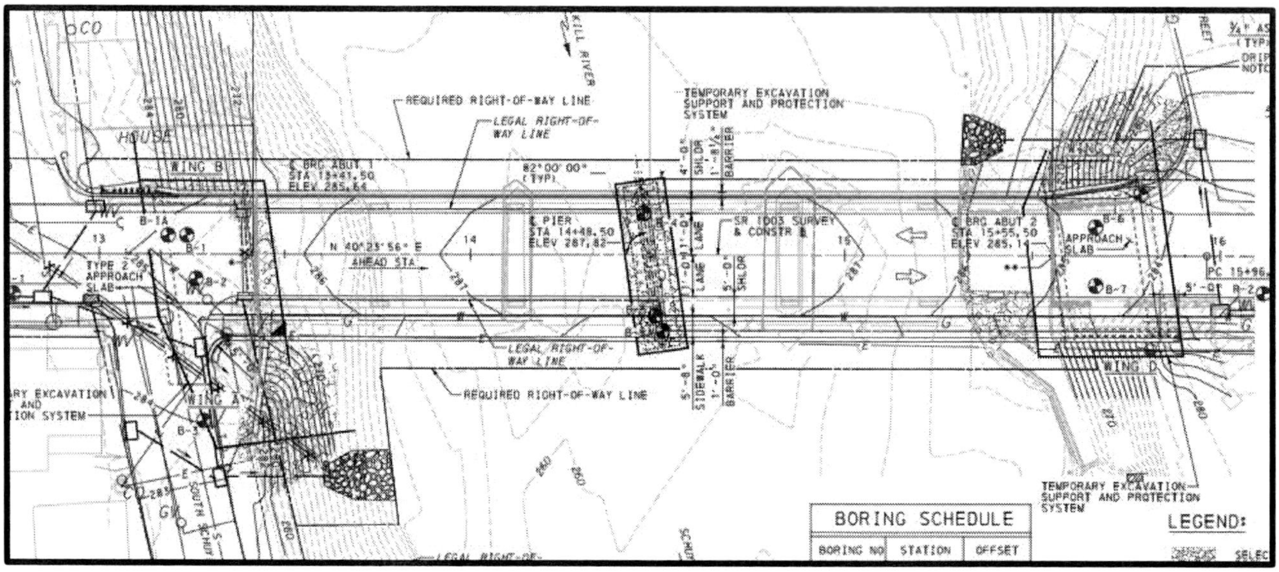

Figure 7: Test Boring Plan

The test borings revealed shallow dolomite bedrock at all the substructure locations at the preliminary proposed bottom of footing elevations. In general, the rock showed less recovery in the epikarst (approximately 10 to 20 feet below top of rock for the abutments and piers respectively) than in the deeper bedrock. The core box (Figure 8) shows a typical rock section. This typical profile does point out some concerning features including low recovery, numerous soil seams and possible voids. Notably, extreme karst features such as top of rock variability, large voids (noted by drill rod drops) and loss of drill water were not observed. The top of bedrock elevation in the structure borings ranges from 257.2 to 272.0 feet in elevation and the existing streambed elevation ranges from 260.0 to 273.0.

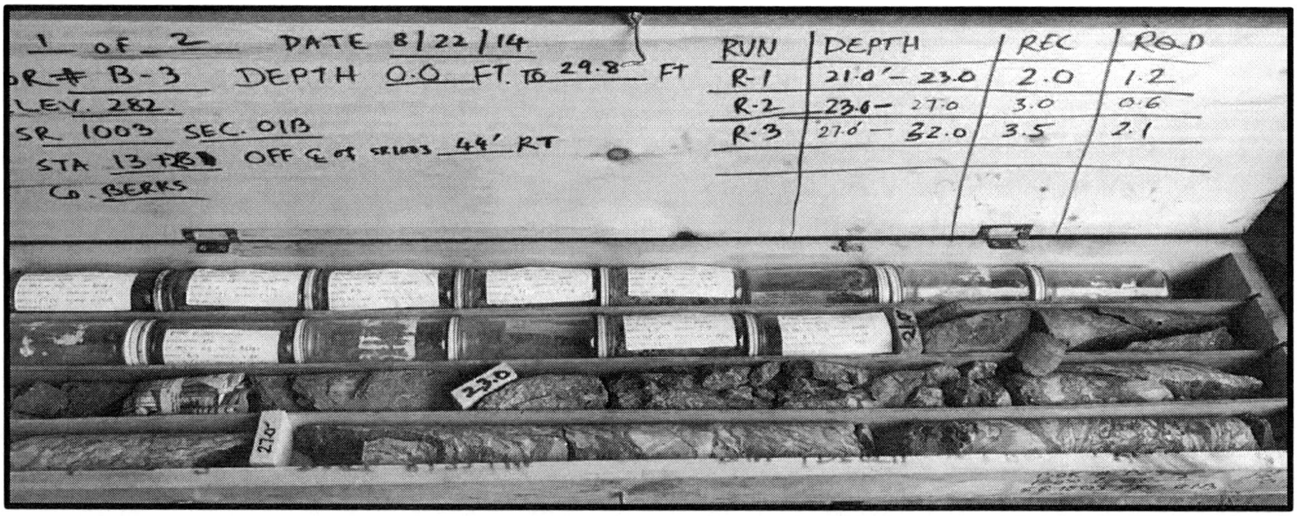

Figure 8: Corebox Photograph

FOUNDATION ALTERNATIVES

The first iteration of the foundation design for this project evaluated several alternatives including a spread footing with limited mobility grouting (LMG) (Option 1), a micropile foundation (Option 2) and pre-drilled H-Piles (Option 3). The alternatives evaluation considered the following concerns:

Type and support condition of the existing foundations
Competency of the rock bearing stratum
Solution cavities within the rock strata
Potential for future solution activity
Deep foundation support within alternating solutions zones
Location of groundwater table
Weathering, hardness, and fracture condition of rock
Constructability
Cost effectiveness

As stated before, the test borings indicated shallow dolomite bedrock at the project site which, based on the test boring logs, exhibited solution activity in the upper rock strata. The rock condition improved significantly with depth, therefore, concerns about solution cavities were evaluated to provide a safe and reliable foundation system

Option 1, a spread footing on bedrock with limited mobility grouting of the upper rock strata, approximately 10 to 11 feet at the abutments and 22 feet at the pier, had a goal of improving the overall recovery of the bedrock to a target of at least 90 percent. The objective of the grouting would be to improve the upper rock strata to distribute the bearing stresses to the deeper, more competent rock mass. Risks considered during evaluation of this option included verification of the post grouting program and shallow grouting adjacent to the river. The estimated cost of this option was $993,000.

Option 2 recommended 7-inch diameter micropiles with 6-inch diameter rock sockets to transfer loads into the more competent rock mass. Risks considered during assessment of this option included the uncertainty of the bedrock condition within the bond zone and potential grout loss in solution features during construction. Additionally, the presence of soil seams, voids and discontinuities could cause difficulty estimating pile tip elevation, bond zone length, and grout quantity and result in overruns, however, proper construction controls could minimize these risks. A 15.0-foot micropile bond length was recommended resulting in a factored capacity of 203 kips. The top of bond zone was selected based on the same considerations examined for the LMG alternative at each substructure. The estimated cost of this option was $877,000.

Option 3 was driven point bearing piles. While not the most intuitive foundation option in karst geology, this option was evaluated for perspective and to provide a proper cost comparison considering the ability of local contractors to self-perform the work. Due to the shallow bedrock profile at the substructure locations the piles would need to be predrilled a minimum of 10 feet and seated at the required depth before driving. The estimated cost of this option was $1,309,000.

Based on the above analysis and considerations Option 2, rock socketed micropiles, was the recommended foundation system because of the least perceived cost and lowest risk. It should be noted that all options have risk in karst bedrock.

An Unusual Challenge

Per the Pennsylvania Department of Transportation's Design Manual Part 4 (DM-4), Section 10. 6.1.2, the bottom of any pile cap must be founded below the depth of scour and frost penetration and have a minimum embedment of 3.0 feet into bedrock if the rock mass is assessed to be "erodible". Per DM-4, Section PP 7.2.4(b)1 (at the time), erodible rock was defined as a rock mass with an RQD of greater than 70% and recovery greater than 90%. This requirement resulted in an acceptable bottom of footing elevation (BFE) at the Pier and Abutment 2 but based on the results of one boring at Abutment 1 a challenge was faced by the design team.

Borings B-1 and B-2 were drilled within the footprint of Abutment 1 and had a top of rock elevation (TRE) of 269.5 ft. and 272.0 ft. respectively. Boring B-3, drilled approximately 30 feet away for a wingwall, had a TRE of 261.0. When evaluating the BFE for Abutment 1 the designer considered this boring, which is common practice at PennDOT and when in a karst environment, due to the inherent unknowns associated with carbonate formations. This evaluation, following DM-4, resulted in a BFE of 258 ft. Additionally, the top of rock elevation at the abutment was above the adjacent ground elevation at the abutment (reference Figure 5). As a result, up to 14 feet of rock excavation (Figure 9) would be required to reach the bottom of pile cap for this option. Added to the challenging constructability of this recommendation, the test borings were only drilled to an average elevation of 240 feet so the micropile tip elevations were below a depth for which we had data.

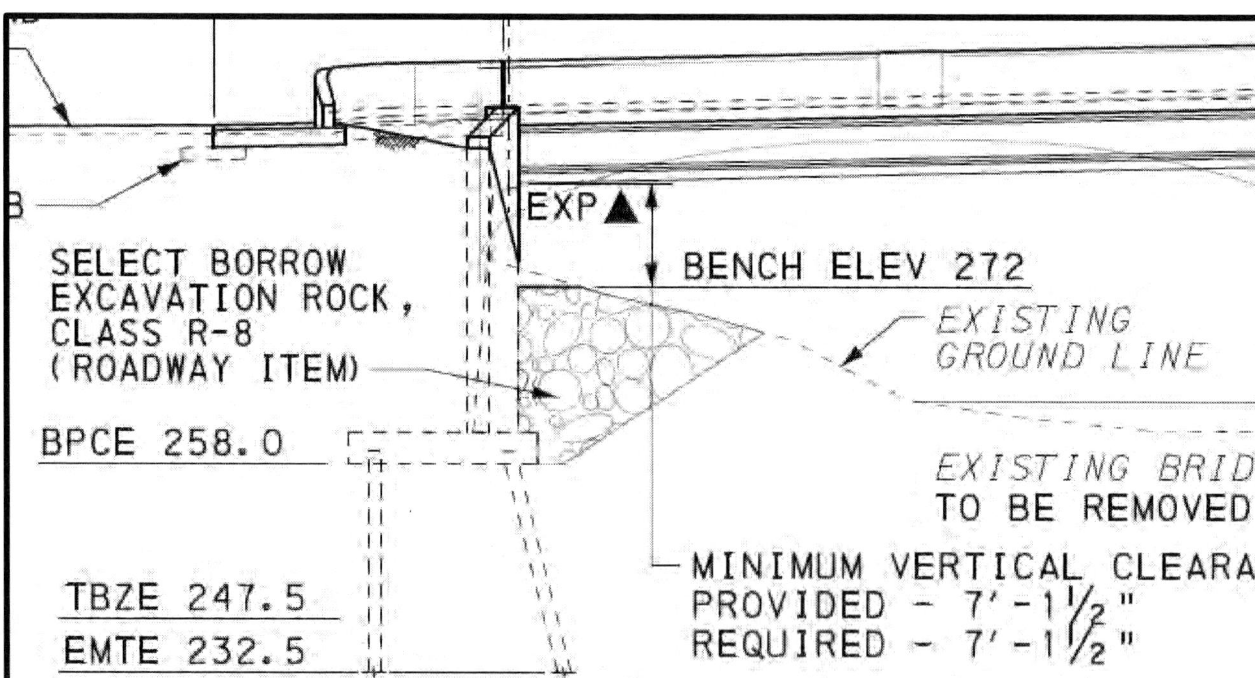

Figure 9: Elevation View at Abutment 1

EXPERIENCE IN THE FACE OF UNKNOWNS

During the review of the foundation design the review team made a field view of the project site to better understand the existing conditions. Two important things were confirmed as a result:

1) The bedrock outcrops at the site indicated a few reasons the test boring data may be misleading.

2) The existing bridge, which was over 100 years old and founded directly on rock, showed no evidence of distress or subsidence related to the carbonate bedrock.

These observations led to a series of review comments and meetings which evaluated several factors related to the proposed foundation design. Two members of the review team were experienced geotechnical engineers with more than 60 combined years of experience with design and foundation performance in carbonate bedrock, as well as having a substantial understanding of evaluation of test boring logs in karst and PennDOT design requirements. One thought was that the near vertical nature of the fractures in the rock often leads to misleadingly low recoveries. Another was that the design, while adequate, safe, and followed the requirements of the Design Manual, should be reconsidered to be shallower. This information, along with concerns about constructability and cost, resulted in a reevaluation of the need to place the bottom of the foundation of Abutment 1 so deep and consider direct bearing on the bedrock with no ground improvement or deep foundations.

The design and review teams worked together for months considering all the data and calculations in the geotechnical report along with the guidance of several engineers and geologists looped into the decision-making process. The review team proposed a spread footing foundation on bedrock embedded three feet into bedrock as determined by the boring logs at Abutment 1, ignoring the wingwall boring. This was considered by the design team and it was agreed that the bottom of the foundation could be raised but there continued to be concerns related to risk based on the unknowns of the geologic formation.

As a result, the design team performed a risk analysis for the foundation alternatives. The analysis included the original three options plus a spread footing option with two methods of additional remediation: a reinforced concrete mat to be placed below the spread footing or sinkhole repair with dental grouting. The reinforced load distribution mat would be approximately four feet wider than the proposed footing and four feet thick and would be designed to span a potential 10-foot void in the rock mass. The dental grouting would be recommended as observed or determined to be needed (Figure 10). While it was understood the potential for continued sinkhole activity would be reduced, any existing voids that were not observed could not be remediated.

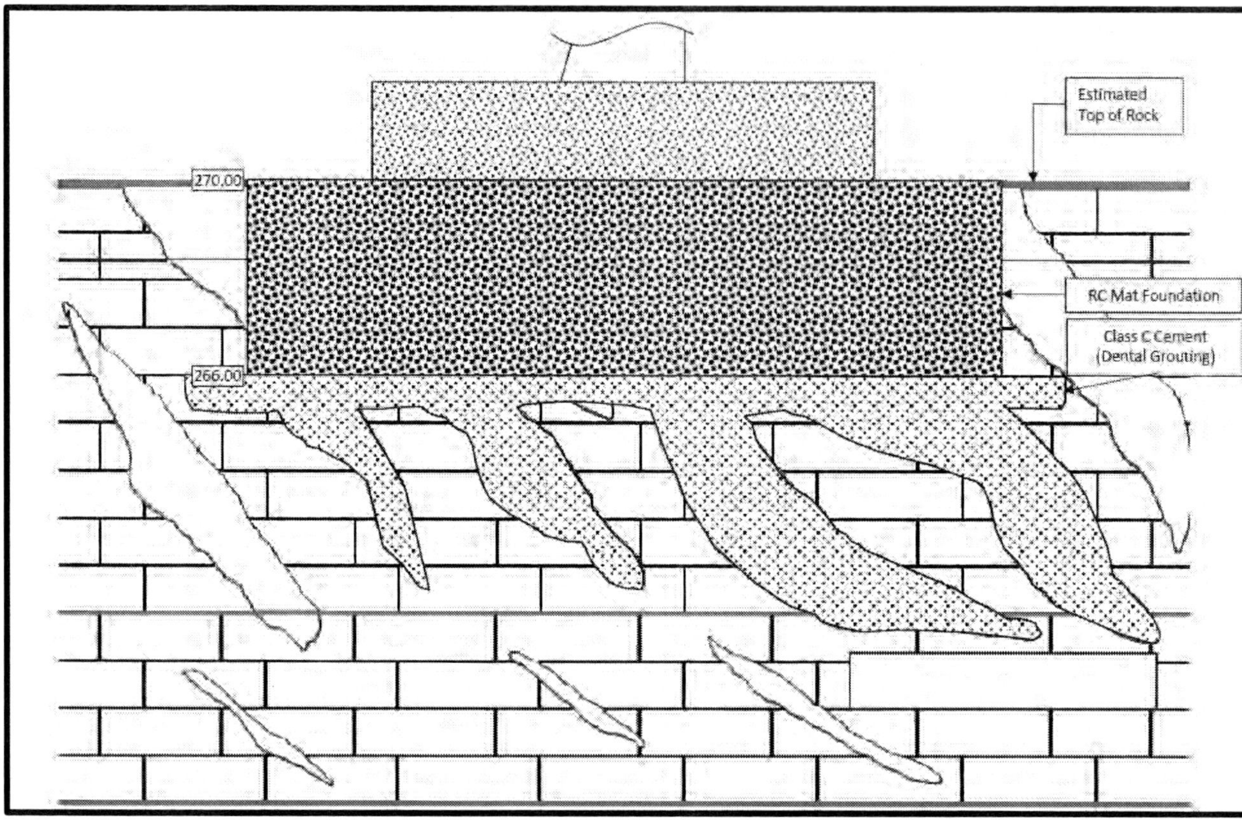

Figure 10: Conceptual Drawing of Subsurface Conditions

The design team concluded the option providing the least risk and lowest cost was the micropile foundation however the 'best value' option was determined to be a spread footing on a reinforced concrete mat (Figure 11). This option assumed some additional risk, which was accepted by the Department, but offered a cost savings of about 25%. As a result, the load distribution mat option was selected, designed, and shown on the plans. It was then determined by the Department and related to the construction team that the need for the mat would be as needed and determined in the field based on inspection of the excavation by the District 5 Geotechnical Engineer. The reinforced concrete mat was affectionately referred to as the "super footing".

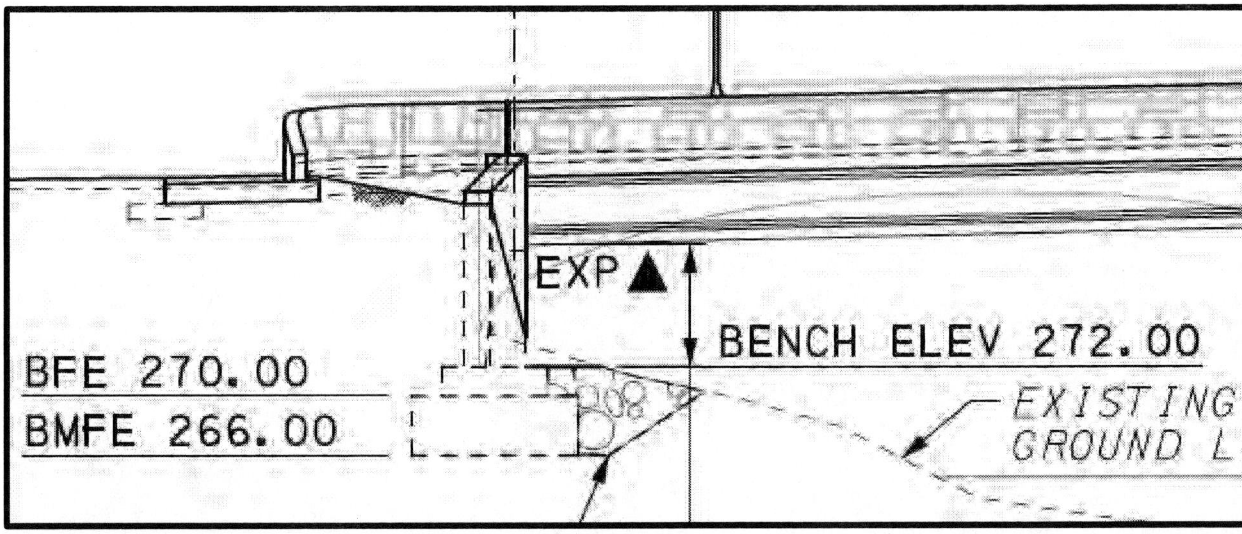

Figure 11: Final Configuration of Abutment 1

An interesting and notable observation about the visual representation in Figure 10 is the conceptualization of voids represented by evaluating the recovery from the test borings. This figure was presented to the Department based on the data from the test borings to help understand what may be happening beneath the ground surface to support considerations for foundation alternates and represents an average rock recovery of 39% below the bottom of the proposed mat. Field observations, coupled with observations of the outcrops and experience, helped the design review team understand this graphic may be misleading and decisions about foundation construction should be made based on direct field observations of the excavations combined with a serious consideration of a practical and realistic understanding of the subsurface conditions.

CONSTRUCTION OBSERVATIONS

Inspections were performed at each of the substructures after excavation to the bottom of footing elevation and are described below with the results of the evaluation and final construction decisions.

Abutment 1

A portion of the Abutment 1 excavation subgrade was inspected at the bottom of footing of elevation of 270.0'. The contractor was asked to excavate a test hole at the other end of the excavation and the bucket was only able to dig a few inches before a rock layer that seemed difficult to remove was encountered. The compacted areas appeared competent (Figure 12) and the remaining portion of the excavation had the same rock layer as described on the test hole. A soil layer approximately 3 inches thick was in the remainder of the excavation and the contractor was directed to remove any soil and place the foundation directly on the rock leaving a thickened footing. Based on the observed subgrade it was determined the mat foundation could be eliminated and the spread footing foundation could be placed on the prepared subgrade without the mat foundation and the footing was noted to be embedded at least two feet into rock.

Figure 12: Abutment 1 Subgrade

Pier

District 5 staff and a design reviewer inspected the subgrade at the bottom of footing elevation of 258.0 ft. There appeared to be more soil material (clay and silt) and weathered rock in this excavation but top of weathered rock was visible a minimum of one foot above the bottom of footing. A few small pools of water existed and appeared to be percolating from the river. Because the bearing rock did not appear to have the quality of the rock subgrade it was recommended to require the load distribution mat foundation installed per the plans. Excavated between the bottom of footing elevation and bottom of mat elevation was a mix of boulders, cobbles and weathered rock with silt-clay soil. No signs of depressions or sinkholes were observed. Notable in Figure 13 is the near vertical bedding of the bedrock which likely contributed to the low recovery during drilling.

Figure 13: Pier Excavation

Abutment 2

The inspection of the Abutment 2 excavation did not indicate any voids or sinkholes in the footprint of the Abutment 2 foundation area. The subgrade consisted of weathered rock with some soil or clay, and the subgrade appeared to be capable of supporting the design loads. Because of the presence of a relatively thin layer of soil (Figure 14) it was recommended the subgrade preparation at Abutment 2 could proceed by over-excavating an additional 6" as well as removing any pockets of soil using dental excavation up to an additional 2 feet in depth. This allowed a mudslab to be placed using a minimum 6" thick Class C concrete. It was determined the load distribution mat was not required.

Figure 14: Abutment 2 Excavation

Again, the near vertical bedding of the rock formation is observed without evidence of voids or solution activity (Figure 15). Abutment 2 was the first substructure excavated and looking at the quality of the rock gave the Department team a real sense of security and verified the expectations based on the reconnaissance.

Figure 15: Near Vertical Bedding in Abutment 2 Excavation Side

CONCLUSIONS

Based on our collective experience with this project the following are the lessons learned by those involved:

- Field views are important and observations made can provide information to fill in gaps in the data and calculations.
- Interpretations of subsurface conditions must be closely evaluated as reasons for low recovery can be varied and experienced individuals are valuable to the evaluation. An important aspect to evaluate is the drilling rate during coring as well as recovery. A void is an interpretation without verification.
- When facing unknowns, it's most important to collaborate with other Geotechnical Engineers so all the risks can be examined and the design team can feel good about a safe, constructable, and economical solution.
- Observation must continue from design all the way through construction to verify the expected conditions. Those involved in design must be able to learn from field observations.

REFERENCES

1. American Association of State Highway and Transportation Officials (20 IO). LRFD Bridge Design Specifications.

2. Berg and Dodge, Atlas of Preliminary Geologic Quadrangle Maps of Pennsylvania, Pennsylvania Bureau of Topographic and Geologic Survey, 1981.

3. Geo-Explorers. lnc. (2016), Foundation Recommendation Report, SR 1003, Section 01B (Wall Street) over Schuylkill River. Leesport Borough. Berks County, PA.

4. Geo-Explorers. lnc. (2014), Reconnaissance Soils & Geological Engineering Report, SR 1003, Section 01B (Wall Street) over Schuylkill River. Leesport Borough. Berks County, PA.

5. Geyer. A.R., Wilshusen, JP. (1982), Engineering Characteristics of the Rocks of Pennsylvania, Pennsylvania Geological Survey. 4th Series.

6. Pennsylvania Department of Transportation (2012). Design Manual, Part 4, Structures, Publication 15.

7. Pennsylvania Department of Conservation of Natural Resources, "The Geology of Pennsylvania", 1999.

Geological Assessment of the Westbound I-40 Slope Failure, Rockwood, Tennessee

D. A. Hannam and R. L. Kath

David A. Hannam, P.G.
WSP / Golder Associates USA
5170 Peachtree Road, Building 100, Suite 300,
Atlanta, Georgia, USA 3034
david.hannam@wsp.com (770) 492-8826

Randy L. Kath, Ph.D., P.G.
Professor of Geology
Department of Geology
University of West Georgia
rkath@westga.edu (678) 839-4063

Prepared for the 71st Highway Geology Symposium, May 2022

Acknowledgements

The authors would like to thank the following individuals for their support and contributions in the work described:

Robert Jowers, P.E. – TDOT
Lori Fiorentino, P.E. – TDOT
Courtney Vissman, P.E. – WSP / Golder Associates USA

ABSTRACT

Interstate 40 (I-40) west of Harriman and east of Rockwood, Tennessee, has a history of slope instability dating back to slope failures that occurred during interstate construction in the early 1960s. Arcuate cracks appeared through the westbound lane between Mile Markers (MM) 342.8 and 343.2 following heavy precipitation during the 2018-2019 winter. Detailed geologic mapping revealed the arcuate cracks were tension scars related to a landslide complex containing several failure surfaces spanning nearly 1,500 feet along the westbound lane.

Accurate detailed geologic mapping applied early in the project allowed development of a site conceptual model that was used to evaluate the cause of landslide movements, evaluate the areal magnitude of the problem, target the geotechnical investigation, and scope the mitigation alternatives analysis.

Detailed geologic mapping conducted on USGS and LiDAR topographic base maps provided a detailed preliminary site model to explain the failure geometry and guided the initial geotechnical investigations. The subsurface and subsequent investigations included sonic and conventional geotechnical boreholes, electrical resistivity imaging (ERI) geophysics, historical aerial photograph review, laboratory analysis, instrument installations (inclinometers, standpipes, and vibrating wire piezometers), rockfall hazard assessment and additional targeted detailed geological mapping. The data were incorporated into a 3D geological model which was used to produced 2D sections used for slope stability analysis.

The final geotechnical design included a suite of tiebacks anchored into the Pennington Formation shale and a more competent upper sandstone member. Geotechnical design challenges included a deep failure surface, low strength of shale and a complexity of ground conditions.

INTRODUCTION

The project site is 1.5 miles northeast of Rockwood, Tennessee, on the southeast slope of the eastern Cumberland Plateau Escarpment, Walden Ridge, near I-40 MM 343, **Figure 1**. Above the westbound lane, sandstones and shale of the Pennsylvanian Gizzard Group and overlying Suwannee Conglomerate overlie the upper sandstone member of the Mississippian Pennington Formation. Calcareous weathered shales of the middle Pennington Formation underlie the sandstone member and continue downslope toward the eastbound lanes. Based on detailed geologic mapping and aerial photographic interpretation, thick colluvial and landslide deposits cover large sections of the project area.

Figure 1: Site location map.

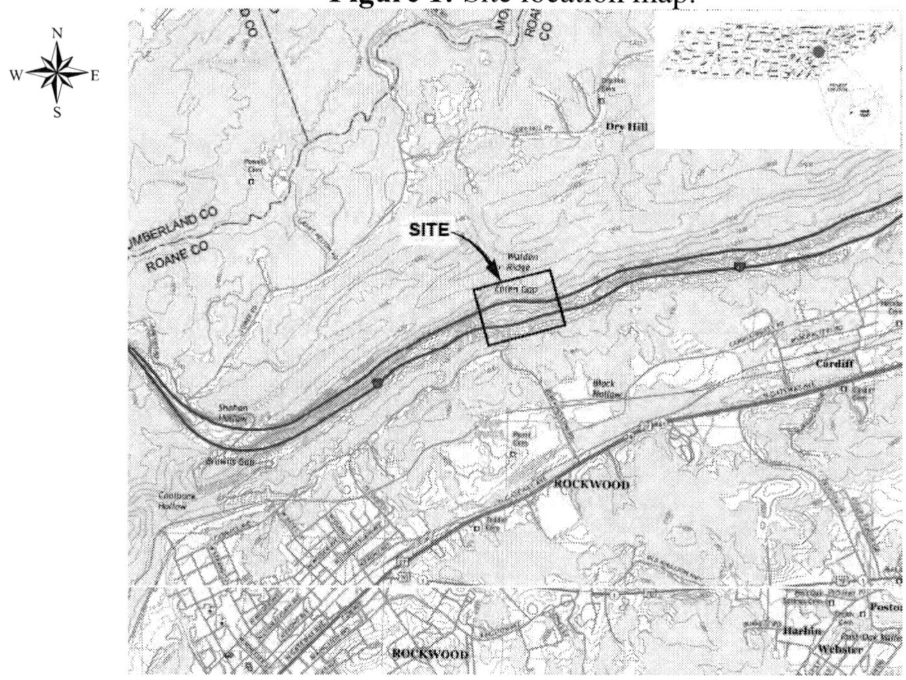

The topographic relief at the site, from the eastbound lane to the top of the ridge is about 550 feet over 1,100 horizontal feet. Elevation at the top of the ridge is just over 1,500 feet above mean sea level (MSL). Elben Gap is formed along a linear feature that transects Walden Ridge.

In early 2019, arcuate cracks were identified by the Tennessee Department of Transport (TDOT) in the westbound lane of I-40 near MM 343 (the westbound and eastbound lanes separate in this area where they traverse the Cumberland Plateau Escarpment) following a winter with heavy precipitation. TDOT records show that arcuate cracks have occurred in this area intermittently since the initial 1960s construction. Given that this 5-mile section of the I-40 has a known history of ground engineering problems (Golder Associates USA Inc. 2009 and 2016, and Royster, D.L., 1973) and the importance of this transportation corridor between Knoxville and Nashville, TDOT contacted Golder to conduct geologic mapping of the area to understand the areal distribution of the rock units, general engineering properties of the rock and/or soils, and to determine the possible source(s) of the arcuate cracks.

HISTORICAL BACKGROUND

Based on the review of archive documents from TDOT, analysis of historical aerial photographs, and geomorphology of landslides, the approximate timeline of events is shown below:

- **1961**: Pre-construction historical USDA aerial photographs show landslides in the immediate area.
- **1967**: I-40 construction has started and north of road construction are three scarps in the project area. Hummocky topography is shown downslope. Fill appears to have been placed over the slide mass.
- **1969**: Several road cuts pass through Colluvium. Road construction has caused a large slump in the eastern part of the site.
- **1970**: A large-scale investigation and analysis for this 5-mile section of I-40 is undertaken by Law Engineering (Law Engineering Testing Company, 1969)
- **1975**: Tension cracking and minor subsidence at the site in the westbound lane is noted in TDOT reports. Horizontal drains and vertical wells are installed in the median.
- **1993:** Additional cracks reported in the westbound lane.
- **1994:** Mitigation work in the median is completed over the next five years including Fill removal, reducing slope angle, and installing lined ditches.
- **2010/2011:** Aerial images show retreating scarps above the westbound lane toward Walden Ridge.

FIELD INVESTIGATION METHODS

Multiple methods were used to collect sufficient geologic and geotechnical data to facilitate remedial design, including detailed site geologic mapping; geotechnical drilling using hollow-stem auger (HAS) and sonic core drilling techniques; and electrical resistivity imaging (ERI) geophysics.

Geologic Mapping

The detailed geologic mapping was performed within and around the site on April 29 through May 1, 2020 using the Cardiff, TN USGS 7.5-minute topographic quadrangle as a general base map along with a LiDAR topographic map and Google Earth imagery. The mapping was focused on geologic features around existing areas of know arcuate zones identified by TDOT on I-40 and the slopes between I-40 and Walden Ridge. Information recorded during geologic mapping includes lithology and mineralogy; orientation and characteristics of structural discontinuities including, faulting, jointing, cleavage, and compositional layering; and depth and type of weathering characteristics of the rock. Map station locations were recorded using a hand-held, Wide Area Augmentation System (WAAS)-enabled Global Positioning System (GPS). The results of the geologic mapping provided an early model for understanding the extent and nature of the arcuate failures transecting the westbound lanes of I-40. Additionally, this detailed geologic mapping provided the basis for developing a geotechnical field investigation to collect data necessary for the slope stability analysis.

Drilling

Thirty-five boreholes drilled up to 300 feet below ground surface (BGS) were advanced between May 2019 and November 2019 using rotary and sonic drilling methods. The sonic method was used to complete all borings receiving an inclinometer. The sonic method provides a large enough diameter borehole to properly install and grout a 2.75-inch diameter casing through difficult drilling conditions of alternating soil and rock.

Geophysics

Data was collected along three ERI lines. ERI Line 1 was collected along the northern shoulder of the westbound lanes of I-40; along the south-facing slopes. ERI Lines 2 and 3 were collected during a second phase of geophysical surveying in the median between the westbound and eastbound lanes. ERI Line 2 was 1,245 feet long and was situated in the median; downslope and parallel to ERI Line 1. ERI 3 was also in the median, oriented perpendicular to Line 2, approximately parallel to the slope. Data from the overlapping arrays were combined to generate a vertical 2-dimensional profile of the subsurface electrical resistivity.

REGIONAL GEOLOGY

The site is contained along the boundary between the Valley and Ridge and Cumberland Plateau physiographic provinces. The Valley and Ridge is composed of Paleozoic-age sedimentary rocks that have been folded into a series of anticlines and synclines broken by numerous thrust (reverse) faults and lateral strike-slip faults. The ridges are primarily held up by layers of sedimentary rock more resistant to weathering, such as sandstone, whereas the valleys are underlain by shale and limestone that readily weathers. The Cumberland Plateau exposes mostly upper Paleozoic rocks that are nearly horizontal and have been highly dissected by river valleys forming rolling hills and shallow valleys. The rocks exposed along I-40 and the slopes between I-40 and Walden Ridge are contained within the Mississippian and Pennsylvanian systems.

The alignment of I-40 nearly parallels Walden Ridge which traverses the Suwannee Conglomerate. The strike of the conglomerate is parallel to the ridge which allows the development of dip joints that dip to the south-southeast. The dip joints provide a mechanism for releasing the Pennsylvanian stratigraphy along planar and curved failure surfaces toward I-40. Additionally, as the escarpment migrates toward the north-northwest and the overlying Pennsylvanian is removed, the underlying Pennington Formation is exposed. The upper Pennington Formation where exposed in the southeastern US is known for unstable subsurface conditions for engineering projects.

SITE GEOLOGIC CONDITIONS

The initial geological mapping was fundamental to the project. The results of the geologic mapping are shown on **Figure 2**. The mapping redirected the early site assumptions, and informed the location and depth of drilling, instrumentation installation and geophysical transects and interpretation. The early geological sections and map generated from field mapping alone proved to be highly accurate, **Figure 3**. The results of the mapping produced a ground model that was refined as additional subsurface investigation data became available. All the investigation data was collated into a 3D geological model generated using Leapfrog, a modelling program by Seequent. The model was used to cut 2D sections used for slope stability analysis and mitigation design.

Figure 2: Geologic map of the main slide area showing cross section locations.

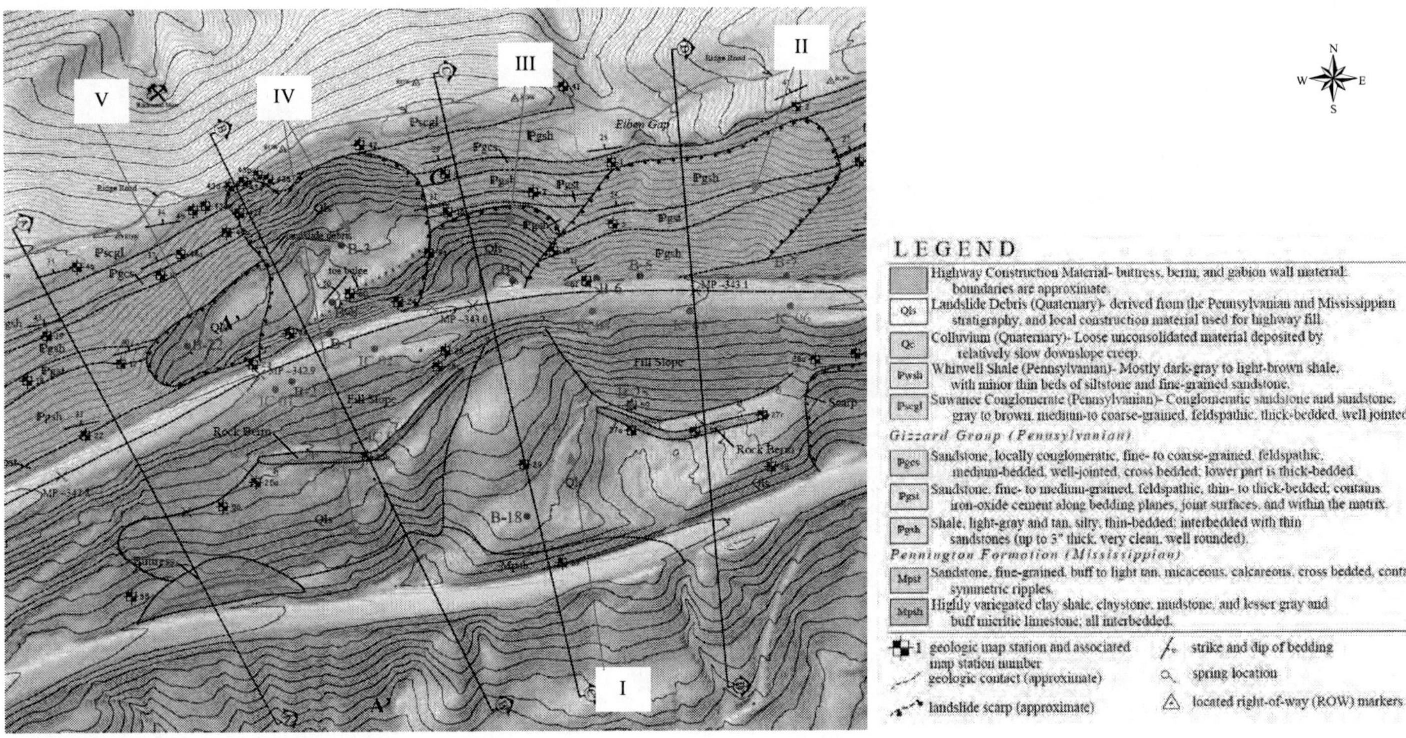

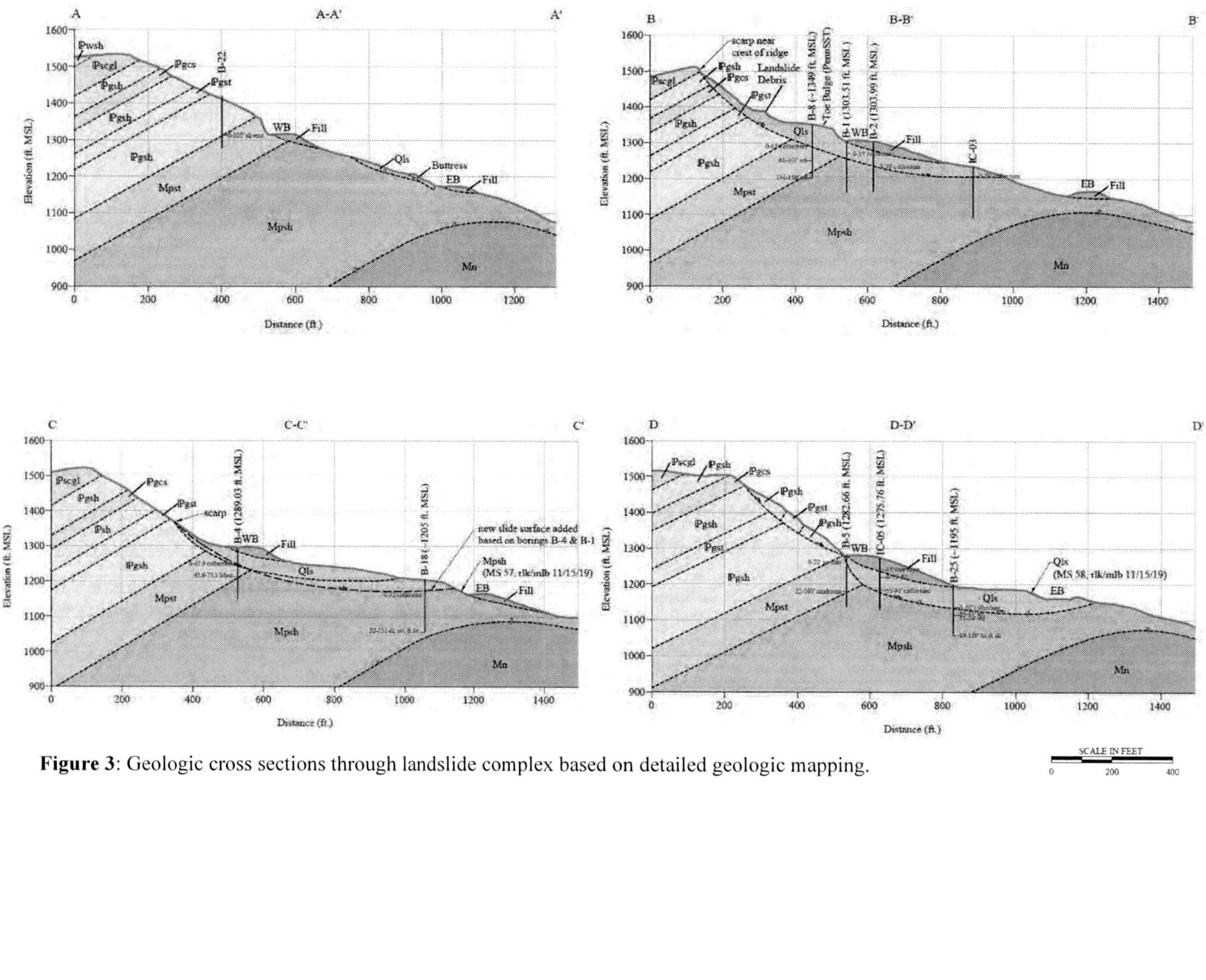

Figure 3: Geologic cross sections through landslide complex based on detailed geologic mapping.

General Site Geology

The site lies along the northwestern flank (limb) of the Rockwood Anticline, **Figure 3**. Lithologic units generally dip to the northwest at a relatively uniform angle. Along Walden Ridge, the Suwannee Conglomerate is well exposed. Underlying the conglomerate are thick units of sandstone, conglomerate, and shales of the Gizzard Group. An upper sandstone member of the Mississippian Pennington Formation underlies the Gizzard Group and is exposed at the site along the roadcuts to the north of the westbound lane. Underlying the sandstone member is shale of the Pennington Formation. The shale contains varying proportions of interbedded sandstone and limestone. The median between the east and westbound lanes contains engineered Fill that was placed during initial road construction.

Site Stratigraphy-

The following section is based on observations from detailed geologic mapping, drilling, and geophysical data.

Engineered Fill

Fill soils, ranging in thickness from 3.5- to 55-feet, underly much of the westbound lane and extended about a third to halfway down the median, terminating at a man-made rock berm. Where Fill overlies Colluvium, differentiating between the two material types can be difficult as both comprise reworked native materials. Fill was encountered as orange brown to yellowish brown and soft to stiff, silt to gravelly, silty sand and as clayey gravel to sand. The gravel is described as fine to coarse sub-rounded to sub-angular and trace cobbles where observed. The plasticity of the clayey soils was variable, ranging from low to high.

Colluvium

Colluvium was recorded in almost all boreholes across the site and may extend beyond the eastbound lane, beyond the project limits. The thickness of Colluvium was highly variable and appeared deepest north of the westbound lane, where a maximum thickness of nearly 100 feet was observed.

Colluvium can be difficult to interpret in boring logs. Colluvium contains reworked native material and can appear similar to underlying residual soils or contain large boulders that can be misinterpreted as bedrock. The Colluvium was a mix of soil zones and coring of large boulders. For example, returns from boring B-10 comprised about 73 feet of sandstone that was determined to be a large, detached sandstone block (forming part of the Colluvium) rather than in-place bedrock. The transition from Colluvium to native deposits is shown in **Figure 4**.

Figure 4: Photographic record of drill core showing interpreted transition from Colluvium to the residual Pennington Shale. Colluvium contains reworked native deposits.

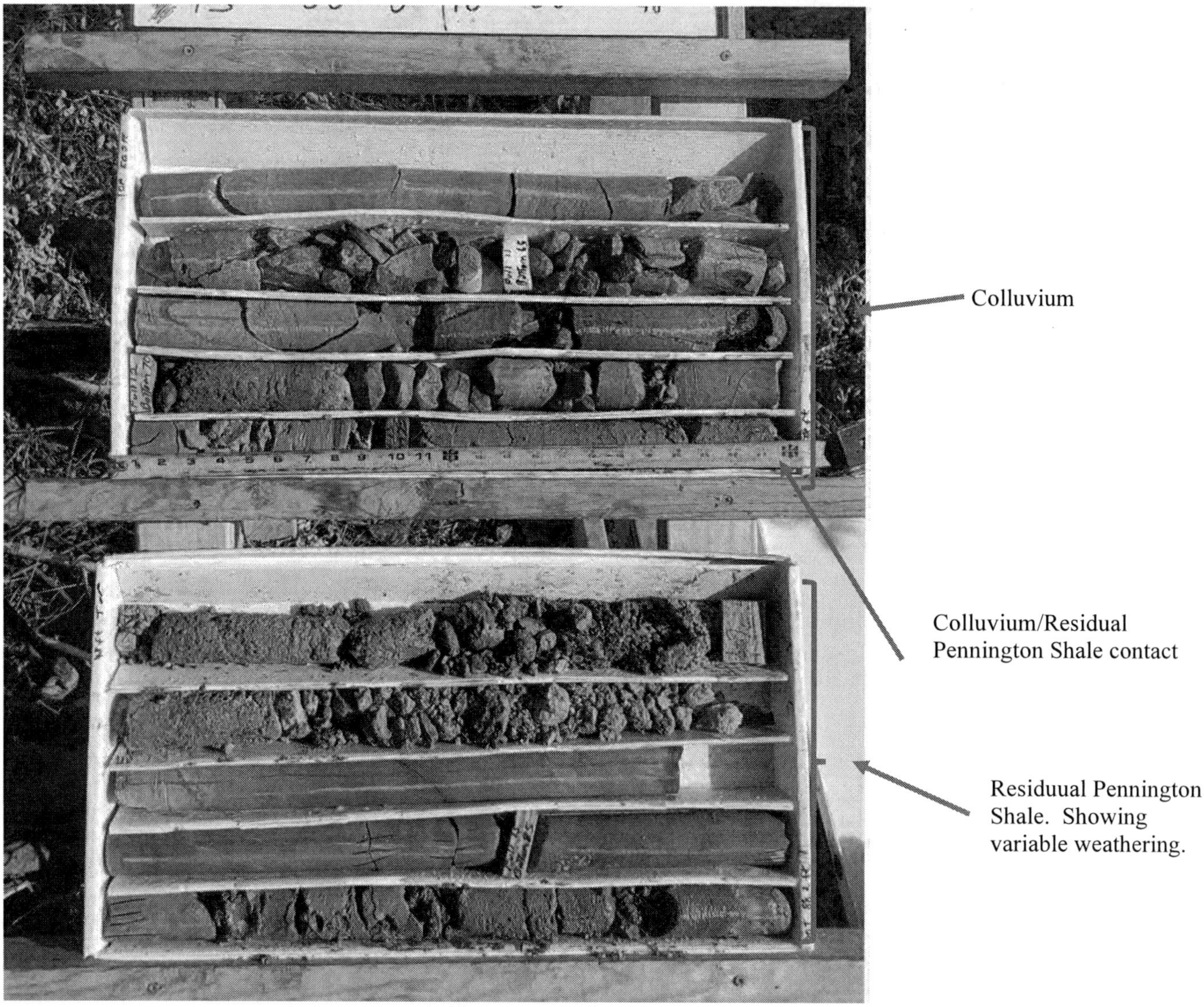

Where recovered, soils within the Colluvium were usually described as light orange-brown clayey sand, sandy clay with trace gravel, or as a gravel. Clay rich samples were described as soft and firm.

Difficult drilling was typical in this formation, with loss of drilling fluid, interspersed rock and clay layers, voids, lost tooling and sections with no sample recovery recorded. Grout takes for monitoring installations were large and surpassed multiple theoretical volumes.

Residual Soils

Residual soils can occur in all bedrock-types but are most notable in the shaly units, i.e., Pennington Shale. The thickness of the residual soils developed on the Pennington Shale was variable. Residual soils directly under the landslide areas were deepest in B-25 where 50 feet of residual soil was observed. Average residual soil thickness below Colluvium was about 15 feet. Residual Soil was generally a grey to yellowish red brown, low to high plasticity clay, or clayey or silty sand.

Pennington Formation
In the project area, the Pennington Formation is divided into an upper sandstone member (Pennington Sandstone) that overlies a shale member (Pennington Shale). The two lithologies are described below.

Pennington Sandstone Member
The Pennington Sandstone member is a 100-foot-thick unit and forms the upper boundary of the Mississippian system. The sandstone is exposed in roadcuts along the north side of the westbound lane in the eastern and western parts of the study area, **Figure 5**. The Pennington Sandstone member was typically observed as fresh to moderately weathered, thin to thick bedded, tan to white, fine- to medium-grained, micaceous, weak- to medium-strong, sandstone.

Borehole recoveries were typically over 60% with rock quality designation (RQD) usually between 40% and 60%. Occasionally, the sandstone was recorded as weak and could be interbedded with weathered clay beds (shale). Defining the boundary between the overlying Colluvium and Pennington Sandstone member was difficult in boreholes through the slide mass above the westbound lane due to the size of large, detached blocks of Pennington Sandstone within the Colluvium, which can appear as in-place bedrock.

Figure 5: Photograph of the Pennington Sandstone member along the westbound lane. (photograph looking northwest)

Pennington Shale Member
The Pennington Shale member is exposed north of the westbound lane towards the eastern boundary of the study area, **Figure 6,** and was encountered in borings below the Colluvium or Pennington Sandstone member along the westbound lane and in the median. Throughout the region, the Pennington Shale member is comprised of shale, mudstone, claystone, limestone and

minor calcareous sandstone. Although lithologies are highly variable, most lithologies are highly colored varying from maroon to dark red to green.

Figure 6: Photograph of an outcrop of the weathered Pennington Shale member in a roadcut along the westbound lane. Seeps and ravelling can be seen in the outcrop (geological hammer for scale).

The Pennington Shale member is variable in composition and weathering characteristics. Highly weathered shales, recorded as clay and similar to residual soils previously described, are commonly observed between more competent Pennington shale beds. The Pennington Shale member was observed as red brown, tan, gray, and usually described as a very weak to weak or weak to medium strong shale. RQDs ranged from <10% at a depth of over 100 feet, to >80%. Typically, RQD ranged from 15% to 45%.

Results from the geophysics generally showed good correlation with the borehole logs and mapping, **Figure 7**. Geophysical ERI profiles across the site indicate that the continuity of the Pennington Shale member is broken by narrow, vertical zones of higher resistivity. A boring drilled in one of the vertical features displayed very poor returns until around 80 feet. Voids, sometimes with a clay infill; flowing sands; and artesian groundwater flow were also recorded during drilling in the Pennington Shale member.

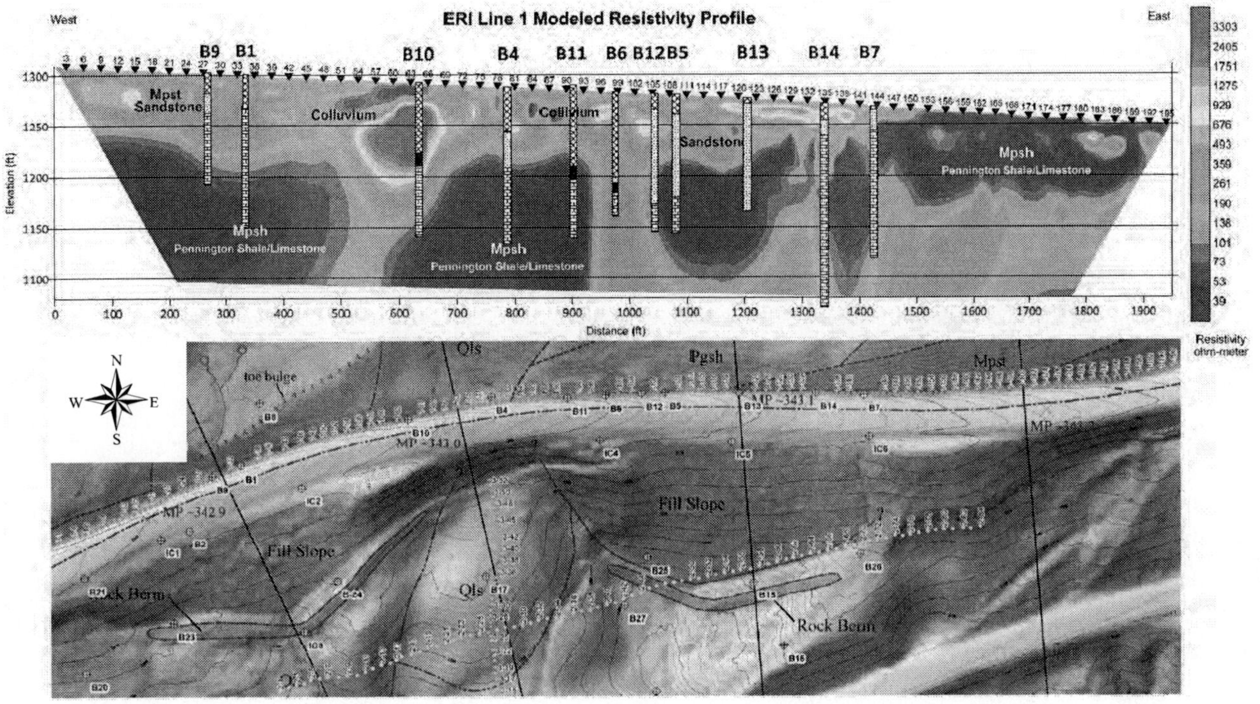

Figure 7: Geophysical ERI results compared to geologic map and boring data. The ERI profile showed a good resolution and correlation with physical data and was used as part of the 3D geological model.

Gizzard Group

The Gizzard Group overlies the Pennington Sandstone member and crops out on the slopes north of the westbound lane. The Gizzard Group comprises interbedded sandstone and shale units. In the slide area, the Gizzard Group was divided into an upper and lower sandstone member which are separated by shale units.

The upper sandstone member is locally conglomeratic, fine- to coarse-grained, feldspathic and cross bedded. The shale between the upper and lower member is typically light-gray to tan, silty, thin bedded and locally contains thin sandstone interbeds. The lower sandstone member is fine- to medium-grained, feldspathic, thin- to thick-bedded and contains iron-oxide cements along the bedding planes.

Recoveries in the lower sandstone were typically 80% or higher but the unit did have zones with RQDs below 20%. Recoveries in the shale were typically high, over 80% with RQDs generally at or higher than 50%.

Suwannee Conglomerate

The Suwannee Conglomerate was observed along the crest of Walden Ridge. The Suwannee is mostly a gray to brown, feldspathic, thick-bedded, well jointed, conglomeratic sandstone and sandstone that locally contains pebbles up to 1 inch (2.54 cm) in diameter.

Geologic Structures-
During geologic mapping of the project area, planar features (bedding and joints) were observed and measured. Lower-hemisphere, equal-area stereonet analysis of bedding and joint sets have the flowing average orientations:

- Bedding 31°/345° (data presented as dip, dip direction)
- Dip Joint 83°/249° (joints that run parallel to direction of dip)
- Strike Joint 68°/163° (joints that run parallel to direction of strike i.e., perpendicular to direction of dip)

In the eastern part of the landslide-complex above the westbound lane, bedding has been rotated approximately 33° (to 54°) due to rotational movement of the slide block.

Groundwater
Groundwater conditions at the site are considered to be complex and influenced by perched groundwater; different groundwater levels between strata; the heterogeneity of Colluvium; differences in permeability between Colluvium and Residual Soil; original, natural topographic drainage patterns now infilled and covered with Colluvium and Fill; surface and subsurface drainage of the I-40; and historical horizontal drains in the median.

Each piezometer and standpipe targeted a specific stratum and the data showed groundwater levels can differ between strata. Interpreted potentiometric contours based on elevations within the Colluvium and Colluvium/ Residual Soil interface were used to create a potentiometric surface. This showed groundwater generally follows topography and flows downwards to the southeast. The potentiometric surface generally matches the slope gradient in the central and eastern areas of the site.

The potentiometric map indicates that groundwater in the western slide appears to be at a higher elevation than in the central and eastern slides. Springs were observed in the slopes of the Western Slide above the westbound lane. The potentiometric surface was added to the geological model.

DISCUSSION OF INSTRUMENTATION AND LABORATORY DATA

Instrument Installation
Inclinometer casings, 2.75-inch diameter, were installed in six borings at the completion of drilling. Grout was lost in boreholes and, in most cases, attributed to voids within the Colluvium. This required multiple stages of grouting and occasional bentonite addition to fill the annulus to the ground surface.

Twenty-two vibrating wire piezometers (VWP) were installed in 12 borings. Between one and three VWP were installed within each of the 12 borings. The VWPs were installed within softer zones of material, geologic contacts – in particular, the Colluvium/residual soil contact or the Residual Soil/Pennington rock contact – or where there was a presence of water, with the ultimate goal of determining the pore pressure at the failure interface. Standpipe piezometers were installed in six boreholes.

Inclinometer Results

Inclinometer displacements were measured at the apparent shear zone from January to March 2020. The inclinometer data often showed a slow creep prior to more displacement. The displacement rate between January and March 2020 increased significantly and displaced an average of about 0.1 inches per month. A summary of the inclinometer data is shown in **Table 1**.

Table 1: Summary of inclinometer data showing shear zone depth, lithology, and cumulative displacement from January to March 2020.

Boring ID	Displacement Depth (ft-bgs)	Lithology at Apparent Shear Zone Displacement	Cumulative Displacement (in)
INC-01	38-42	Residual Soil	0.4
INC-02	58-62	Residual Soil	0.3
INC-03	46-50	Residual Soil	0.3
INC-04	-	-	NA
INC-05	90-94	Colluvium/Pennington Formation	0.2
INC-06	38-42	Residual Soil/ Pennington Formation	0.1

The inclinometer data showed all displacement was deeper than 38 feet bgs (inclinometer locations are shown in **Figure 2**. Correlation with boring data indicates the base of the slides occurs in the soft Residual Soil or at the interface of Colluvium and Pennington Formation.

Laboratory Data and Material Properties

Soil and rock samples were collected during the drilling investigation. Laboratory tests and *in situ* observations included triaxial consolidated undrained and drained, direct shear, natural moisture, plasticity index, RQD, recovery, unconfined compressive strength (UCS), and engineering descriptions of soil and rock. These data were used for the back analysis, which was used to obtain material parameters for geotechnical design.

Failure Mechanisms

The failure mechanism for each landslide differs slightly. The main influencing factors are: Differential weathering, the Pennington Sandstone member, accumulation of colluvial material, differing permeabilities between Colluvium and underlying residual soils of the Pennington Shale member, and low shear strength properties of the Pennington Formation residual soils.

Differential Weathering

The massive sandstones of the overlying Gizzard Group are pervasively undercut in scarp slopes as the Gizzard Group shale weathers and the sandstone is released along a strike parallel joint (strike joint). After continued undercutting the sandstones eventually fail, predominantly along their strike joint, **Figure 8**. This failure mechanism appeared to have occurred as recently as 2010/2011 in the Western Landslide. Elongated boulders up to 30-feet-long from recent rockfall failure north of westbound lane were observed during geologic mapping.

Figure 8: Example of differential weathering and strike parallel jointing in the Gizzard Group.

Influence of the Pennington Sandstone Member
The Pennington Sandstone member is massive and appears to act temporarily as a retaining structure confining the landslides to the overlying Gizzard Group, as seen in the west of the site, **Figure 2**. Sufficient loading and undercutting from weathering of the Pennington Shale member can cause Pennington Sandstone member to fail as has occurred in the Western and Central slides. The thickness and massive structure of the Pennington Sandstone member combined with the overlying landslide material, can result in a large failure with a thick accumulation of Colluvium downslope.

Accumulation of Colluvium
Continued failures caused by differential weathering result in the accumulation of Colluvium. The Colluvium drapes the hillside. The elevation of the base of the Colluvium can be varied because it can infill the original topography.

Differing Permeabilities Between Colluvium and Underlying Residual Soil
The residual soil derived from the Pennington Shale member has a low permeability. The overlying Colluvium is generally unconsolidated with grain sizes ranging from clay to large boulders and generally has a higher permeability than the underlying residual soil. This causes a scenario with groundwater accumulating at the base of the Colluvium and saturating the residual soil.

Low shear strength properties of the Pennington Shale Member Residual Soil
The Pennington Shale member is typically a varied calcareous shale, mudstone, and sandstone with beds of limestone. The shale can weather to a weak, highly plastic, impermeable clay. The

weathering zone is variable and weathered zones can occur at depth within otherwise strong rock. The highly plastic, weak clay combined with the groundwater, steep slopes, residual shear strength from creep and historical failures and loaded with Colluvium results in a slope that is highly susceptible to landslides.

Landslide Geomorphology
The individual landslides, referenced below, and geology are shown on the geologic map in **Figure 2,** and the geologic cross-sections are shown in **Figure 3.**

Slide I (Eastern Slide, Figure 3 D – D')
The Eastern Slide is at the east and directly below the westbound lane. The Eastern Slide is thought to extend at least to the most-eastern crack observed in the westbound lane. The head scarp for the Eastern Slide is not exposed as it is overlain by Fill material from construction of I-40. Borehole data appears to indicate the Eastern Slide has the deepest areas of Colluvium at the site. The southern extent of Colluvium was also not delineated as it appears to extend downslope, beyond the eastbound lane. A cross-section through Slide I is shown in **Figure 3, Section D – D',** below the westbound lane.

Slide II (Slump, Figure 3 D – D')
The Slump overlies the Pennington Sandstone member above the Eastern Slide. Based on historical photographs, the Slump is believed to have been caused by removal of the Pennington Sandstone during construction. A cross-section through Slide II is shown in **Figure 3, Section D – D',** above the westbound lane.

The Slump is a slide within the Gizzard Group and considered to be a relatively shallow. The location of the head scarp is not clear. As the Gizzard Group sandstone is displaced and the Suwanee Conglomerate not displaced, the head scarp is currently between these two units. The head scarp is mapped at the base of the Suwanee Conglomerate. The Slump extends down to the top of the Pennington Sandstone member outcrop in the east. As the Pennington Sandstone outcrop is hidden further west, the extent of the Slump is not clear, but thought to extend below the westbound lane.

The displaced mappable units were traced across the slopes of Roane Mountain east and west the Site. Geologic mapping indicated the vertical displacement of the Gizzard Group sandstone ranged from a few feet in the east to approximately 50 feet in the west of the Slump. The displaced sandstone also appeared rotated 33°, with bedding dipping at an angle of 54° compared to an average of 31° for the regional bedding.

In the eastern part of the Slump, the Pennington Sandstone member separates the Slump from the underlying Eastern Slide. In this area, the Slump is not considered to be directly loading the Eastern Slide.

In the western part of the Slump, the greater displacement may be because the slump overrides part of Slide III in this area. As the Slide III appears to have removed the Pennington Sandstone member, the Slump is considered to be directly loading the landslide lower down the slope.

Slide III (Central Slide, Figure 3, C – C')

The Central slide is in the approximate center of the site and above the westbound lane. The head scarp is near the Pennsylvanian Gizzard Group Sandstone, about mid-slope between the westbound lane and ridge crest. The slide has a relatively flat topography in the mid and toe section in the median. The head of the Central slide rises steeply towards the head scarp. The southern extent of Colluvium is near the road cut for the eastbound lane. The slide seems to have occurred relatively early as adjoining slides appear to cut through the original slope morphology. A cross-section through Slide III is shown in **Figure 3, Section C – C'**.

Slide IV (Western Slide, Figure 3, B – B'))

The Western slide is directly west of the central slide. The head scarp extends to the top of the ridge in the Suwanee Conglomerate, **Figure 9**. The Western slide appears more as draped Colluvium over the Pennington Formation as compared to the deeper Central and Eastern slides. The head scarp appears to have retreated as recently as 2010/2011 based on Google Earth aerial photographs.

A ridge of displaced sandstone boulders can be seen along the surface of the slide, above the westbound lane. This is thought to be displaced Gizzard Group Sandstone from further up the slope. The western edge of the slide coincides with the western crack observed in the westbound lane. The edge is marked by an outcrop of in-place Pennington Sandstone member along the westbound lane. The southern extent of Colluvium is near the road cut for the eastbound lane. A cross-section through Slide IV is shown in **Figure 3, Section B – B'**.

Figure 9: Large blocks of Suwanee Conglomerate from rockfall at the crest of the Slide IV. Blocks are overgrown with vegetation. For scale, the blocks are mini-bus size.

Slide V (Far-Western Slide)

Slide V is the furthest west and entirely above the westbound lane. The southward trajectory of the slide appears to have been limited by the Pennington Sandstone member. The slide cuts through the Gizzard Group sandstone member. This slide does not appear to impact the westbound lane and so was not investigated as part of the project.

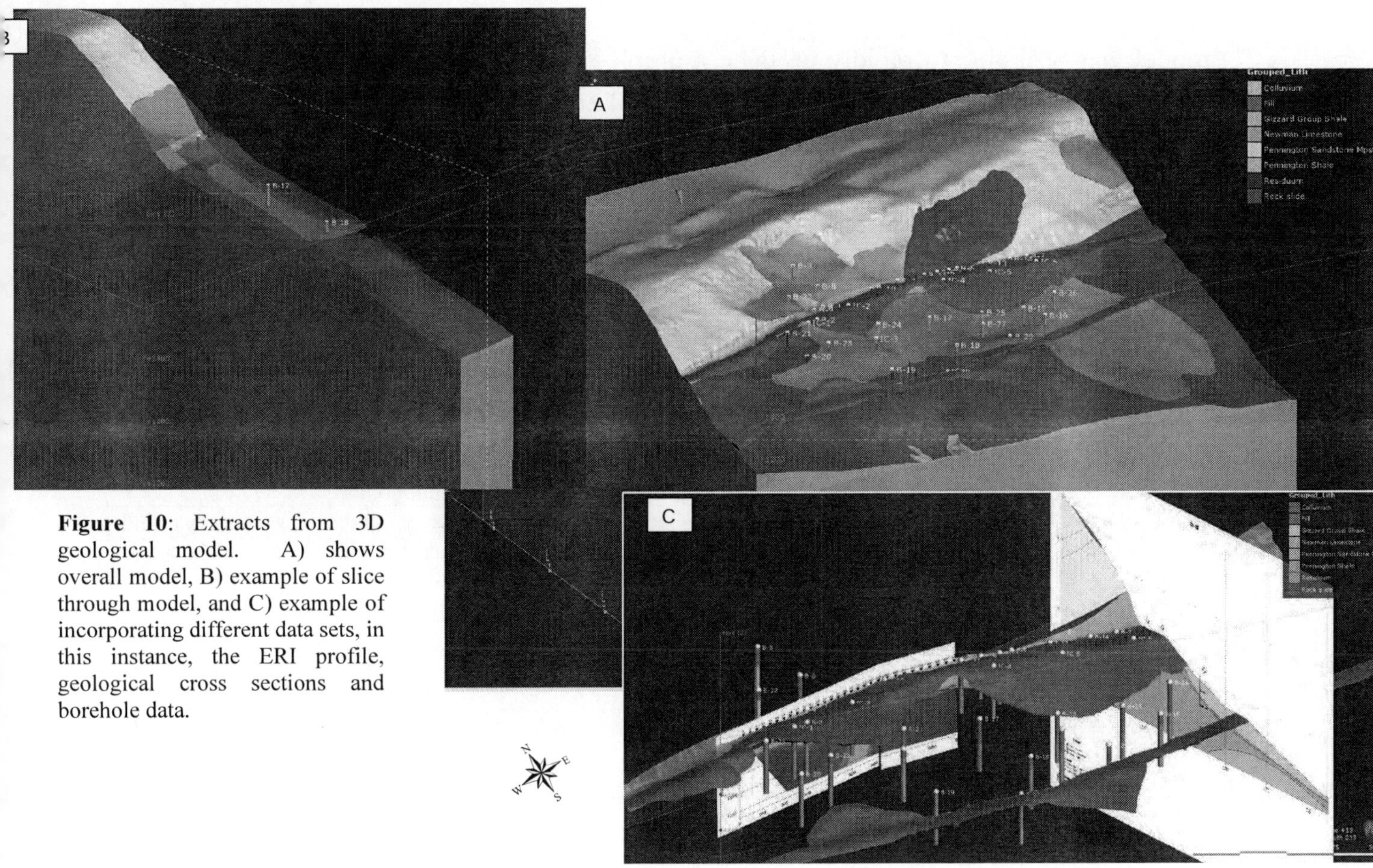

Figure 10: Extracts from 3D geological model. A) shows overall model, B) example of slice through model, and C) example of incorporating different data sets, in this instance, the ERI profile, geological cross sections and borehole data.

GEOLOGICAL MODEL

Using Leapfrog to create a 3D model was critical to project success. The complex spatial distribution and critical depth of problem soils (i.e., Fill, Colluvium and Residual Soils), a variable slip surface and the competent units (i.e., Pennington Sandstone member used for anchoring) were fundamental to the stability analysis and engineering design.

Interpretation of these parameters was dependent on an understanding on the complex geomorphology, failure mechanisms and landslide history. The model needed to incorporate varied types of data, such as longitudinal geophysical profiles, vertical boring logs, inclinometer data and geological mapping A 3D modelling tool like Leapfrog, allowed the multiple datasets to be integrated and interpreted with a knowledge of the landslide geomorphology, **Figure 10**.

A 3D model was also able to rapidly produce multiple sections that were imported to CAD to create surfaces that were used for design sheets and imported into SLIDE (RocScience, 2018) for 2D analysis.

A summary of the problems encountered with a large complex landslide and the benefits of incorporating the data into a 3D model are shown in **Table 2**.

Table 2: Summary of Problems and Solutions of Using a 3D Model for Complex Landslide Projects

Problem	Solution by Using 3D Model
Variable types of data sets, i.e., vertical borings logs, linear ERI profiles and geological mapping	Multiple data sets could be combined to help understand spatial relationships
Large complex landslide geometry and distant data points	Data could be combined into single model and allow interpretation between data points
Variable location and depth of problem soils and stable materials	Geological interpretations, landslide history and geomorphology combined with field data in model to predict distribution of key (i.e., Colluvium, Fill, Residual Soil, base of slip surface, stable sandstone for anchoring)
Multiple slope stability sections required	Can rapidly cut multiple sections and import into other computer programs
Additional data added to project after the model has been created	3D modelling program allows additional data to be added, model alternations and recut sections quickly and easily.

DISCUSSION OF ENGINEERING ANALYSIS AND MITIGATION DESIGN

Back Analysis

Back analysis was performed at twelve cross-sections to estimate the average mobilized shear strength of the Residual Soil and Colluvium for the site. The two-dimensional generalized limit equilibrium (GLE) method was used and was implemented in the software program SLIDE (RocScience, 2018). Where available, inclinometer data was used to guide the failure surface.

The results of the back analysis are provided in **Table 3**.

Table 3: Geotechnical Design Parameters Derived from Back Analysis

Material	Dry Unit Weight (pcf)	Moist Unit Weight (pcf)	Cohesion (psf)	Effective Friction Angle (°)
Fill	125	133	150	33
Colluvium (above WB*)	120	130	100	25 to 38
Colluvium (below WB*)	120	128	150	11 to 19.5
Residual Soil	115	125	150	11 to 19.5
Pennington Sandstone	145	150	N/A	N/A
Pennington Shale	145	150	N/A	N/A

*WB = Westbound Lane

Forward Analysis and Anchor Design

Ground anchors were used for the slope mitigation design. The anchor rows, bonded and unbonded length, inclination, and spacing varied depending on the force requirements and relative location of the stratigraphic units. Example anchor layouts are shown in **Figure 11**.

In general, the application of the ground model was used to design ground anchors that extended beyond the slip surface into the Pennington Shale member, or higher up the slope, extended into the Pennington Sandstone member.

The method used to determine the required anchor stabilization forces was in general accordance with the limit equilibrium approach from Sabatini, et al. (1999). Anchor loads were applied as concentrated active forces resisting motion. The resulting critical failure surface and FS under the loads applied was evaluated to achieve a FS greater than 1.3. Compared to back analyses, some sections with anchor stabilization had about the same or deeper failure surfaces due to applied active forces. The required anchor force ranged from 25 to 285 kip/ft.

Anchor Design Considerations

Three different size ground anchors, with three, seven, and nine-strands were selected for stabilization. Factors contributing to the anchor design are:

- Single anchor capacity
- Anchor spacing
- Anchor length
- Anchor protection

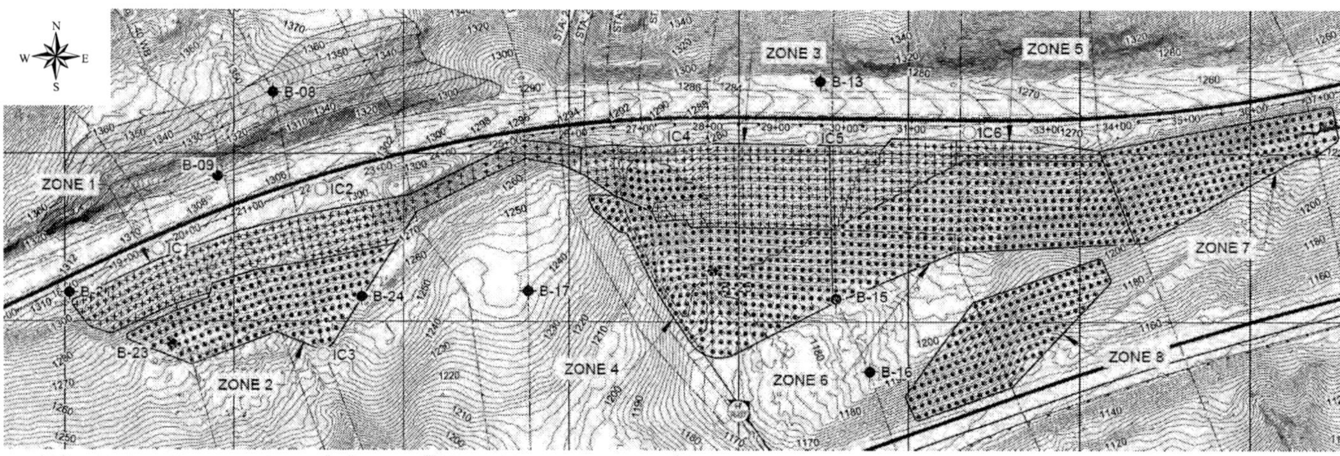

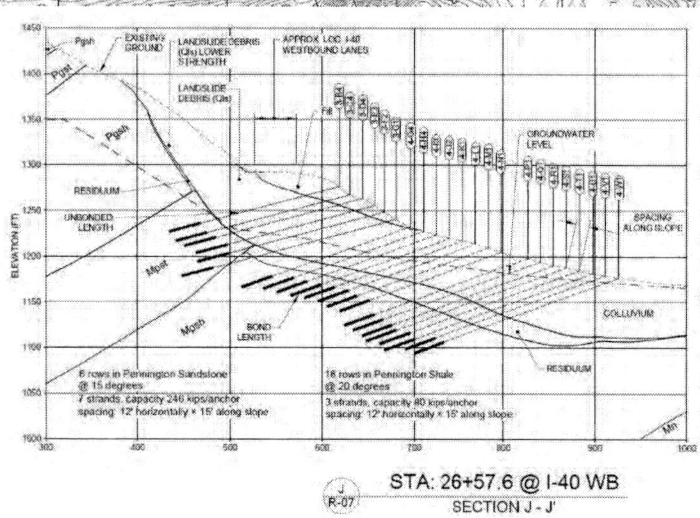

Figure 11 Example of anchor layout and cross-sections. Anchor free length, bonded length and inclination are shown as well as target lithologies below the cirtical slip surface into Pennington Shale or Pennington Sandstone members.

Single Anchor Capacity
Pullout resistance was estimated using engineering experience and published data.

The Penington Shale member was characterized as a soft shale because of the weathering characteristics observed resulting in an estimated grout to ground ultimate bond strength of 5 kips per square foot (ksf, ~35psi). A value of 22 ksf (~150 psi) was used for the ultimate anchor bond strength in the competent Pennington Sandstone. The ultimate anchor bond strengths were within American Association of State Highway and Transportation Officials (AASHTO) recommended limits.

For tendon capacity, the maximum design tendon load was 60% of the ultimate load of the selected tendon (Ground Engineering Systems, Williams Form Engineering Corp, No.116.2). The design loads for ground anchors in the shale were limited by the pullout capacity and the design loads for ground anchors in sandstone were limited by anchor block bearing capacity. A summary of anchor details are included in **Table 4**.

Table 4: Summary of Tendons, Anchor Bond Strength and Design Loads

Load Bearing Stratum	Anchor Size	Minimum Hole Diameter	Assumed Bond Strength (ksf)	Maximum Design Load (kips)
Pennington Shale	3-strand	4.5 in	5	80
Pennington Sandstone	7-strand	4.5 in	22	246
	9-strand	5.6 in	22	317

Anchor Spacing
The Pennington Shale had a low bond strength and because of the large stabilization forces required the spacing was designed at 12 feet horizontally and 15 feet along slope face.

Anchor (Minimum Free) Length
The total length of each anchor is the sum of the free or unbonded length and bond length. The miminum free length was determined by 1) extending anchors to a distance 15 feet into the estimated surface of load-bearing bedrock and past the critical failure plane by at least 15 feet, and 2) at a distance in the appropriate ground (rock) and at a sufficient depth to provide necessary overburden pressure for rock wedge stability.

CONCLUSION
Early geological mapping was key to the success of this project. The early geological model was critical in understanding the problem and directing the solution, from the field investigation through to the detailed design.

The project was also able to successfully combine the field mapping with a range of ground investigation data, including drilling core logs, inclinometer data, laboratory data and geophysical transects into a single 3D model. This allowed visualization of the problem and made for a much efficient and accurate analysis and design.

The project also highlighted the importance of good soil and rock core logging and experienced geological interpretation. This was most critical in the colluvial material which contained up to 100 feet of reworked native deposits.

The engineering mitigation design included a series of tiebacks anchored below the slip surface into the Pennington Formation shale and the more competent sandstone member

REFERENCES

- Reports
  1. Golder Associates USA Inc., I-40 Landslide Evaluation, Rockwood, Roane County, Tennessee, Phase 1 Report, Project No. 07390089-01. October 19, 2009
  2. Golder Associates USA Inc., 2016. Emergency Drainage System Construction, Geotechnical Exploration, and Slope Stabilization Recommendations, I-40 MP 342 Landslide Evaluation, Phase 2, Roane County. Project No. 07390089-01. March 11, 2016.
  3. Golder Associates USA Inc., Geotechnical Report. I-40 Westbound Landslide Remediation Near Milepost 342 at Rockwood Mountain. 19122349. May 2020.
  4. Law Engineering Testing Company. Report of Landslide Investigation, Interstate Highway Project I-40-6 (40) 340, Roane County, Tennessee. Project No. EC-239. June 25, 1969
- Federal Government Report
  1. American Association of State Highway and Transportation Officials (AASHTO) Load and Resistance Factor Design LRFD Bridge Design Specifications, Ninth Edition, Publication No. 978-1-6051-738-2 LRFDBDS-9. 2020.
- Computer Program
  1. Rocscience. *SLIDE*, Version 8.016. 2018
- Conference Proceedings
  1. Royster, D.L., 1973. Highway Landslide Problems Associated with the Escarpment Areas of the Cumberland Plateau in Tennessee. Proceedings of the 24th Highway Geology Symposium, Sheridan, Wyoming, p. 3-23. August 9-10, 1973.
- Maps
  1. Tiedemann, H.A., Jewell, J.W., and Swingle, G.D. Geologic Map and Mineral Resources Summary of the Cardiff Quadrangle, 1:24,000-scale, Tennessee Division of Geology. 1965
  2. United States Geological Survey, 1:24,000-scale topographic map, Cardiff, TN. 2010

Accelerated Geotechnical Investigation of the Sterling Highway Realignment – Cooper Landing, Alaska:

Adam Koslofsky, R.G., C.E.G.
Landslide Technology (a division of Cornforth Consultants, Inc.)
10250 SW Greenburg Rd, Ste 111
Portland, OR 97223
(503)-452-1200
adamk@landslidetechnology.com

Logan Allender, P.E.
Landslide Technology (a division of Cornforth Consultants, Inc.)
10250 SW Greenburg Rd, Ste 111
Portland, OR 97223
(503)-452-1200
logana@landslidetechnology.com

Darren Beckstrand, R.G., C.E.G., C.P.G.
Landslide Technology (a division of Cornforth Consultants, Inc.)
10250 SW Greenburg Rd, Ste 111
Portland, OR 97223
(503)-452-1200
darrenb@landslidetechnology.com

Keri Nutter, C.P.G.
DOWL, LLC.
4041 B Street
Anchorage, AK 99503
(907)-562-2000
knutter@dowl.com

Prepared for the 71st Highway Geology Symposium, May, 2022

Acknowledgements

The author(s) would like to thank the individuals/entities for their contributions in the work described:

Mitch Miller, PE - Alaska DOT&PF
Jonathan Tymick, PE – Alaska DOT&PF
DOWL Project Design Team

Disclaimer

Statements and views presented in this paper are strictly those of the author(s), and do not necessarily reflect positions held by their affiliations, the Highway Geology Symposium (HGS), or others acknowledged above. The mention of trade names for commercial products does not imply the approval or endorsement by HGS.

Copyright Notice

ABSTRACT

The Alaska Department of Transportation & Public Facilities (DOT&PF) is realigning a 15-mile section of the Sterling Highway on the Kenai Peninsula, southwest of Anchorage, Alaska. An initial timeline for the CM/GC project required geotechnical investigations to commence in 2020, with a desired project completion date in late 2024. Landslide Technology was part of a team with DOWL selected to conduct the geotechnical investigations. The efforts to execute this geotechnical investigation program presented an opportunity to develop mapping and management systems to deliver exploration results to the project team in nearly real-time, and allow DOT&PF to advance their goal of rapid design and construction on a CM/GC project.

Subsurface explorations across undeveloped backcountry were performed between June and December 2020, with winter-access drilling occurring between March and April 2021. A total of 218 borings, 105 test pits, and 516 peat probes comprising 15,789 feet of drilling were completed and logged by thirteen engineers and geologists from the design team and DOT&PF. Up to five drill rigs and 24-hour shifts operated concurrently during 2020, requiring up to seven inspectors during a 24-hour period. Overland access limitations and challenges included muskeg/wetlands, steep slopes, and culturally/environmentally restricted areas.

The project's concurrent progress with design and construction required rapid updates of progress, summary logs, lab testing results, and daily coordination between agencies, consultants, and contractors. ArcGIS Online and ESRI's Collector App were used to map test hole locations, adjust exploration plans based on field results, populate drill progress dashboards, and quickly present data to the design team via a map interface.

INTRODUCTION

The Sterling Highway connects Southcentral Alaska to the Kenai Peninsula. Cooper Landing is a popular fishing and wildlife watching destination 100 miles south of Anchorage. Recreational opportunities draw thousands along the Sterling Highway as it follows the winding Kenai River. The high traffic volume and narrow, winding road contribute to congestion and numerous traffic incidents. To mitigate these safety concerns and anticipated traffic volumes, the Alaska DOT&PF plans to construct a 15 mile corridor realignment north of the existing highway; a key element of the project is a more than 800-foot single span bridge over the Juneau Creek Canyon near the corridor midpoint. The realignment will divert traffic around the town of Cooper Landing and the Kenai River through previously undeveloped wilderness and US Forest Service Land as shown in Figure 1.

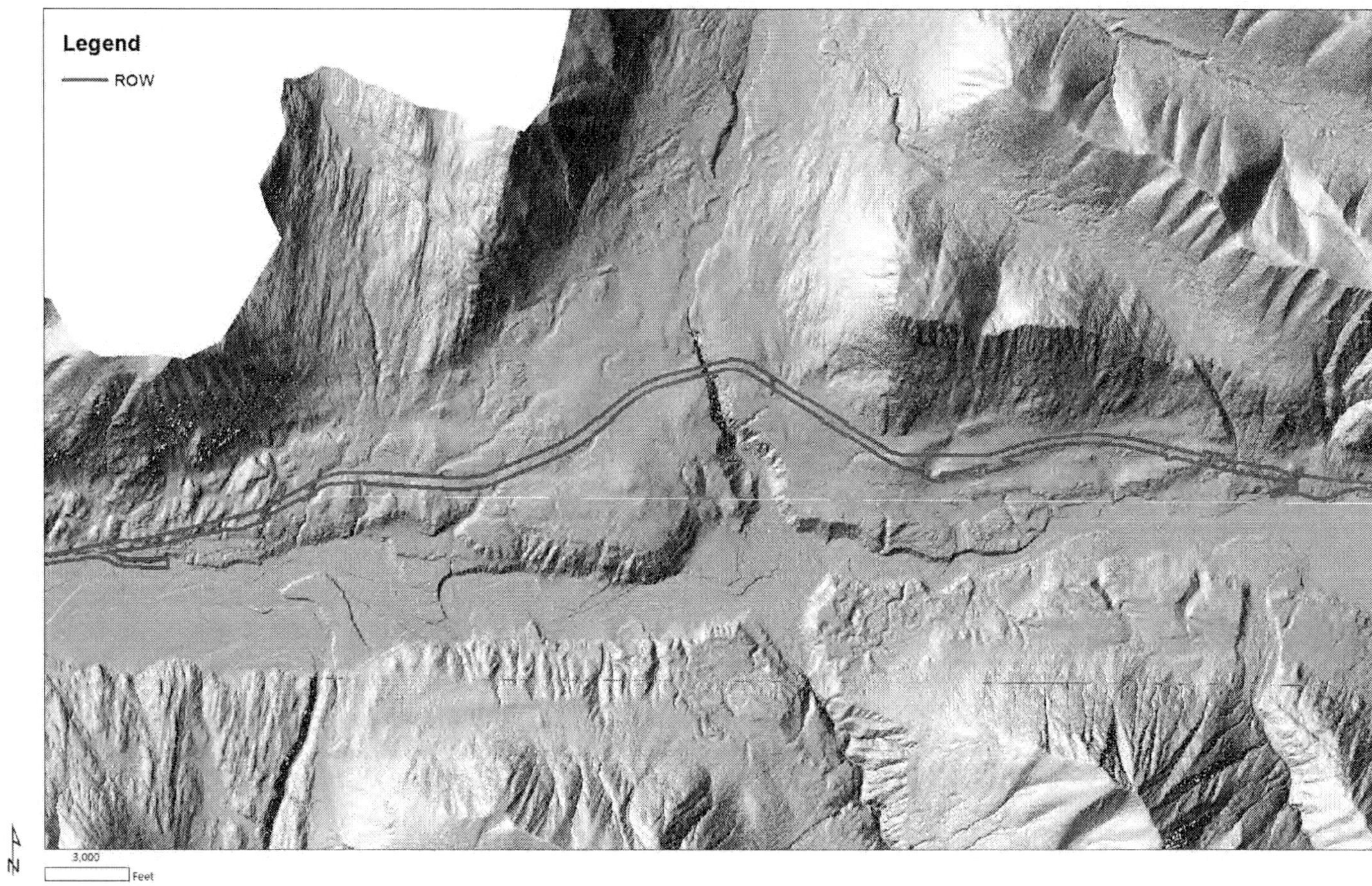

Figure 1 – Sterling Highway Realignment

The geotechnical design team was tasked with completing a fast-paced geotechnical investigation to help Alaska DOT&PF meet an accelerated design and construction schedule. To meet the initial project design schedule, multiple drilling teams were deployed along the project corridor to quickly collect data along the first seven miles of the project corridor in June 2020; this required multiple drilling subcontractors and engineers and geologists working on shift-based schedules. The challenges the design team faced included a large number of borings and test pits, difficult access, limited working windows, sharing data quickly with multiple partners, changing designs and right-of-way limits, and multiple subcontracted drilling teams.

To help mitigate the challenges faced by the CM/GC team, the geotechnical team utilized ArcGIS Online along with the Collector App to share information, modify investigations, and coordinate with the engineers and geologists conducting the subsurface investigations.

Additionally, this large field-based effort commenced during the first months of the SARS-CoV-2 pandemic, which added an unanticipated level of field logistics and worker health and safety to be overcome with travel logistics, limited available lodging, the remote project location, and continually evolving requirements from government entities (CDC, OSHA, DOT&PF, etc.) and private employers' safety plans.

EXPLORATION PLANNING

The geotechnical design team of Landslide Technology (LT) and DOWL were tasked with planning and implementing a geotechnical investigation of the realignment. To prepare for the fieldwork, LT and DOWL overlaid the cut/fill limits with LiDAR imaging and placed that into ArcGIS Online. Subsurface exploration locations were selected based on FHWA recommended guidelines regarding spacing, proposed structures, and anticipated access and potential drill pads. An example of planned explorations is shown in Figure 2.

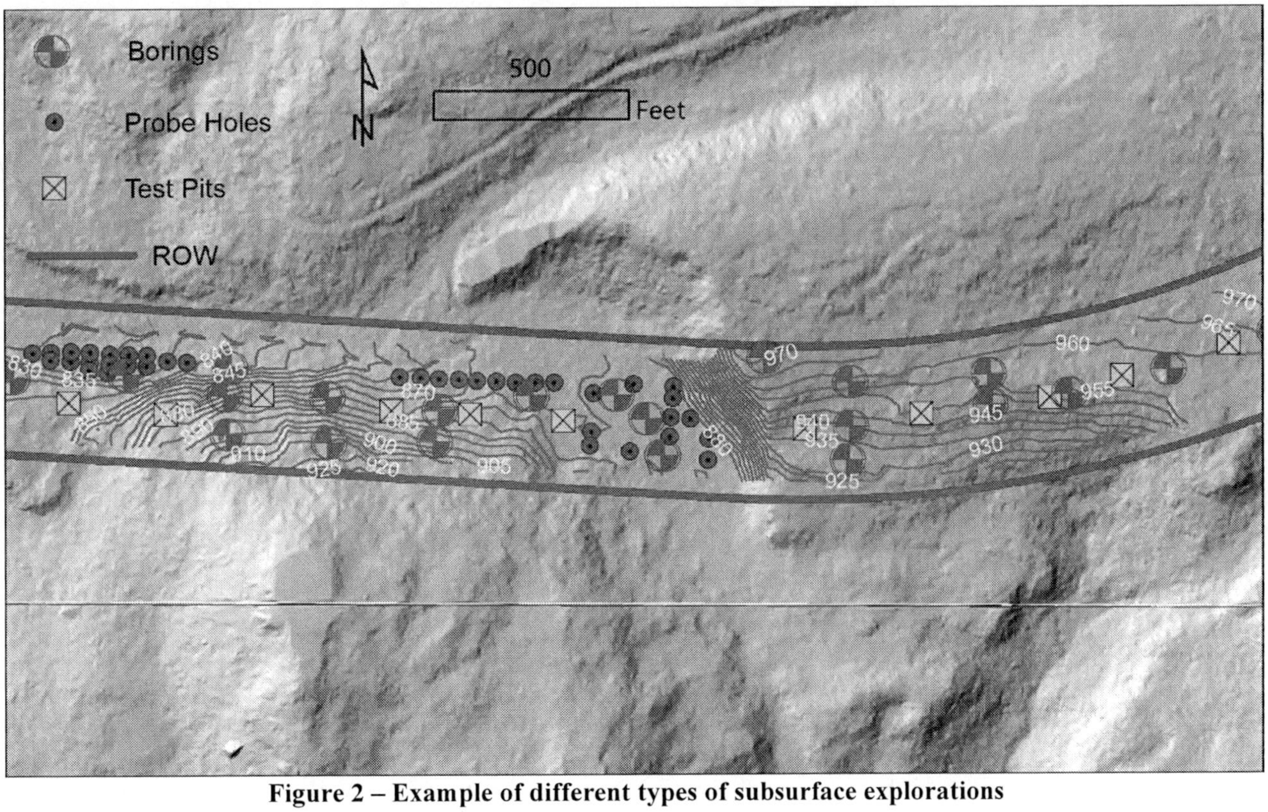

Figure 2 – Example of different types of subsurface explorations

Placing the borings into ArcGIS Online automatically geolocates the planned exploration locations. Detailed attributes were assigned to each position, including planned depths, purpose, instrumentation, station and offset, elevation, drill type and access. This information was accessible via both ArcGIS Online, and the Collector App, as shown in Figure 3, that allowed inspectors to quickly and efficiently locate and edit borings in the field. Map and data were accessible both online and offline.

EXPLORATIONS

Prior to the start of the drilling program, a reconnaissance was performed to ground truth the planned explorations, identify access issues, and stake locations. The reconnaissance team used Android OS tablets and the Collector App to field truth and test both the exploration locations and application. No active cellular or internet connection was needed once the project had been successfully loaded.

Following reconnaissance efforts, tree clearing crews began clearing the planned alignment for access and preconstruction activities. Many of the stakes used to mark exploration locations were damaged or lost during the clearing activities, but the georeferenced locations on ArcGIS Online and the Collector App made relocating the planned explorations simple and quick.

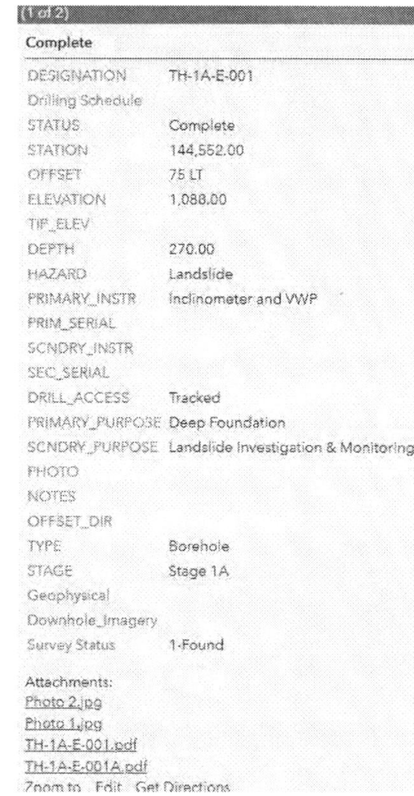

Figure 3 – Example of data entered for borings

Explorations included several drilling and coring techniques, downhole oriented imagery, several inclinometers and piezometer installations, and downhole seismic for critical structures. Test pits, peat probes, and borings were all conducted simultaneously. Test pit and peat probe results were used to modify the drilling program for access and changes to schedule, specifically in the large muskeg areas observed onsite. Three drilling subcontractors and the State of Alaska were onsite with up to five drill rigs with two drill rigs running 24-hour shifts beginning in June 2020. LT and DOWL rotated a group of up to seven engineers and geologists. LT supplied full time field management to coordinate subsurface explorations, perform quality control, generate summary boring and test pit logs, and select samples for laboratory testing.

With so many explorations underway simultaneously and the need to share information in near real-time with the CM/GC team, the use of ArcGIS Online allowed rapid delivery of summary logs, lab results, and other critical information. Exploration locations were adjusted in the field as needed based on access limitations or changing project requirements. Borings and test pits were assigned to drill crews as determined by ability and availability of the drilling crew and equipment. Explorations were initially tagged as "Not Started" until a rig was in position to begin the exploration. The tag was changed to "Started/Not Complete" and designated with a name, and a yellow highlight to show work had begun. Upon completion of the exploration (including any instrumentation or backfilling) the tag was changed to "Completed" and given a green highlight. Each of these designations cued a different highlight on the online mapping platform to allow rapid assessment of drilling location and progress. ArcGIS Online was updated daily with this information and was able to viewed and tracked by the entire team via password protected URLs.

Summary logs, oriented downhole imaging, and photos were uploaded to each boring location and could be viewed online, or downloaded as needed. An example of available files can be seen at the bottom of Figure 3 under Attachments.

As changes to the planned grade, cut/fill limits, and alignment shifted, exploration locations and depths were shifted in real-time and allowed inspectors to stay updated with objectives and planned grades. The near real-time uploading of information allowed the geotechnical design team to adjust boring lengths, add/delete borings as needed, and change instrumentation objectives saving the project valuable time and costs.

To track the progress of the overall project and share information of work completed by each rig per shift, a daily check-in system was used by the inspectors. An online form was developed for each inspector to complete on a daily basis. To simplify the form, drop down menus were used as much as possible as shown inf Figure 4.

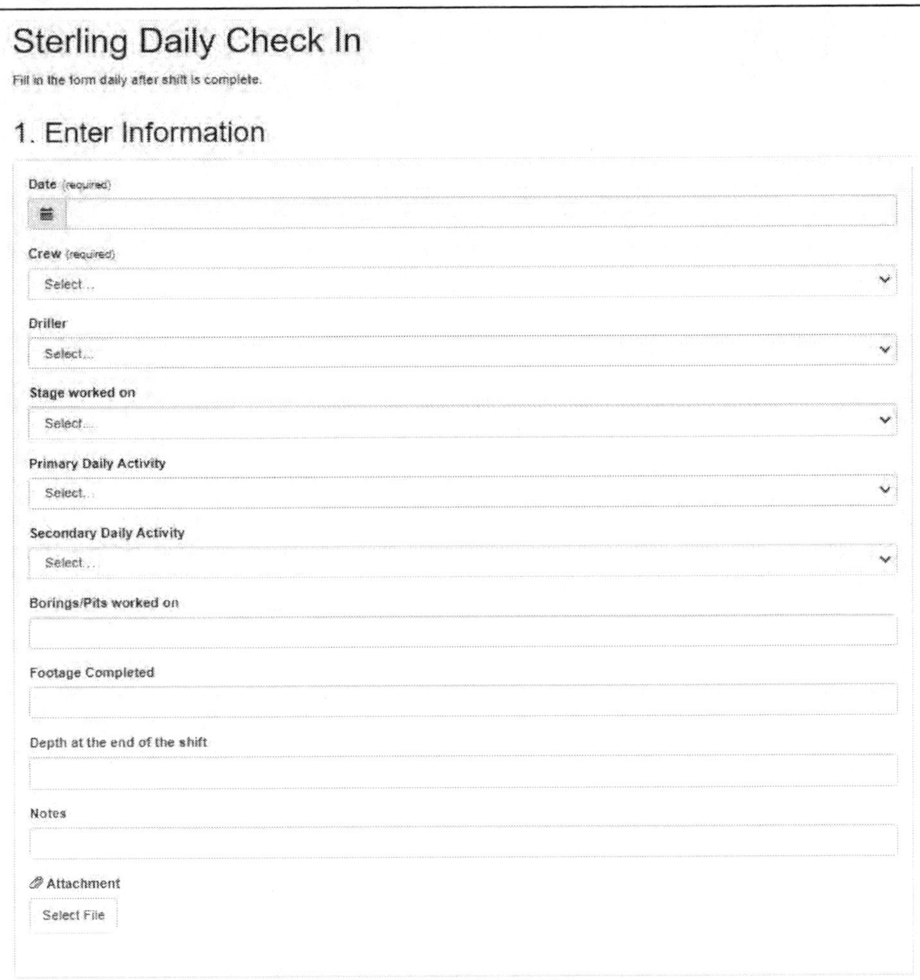
Sterling Daily Check In

Fill in the form daily after shift is complete.

1. Enter Information

Date (required)

Crew (required)

Select...

Driller

Select...

Stage worked on

Select...

Primary Daily Activity

Select...

Secondary Daily Activity

Select...

Borings/Pits worked on

Footage Completed

Depth at the end of the shift

Notes

Attachment

Select File

Figure 4 – Daily Check-in Form

The form contained date, drill crew, driller, boring information, activities performed, footage and depth at the end of shift information. The inspector then selected the approximate location on a map where the work was performed.

This information was displayed to the team in an Explorations Progress Dashboard Figure 5). The dashboard contained summary of work performed each shift by crew, the total number of borings and test pits as well as number of completed explorations.

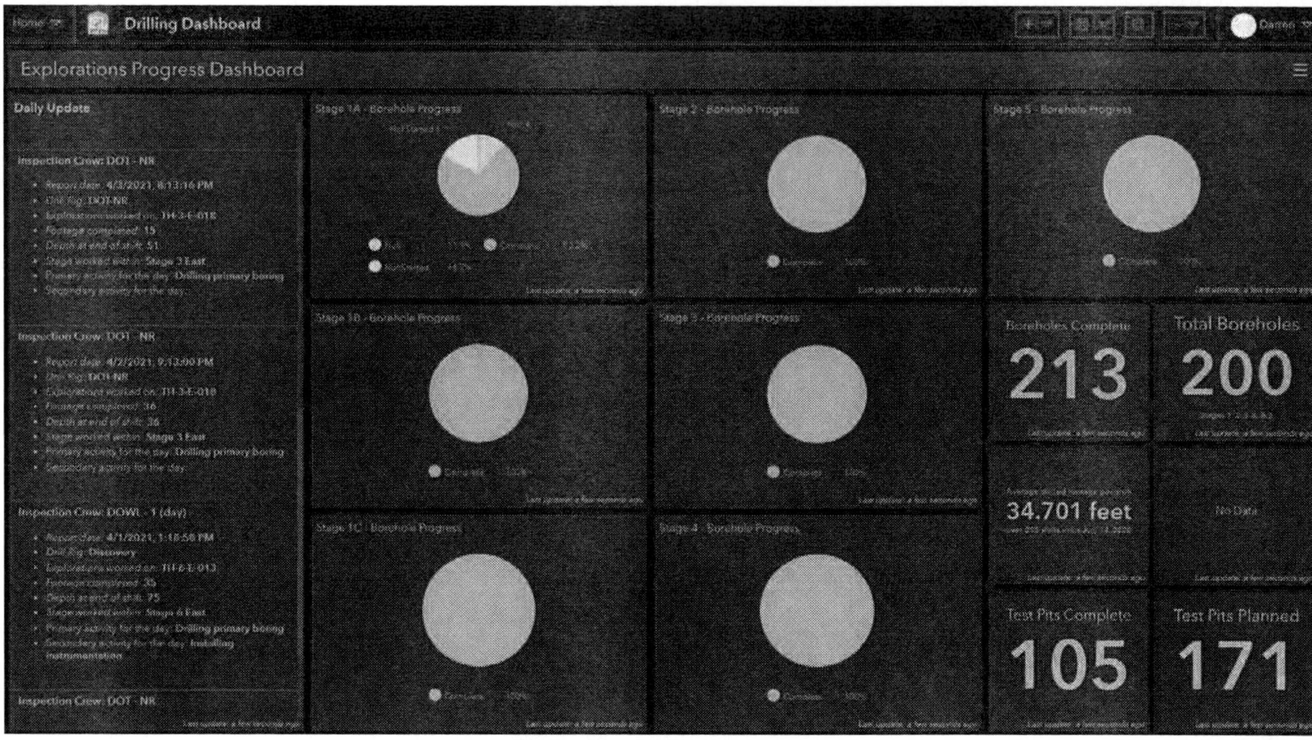

Figure 5 – Drilling Dashboard

The dashboard was also set up to track average footage per day, per rig. For the 218 borings completed totaling 15,789 feet, an average of 34.7 feet per rig, per shift was completed. This footage rate includes setup and teardown, mobilization to and from locations in challenging terrain such as muskeg or steep slopes, instrumentation installations, oriented downhole imaging work, in-situ testing, and rig breakdowns to give an accurate representation of full progress on project of this nature. This average rate well represents the overall progress vs no production and high production days such as downtime or getting 70 feet per shift.

SUMMARY

Innovations and rapid data sharing identified design challenges quickly. Conditions such as dense till, moisture sensitive silt, potentially unstable abutments, localized high groundwater pressure, and stability and settlement concerns, how to deal with peat, and where borrow sources and waste areas were could be identified and addressed early on due to having this online geodatabase and mapping platform.

Real-time sharing with a large CM/GC team that included the design team and contractor allowed for rapid adjustments to the design and field efforts. This helped the field manager coordinate concurrent multiple drilling efforts across a large project corridor, and keep the team aligned. The application used to communicate data from the multiple field crews on a daily basis, and track daily progress on the project was useful in budget tracking and resource loading.

The use of the these tools and real-time data sharing helped the team overcome serious logistical and access challenges with five concurrent drill crews in a very short window of time.

Potential Liability Associated with Unstable Slope Management Programs

Timothy R. Wyatt, Ph.D., P.E.
GeoLaw®, Conner Gwyn Schenck PLLC
306 E. Market Street, Suite One
Greensboro, North Carolina 27420
(336) 369-8290
twyatt@cgspllc.com

Prepared for the 71st Highway Geology Symposium, May 2022.

Acknowledgements

The author wishes to acknowledge the Transportation Research Board of the National Academies for sponsoring the research described in this paper, under National Cooperative Highway Research Program (NCHRP) Project 20-06, Legal Problems Arising out of Highway Programs. A full report of the results of this research is available as NCHRP Legal Research Digest No. 82 (May 2020).

Disclaimer

Statements and views presented in this paper are strictly those of the author, and do not necessarily reflect positions held by their affiliations, the Highway Geology Symposium (HGS), or others acknowledged above. The mention of trade names for commercial products does not imply the approval or endorsement by HGS.

Copyright

ABSTRACT

Personal injury or property damage resulting from highway slope failures often result in tort claims made against State Departments of Transportation (DOTs). Although State DOTs have a legal duty to maintain highways in a reasonably safe condition for travel, it is generally understood that it is not feasible to completely eliminate the risk of highway slope failure. In an effort to manage the cost and risk (legal and otherwise) of highway slope failures, many State DOTs have adopted unstable slope management programs, such as the Rockfall Hazard Rating System (RHRS) developed with the support of the Federal Highway Administration. Program capabilities vary widely from state to state, ranging from project ranking systems for capital-intensive slope remediation projects in some states, to geotechnical asset management programs to support routine maintenance throughout the slope life cycle in other states. This paper will examine how these programs influence the outcome of tort claims against State DOTs in lawsuits involving highway slope failures, including how the programs influence the court's analysis of immunity and negligence. It will be seen that, while unstable slope management programs can help State DOTs avoid liability for decisions to defer capital-intensive slope remediation projects, they generally do not allow State DOTs to avoid liability for failure to perform routine maintenance of highway slopes.

INTRODUCTION

Slope failures such as landslides and rockfalls pose risks for highway owners such as State Departments of Transportation (DOTs), such as personal injury or property damage suffered by travelers on the highway due to the falling or sliding debris, or due to the dangerous condition of an unrepaired highway after a slope failure event.

Personal injury or property damage resulting from highway slope failures often result in tort claims made against State DOTs. Although State DOTs have a duty to maintain highways in a reasonably safe condition for travel, it is generally understood that it is not feasible to completely eliminate the risk of highway slope failure. Courts, claims boards, or other tribunals considering such tort claims will undertake an analysis of governmental immunity.

In 1946, with the enactment of the Federal Tort Claims Act (FTCA), the federal government consented to be sued in tort. The FTCA provides, at 28 U.S.C. § 2674, that the federal government is generally liable for actual damages caused by its negligence "in the same manner and to the same extent as a private individual under like circumstances." However, the FTCA contains an exception from liability, at 28 U.S.C. § 2680(a), for the federal government's "failure to exercise or perform a discretionary function or duty." Thus, the federal government retains immunity for negligence in the performance of discretionary (as opposed to ministerial) activities. Discretionary activities are those that involve the government's exercise of discretion, judicial reasoning, or policy-making.

In the years following passage of the FTCA, most state legislatures followed the lead of Congress, and enacted statutory waivers of immunity applicable to the state government. Most statutory waivers of immunity for state governments include the discretionary function exception, closely mirroring the language of the FTCA. In most states where the discretionary function exception is not expressly incorporated into the statute, the courts have read an implied discretionary function exception into the statute. In states where there is not a discretionary function exception to tort liability, courts often find immunity through other judicial doctrines. Whether the discretionary function exception has been conferred by the legislature or the judiciary, courts reserve immunity for decisions concerning public policy, such as planning decisions, that involve the consideration and balancing of social, economic, and political factors by an agency authorized to make such decisions.

The discretionary function exception nominally immunizes State DOTs for their negligence in performing activities that involve the exercise of discretion (such as highway planning), but not in performing operational-level activities that do not involve the exercise of discretion. Further, because the State DOT has a duty to maintain highways in a reasonably safe condition for travel, the discretionary function exception does not apply to ministerial or operational activities such as highway construction and maintenance.

In slope failure cases, it is widely recognized that the duty to maintain the highway in a reasonably safe condition includes a duty to maintain the slopes adjacent to the highway in a reasonably safe condition to prevent danger to travelers from slope failure. To avoid liability in the latter situation, State DOTs must demonstrate that they were not negligent. This might be accomplished by demonstrating that reasonable efforts were made at the operational level to maintain the highway at an acceptable level of safety, and that upgrading the highway would not be economically feasible given limited funds and higher priority capital improvement projects.

Where there is personal injury or property damage on the highway due to slope failure, plaintiffs trying to hold the State DOT liable will typically attempt to portray the State DOT's activities as operational or ministerial (*e.g.*, negligent maintenance of the highway or the slope). The State DOT, on the other hand, will argue that its actions or inaction were allowable exercises of discretion (*e.g.*, policy decisions) in order to invoke the discretionary function exception.

In an effort to manage the cost and risk (legal and otherwise) of highway slope failures, many State DOTs have adopted unstable slope management programs, such as the Rockfall Hazard Rating System developed with grant funding from the Federal Highway Administration (FHWA). This paper examines how unstable slope management programs influence the outcome of tort claims against State DOTs in cases involving highway slope failures, including how they influence the court's analysis of immunity and negligence. It is seen that, while unstable slope management programs can help State DOTs avoid liability for decisions to defer capital-intensive slope remediation projects, they generally do not allow State DOTs to avoid liability for failure to perform routine maintenance of highway slopes.

UNSTABLE SLOPE MANAGEMENT PROGRAMS AND LIABILITY

Use of Unstable Slope Management Programs to Avoid Liability

Although unstable slope management programs were intended, in part, to help State DOTs avoid tort liability for highway slope failure, there are only a handful of reported court cases in which unstable slope management programs are considered at any length by the court. The cases generally support the notion that unstable slope management programs (with their hazard priority rankings and benefit-cost decision-making support) qualify for the discretionary function exception to the extent they are used to evaluate capital projects such as extensive remediation of hazardous slopes or road relocation. However, it is widely understood that the discretionary function exception does not extend to a State DOT's duty to maintain the highway in a reasonably safe condition for travel, and the cases generally do not excuse a State DOT's negligent failure to perform routine maintenance of highway slopes even when the slope in question is not a high priority under the State DOT's unstable slope management program.

Cases Finding Broad Immunity

An unstable slope management program that includes priority rankings of slope hazards and benefit-cost decision-making tools may be used to argue that the State DOT is entitled to discretionary immunity when an accident results as an alleged result of deferred slope remediation. This strategy has been most successful for State DOTs in the Washington state courts, in cases involving the WSDOT Unstable Slope Management System (USMS).

In 2014, in *Helm v. State, Department of Transportation* (*1*), the USMS appeared to be the primary factor enabling WSDOT to avoid liability for a broad array of alleged negligent acts, ranging from deferred slope remediation to inadequate routine maintenance to failure to warn, with respect to personal injury resulting from a 2006 rockfall on I-90. The rockfall that resulted in the plaintiff's injury took place at "Slope 1867," one of 3000+ slopes incorporated into the

USMS. The night before the plaintiff's accident, via a computer-aided dispatch (CAD) log, the Washington State Patrol reported a small rockslide to WSDOT. However, only after the plaintiff collided with a rock in the road, fifteen hours after the CAD report, did WSDOT place a warning message on its variable message sign.

In 2009, the plaintiff sued WSDOT for negligence, alleging that WSDOT "failed to properly maintain I-90" and also that WSDOT "failed to warn motorists about rockfall." WSDOT moved for summary judgment (*i.e.*, judgment in its favor as a matter of law, without incurring the expense of a trial) as to all of plaintiff's negligence claims, arguing that its use of the USMS entitled it to discretionary immunity. WSDOT's summary judgment motion was supported by the declaration of WSDOT's Chief Engineering Geologist Tom Badger, who explained that WSDOT uses the USMS to prioritize slope remediation projects given limited funding. In its most recent evaluation in 2005, Slope 1867 scored 351 points on the USMS scale of 33 (representing a minimum score of three points for each of the eleven USMS categories) to 891 (representing a maximum score of 81 points for each of the eleven USMS categories). Although Slope 1867 posed a significant rockfall hazard, and scored slightly above the 350 points required by WSDOT to qualify for full slope remediation, there were a number of slopes with a higher hazard priority ranking. Mr. Badger declared that WSDOT elected to defer remediation of Slope 1867 until a planned future construction project that involved relocation of a portion of I-90, during which Slope 1867 would be eliminated.

Upon hearing WSDOT's motion for summary judgment, the trial court found "that the USMS as a system qualified for discretionary immunity," so that slope remediation decisions based on the USMS could be entitled to the discretionary function exception. However, the trial court denied WSDOT's motion for summary judgment, as there was not sufficient factual background to determine whether WSDOT had actually performed a benefit-cost analysis, balancing the risks and advantages of deferring remediation of Slope 1867. Therefore, it would be for the jury to determine whether WSDOT had actually exercised its discretion in deciding to defer slope remediation.

At trial, Mr. Badger testified about the role of the USMS, and how it was used by WSDOT geologists under his direction to prioritize slope remediation projects, and specifically in the decision to defer remediation of Slope 1867 until the relocation of I-90 in 2014 or later. The plaintiff conceded that the decision to defer full remediation of Slope 1867 was within WSDOT's discretion, and instead argued that WSDOT should have undertaken lesser mitigation measures including routine ditch maintenance or installing interim protective devices. The plaintiff attempted to elicit testimony regarding appropriate maintenance or interim protective measures from its expert witness, a professional engineer. However, relying on Mr. Badger's declaration that slope remediation decisions are made by geologists, WSDOT moved to exclude the plaintiff's engineering expert from testifying as to any maintenance measures involving the slope, suggesting that such testimony would constitute the unlicensed practice of geology.

In its written order restricting the plaintiff's expert witness from testifying about slope remediation, the trial court defined slope remediation broadly as "work that relates to the slope," specifically including rock scaling and "protective devices such as rock screens and cable netting"—measures typically understood to fall short of the full slope remediation measures (*i.e.*, excavation or relocation) about which Mr. Badger testified. The broad definition of slope remediation used by the trial court was likely a significant factor in the outcome of the *Helm* case. It prevented the plaintiff's engineering expert from testifying about anything involving the slope, effectively limiting his testimony to potential safety measures such as concrete barriers on the road surface itself. The trial court's definition of slope remediation also effectively extended discretionary immunity to all "work that relates to the slope," such as rock scaling or protective devices installed on the slope itself, as the trial court had previously ruled at summary judgment that the decision to defer slope remediation based on the USMS would be entitled to discretionary immunity if a benefit-cost analysis was actually performed.

This was one in a series of questionable and potentially impactful evidentiary rulings made by the trial court in favor of WSDOT. When the plaintiffs attempted to introduce into evidence a 2005 report on slopes along I-90 in Snoqualmie Pass authored by Mr. Badger (which described Slope 1867 as "high risk" and "high hazard"), WSDOT opposed it on the grounds that potential mitigation measures documented in the report, such as rock fences used on other slopes, would be prejudicial to WSDOT. The trial court agreed, stating that the jury was not qualified to determine whether protective devices and other mitigation measures used on other slopes would have been appropriate on Slope 1867, although a licensed geologist could testify about that. However, when the plaintiff attempted to elicit testimony from Mr. Badger about these potential mitigation measures, and he professed to not recall the contents of his 2005 report, the trial court refused to allow the plaintiff to use the report to refresh Mr. Badger's recollection. The plaintiff was effectively prevented from eliciting testimony from either expert witness regarding potential protective devices or other mitigation measures that could have been used on the slope itself.

Evidentiary rulings such as excluding the 2005 report also handicapped the plaintiff's argument that WSDOT had notice of a dangerous condition at Slope 1867 and should have taken action to warn travelers. On WSDOT's motion, the trial court excluded from evidence the CAD report of a rockfall, fifteen hours prior to the plaintiff's accident. If WSDOT could have been charged with fifteen hours notice of a dangerous condition, it would likely not have been able to rely on discretionary immunity.

The jury instructions included an instruction that WSDOT's use of the USMS "involves a basic governmental policy" (namely, "prioritization" of slope hazards), and that WSDOT "is immune from liability for decisions in which it is determining basic governmental policy." The verdict form asked whether WSDOT "balanced the risks and advantages of delaying remediation of slope 1867," to which the jury responded "Yes," indicating that WSDOT was entitled to discretionary immunity for its decisions regarding slope remediation. Therefore, WSDOT had no liability for the plaintiff's injuries.

The plaintiff appealed, contending that the jury instructions were confusing, in that it was unclear what "slope remediation" activities qualified for discretionary immunity. Because the plaintiff did not contest WSDOT's discretion to delay full remediation of Slope 1867, the plaintiff argued that the discretionary immunity instruction should not have been given. Moreover, given the trial court's broad definition of "slope remediation" in its written order restricting the plaintiff's expert witness from testifying about slope remediation, the plaintiff argued that jurors may have been confused into believing that, because WSDOT balanced the risks and benefits of deferring full remediation of Slope 1867, it was entitled to discretionary immunity for failing to undertake lesser mitigation measures, such as routine ditch maintenance or installation of protective devices, despite the fact that there was no evidence that WSDOT had balanced risks and benefits of these lesser mitigation measures. The plaintiff also appealed the trial court's numerous evidentiary rulings, which effectively prevented the plaintiff from putting on evidence of slope protective devices and other mitigation measures available to WSDOT, and also from putting on evidence of WSDOT's notice of a dangerous condition at Slope 1867 prior to the accident.

However, the Washington Court of Appeals affirmed the trial court, holding that the evidentiary rulings were within the trial court's discretion. Because so much of the plaintiff's evidence (including its expert witness testimony) was excluded, the jury was left to rely primarily on Mr. Badger's testimony regarding the USMS to determine that WSDOT was entitled to discretionary immunity for its slope management decisions.

In 2015, in *Pszonka v. Snohomish County* (*2*), WSDOT employed a similar litigation strategy involving a declaration from Mr. Badger regarding the USMS, but instead of seeking discretionary immunity, Mr. Badger's declaration was used to obtain a concession from the plaintiffs that WSDOT did not negligently maintain its highway slopes. *Pszonka* involved the consolidated claims of individuals injured in the March 2014 Oso landslide, one of "the most destructive landslides in United States history," which "killed 43 people, injured others, and destroyed the property in its path." A nearly mile-long section of a nearby highway, State Road 530, was "covered by debris measuring 20 feet deep in some places." The plaintiffs included the estate of one decedent who "was traveling eastbound on State Route 530 at the time the landslide overran the highway." The plaintiffs alleged that various governmental entities including WSDOT were at fault for the plaintiffs' injuries. Specifically, the plaintiffs alleged that WSDOT "violated its statutory and common law responsibilities to ensure that Rte. 530 was 'reasonably safe for ordinary travel.'" (*3*)

In May 2015, the State of Washington moved to dismiss all claims against WSDOT, not on the basis of immunity, but rather on the grounds that WSDOT was not negligent; *i.e.*, that it satisfied its duty to "maintain its roadways in a condition that is reasonably safe for ordinary travel." WSDOT's motion to dismiss was supported by the declarations of senior engineering personnel. The declaration of WSDOT's Northwest Region Highway Engineer, Dave Crisman, stated that the highway section in question had "never been damaged or destroyed by a landslide," that there was no place "to locate the highway that is guaranteed to be safe from a landslide," and that the "highway satisfied all applicable engineering standards and was reasonably safe for ordinary travel." In order to make its highways reasonably safe for ordinary travel, Crisman declared that "WSDOT uses and relies upon accepted, tested, researched engineering standards in the design and construction of its state highways," including "the research, testing, and experience of federal and state transportation agencies across the nation."

As further evidence of WSDOT's application of reasonable engineering practices to reduce risk to the traveling public, the declaration of Mr. Badger, WSDOT's Chief Engineering Geologist, provided details about WSDOT's use of the USMS:

> The development of WSDOT's USMS began in the mid 1990's, when a new project programming approach was implemented for WSDOT's highway construction program. This new approach involved prioritizing and programming

> projects based on the extent which they addressed highway deficiencies along WSDOT's highway system. . . ..
>
> The first step in this comprehensive system is to identify the slopes. The slope has to be *a known unstable slope that has a history of causing maintenance problems on a state highway.* Each slope is then rated using a numerical rating system that evaluates risk factors to the highway facility. . . .. Each rating category is scored using point values ranging from 3 to 81, and then totaled to yield a numerical rating for each slope.

The suggestion was that WSDOT had met or exceeded its obligation to protect highways from slope failures through its establishment of a "comprehensive system" for unstable slope management. However, despite WSDOT's efforts, Mr. Badger declared that the slope that failed resulting in the Oso landslide had "never in the history of the highway caused a maintenance problem." Because it was not an "unstable slope that has a history of causing maintenance problems on a state highway," the slope had never been included in WSDOT's "comprehensive" USMS inventory. WSDOT's implication may have been either that the Oso landslide was not foreseeable, or that there must be reasonable limits to a State DOT's duty to maintain slopes, and that this particular slope was outside of those limits.

In response, instead of simply contending that the slope was part of the highway to be maintained and that WSDOT was negligent by failing to include the slope in its USMS, the plaintiffs conceded "that they do not contend that WSDOT is implicated in this case because SR 530 was defectively designed or maintained." Instead of relying on the recognized principle that a State DOT has a duty to maintain all of its highways in a reasonably safe condition, the plaintiffs argued that WSDOT had a "duty to investigate, monitor, and warn about the dangers" of the site, as well as a "duty to coordinate" or "duty to engage" with other state agencies. The implication was that if WSDOT had shared information and expertise regarding the site, steps would have been taken to mitigate the hazard. In support of this argument, the plaintiffs pointed specifically to WSDOT's USMS: "The declarations of Messrs. Badger and Crisman establish that WSDOT has the resources and skill to 'proactive[ly] stabiliz[e] known unstable slopes.' . . . Since the 'mid-1990's,' WSDOT has managed landslide risks, by ranking them, developing design and cost estimates for mitigating those risks and then prioritizing the mitigation of landslide risks before those risks turn into tragedy."

The plaintiffs also rebutted WSDOT's suggestion that the landslide was not foreseeable, referencing documents indicating that in 1995, the state was concerned that a WSDOT bridge ("the crossing of SR 530 over the river just downstream of the slide") was "at risk from the predicted catastrophic failure" of the slope. Given WSDOT's expertise in unstable slope management, the plaintiffs suggested that "the skill and resources of WSDOT" should have been deployed "to proactively mitigate the dangers posed" by the slope, including the "known risk . . . posed to WSDOT-managed property" (*i.e.*, the SR 530 bridge). With the plaintiffs arguing that WSDOT should have better protected its highway, it is curious why the plaintiffs conceded that WSDOT was not negligent in maintaining the highway.

WSDOT's motion to dismiss was resolved by consent agreement (*i.e.*, an agreement between the parties *in lieu* of a court ruling) in June 2015, with the plaintiffs stipulating that they “do not claim that a defective design or maintenance condition on SR 530 caused the roadway not to be safe for ordinary travel,” and dismissing claims against WSDOT for negligent design or maintenance. In return, WSDOT withdrew its motion to dismiss as to the plaintiffs’ other theories of WSDOT negligence, such as the duty to warn and the “duty to coordinate.” (*4*) This consent agreement would appear to have been a major tactical victory by WSDOT, as the dismissed claim for negligent maintenance arguably encompassed the plaintiffs’ best argument for recovery against WSDOT—*i.e.*, that WSDOT’s duty to maintain the highway in reasonably safe condition for travel required it to take proactive steps to investigate and mitigate the dangerous condition posed by the slope before it catastrophically failed.

Notwithstanding the June 2015 consent agreement between the parties resolving WSDOT’s motion to dismiss, in November 2016, shortly after Snohomish County was dismissed from the lawsuit on immunity grounds, the State of Washington (without admitting liability) consented to a judgment in the amount of $50 million, to resolve all remaining personal injury claims against all state agencies arising from the Oso landslide. (*5*) One will never know how different the outcome would have been if the negligence claims against WSDOT had not been dismissed in June 2015. However, it is interesting that WSDOT did not seek discretionary immunity for slope remediation based on the USMS, particularly considering the fact that its motion to dismiss in *Pszonka* was filed in May 2015, seven months after issuance of the *Helm* appellate decision affirming broad discretionary immunity for WSDOT for slope remediation. It seems that it would have been a worthwhile strategy for WSDOT to pursue discretionary immunity for slope maintenance based on the USMS, and then argue that the immunity encompassed the alleged duties to warn and coordinate.

Both the *Helm* and *Pszonka* cases illustrate the defensive use of an unstable slope management program by a State DOT in tort litigation. Although the mere existence of an unstable slope management program is not likely to completely immunize a State DOT from liability for slope failure, a State DOT may be able to use the program to show that it balanced the risks and advantages of deferring capital improvements, so that the State DOT’s failure to remediate the slope will be entitled to the discretionary function exception. Alternatively, the same facts can be used to demonstrate that the State DOT was not negligent, as the facts may show that the State DOT considered the hazard posed by the slope in question, but made a reasonable decision to focus its limited resources on remediating slopes with higher hazard priority ratings, or on projects that would have a higher benefit-cost ratio.

Where the slope in question does not have a high hazard priority rating in the unstable slope management program, the State DOT may be able to effectively argue that it was not negligent because it had no notice of a dangerous condition on the highway. On the other hand, where the failed slope has a high hazard priority rating in the unstable slope management program, plaintiffs will use that information to argue that the State DOT negligently failed to exercise its discretion by taking action to address the known dangerous condition. While the unstable slope management program can be very helpful in avoiding liability for failing to fully remediate a hazardous slope, undertaking lesser mitigation measures and routine maintenance activities can help the State DOT prove that its maintenance of the hazardous slope was reasonable, as discussed in the following Section.

Cases Finding Liability for Negligent Maintenance

In 2001, in *Medina v. State*, the use of a rockfall hazard rating system failed to absolve the Colorado DOT from liability for injury due to a rockfall, where the Colorado Governmental Immunity Act (CGIA) did not contain a discretionary function exception from the general waiver of immunity for injuries resulting from failure to maintain a public highway. Instead, the CGIA at the time provided a more narrow exception covering "injuries solely attributable to the inadequate design of a public highway." In *Medina*, the Supreme Court of Colorado endeavored to "clarify the relationship between 'maintenance' and 'design' under the [CGIA], thereby demarcating the scope of the state's duty to maintain a public highway." (*6*)

Medina involved a 1996 rockfall on U.S. Highway 6 in which a boulder struck a bus, injuring passengers. Moving to dismiss on the basis of immunity, Colorado DOT submitted the affidavit of Richard D. Andrew, "the state geologist in charge of evaluating the state's highways for rockfall hazards." In the affidavit, Mr. Andrew described the Colorado RHRS, which included a preliminary rating of slopes adjacent to Colorado highways, followed by a more detailed priority rating of the slopes that, based on the preliminary rating, were deemed to pose "the most serious threat of danger from rockfall activity." Since the initiation of the Colorado RHRS in 1991, the slope in question had been assigned a preliminary rating "indicating the highest risk of rockfall activity," and it ranked 381st out of the approximately 700 slopes that received a detailed rating. In his affidavit, in an effort to invoke the statutory design immunity, Mr. Andrew described the rockfall hazard at the site in question as a condition resulting from design, as opposed to negligent maintenance or construction:

> This area of the highway was *designed* with no shoulders, no roadside ditches and very steep highway clearance rock cuts. The *design methods* that would have mitigated the rock fall potential in this area would be a ditch catchment at the base of the cut slope, highway shoulders, rock bolting, wire mesh or a combination of these methods. It was the *original design* of the highway cut slope through this area that allowed the rock to reach the traveled portion of the road and not construction or lack of maintenance.

The plaintiffs seized on Colorado DOT's rockfall hazard ratings as evidence that Colorado DOT had knowledge of the dangerous condition, or at least that the injuries were reasonably foreseeable. To invoke the CGIA waiver of immunity for dangerous conditions on public highways, the plaintiffs alleged that Colorado DOT negligently failed to maintain the highway "free from dangerous conditions." The plaintiffs alleged that Colorado DOT breached its duty to maintain by, among other things, "not installing devices to prevent boulders from falling on the highway," such as the rock bolts or wire mesh suggested by Mr. Andrew's affidavit. In addition to the duty to maintain, the plaintiffs also alleged that, given the actual knowledge of the rockfall hazard rating at the site in question, Colorado DOT was negligent by failing to warn travelers, or by failing to close the highway and direct traffic to alternate routes.

Relying on Mr. Andrew's affidavit that the rockfall hazard was attributable to design, Colorado DOT moved to dismiss based on the highway design exception to the CGIA waiver of immunity. The trial court denied the motion to dismiss, finding that "[t]he dangerous condition in which the plaintiffs were injured existed because of the government's lack of maintaining the roadway, rather than from a design perspective." The trial court thus appeared to conclude, without an evidentiary hearing, that Colorado DOT was liable for the injuries. Colorado DOT asserted an interlocutory appeal (*i.e.*, an appeal of the ruling on Colorado DOT's motion to dismiss, prior to trial of the case) pursuant to the CGIA.

The Colorado Court of Appeals reversed a significant portion of trial court's ruling, concluding that the highway design exception to the CGIA waiver of immunity barred a number of the plaintiffs' claims of negligent conduct by Colorado DOT. First, as to the allegation that Colorado DOT was negligent by failing to warn travelers, the court held, "The failure to warn of a hazard by posting warning signs is a design defect for which immunity has not been waived." Second, as to the allegation that Colorado DOT was negligent by failing to install devices to prevent boulders from falling on the highway, the court was persuaded by Mr. Andrew's affidavit that Colorado DOT was immune because the highway was designed without such safety devices. However, as to the "general allegations" that Colorado DOT "negligently failed to maintain the highway and keep it free from a dangerous condition," the appellate court affirmed the trial court's denial of the motion to dismiss, concluding that "a failure to maintain the highway and cut slope in their designed or constructed state" was within the CGIA waiver of immunity. Therefore, Colorado DOT had exposure to the extent the plaintiffs' injuries arose from the failure to maintain the highway as designed, and the appellate court did *not* overturn or even address the trial court's finding that the plaintiffs' injuries were the result of a dangerous condition caused by Colorado DOT's failure to maintain the roadway. (*7*)

The Supreme Court of Colorado agreed to review the decision of the Court of Appeals. As to the alleged negligent failure to warn, the court sided with Colorado DOT, affirming "that the CGIA has not waived the state's immunity for such a claim." As to the alleged negligent failure to maintain, the court provided even greater relief to Colorado DOT, effectively overturning the trial court's finding that the plaintiff's injuries resulted from a dangerous condition created by Colorado DOT's failure to maintain the highway. "Without evidence establishing the original state of being, repair, or efficiency of the road, it is impossible to determine whether Plaintiffs' injuries were caused by a dangerous condition of the road that developed subsequent to the initial design and construction of the road or whether their injuries were caused by a dangerous condition that inhered in the design itself." Demarcating where Colorado DOT's duty to maintain arises, the Court explained:

> When a dangerous condition of a roadway develops subsequent to the initial construction and design of a public highway due to a failure to maintain, the state is required to take the steps necessary to return the road to the same general state of being, repair, or efficiency as initially constructed, but nothing more. This is because a failure to return the road to the same general state of being, repair, or efficiency as initially constructed would increase the risk of injury above that deemed to be acceptable during the design stage.

Although the site in question had been assigned a preliminary rating "indicating the highest risk of rockfall activity" at the initiation of Colorado's RHRS in 1991, there was no specific evidence of the site's rockfall hazard *as designed*, or whether the rockfall hazard had become more severe due to lack of maintenance. An evidentiary hearing would be required to determine whether the rockfall hazard at the time of the accident was *solely* attributable to design, and thus whether the

CGIA waiver of immunity for dangerous highway conditions had any applicability to this case. This would involve determining "the original state of being, repair, or efficiency of the road as initially constructed," and then determining whether the state of the road had subsequently deteriorated due to a lack of maintenance so as to cause or exacerbate the dangerous condition that resulted in the plaintiffs' injuries.

As to the alleged negligent failure to install protective devices such as rock bolts or wire mesh, the court sided with plaintiffs, indicating that Colorado DOT could have a maintenance duty to install protective devices, even if not included in the original design, if protective devices "are necessary to return the road to its original state of being, repair, or efficiency as initially constructed." In reaching this conclusion that the duty to maintain may include installation of mitigation measures that were not included in the original design, the court was persuaded by an affidavit from the plaintiffs' expert consultant: "In my opinion, the installation of rock bolts and wire mesh can be used in a wide range of applications from initial design of rock slopes to *maintenance and remediation* of rockfall hazards. Rock bolts and wire mesh are routinely installed *following initial design* and construction to mitigate the risk of rockfall." (*10*)

In a concurring opinion, some of the justices appeared to lament that Colorado DOT was potentially subject to liability in this case, in light of Mr. Andrew's affidavit concerning Colorado DOT's RHRS. The concurring opinion recommended that the legislature adopt a general "discretionary function exception" broad enough to immunize the state from rockfall injury based on prioritization of rockfall hazards:

> Given a finite budget, and a state with aging road systems through mountainous areas, the state should have some degree of flexibility to determine the best uses of its resources. To preserve this flexibility, other jurisdictions around the country have excepted discretionary functions from waivers of governmental immunity. We have no such exception.

The concurring opinion suggested that a discretionary function exception "could allow for a more measured approach to highway maintenance." It is unlikely that a discretionary function exception would have resulted in a different outcome in *Medina*, since courts routinely find that highway maintenance is an operational or ministerial activity not subject to the discretionary function exception. The Colorado design immunity statute served the purpose of a discretionary function exception, immunizing Colorado DOT from its decision to locate the highway in an area prone to rockfall, and also for its decision not to undertake capital improvements that would make the highway safer than originally designed. Courts rarely extend the discretionary function exception to excuse a State DOT's failure to perform routine maintenance or other mitigation measures to maintain the highway in a reasonably safe condition for travel.

For example, in 2017, in *O'Grady v. State*, where an RHRS was in place at the time of a rockfall, the Hawaii DOT was deemed to be negligent for (among other things) its maintenance district's failure to "consult[] regularly with a geotechnical engineer who had information regarding the findings of the RHRS project," and such negligence did not fall within the discretionary function exception to immunity. (*8*) The *O'Grady* plaintiffs were driving along a state highway when the rockfall occurred in 2007, resulting in personal injury. Hawaii DOT had implemented a statewide RHRS in 2004. The rockfall site in question received a preliminary

"A" rating, and in developing the detailed RHRS rating, the site received the highest possible score with regard to the individual categories of differential erosion and block size volume. However, the high RHRS hazard rating had not resulted in remediation of the slope, as "there was minimal integration between the Hawaii District Engineer and the State's Rockfall Hazard Project results." The plaintiffs alleged that Hawaii DOT was negligent in ways including but not limited to the maintenance district's lack of awareness of the RHRS project, the RHRS project manager's failure to share the RHRS results with the maintenance district, and the failure to take action to remediate the slope given the high RHRS rating.

Hawaii DOT attempted to use the RHRS project to demonstrate that it was not liable for the plaintiff's injuries. Hawaii DOT argued that the RHRS was implemented, in part, to discharge its duty to maintain roads in a reasonably safe condition: "DOT intended to use the RHRS to prioritize large-scale projects . . ., as rockfall mitigation based on the RHRS would have been subject to legislative appropriations or federal funding." Hawaii DOT engineers and their RHRS consultant considered several different weighting methodologies to calculate a detailed ranking of all "A" sites, and the rockfall site was not ranked in the top twenty sites using any methodology. Considering the limited resources available to remediate all rockfall hazards, Hawaii DOT contended that its decision not to remediate the site was reasonable. Alternatively, Hawaii DOT asserted that it was not liable due to the discretionary function exception: "The RHRS does not prescribe what is to be done after the ratings are determined. . . . Instead, the decisions about what to do are made within the discretion of the engineers." Hawaii DOT argued that its geotechnical department's decision not to report RHRS preliminary ratings to its maintenance department was also subject to the discretionary function exception.

The trial court concluded that, although the "decision to undertake a large-scale rockfall prevention or mitigation project . . . may fall within the discretionary function exception[,] the State should not escape liability under the discretionary function exception merely by choosing to address rockfalls onto a State highway only with large-scale projects and declining to use routine, everyday maintenance to address the risk." The trial court concluded that the Hawaii DOT maintenance district should have "had a system of routine ongoing maintenance" and also should have "consulted regularly with a geotechnical engineer who had information regarding the findings of the RHRS project," among other things, but failed to do so. Therefore, Hawaii DOT was negligent, having breached its "duty of care to travelers on a state highway to maintain the highway so it is reasonably safe for travel" (which the trial court expressly found to include the duty "to maintain the areas adjacent to the highway so that the highway is reasonably safe from rockfalls").

Notwithstanding Hawaii DOT's negligence, however, the trial court concluded that there was no liability because the plaintiffs failed to prove that their injuries were caused by Hawaii DOT's negligence. Specifically, the trial court reasoned that even if Hawaii DOT had not been negligent, and had integrated the RHRS findings into its maintenance decision-making, the rockfall may not have been prevented if Hawaii DOT had not received funding from the state legislature or federal government to remediate the rockfall site. Supporting this conclusion was the trial court's finding that the "purpose of the RHRS was to identify the rockfall hazards adjacent to State highways," and then "to use the information garnered from the RHRS project to choose large-scale projects which would be funded by the Legislature of the State of Hawaii . . . and with Federal funding." The trial court thus viewed the RHRS as a mechanism for obtaining funding for remediation projects, and treated the plaintiffs' failure to prove the availability of remediation funding as a break in the chain of causation between Hawaii DOT's negligence in handling the RHRS results and the injuries suffered by the plaintiffs.

On appeal, the Hawaii Supreme Court vacated the trial court's judgment. The trial court erred by requiring the plaintiffs to prove that there was available funding to remediate the slope, effectively placing the burden on the plaintiffs to prove that the rockfall would not have occurred if Hawaii DOT had not been negligent. Once the trial court concluded that Hawaii DOT was negligent, all that was required for plaintiffs to establish liability was to show that Hawaii DOT's negligence was a "substantial factor" in the injuries suffered by the plaintiffs. In remanding to the trial court to apply the proper standard, the Hawaii Supreme Court strongly suggested the correct ruling, noting that no one had appealed the trial court's determination that Hawaii DOT was negligent, and stating that the plaintiffs do not have a "significant burden" to prove that Hawaii DOT's negligence was a "substantial factor" causing their injuries. In addition, although the trial court did not expressly invoke the discretionary function exception, its findings evidenced concern that Hawaii DOT might not have had sufficient funding to remediate all hazardous slopes identified in the RHRS. On remand, the Hawaii Supreme Court advised the trial court "that such rockfall mitigation efforts at the operational level would not involve the consideration of broad public policies," and therefore "the State's breach of its duty of care . . . does not fall within the discretionary function exception."

The *Medina* and *O'Grady* cases illustrate that, while unstable slope management programs can help State DOTs obtain immunity for failing to undertake large-scale slope remediation projects, the State DOT is unlikely to avoid liability for failing to maintain its highways in a reasonably safe condition for travel. The question is whether unstable slope management programs can help a State DOT avoid liability for failing to undertake lesser mitigation measures that fall somewhere between full remediation and routine maintenance (such as rock scaling or installation of protective devices on the slope). Most unstable slope management programs were originally "worst-first" programs, resulting in hazard priority rankings that effectively identified where to spend resources for full slope remediation. As the programs evolve into geotechnical asset management programs, State DOTs will be able to balance the risks and advantages of a range of mitigation measures other than full remediation. While the State DOT may never be entitled to immunity for failure to undertake lesser mitigation measures, the use of a geotechnical asset management program may help the State DOT show that it was reasonable, and thus not negligent, by directing its limited mitigation resources to other slopes based on a benefit-cost analysis.

Defending Limitations of Unstable Slope Management Programs

State DOTs may be concerned that, as in the *Medina* and *O'Grady* cases discussed in the previous Section, tort plaintiffs will attempt to use the State DOT's unstable slope management program to demonstrate liability of the State DOT. For example, where the slope in question has a high hazard priority ranking in the unstable slope management program, plaintiffs will likely argue that the State DOT had knowledge of a dangerous condition on the highway. Where the State DOT fails to take action sufficient to prevent slope failure, plaintiffs will likely argue that given the high hazard priority ranking, it was not within the State DOT's discretion to defer remediation, or that the State DOT did not actually exercise its discretion by considering other mitigation options. Given these concerns, it is reasonable to question whether State DOTs are exposing themselves to liability by implementing an unstable slope management program, if the data in the programs can be used against the State DOT.

Failing to Implement a Program

In 2008, in *Terbush v. United States*, the federal government avoided liability for the death of a rockclimber due to a rockfall at Yosemite National Park (YNP), under the discretionary function exception to the FTCA, despite (or perhaps because of) its failure to implement an RHRS. (*9*) The *Terbush* plaintiffs (parents of the deceased rockclimber) sought to hold the government liable in negligence, alleging, among other things, that the National Park Service (NPS) knew or should have known of the rockfall hazard and negligently failed to warn visitors of the hazard. This theory was supported by the expert opinion of geology professor Chester Watts that rockfalls "are in fact predictable to a great extent by scientific analysis of the rock formation and conditions" including localized water and rockfall history. The government, on the other hand, argued that the discretionary function exception barred the plaintiffs' claims.

The U.S. District Court for the Eastern District of California dismissed the lawsuit in 2005, concluding that the case "did not involve a routine decision regarding maintenance" nor the government's "simple failure to perform a mandatory duty under an established, specific policy or pursuant to scientific, objectively determinable standards." Therefore, the court concluded that the discretionary function exception to the FTCA deprived the court of subject matter jurisdiction over the plaintiffs' negligence claims, and allowed the government to avoid liability for failing to implement a geologic hazard rating system. (*10*)

On appeal in 2007, the U.S. Court of Appeals for the Ninth Circuit largely agreed that the government's failure to warn of rockfall hazard potential was covered by the discretionary function exception, as the process of identifying potential hazards and determining which hazards warrant a warning involve the exercise of discretion. The Ninth Circuit also agreed that the alleged "negligent design and construction" was the type of decision traditionally subject to the discretionary function exception, similar to the decision to locate a highway in an area prone to rockfall. However, on appeal, the plaintiffs "shift[ed] the focus of their claim" from negligent design and construction to negligent maintenance. The Ninth Circuit agreed that "the parties and the district court to some degree lumped the question of maintenance together with the other claims regarding design and construction." The Ninth Circuit thus reversed the district court's ruling that the discretionary function exception barred the plaintiffs' claims as to negligent maintenance. In remanding back to the district court, the Ninth Circuit recognized that "matters of routine maintenance are not protected by the discretionary function exception because they generally do not involve policy-weighing decisions or actions," although some maintenance decisions (such as full slope remediation) are "far from routine and may involve considerable discretion that invokes policy judgment." On remand, therefore, it would be up to the district court to determine whether the government's alleged negligence involved routine maintenance. (*9*)

On remand, the expert witness for the plaintiffs, geology professor Chester F. Watts, suggested that implementation of an RHRS was a routine maintenance obligation: "Standards of care and maintenance require that exposure of the public to rockfall hazards be minimized in every way possible, including remediation, warnings, and relocating infrastructure." Dr. Watts identified "federal and state highway agencies" as having developed objective scientific standards as well as the standard of care for rockfall hazard prevention, noting specifically that FHWA had "established procedures for quantifying rockfall hazards to the public referred to as the Rockfall Hazard Rating System (RHRS)," and that other government agencies such as NPS could "modif[y] RHRS to fit their needs." Dr. Watts suggested that NPS had an even greater obligation to implement RHRS than highway agencies do, contrasting the minimal time exposure of motorists to rockfall hazards, based on vehicle travel speeds, with the "hours and days" that park visitors such as campers may be exposed to rockfall hazards.

Ultimately, however, the government was successful in arguing that the plaintiffs, in shifting their focus to the alleged negligent failure to implement an RHRS, were attempting to relitigate their claim for "negligent design and construction," which the Ninth Circuit had affirmed was precluded by the discretionary function exception. The government argued that Dr. Watts had "modified his statements to now express the same opinions which focused on construction and management before the 2005 dismissal and subsequent appeal, but to now attribute them to deficient maintenance." The court dismissed the plaintiffs' lone remaining claim for negligent maintenance in 2010. (*11*) The absence of an RHRS probably contributed to that, as there was no system in place for recording periodic inspections and developing ratings to identify potential remediation activities. In that respect, the absence of an RHRS may have helped the government avoid liability at the dispositive motion stage, and avoid a trial, as rockfall hazard ratings had not become "routine maintenance" activities at Yosemite.

Because the *Terbush* court rejected the plaintiffs' argument that the standard of care for slope management includes the use of an unstable slope management program such as an RHRS, this opinion could be persuasive authority that a State DOT is not negligent for failing to implement a program. On the other hand, the opinion should not be read to suggest that State DOTs should not implement unstable slope management programs to avoid generating evidence of liability for slope failures. *Terbush* did not involve injury on a highway, so it did not involve the recognized duty to maintain highways in a reasonably safe condition for travel. Because of the duty to maintain, State DOTs need to demonstrate reasonable efforts to maintain the highway in a safe condition. In addition to a routine maintenance program at the operational level, the existence of an unstable slope management program can help State DOTs demonstrate that they discharged their maintenance duty in slope failure cases, as long as the State DOT actually uses the program to make rational decisions about slope remediation projects.

Failure to Upgrade Program

Unstable slope management programs have many recognized limitations. The calculations are not rigorous or high-fidelity predictions of slope failure; the slope hazard ratings are relatively simplistic calculations. State DOTs adopting unstable slope management programs often advertise that they have made improvements over the programs used by other State DOTs. The question naturally arises whether State DOTs can incur liability by failing to adopt improvements or make upgrades to their unstable slope management programs.

In 2018, in *Gray v. State*, NYSDOT avoided liability for personal injury to travelers who were seriously injured by the "soil veneer failure" of a slope included in NYSDOT's rock slope rating inventory. (*16*) The slope in question had previously experienced rockfalls in the 1980s and 1990s, which had resulted in traffic accidents and vehicle damage. The slope ranked 361st using NYSDOT's rock slope rating procedure, with a NYSDOT geologist testifying at trial that "the slope's relevant risk rating indicated that it was at less of a risk of slope failure than 360 other slopes in the state." The court observed that under New York law, NYSDOT's "duty to maintain its roadways in a reasonably safe condition" extends to "conditions adjacent to the highway" such as the slope, and NYSDOT "may be found liable where it has actual or constructive notice of a hazardous [or dangerous] condition and fails to take reasonable measures to remedy the danger." There was some question whether NYSDOT adequately performed its routine maintenance obligations to guard against rockfall hazards, such as regular inspections or other rockfall mitigation measures. However, the slope failure that injured the plaintiffs was a soil veneer failure or "mudslide," not a rockfall. This was not a failure mode that was considered in the NYSDOT rockfall rating procedure.

The case went to trial in 2016, nearly ten years after the accident and more than seven years after the plaintiffs filed a lawsuit against NYSDOT. At trial, the NYSDOT geologist testified that "a rock fall inspection would not have provided any information relevant to whether the subject slope was at risk of a potential mudslide." An NYSDOT geotechnical engineer testified that, although NYSDOT "had never inspected the subject slope for soil stability," potential rockfall remediation measures that NYSDOT might have taken such as installing wire mesh on the slope "would not have reduced the risk of a mudslide." Therefore, the New York Court of Claims ruled, and the Appellate Division of the New York Supreme Court affirmed in 2018, that the plaintiffs failed to show that NYSDOT had notice of a soil slope failure hazard at the time of the 2006 incident, and thus NYSDOT was not liable. Presumably the outcome would have been less favorable to NYSDOT if the plantiffs had been injured by a rockfall rather than a mudslide, given NYSDOT's failure to show that it had performed routine maintenance to address rockfall concerns. Likewise, if NYSDOT's slope rating procedure accounted for soil failure modes (slides) in addition to rock failure modes (falls), NYSDOT might have been charged with notice of the soil slope failure hazard, subjecting it to liability.

Following that reasoning, it is reasonable to question whether State DOTs are exposing themselves to liability by, for example, enhancing their unstable slope management programs to include soil slopes in addition to rock slopes. Similarly, State DOTs may be concerned that they are taking on liability by upgrading their "worst-first" unstable slope management programs to geotechnical asset management programs that consider a wider range of mitigation measures instead of just full remediation. Following the logic of *Gray*, if the State DOT's existing unstable slope management program does not perform soil slope hazard ratings, or does not consider interim mitigation measures short of full slope remediation, then perhaps the State DOT cannot be charged with notice and can escape liability on that basis.

However, a contrary view is that if the technology is available to consider alternate failure modes and alternate mitigation measures, the State DOT could be negligent by failing to upgrade its unstable slope management program to consider a wider range of alternatives. Although State DOTs are not required to implement geotechnical asset management programs, FHWA has recommended that they do so, and plaintiffs may argue that failure to follow FHWA's recommendation indicates negligence by the State DOT. Merely because the geotechnical asset management program allows the State DOT to consider a wider range of slope mitigation options does not obligate the State DOT to mitigate every unstable slope in its inventory. As long as the State DOT actually uses the geotechnical asset management program to make rational decisions with respect to selecting slope mitigation projects (*e.g.*, based on a benefit-cost analysis and considering limited funding), supplemented with a routine maintenance program at the operational level, the State DOT should be able to demonstrate that it was not negligent and avoid liability for injuries due to slope failure.

CONCLUSION

State DOTs are generally subject to statutory waivers of governmental immunity, subjecting the State DOT to potential tort liability when individuals suffer personal injury or property damage as a result of highway slope failures. Although most immunity waivers contain a discretionary function exception, retaining immunity for certain State DOT decisions such as the decision to locate a highway in an area prone to slope failure, the State DOT has a recognized duty to maintain the highway in a reasonably safe condition for travel. In tort claims arising from highway slope failure, liability will typically depend on whether the State DOT fulfilled its duty to maintain the highway or was negligent.

Unstable slope management programs such as the Rockfall Hazard Rating System used by a number of State DOTs can be useful tools to reduce liability for slope failures. They provide a framework for State DOTs to identify hazardous slopes most in need of remediation, supporting decision-making regarding allocation of limited resources for capital improvements. These programs will become more useful over time, as they evolve into geotechnical asset management programs, allowing State DOTs to consider a range of mitigation measures, accounting for life cycle maintenance costs, in order to optimally allocate slope maintenance resources across the state highway system to minimize the risk of personal injury or property damage due to slope failure. To the extent that unstable slope management programs help State DOTs avoid catastrophic slope failures, they certainly reduce the State DOT's liability.

However, all highway slope failures cannot be prevented. When there is personal injury or property damage due to highway slope failure despite the use of an unstable slope management program, the State DOT's use of the program can still play a role in reducing its liability. State DOTs can typically take advantage of the discretionary function exception for decisions grounded in social, economic, and political policy, which involve a conscious balancing of risks and advantages of various alternatives. Selecting slope remediation projects given limited resources is the type of decision that is generally understood to be within the State DOT's discretion, warranting immunity. Unstable slope management programs provide a rational decision-making framework to assist State DOTs in selecting highway slope remediation projects, demonstrating that the State DOT actually exercised its discretion.

However, State DOTs should not presume that the adoption of an unstable slope management program will absolve them from liability in tort for highway slope failures. If the State DOT does not actually use the program to make decisions regarding slope remediation, it may be unable to demonstrate that it exercised its discretion. Further, even though the State DOT may be entitled to discretionary immunity for its decision not to remediate the slope, the State DOT still must demonstrate that it fulfilled its duty to maintain the highway in a reasonably safe condition. The State DOT will need to demonstrate that it performed routine maintenance of slopes, such as regular inspection and debris removal, which is generally understood not to qualify for the discretionary function exception. Depending on the facts, the State DOT may need to demonstrate that it considered and undertook additional mitigation measures, such as rock scaling and installation of protective devices, in order to show that it was not negligent. Courts will consider whether the State DOT's mitigation activity was reasonable and conformed with the State DOT's duty to maintain the highway in a reasonably safe condition.

As unstable slope management programs evolve into geotechnical asset management programs, they can help State DOTs consider a range of mitigation measures, and help make decisions regarding allocation of slope maintenance resources. Although maintenance decisions will typically not qualify for the discretionary function exception, evidence that the State DOT used its unstable slope management program to adequately balance the risks and advantages of potential slope hazard mitigation measures will help the State DOT demonstrate that it was not negligent, and ultimately avoid liability on that basis. On the other hand, where the State DOT adopts a program to help determine slope hazard mitigation measures, but fails to act on the analysis by undertaking the suggested mitigation measures, that inaction can be used by plaintiffs as evidence of the State DOT's negligence. Whether used to avoid liability on the basis of discretionary immunity or fulfillment of the duty to maintain highways, unstable slope management programs are only useful to the extent they are actually used by State DOTs to balance the risks and advantages of slope hazard mitigation.

REFERENCES

1. Washington Ct. of Appeals 2014. Helm v. State, Dep't of Transportation, 184 Wash. App. 1010, No. 71664-6-1. Available at https://www.courts.wa.gov/opinions/pdf/716646.pdf.
2. Washington Supreme Ct. 2019. Pszonka v. Snohomish County, 439 P.3d 1068, 193 Wash.2d 1009.
3. Washington Ct. of Appeals 2018. Regelbrugge v. State, 432 P.3d 859, 7 Wash. App. 29.
4. Washington Super. Ct. 2015. Stipulated Order Resolving State's Pending Motion, Pszonka v. Snohomish County, No. 14-2-18401-8.
5. Washington Super. Ct. 2016. Stipulated Judgment Against State, Pszonka v. Snohomish County, No. 14-2-18401-8.
6. Colorado Supreme Ct. 2001. Medina v. State, 35 P.3d 443.
7. Colorado Ct. of Appeals 2000. Medina v. State, 17 P.3d 178.
8. Hawaii Supreme Ct. 2017. O'Grady v. State, 398 P.3d 625, 140 Haw. 36.
9. U.S. Ct. of Appeals for the 9th Cir. 2008. Terbush v. United States, 516 F.3d 1125.
10. U.S. Dist. Ct. for the E. Dist. of California 2005. Terbush v. U.S., No. 02-CV-05509.
11. U.S. Dist. Ct. for the E. Dist. of California 2010. Terbush v. U.S., No. 02-CV-05509.
12. New York Supreme Ct. Appellate Div. 2018. Gray v. State, 159 A.D.3d 1166, 72 N.Y.S.3d 208.

Advancements in Investigating, Testing, and Treatment of Acid Producing Rock – SR 15 Section 088, Central Susquehanna Valley Transportation, Snyder County, Pennsylvania

Andrew J. Smithmyer, P.G.
Gannett Fleming, Inc.
207 Senate Avenue
Camp Hill, PA 19403
(717) 886-5460
asmithmyer@gfnet.com

Jason M. Gardner, P.E.
Gannett Fleming, Inc.
207 Senate Avenue
Camp Hill, PA 19403
(717) 886-5429
jgardner@gfnet.com

Prepared for the 71st Highway Geology Symposium, May 2022

Acknowledgements

The authors would like to thank PennDOT Engineering District 3-0 and the Pennsylvania Department of Environmental Protection for their work on the various aspects of this project.

Disclaimer

Statements and views presented in this paper are strictly those of the author(s), and do not necessarily reflect positions held by their affiliations, the Highway Geology Symposium (HGS), or others acknowledged above. The mention of trade names for commercial products does not imply the approval or endorsement by HGS.

ABSTRACT

The Central Susquehanna Valley Transportation (CSVT) Southern Section is a new, four lane, limited access highway located in central Pennsylvania. The alignment traverses the Devonian age Hamilton Group and Trimmers Rock Formation consisting primarily of siltstone and shale that upon preliminary testing contain concentrations of acid producing sulfide minerals (%Sulfur $\geq$0.5%) that warranted treatment based on past standards of practice. Significant excavation (233,400 cubic yards) through the acid producing rock (APR) could not be avoided due to highway grade and established alignments. The geologic structural setting and the syngenetic origin of the sulfide minerals necessitated a detailed subsurface investigation with extensive laboratory testing of rock core to complete acid base accounting (ABA) to support the treatment and disposal methods.

The guidelines for the identification, treatment and disposal of APR originate from the mining industry with several state department of transportation agencies developing guidance documents more aligned to suit the civil construction realm over the past ten to fifteen years. Due to the extensive site characterization and large laboratory data set developed, an opportunity to refine the previously established APR treatment rates was undertaken.

APR treatment calculations for several net neutralization potential (NNP) results were completed to initially determine a range of supplemental alkaline material (SAM) required to treat the estimated volume of APR. The ABA results indicated the NNP of the APR to be variable, therefore a weighted factor of safety analysis was completed to evaluate the impact that SAM treatment rates would have on the entire rockmass. The weighted factor of safety results shows that SAM treatment rates lower than previously published treatment guidelines can be considered if extensive laboratory testing and detailed subsurface characterization of the APR is conducted.

INTRODUCTION

The SR 15, Section 088 project, also known as Central Susquehanna Valley Transportation (CSVT) Southern Section, is a new 6.5 mile, four-lane, limited-access highway located in Monroe Township and Shamokin Dam Borough, Snyder County, Pennsylvania. The CSVT Southern Section begins at the SR 11/SR 15/SR 522 interchange located just north of Selinsgrove, PA and extends to the CSVT Northern Section, which starts west of SR 15, approximately ⅓ mile south of County Line Road (SR 1022). When completed in 2028 the CSVT Southern Section will reduce commercial vehicle traffic along the highly congested "Golden Mile" portion of SR 11/SR 15 between Selinsgrove Borough and Shamokin Dam Borough. A project location map is included as Figure 1.

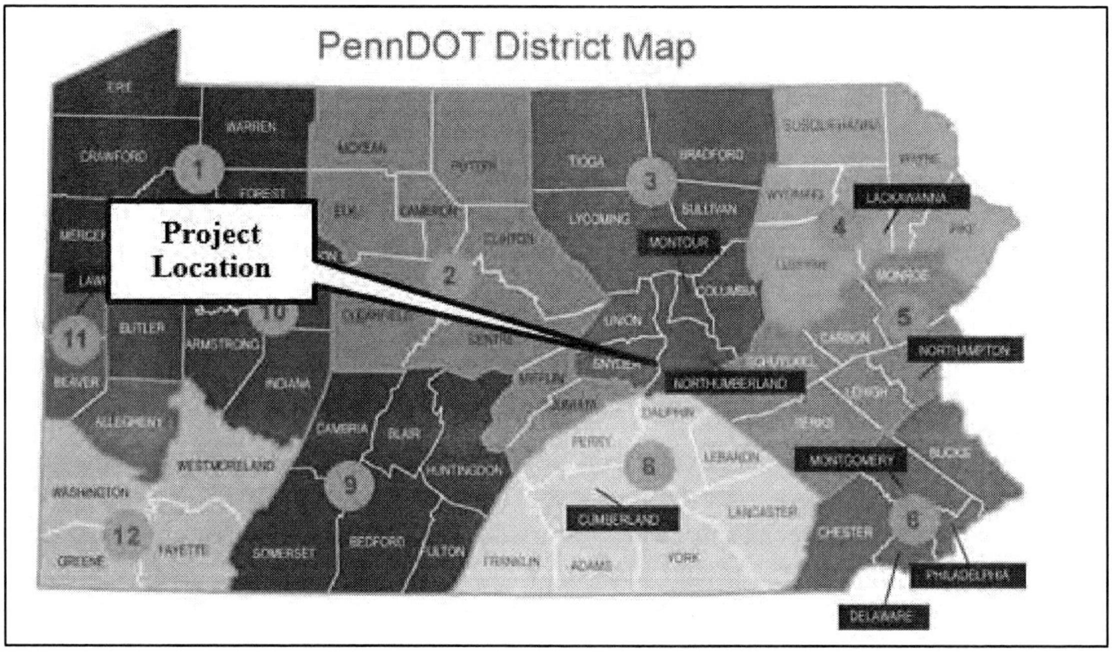

Figure 1 – Project Location Map

The construction of the CSVT Southern Section will require embankments approximately 90 feet in height and cut slopes of approximately 120 feet. The alignment traverses the Devonian age Hamilton Group and Trimmers Rock Formation consisting primarily of siltstone and shale that upon preliminary testing contained concentrations of acid producing sulfide minerals (%Sulfur $\geq$0.5%) that warranted special handing, treatment, and disposal based on past standards of practice. The preliminary results initiated an extensive testing and subsurface characterization of the rockmass within the proposed highway cuts.

SITE GEOLOGY

The CSVT Southern Section alignment at the SR 11/SR 15/SR 522 interchange traverses in a northwest direction for approximately 1.5 miles at which point the alignment turns to the northeast, oriented parallel to bedrock strike. A Geology Map containing the CSVT alignment is included as Figure 2 below.

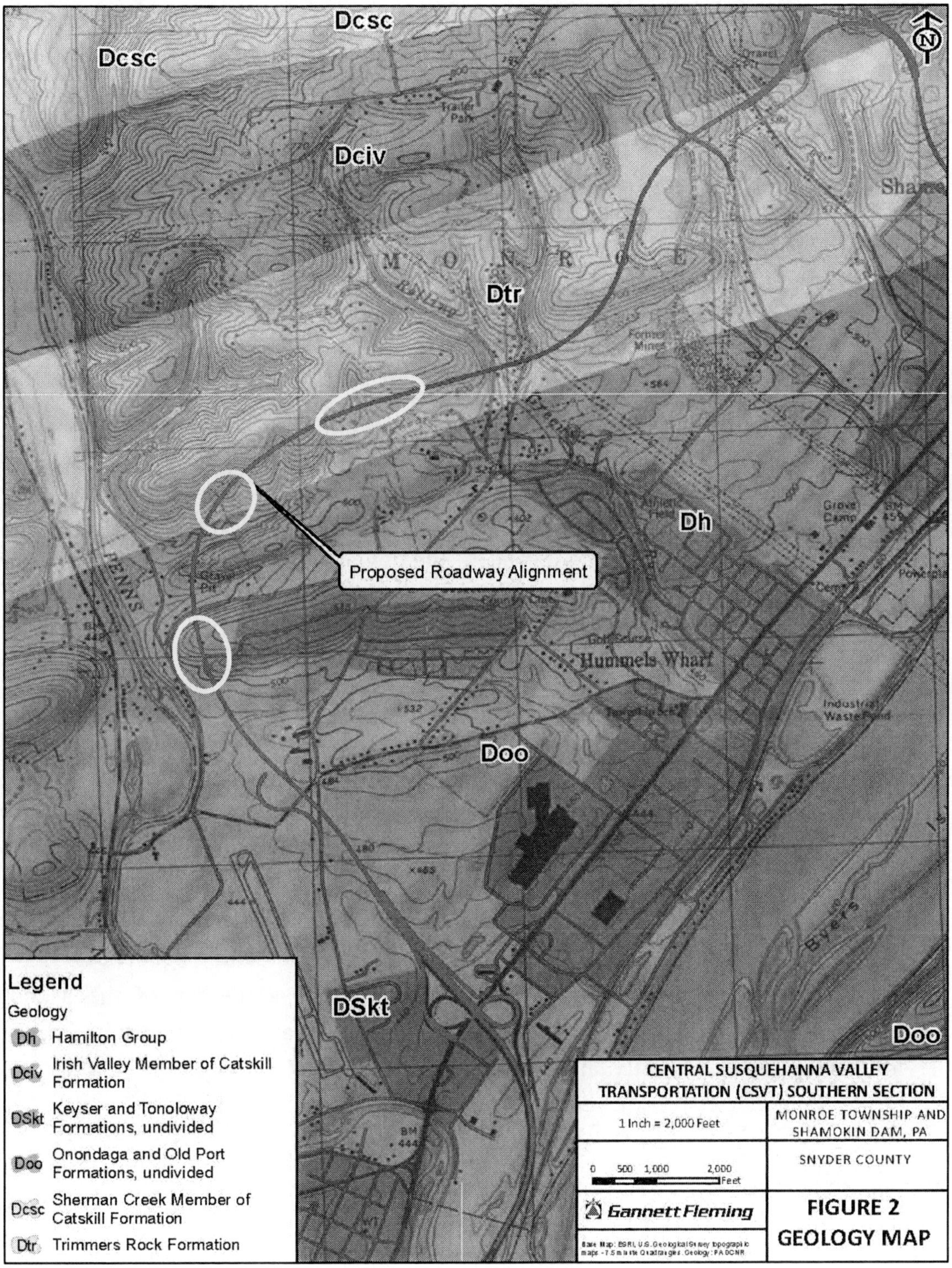

Figure 2 –Geology Map

The site lies within the Appalachian Mountain Section of the Ridge and Valley physiographic province. The surrounding topography has been developed through erosional processes of the regional drainage network and reflects the bedrock structural trends and relative resistance of the rocks to erosion. The CSVT Southern Section alignment crosses six distinct geologic units, spanning from the Lower Devonian to the Upper Devonian, (408 to 360 million years ago) becoming younger to the north and represents an overall transition from shallow marine to deltaic depositional conditions.

The underlying rock units, described in ascending order within the project area include: the Keyser and Tonoloway Formations, undivided, the Onondaga and Old Port Formations undivided, the Hamilton Group (Marcellus Formation and Mahantango Formation), the Trimmers Rock Formation, and the Irish Valley and Sherman Creek Members of the Catskill Formation. Of these formations, the Hamilton Group and Trimmers Rock Formation were identified to contain sulfide bearing minerals. These two geologic units are described in more detail below.

The Hamilton Group consists of the Marcellus and Mahantango Formations which are described in ascending order. The Marcellus Formation is approximately 240 feet thick and consists of dark-gray to black, highly fissile, shales containing locally abundant pyrite and few fossils *(1)*.

The Marcellus Formation is documented as potentially an APR unit *(2)*. Shale generally predominates but tends to become siltier and less fissile upward. A thin limestone unit occurs near the middle of the Marcellus and represents the Purcell Limestone Member, but has also been called the Upper Selinsgrove Limestone *(2)*.

The Mahantango Formation consists of the following four members:

- Fisher Ridge, consists of medium-gray to olive-gray, commonly laminated silty claystone, siltstone, and some very fine-grained sandstone.
- Montebello Sandstone, consists of light-olive- to medium-light-gray, very fine- to medium-grained sandstone, commonly having abundant marine fossils and containing interbeds of siltstone and silty claystone.
- Sherman Ridge, consists of light-olive- to medium-gray silty claystone with zones of siltstone and very fine-grained sandstone in upward coarsening sequences.
- Tully Limestone, a thin, but important marker bed at the top of the Mahantango Formation consisting of 10 inches of medium-dark-gray shale limestone and 2 feet of dark-gray calcareous silty shale, both abundantly fossiliferous.

The Trimmers Rock Formation consists of olive gray and medium gray siltstone and silty shale with some very fine grained sandstone in its upper part. Measured thickness is 2,000 feet at nearby Shamokin Dam.

The geologic structure is dominated by an east-west trending anticline with the axis located at the southernmost section of the CSVT alignment. The Onondaga and Old Port Formations are mapped as a finger-like feature in this area and suggests a localized flexure or warping of the bedrock where the plunge of the fold axis is nearly horizontal. The northwest limb of the anticline dips to the northwest at approximately 40 degrees.

ACID PRODUCING ROCK & HISTORICAL BACKGROUND

Acid Producing Rock (APR) is rock which contains iron sulfide minerals such as pyrite, marcasite, and pyrrhotite with pyrite being the most prevalent sulfide mineral in sedimentary rocks within Pennsylvania's Appalachian Plateaus and Ridge and Valley Provinces. When these minerals are altered during oxidation (exposed to both air and water), ferrous sulfate and sulfuric acid are produced, potentially resulting in the generation of acid rock drainage (ARD). The sulfuric acid can generate acidic runoff containing high levels of dissolved metals, resulting in water quality degradation by reducing the pH, lowering the dissolved oxygen available, and mobilizing heavy metals such as iron, aluminum, magnesium, and zinc. Rock containing more than 0.5 percent by weight pyrite and having little to no alkaline content have the potential to be significant sources of ARD when exposed during construction. The APR identified in the CSVT alignment is syngenetic in origin, or formed entirely from the original sediments and disseminated throughout the rockmass.

The identification, handling, treatment and disposal of APR encountered during highway construction projects has its roots in the mining industry. The treatment of APR and prevention of ARD began with the Surface Mining and Conservation and Reclamation Act of 1971. The act required a mining plan provide a practical method to avoid acid mine drainage (AMD) or other stream pollution. In the ensuing decades the requirement advanced laboratory testing methods, treatment techniques, and disposal of both ARD and APR.

Great attention to the identification, handling, treatment and disposal of APR began in the early 2000's when in 2003 approximately 1 million tons of APR was exposed during the construction of Interstate 99 at Skytop in Centre County Pennsylvania *(3)*. The cut exposed pyrite veins associated with zinc-lead deposit (epigenetic) that was unidentified during design. Shortly after placement of this material, acidic runoff was identified impacting streams and groundwater and delayed construction, resulting in years of treatment at a cost of over 100 million dollars. This prompted several state agencies (i.e., Department of Environmental Protection and PennDOT) to develop detailed guidance documents to assist engineers and contractors when encountering APR on large earthwork projects.

In 2006, shortly after the Skytop incident, PennDOT, Central Office authored a chapter dedicated to APR in its Publication 293- Geotechnical Engineering Manual *(4)*. The chapter provides guidelines, recommendations, and considerations, for the investigation, testing, identification, prevention and treatment of potential APR and ARD in highway projects and has undergone several revisions since its initial publication.

Similarly, in 2007 Tennessee Department of Transportation (TDOT), issued *Guideline for Acid Producing Rock Investigation, Testing, Monitoring, and Mitigation (5)*. The document was developed to address the increasing number of projects in Tennessee encountering APR and to provide a consistent set of recommendations for the investigation, prevention, and mitigation of APR.

SUBSURFACE INVESTIGATION AND LABORATORY TESTING PROGRAM

In 2016 during the final design boring program, pyrite was observed during examination of rock cores. A typical occurrence of pyrite in recovered core is presented in Figure 3. A total of 26 borings consisting of 1,450 lineal feet of rock core and 481 Acid Base Accounting (ABA) tests were completed to obtain an initial assessment of the presence of APR and evaluate the extent of oxidized caprock, along a nearly 1.5 mile alignment. The laboratory results confirmed that sulfide bearing rock would be encountered during excavation, and after discussions with PADEP and PennDOT District 3-0 it was decided to move the alignment between 50 and 100 feet to the south of the original alignment to reduce the depth of excavation and anticipated excavation quantities by approximately 0.75 million cubic yards.

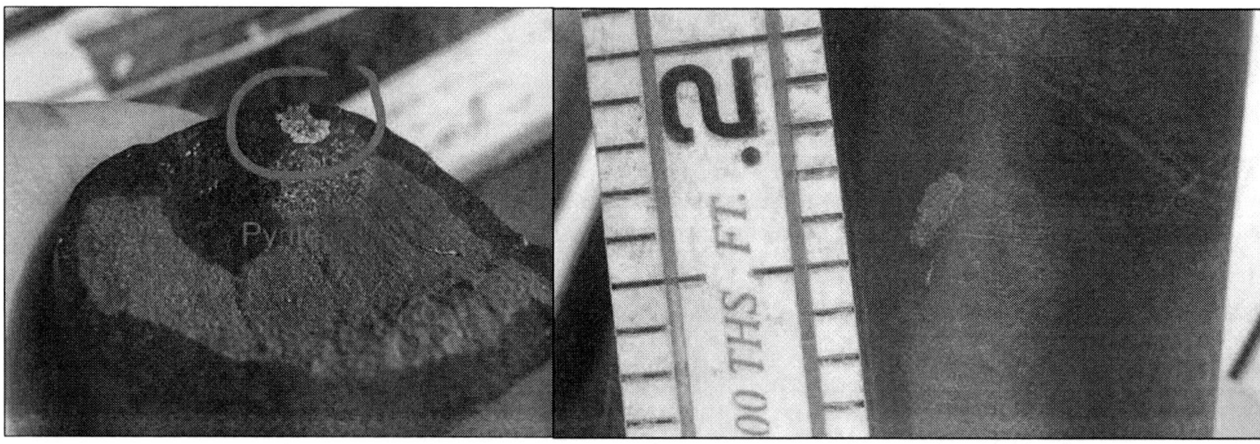

Figure 3 – Observed pyrite in Marcellus Shale Formation

The revised alignment required three cut slope locations requiring the excavation, treatment and disposal of APR. A summary of the cut slope excavations is provided in Table 1 and locations presented in Figure 4.

Table 1 – Summary of Cut Slopes in APR

Cut Slope	Geologic Formations	Station Limits (SR 15 Baseline)		Number of Borings	Approximate Excavation Volume
Cut No. 1	Hamilton Group (Marcellus Sh. Fm., Purcell Mbr.) and Mahantango Fm.	610+00 to 621+00 LT	606+00 to 621+00 RT	21	92,000 CY
Cut No. 2	Trimmers Rock Fm.	642+50 to 647+00 LT	NA	2	8,000 CY
Cut No. 3	Trimmers Rock Fm.	648+50 to 667+00 LT	650+25 to 654+25 RT; 655+50 to 668+00 RT	28	133,000 CY

Note: APR was not identified in Cut No. 4. Due to its limited depth the cut is within oxidized cap rock.

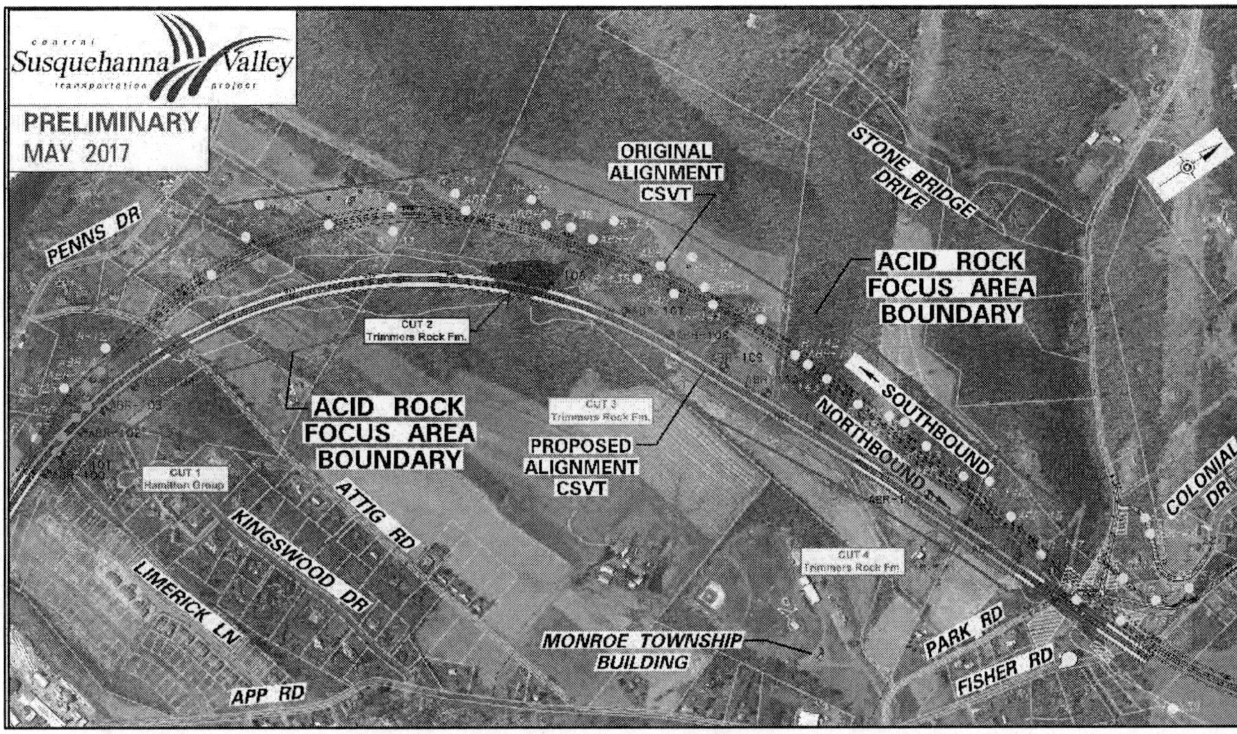

Figure 4 – Cut Slope Locations in APR

An additional 40 borings were completed with laboratory testing in two phases in 2017 along the new alignment. Laboratory results were evaluated and during final design in 2019 and an additional 16 borings were completed and submitted for testing to assist delineating the APR. The borings were drilled vertically, and the locations considered the dip of the bedrock in order to provide complete coverage of all beds that would be encountered during excavation. A total of 113 tests (Cut No. 1, 57 tests, Cut No. 2, 2 tests, and Cut No. 3, 54 tests) provided full depth sampling of the rock units encountered when excavated during construction. Figure 5 illustrates the number and distribution of borings to characterize a portion of Cut No. 3.

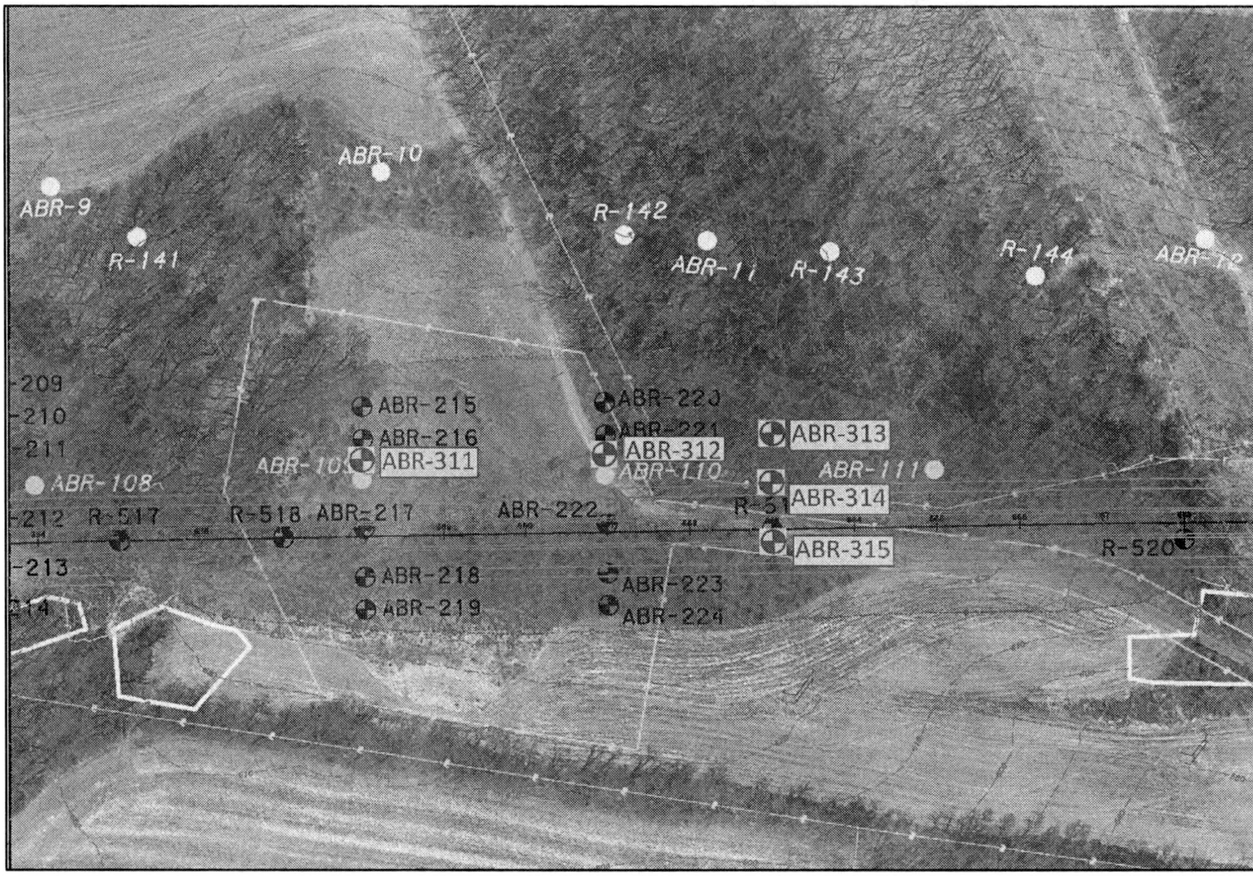

Figure 5 – Boring Layout at Cut Slope No. 3

ACID BASE ACCOUNTING

Acid base accounting (ABA) is a series of calculations that provide values used to assess the ability of a rockmass to produce acid or alkaline conditions. The results of these calculations can be used as a guidance tool by determining the total amount of acidity and alkalinity that a rockmass has the potential to produce.

The three laboratory tests that are required to complete ABA calculations are: 1) The “Fizz Rating, 2) Neutralization Potential (NP), and 3) Total Percent Sulfur. The test methods and required sample volume is provided in Table 2.

Table 2 – Acid-Base Accounting Test Methods		
Test	Test Method	Required Test Specimen passing the No. 60 sieve (AASHTO T 27)
Fizz Rating	Sobek Method	0.5 grams
Neutralization Potential	Sobek Method Siderite Correction	2 grams
Total Percent Sulfur (%S)	High Temperature Combustion Method (ASTM D-4239)	0.5 grams

The % Sulfur and the NP results obtained from the laboratory testing are used to determine the following:

- Maximum Potential Acidity (MPA), where MPA = (Total % Sulfur) x (31.25 ppt $CaCO_3$/1% Sulfur)
- Potential Ratio (PR), where PR = NP/MPA
- Net Neutralization Potential (NNP), where NNP = NP – MPA

The interpretation of the MPA, PR, and NNP results and corresponding treatment recommendations is summarized in Table 3. In summary % Sulfur values ≥ 0.5% may produce significant acidity. NNP results greater than 20 ppt are characterized as alkaline and do not require treatment, NNP results less than 0 parts per thousand (ppt) are likely to produce acidity, and values between 0 and 20 ppt may result in acidic or alkaline conditions. Potential Ratio values greater than 2 indicate alkaline conditions, and less than 1 indicate acidic conditions could develop. PR values between 1 and 2 may result in acidic or alkaline conditions.

Table 3 – Acid-Base Accounting Interpretations						
NNP (ppt)	PR	Fizz Rating	NP (ppt)	% Sulfur	Interpretation	Action
-	-	≥1	>30	-	Significant source of alkalinity	No treatment/disposal of material required
>30	-	-	-	-	Very likely to produce alkalinity	
20 – 30	>2	-	-	-	Likely to produce alkalinity	
0 – 20(1)	1 -2	-	-	-	May produce alkalinity or acidity	Treatment may or may not be required
<0	<1	-	-	-	Likely to produce acidity	Treatment and disposal of material required
-	-	-	-	>0.5	May generate significant acidity	

Note: (1) A NNP value of ≥12 ppt $CaCO_3$ is considered favorable for alkaline conditions to be maintained.
Source: PennDOT Publication 293, Chapter 10 – Acid Producing Rock, December 2020 (*4*).

INTERPRETATION OF ABA CALCULATIONS

Continuous testing was completed generally in three feet sample lengths of core. The % Sulfur, NP, NNP, and lithologic description were plotted on cross sections to determine the limits of APR that would require treatment prior to disposal. An estimate of the oxidized zone or oxidized cap rock was defined as generally rock containing <0.04% Sulfur. Laboratory results and ABA calculations that resulted in total %Sulfur values >0.5% coupled with little or no neutralization potential, (NNP <20) were characterized as potential APR and prompted delineation and development of a treatment program. A portion of cross section at Station 653+00 with laboratory results, ABA calculations, delineated oxidized cap rock, identified APR, and orientation of geologic structure is presented in Figure 6.

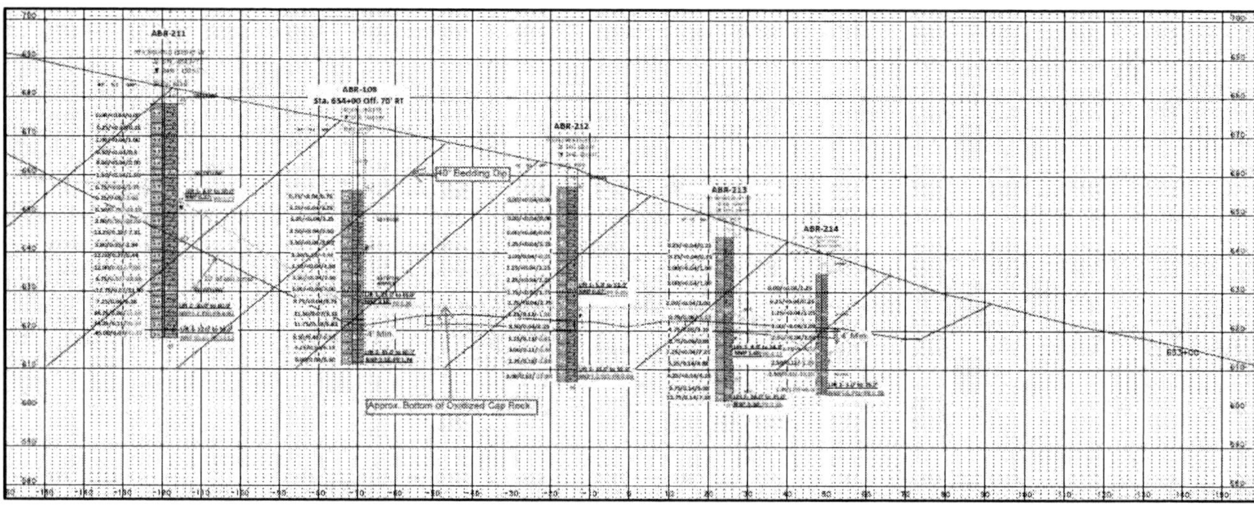

Figure 6 –Laboratory and ABA Calculation Results at Station 653+00

TREATMENT EVALUATION OF APR

Treatment of APR is achieved by adding supplemental alkaline material (SAM) to APR to maintain an alkaline environment and neutralize any potential generation of acidity. Excavated APR is treated prior to disposal on site with limestone or dolomite having a neutralization potential of at least 50 ppt $CaCO_3$.

The statistical metrics summarized in Table 4 illustrate the variability of MPA and NP results calculated for Cut No. 3.

Table 4 – Cut No. 3 Acid Base Accounting Results				
Metric[1]	MPA[2]	NP (ppt)	PR	NNP (ppt)
Min.	0	0	0	-49.0
Max.	59.0	18.7	14.4	16.8
Average	9.5	7.6	2.4	-1.9
Median	3.44	7.5	1.4	2.13
Standard Deviation	12.03	5.3	2.9	13.6

Note: (1) Results are based on 79 laboratory samples located below the estimated top of oxidized cap rock.
(2) An MPA of zero indicates a % Sulfur value of <0.04% or not detected by laboratory method.

The variability can be attributed to the varying concentrations of syngenetic pyrite formed in the sediments during deposition and diagenesis that are disseminated throughout the rockmass as well as varying amounts of alkaline content. This variability prompted PennDOT to select a treatment rate based on the lowest NNP value obtained. The treatment target for Cut No. 3 was intended to increase the lowest NNP value (-49.0 ppt) to 24 ppt $CaCO_3$ which is more conservative than treatment guidance suggested in PennDOT Publication 293 which recommends treatment by increasing the calculated average NNP of the APR with a quantity of SAM to achieve a target NNP of 24 ppt $CaCO_3$.

Due to the large quantity of APR requiring treatment, the large number of ABA tests completed, and extensive subsurface characterization, subsequent calculations were completed to provide PennDOT with several treatment rates for consideration with the intent of striking a balance between providing adequate treatment rates and cost.

Additional ABA Calculations and Results

The treatment levels are based on the following: lowest NNP, average NNP, and the 25th percentile NNP, to achieve a factor of safety of 2.0 were calculated using only the NNP values with corresponding %Sulfur values $\geq$0.5% for each cut slope location. In addition, a sensitivity analysis was completed to determine the amount of SAM required to treat the lowest NNP for a range for factors of safety between 1.0 and 2.0. Results for Cut Slope No. 3 are presented in Table 5 below.

Table 5 – Cut No. 3 SAM Addition Results for NNP Treatment Level Thresholds				
NNP Levels	NNP Value(1)	NNP Deficiency ($CaCO_3$ ppt)	Tons of 96% CCE Required/1000 Tons ABR(2)	Factor of Safety(3)
Avg. NNP	-20.68	32.6	68.1	2.0
Lowest NNP	-49.06	61.1	63.6	1.0
		76.3	79.5	1.25
		91.6	95.4	1.5
		106.9	111.3	1.75
		122.1	127.2	2.0
25% Percentile NNP	-25.9	37.9	79.0	2.0

Notes: (1) The NNP values are based on 19 test results with % Sulfur values ≥0.5% which range from 0.52% to 1.89%.
(2) Calcium Carbonate Equivalent (CCE) of an alkaline material is related to its purity. For example, pure calcitic limestone ($CaCO_3$) has a CCE value of 100% and pure dolomite $(CaMgCO_3)_2$ has a CCE of 109%
(3) Factor of safety of 1.0 is equal to an NNP value of 12 ppt $CaCO_3$.

Since these values are based on only NNP values with corresponding %Sulfur values ≥0.5%, an evaluation of the proposed SAM quantities and its effect on the entire rockmass below the oxidized cap rock, was completed.

Several SAM treatment rates were evaluated for each laboratory sample NNP result and a weighted factor of safety was determined for the rockmass. The SAM quantities were applied to 79 laboratory samples located below the estimated top of oxidized cap rock. The NNP values for the 79 samples range from 16.88 to -49.06. The results are presented in Table 6 below.

Table 6 – Cut No. 3 Weighted Factor of Safety Calculation Summary					
SAM Application Rate (Tons 96%CCE Sam/1000 tons APR)	Factor of Safety	Treatment NNP Threshold	Overall Rockmass Factor of Safety		
			High	Low	Average
79.0	2.0	25th percentile	75.8	1.2	16.3
95.4	1.5	lowest	91.6	1.5	19.7
63.6	1.0	lowest	61.0	1.0	13.2
68.0	2.0	average	65.4	1.1	14.0
34.0	1.0	average	32.7	0.53	7.0

The results presented in Table 6 indicate the SAM applied to the rockmass provided a treatment with significant reserve capacity for acid neutralization should localized zones of treated and encapsulated rock produce acid. After consultation with PennDOT District 3-0 and presenting the weighted factor of safety calculations that demonstrated significant reserve capacity, the treatment of APR based on the lowest NNP value to a FS = 1.5 as an alternative to the initial treatment to a FS = 2.0 was selected. This revision was deemed an appropriate treatment rate for the following reasons:

- Although the laboratory data was variable, a high level of confidence that the range of results was confirmed with complete sampling of the APR.
- The pyrite is of sedimentary origin, disseminated throughout the rockmass and not associated with sulfide deposits of hydrothermal origin (i.e., veined pyrite), ruling out any anomalies.
- The excavated APR consists of siltstone, shale and fine grained sandstone and is expected to be well graded with a significant portion of fines, reducing the likelihood of SAM migration within the treated rock.

The laboratory data, ABA calculations and rationale for the proposed treatment rate was presented to PADEP Environmental Cleanup and Brownfields (ECB) for review and concurrence in May 2020. In June 2020, PADEP-ECB completed a review of the calculations and proposed treatment quantities and concurred with the proposed SAM treatment quantities.

A mixture of SAM comprised of 25% 2A, and 75% agricultural lime with a minimum CCE of 96% was specified as the most appropriate mixture based on the anticipated characterization of excavated APR. Modifying the SAM mixture during construction based upon the particle size distribution of the excavated material was provided in a special provision. The 96% CCE is based upon the availability of local limestone sources in close proximity to the project site.

COST ESTIMATE

Table 7 – Cost Savings Analysis

Cut Slope	Tons of 96% CCE Required/1000 Tons ABR	Initial Cost Based on lowest NNP to a FS = 2.0	Revised Cost Based on lowest NNP to a FS = 1.5
Cut No. 1 - Sta.609+00 to 613+00	66.6	\$284,440	\$213,331
Cut No. 1 - Sta.614+00 to 621+00	50.4	\$187,750	\$140,800
Cut No. 2 - Sta.644+00 to 646+00	78.4	\$63,920	\$47,940
Cut No. 3 - Sta. 651+00 to 653+00 and 656+00 to 665+50	95.4	\$1,152,000	\$864,000
Total Estimated Treatment Cost		\$1,668,110	\$1,266,071

Note: Assumes 96% CCE SAM at \$32/ton.

Table 7 presents a costs savings analysis for each cut slope location. The selection to treat the APR to a F.S. of 1.5 based on the lowest NNP value instead of a F.S. of 2.0 resulted in a cost savings of approximately \$422,025. The additional drilling required to obtain a comprehensive test results and complete subsurface characterization was approximately \$130,000.

CONCLUSIONS

Due to the estimated quantity of potential APR to be excavated during construction, the identification of pyritic bearing rock along the CSVT Southern Section alignment provided an opportunity to develop a comprehensive set of laboratory test results and complete ABA calculations. A summary of the results of the investigation and conclusions are:

1. When APR is identified, cannot be avoided, and significant disturbance or excavation is unavoidable a subsurface and laboratory testing program should be a phased approach that evaluates the variability of the APR.

2. ABA interpretations are not often straightforward, particularly when sample results have a NNP value between 0 and 20 as the material may or may not produce acid conditions.

3. Complete initial treatment evaluations using a subset of the laboratory data consisting of only %Sulfur values $\geq$0.5% as conservative method. To determine a range in potential SAM treatment quantities for initial consideration, calculate the amount of SAM needed to increase the NNP based on the following: the lowest NNP, the 25th percentile NNP, and the average NNP laboratory result for varying factors of safety between 1.0 and 2.0 is recommended.

4. If the NNP results are found to be variable, complete a weighted factor of safety analysis using a subset of the laboratory data consisting of all laboratory results below the oxidized cap rock. This analysis accounts for the variability of NNP throughout the rockmass and evaluates the overall rockmass factor of safety when a selected quantity of SAM is applied to the entire rockmass.

5. In addition, the following factors should be taken into consideration when selecting an APR treatment rate:
   The volume of APR to be treated.
   Will the treated APR impact the cut/fill balance?
   What level of risk is the owner willing to accept?

6. This project afforded the opportunity to develop a data set that both the designer and owner had a high level of confidence that it accurately characterized the APR rockmass.

7. The selection of an appropriate treatment rate is not straightforward, a balance between cost and risk must be taken into account.

REFERENCES

1. MacLachlan, D. B., Hoskins, D. M., and Payne, D. F., 1995, Bedrock geology of the Freeburg 7-1/2' quadrangle: Pennsylvania Geological Survey, 4th ser., Open File Report 95-04.

2. Pennsylvania Geological Survey, (2004), Geologic units containing potentially significant acid-producing sulfide materials: Pennsylvania Geological Survey 4th ser. Open File Report OFMI 05-01.1, 1 map, scale 1:500,000.

3. Hammarstrom, J. M., Brady, Keith, and Cravotta, III, C. A., 2005a, Acid-rock drainage at Skytop, Centre County, Pennsylvania, 2004: U.S. Geological Survey, Open-File Report 2005-1148, 45 p.

4. PennDOT Publication 293 – Geotechnical Engineering Manual, December 2020 edition.

5. Golder Associates, Inc., 2007, Guideline for acid producing rock investigation, testing, monitoring, and mitigation: prepared for Tennessee Department of Transportation, 108 p.

Investigation, Design, and Construction of a Debris Flow Barrier System for a Repetitively Failing Slope Along I-40 Near the Buncombe/McDowell County Line in North Carolina

Melissa E. Landon, PhD, PE
WSP Golder
226 York Street, Box 9.
York, Maine 03909
(207) 606-8322
Melissa_landon@golder.com

Jay R. Smerekanicz, PG, CPG
WSP Golder
670 North Commercial Street, Suite 103
Manchester, New Hampshire 03101
(603) 493-6274
Jay_smerekanicz@golder.com

Peter C. Ingraham, PE
Scarptec, Inc.
P.O. Box 326, Monument Beach, Massachusetts 02553
(603) 493-6274
peter@scarptech.com

Jody Kuhne, PG, PE
North Carolina Department of Transportation
11 Old Charlotte Highway
Asheville, North Carolina 28803
(828) 298-3874
jkuhne@ncdot.gov

D. Matthew Mullen, PE
North Carolina Department of Transportation
11 Old Charlotte Highway
Asheville, North Carolina 28803
(828) 298-3874
dmmullen@ncdot.gov

Roger Moore, PE, PG
Ameritech Slope Constructors, Inc.
21 Overland Industrial Boulevard
Asheville, North Carolina 28806
(828) 633-6352
rmoore@ameritech.pro

Prepared for the 71st Highway Geology Symposium, May, 2022

Disclaimer

Statements and views presented in this paper are strictly those of the author(s), and do not necessarily reflect positions held by their affiliations, the Highway Geology Symposium (HGS), or others acknowledged above. The mention of trade names for commercial products does not imply the approval or endorsement by HGS.

ABSTRACT

Due to the increase in both the occurrence and intensity of precipitation events, debris flows have plagued I-40 at Swannanoa Gap near the Buncombe/McDowell County line in North Carolina over the past few decades. A 400-foot-tall slope has repeatedly experienced failures between 1991 and 2018 that have resulted in mud and debris flowing over the highway. The overburden material consists of silty clayey gravel and cobble colluvium over saprolite developed from highly weathered Precambrian schist and gneiss. The failures are characterized as being an "explosive" mix of supersaturated mud and debris that has a large impact area yet a small volume. For events prior to 2018, mitigation included excavation of material and the head scarp, installation of horizontal drainage and slope runoff protection, and increasing the catchment area. Investigation of a 2018 event that consisted of a 100-foot to 150-foot slide following a large rainfall event included a field study, drone survey, LiDAR survey, and finding evidence of small diameter open seepage "pipes" in the colluvium that indicates large pressure heads and concentrated flow that led to the "explosive" nature of debris flows. However, these mitigation efforts were not sufficient to retain the 2018 extreme event.

Therefore, and alternative mitigation system using a multi-tiered barrier system was designed and constructed to address larger debris flow events. Design parameters for the barrier system included predicted future potential debris flow volumes, velocities, and heights from simulations using RAMMS::DEBRISFLOW 3D simulation software. The simulations were based on existing site topography and remaining volume of soil at the head scarp, and the model was calibrated based on the previous slide topography and estimated volume. Design also included selection of the geometry and load specifications of the barrier system and the rock and tie-back anchors used to hold the barrier system in place. Because of the volume of potential debris flow material that remained on the slope, a two-tiered shallow landslide retention system was designed, specified, and installed in 2019.

INTRODUCTION

The project site is located on Interstate 40 east of Asheville, North Carolina in McDowell County (Figure 1). The roadway in this area includes truck climbing lanes on both sides, and a mandatory truck stop at a rest area on the east bound side for trucks to verify operational braking systems. The soil slope on the westbound I-40 (north side) at Swannona Gap mile marker 67.4 has experienced repeated debris flows since 1991, which have negatively-impacted this vital east-west transportation corridor. Due to right-of-way restrictions associated with the adjacent Pisgah National Forest, it is not possible to regrade the slope to remove the debris flow hazards. Given this restriction, previous mitigation efforts by the North Carolina Department of Transportation (NCDOT) included construction of: a double, U-shaped, concrete-lined ditch to convey stormwater and minor debris across the slope to the toe of the slope; a rip rap lined drainage channel to contain larger flows; and temporary concrete barriers at the shoulder to contain debris. These mitigation efforts are illustrated in Figure 2.

The most recent debris flow occurred on May 30, 2018. This paper discusses the analysis and design of the most recent debris flow mitigation efforts. Understanding the geologic and geotechnical conditions, right-of-way challenges, and recent innovations in 3-D debris flow modeling were essential to design and construction of a more robust debris flow mitigation.

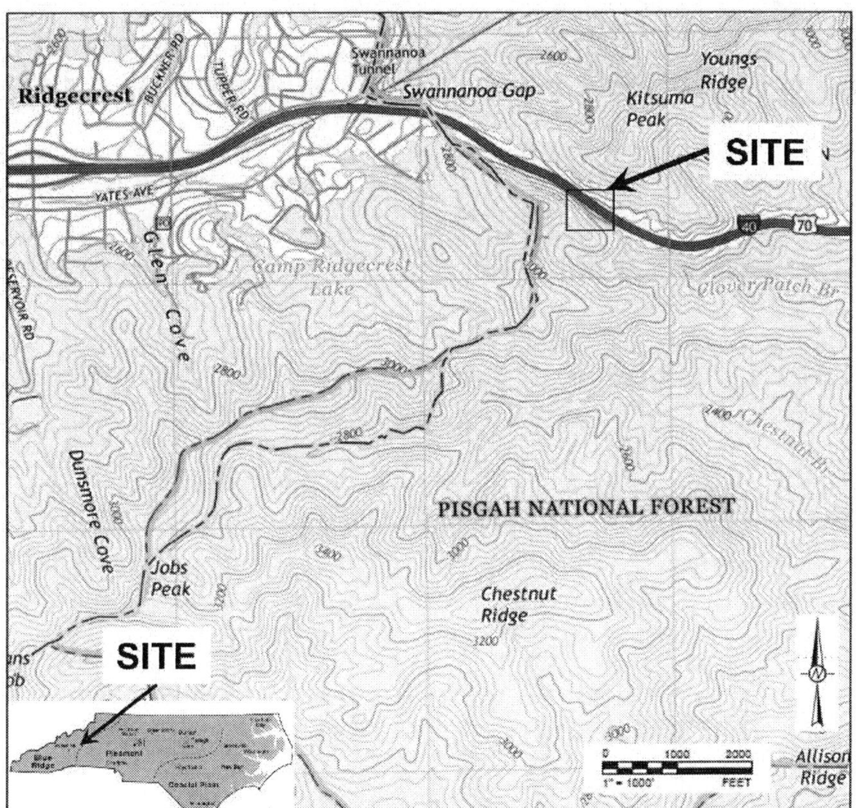

Figure 1. Site Location and Physiographic Map (USGS, 2016a,b)

Figure 2. View of slope showing reoccurring debris flows and key mitigation features (Google Earth Image, 2018).

SITE GEOLOGY

The project site is located within the Blue Ridge physiographic province in western North Carolina. The Blue Ridge is a deeply dissected mountainous area of numerous steep mountain ridges with intermontane basins and trench valleys that intersect, producing its rugged mountain character. The Blue Ridge contains the highest elevations and the most rugged topography in the Appalachian Mountain system of eastern North America (NCDEQ, 2015).

The Blue Ridge physiographic province lies in a region bounded to the southeast by the Brevard fault zone and to the northwest by the Blue Ridge fault systems (Holston-Iron Mountain, Great Smoky and Cartersville faults). These faults transported crystalline thrust sheets composed of Precambrian basement, late Precambrian-early Paleozoic metasedimentary and metavolcanic rocks, and Paleozoic plutons northwestward over Paleozoic sedimentary rocks of the Valley and Ridge province. The Blue Ridge province contains well-exposed Middle Proterozoic basement gneisses, Late Proterozoic plutons, Late Proterozoic metavolcanic and metasedimentary rift sequences, and thick early Paleozoic rifted continental martin and planform deposits. These rocks were involved in foreland thrusting along the western flank of the Appalachian orogen and record multiple periods of Paleozoic-aged deformation associated with the formation of the southern Appalachian orogen (Hatcher and Goldberg, 1991).

Bedrock of the site is mapped as the Neoproterozoic Alligator Back Formation and graphitic schist and metasandstone subunit. This consists of dark gray to greenish gray to medium gray, fine- to medium-grained, well foliated to mylonitic, equigranular to inequigranular, lepidoblastic to porphyroblastic, graphitic schist that is composed of sericite, quartz, graphite, feldspar, chlorite, kyanite, pyrite, and accessory minerals (Figure 3). This is interlayered with lesser amounts of metasandstone, metasiltstone, schistose metagraywacke, schist, and phyllite. The site is also mapped about 3,000 feet northwest of the Brevard fault zone. Foliation dips gently (15° to 25°) to the southeast, with at least three major near vertical joint sets (Cattanach et al., 2014). A deep mantle of reddish brown, clayey, saprolitic soil has developed on portions of the bedrock. This forms the colluvial soil in the upper portion of the slope. Bedrock is exposed on the west side of the slope, and subcrops are scattered in the middle and lower portions of the slope, which were exposed by prior debris flows and mitigation construction.

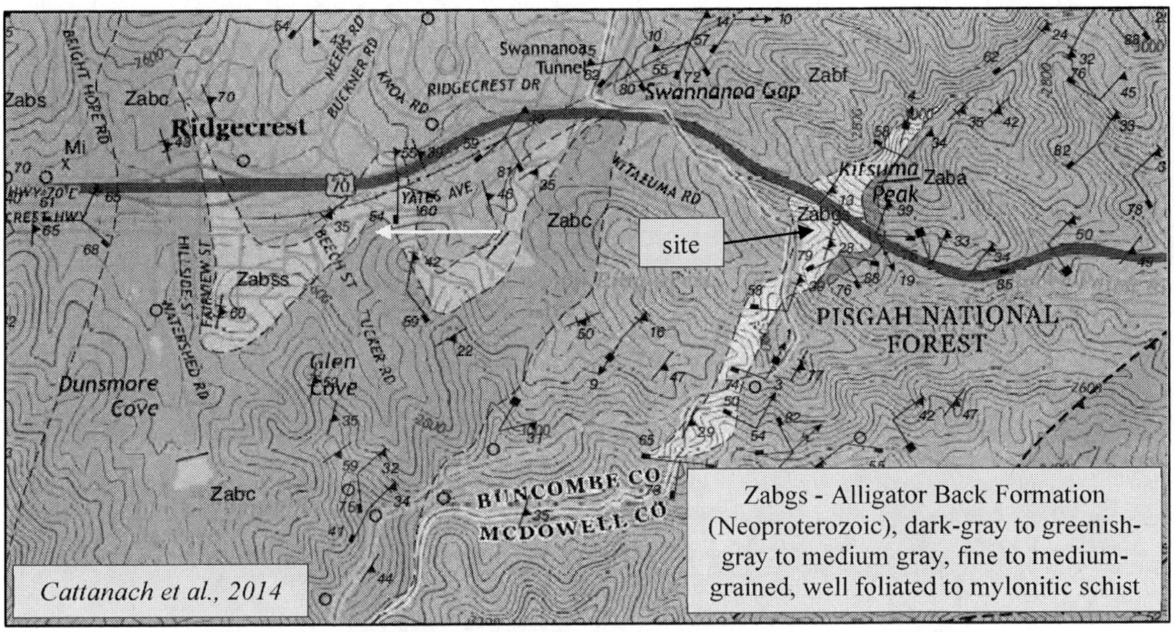

Figure 3. Bedrock geologic map (Cattanach et al., 2014)

Bedrock of the site is mapped as the Neoproterozoic Alligator Back Formation and graphitic schist and metasandstone subunit. This consists of dark gray to greenish gray to medium gray, fine- to medium-grained, well foliated to mylonitic, equigranular to inequigranular, lepidoblastic to porphyroblastic, graphitic schist that is comprised of sericite, quartz, graphite, feldspar, chlorite, kyanite, pyrite, and accessory minerals (Figure 4). This is interlayered with lesser amounts of metasandstone, metasiltstone, schistose metagraywacke, schist, and phyllite. The site is also mapped about 3,000 feet northwest of the Brevard fault zone. Foliation dips gently (15° to 25°) to the southeast, with at least three major near vertical joint sets (Cattanach et al., 2014).

A deep mantle of reddish brown, clayey, saprolitic soil is present on portions of the bedrock. This forms the colluvial soil in the upper portion of the slope. Bedrock is exposed on the west side of the slope, and subcrops are scattered in the middle and lower portions of the slope, which were exposed by prior debris flows and mitigation construction.

SITE CONDITIONS AND 2018 DEBRIS FLOW

The most recent debris flow occurred on May 30, 2018. Figure 4 shows the base of the debris flow after partial cleanup to remove soil from the roadway. Figure 5 shows the middle and upper portions of the debris flow. Figure 5 shows both the upper portion of the debris flow near the head scarp and middle of the debris flow. Notice the water flowing down the debris flow surface in both Figure 4 and Figure 5. During site reconnaissance, we identified "soil pipes" with diameters ranging from 0.5 feet to 1.0 feet near the head scarp that are shown in Figure 6. These pipes likely played a role in saturating the colluvial soils and formation of the debris flow. NCDOT reported they removed between 1000 cubic yards and 2000 cubic yards of soil from the roadway following the debris flow.

Figure 4. Debris flow cleanup on I-40 westbound at the base of the slope (NCDOT image from May 30, 2018 drone video).

Figure 5. Debris flow at the head scarp (left) and mid-slope (right).

Figure 6. Soil pipes exposed at head scarp from May 30, 2018 debris flow. (Photograph from June 27, 2019).

PROCUREMENT

NCDOT performed a preliminary analysis of the site, considering any improvement must remain in the right-of-way and construction would be constrained by the steep slopes. NCDOT selected a debris flow barrier concept where barriers are placed on the path of the previously constructed concrete-lined ditch to mitigate further debris flows. Preliminary studies performed by NCDOT indicated a barrier having a maximum pressure level (MPL; i.e., capacity) of 150 kiloNewtons per square meter (kN/m^2) and a maximum energy level (MEL) of 500 kiloJoules (kJ) as manufactured by Geobrugg® (SL-150 Shallow Debris Flow Barrier) might be sufficient. However, more detailed analyses were needed to check the design assumptions, size the barrier, and design the barrier foundations. NCDOT subsequently let the project as a design-build procurement, which would include: geotechnical drilling and geologic mapping to collect geotechnical data for final design; analyses of MPL and MEL for a debris flow barriers; design of the debris flow barrier; and design of a permanent concrete barrier wall at the slope toe.

FIELD INVESTIGATION

Nine (9) geotechnical borings were drilled to identify subsurface soil type and depth to bedrock to support foundation design for the debris flow barriers. Standard Penetration Testing was performed on the steep slope in late June 2019 using a remote-controlled Geoprobe® track rig using both solid stem and hollow stem augering methods. Depth to bedrock ranged from 1.5 feet to 4.1 feet below the ground surface (bgs) for eight (8) borings and 17 feet bgs for one (1) boring, above which both saprolitic and colluvial soils (some saturated) encountered. Surficial soils consisted of medium brown to red brown, dry to saturated, loose, sandy, gravelly and clayey silt, deposited by prior debris flows. In some places, these overlie both a tan, dry, silty sand fill used to construct the drainage ditch and tan-brown, fine to very fine grained, dense, extremely weak to very stiff, completely weathered, moist saprolite. Bedrock consists of medium tan-gray, fine to very fine grained, strongly foliated, very dense, extremely weak to very stiff, completely to highly weathered, damp phyllite and schist, with quartz veins and manganese oxide staining. Saprolite is at least 19 feet thick.

DEVELOPING THE DESIGN DEBRIS FLOW

In order to design an appropriate debris flow barrier system and foundations that could mitigate the effects of a potential future debris flow and impacts to I-40, a design debris flow was required. The design debris flow requires estimates of the volume (area and depth), slope angle, and density of the initiating debris flow, as well as the downslope geometry and predicted maximum velocity, travel time, discharge, and flow height. These parameters are required inputs for the barrier system design, and required three-dimensional (3D) numerical simulations of the existing slope geometry and materials in order to establish.

We developed and analyzed the design debris flow using the Rapid Mass Movement Simulation (RAMMS) Debris Flow software (RAMMS::Debris Flow; ETH 2019). RAMMS::Debris Flow uses a Voellmy-fluid friction model and a block release area for unchannelized flows. NCDOT generated a digital elevation model (DEM) of the slope geometry following the 2018 debris flow that was used to generate the 3D surface in the Debris Flow model. This information provides the slope angle at the area of debris flow initiation, as well as downslope for the continued flow. We then used the 2018 debris flow characteristics, information gathered from the field investigation, and engineering judgement to further develop and calibrate the Debris Flow model. The Debris Flow model requires the input of geometric parameters of sediment depth, volume, and area of a debris flow. We established these for the 2018 debris flow by evaluating the boring log sediment thickness, depth of the release at the head scarp, upper area of the debris flow thought to have been involved in the initial release, and photographs and drone footage of the post-flow slope. NCDOT provided an estimated volume of sediment created by the 2018 debris flow of between 1000 and 2000 cubic yards based on cleanup efforts, and these estimates further honed our interpretation of the debris flow initiation for model calibration.

Table 1. RAMMS::Debris Flow Material Input Parameters Defined

Parameter	Definition	Values
ρ	Total density of debris	Default: 2000 kg/m^3
μ	Tangent of the internal shear angle. Accounts for the resistance of the solid phase. Dominates when flow is close to stopping.	0.05 to 0.40
ξ	Relates to the viscous or turbulent fluid phase and hydrodynamics of the flow. Dominates when the flow is running quickly.	100-200 granular 200-1000 muddy

The Debris Flow model also requires input of material properties of density (ρ), internal shear angle (μ), and fluid phase hydrodynamic flow parameter (ξ), at a minimum, and the software manual provides ranges of possible values to choose based on the characteristics of the site sediments (Table 1). We evaluated a range of these properties based on the known colluvium sediment and the presence of flowing water (Figure 4 through Figure 6). The Debris Flow model additionally allows inputs of material yield stress or an erosion model that allows the debris flow to pick up additional sediment as it travels downslope. We opted to not use these parameters, as limited data were available to calibrate them from the previous debris flows at the site.

We performed a parametric study using nine (9) different models of the assumed initial release geometry (area, height, and volume) and material properties for the 2018 debris flow to calibrate the Debris Flow model. Part of the parametric study was to establish the importance of the target volume, sediment depth, and sediment properties ρ, μ, and ξ on the resulting maximum velocity, pressure, shear stress, and height of the flow, where modeled debris flow run out onto the area of I-40 from the model was visually compared with the run out images from the actual debris flow. Table 2 provides a summary of the ranges of target volume with variable depth at a constant release area (Figure 7), ρ, μ, and ξ were varied. For the parametric study, three values of each parameter were chosen, and only one parameter at a time was varied (e.g., target volume at a constant release area and variable depth varied, while ρ, μ, and ξ remained constant). Figure 8 provides results for the best fit model (Table 2) maximum height, velocity, pressure, and shear stress. We visually compared the modeled debris flow areas on the slope and the run out into the area of I-40 with the drone footage and photographs from the 2018 debris flow.

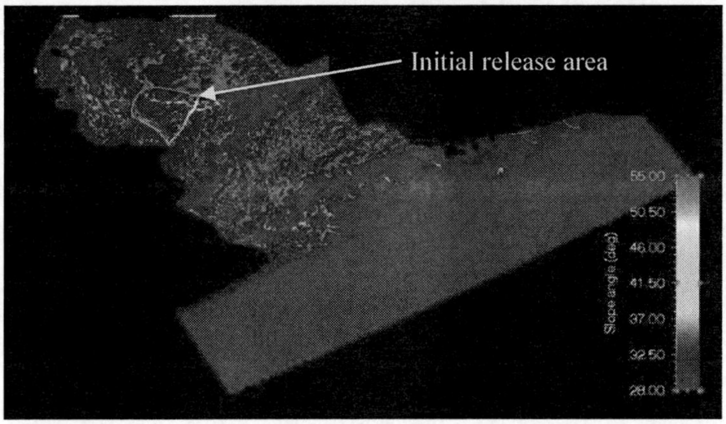

Figure 7. RAMMS::Debris Flow model showing the slope DEM and initial release area.

Table 2. RAMMS::Debris Flow Calibration Model Parameters and Results based on observations of the site's 2018 debris flow.

	Input Parameters							**Results**		
	Avg. Slope Angle °	**Target Volume (ft^3)**	**Area (ft^2)**	**Depth (ft)**	**ρ (pcf)**	**μ (-)**	**ξ (-)**	**Max. Velocity (ft/s)**	**Max. Pressure (psf)**	**Max. Shear Stress (psf)**
Range	29 to 35	27,270 to 53,670	7,900	2.6 to 5.3	120 125 130	0.25 0.30 0.35	100 200 300	5 - 28	1555 - 3360	580 - 1150
Best Fit	35	39,160	7900	3.7	130	0.30 0.35	200 100	27 20	2875 1555	850 740

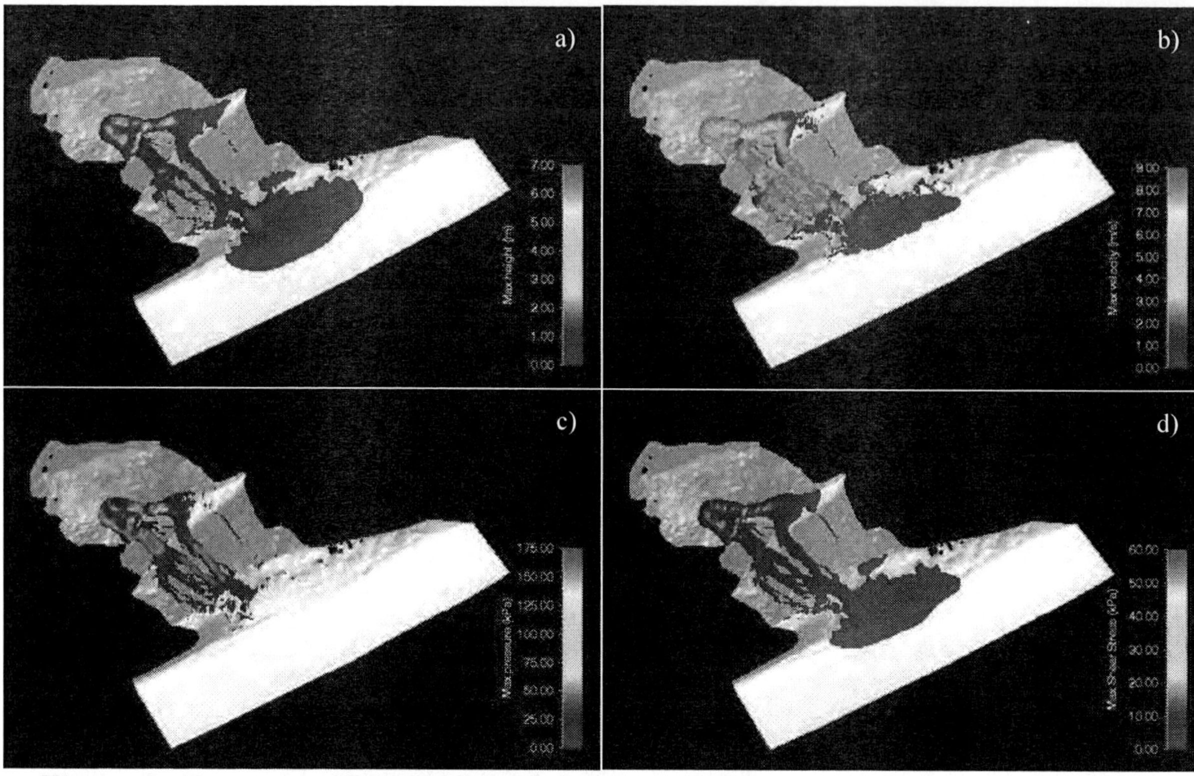

Figure 8. Example of RAMMS::Debris Flow calibration model results showing a) maximum height, b) maximum velocity, c) maximum pressure, and d) maximum shear stress for the Table 2 best fit scenario (μ = 0.30 and ξ = 200) debris flow.

The parametric study findings showed: material density has little effect on the model results; an increase in internal shear angle μ results in a decrease in debris flow velocity; an increase in the viscous flow parameter ξ results in increases in maximum velocity, height, pressure, and shear stress of the debris flow. An increase in the debris flow volume increases all resulting maxima, leading us to use the mid-range of the NCDOT-estimated volume of 1450 cubic yards in all subsequent analyses. Table 2 provides the parameters we determined were the most reasonable best fit that represented the conditions observed after the 2018 debris flow. These observed conditions used to determine best fit parameters included the extend of the debris at the toe of the slope on I-40, evidence of soil pipes, water in the sediment, and water flowing from the slope after the event, and the colluvium properties and depth above bedrock.

In addition to the nine (9) calibration models performed, we performed one (1) additional model that used μ = 0.35 and ξ = 100 for comparison to the best fit model that used μ = 0.30 and ξ = 200. We know the 2018 debris flow occurred after a period of heavy rains in the area. Based on this and the presence of the soil pipes and flowing water observed following the debris flow, we were comfortable with the modeled μ = 0.30 and ξ = 200 values, which represent higher water content sediments. However, we additionally wanted to consider a design debris flow where less water would be present in the slope and sediment had a higher internal friction and was less "muddy" by using μ = 0.35 and ξ = 100. Table 2 shows that the resulting velocity, pressure, and shear were greater for a debris flow mass with more viscous parameters, and thus, we adopted the parameters of μ = 0.30 and ξ = 200 for the design debris flow scenarios.

Following establishment of the material parameters for the design debris flows, we identified three (3) new potential debris flow initiation areas and volumes (Figure 9) based on elevations on the slope, slope angles (high), and an estimated 4.3 foot colluvium depth from the field investigation. We modeled these three (3) areas in RAMMS::Debris Flow using the same DEM with the best fit ρ, μ, and ξ parameters from the calibration models (Table 2) and obtained the resulting velocities, pressures, and shear stresses provided in Table 3 These were subsequently used for design of the debris flow barrier.

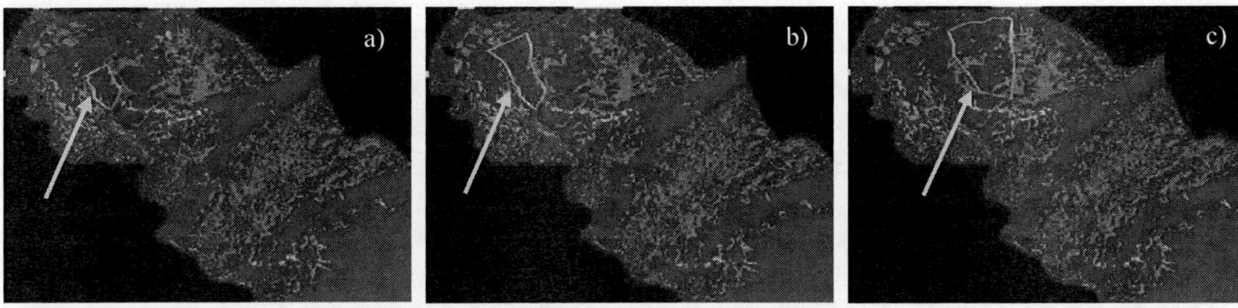

Figure 9: Design Potential Debris Flow Release Areas with 4.3 feet Colluvium Depth: a) 11,920 cubic feet; b) 23,750 cubic feet; c) 51,485 cubic feet.

Table 3. RAMMS::Debris Flow Model Parameters and Results for the design debris flows.

	Input Parameters							**Results**		
Design Debris Flow #	**Avg. Slope Angle °**	**Target Volume (ft^3)**	**Area (ft^2)**	**Depth (ft)**	**ρ (pcf)**	**μ (-)**	**ξ (-)**	**Max. Velocity (ft/s)**	**Max. Pressure (psf)**	**Max. Shear Stress (psf)**
1	29	11,920	2,350	4.3	130	0.30	200	24.5	2455	470
2	27	23,750	4,850	4.3	130	0.30	200	26.5	2875	440
3	29	51,485	10,240	4.3	130	0.30	200	30.5	3750	395

BARRIER DESIGN

Barrier Selection

The design debris flow barrier selected by NCDOT, the Geobrugg® SL-150 Shallow Debris Flow Barrier. The SL-150 barrier selected has a 3.5 m (11.5 feet) height, 72 m (236 feet) length, and 8 m (26.2 feet) post spacing. The barrier was sized using the Geobrugg® Shallslide online dimensioning tool (Geobrugg, 2019a) and the RAMMS::Debris Flow release areas, material parameters, and results (Table 3) for the three (3) design debris flows. We assumed the barrier location along the slope and determined the distance from the bottom of each release area (breakout zone) to the barrier and assumed a debris flow spread angle of 10° (maximum). We used the width of starting volume, starting volume, material density, slope angle, and peak discharge of the debris flow from each RAMMS::Debris Flow model. Lastly, we used a minimum global safety factor of 1.3, a dynamic load coefficient of 1.0 (maximum), and assumed a horizontal inclination of retained material behind the barrier following the design debris flow for all design debris flows.

The Shallslide used these input parameters to evaluate the capacity of the design debris flow barrier to withstand the dynamic impact and retain the volume for the design debris flows. The results indicated that while one SL-150 barrier system of 3.5 m height and 72 m length with 8 m post spacing would not be sufficient to withstand the dynamic impact and retain the released volume of each of the three (3) design debris flows. Thus, a double barrier system of the same type was planned, where a second barrier was designed downslope from the first to absorb and retain the overflow from the upstream barrier during the debris flow.

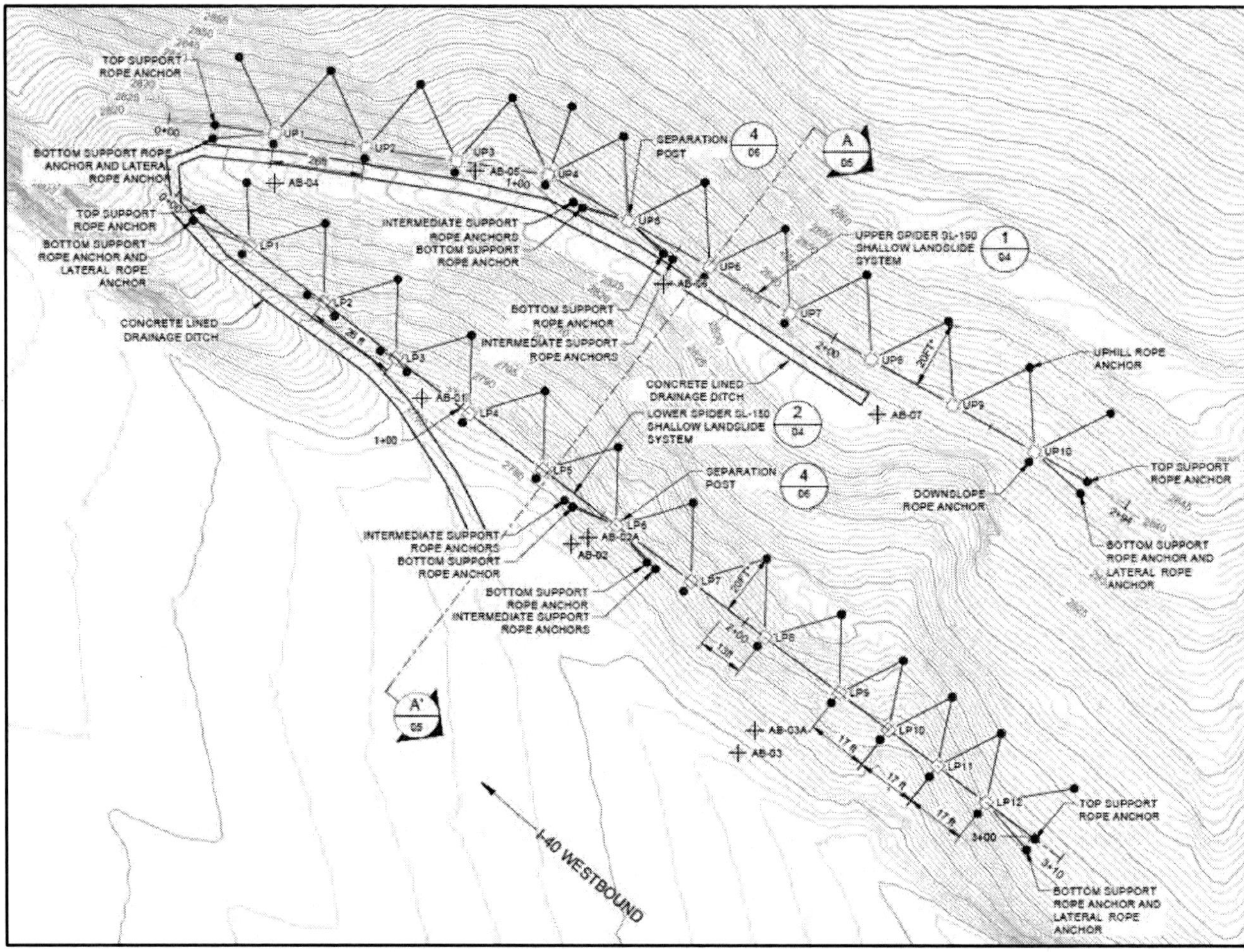

Figure 10: Double Tier Debris Flow Barrier Layout.

Barrier Layout

Figure 10 shows a plan view of the debris flow barrier system developed for the site, which includes the upper and lower barriers, foundation locations, and tiebacks installed both laterally behind and in front of and in back of the barriers. The design is based on the recommendations provided by the manufacturer in the SL-150 product manual (Geobrugg, 2019b). The design incorporates dual lateral and intermediate anchors in plane with the barriers. Figure 11 shows the cross-section view of the debris flow barrier system. The barriers are located on the outside edge of the previously installed concrete ditch in order to maintain the ditch functionality in conveying surface water from the upper slope to the toe of the slope to minimize infiltration and soil saturation.

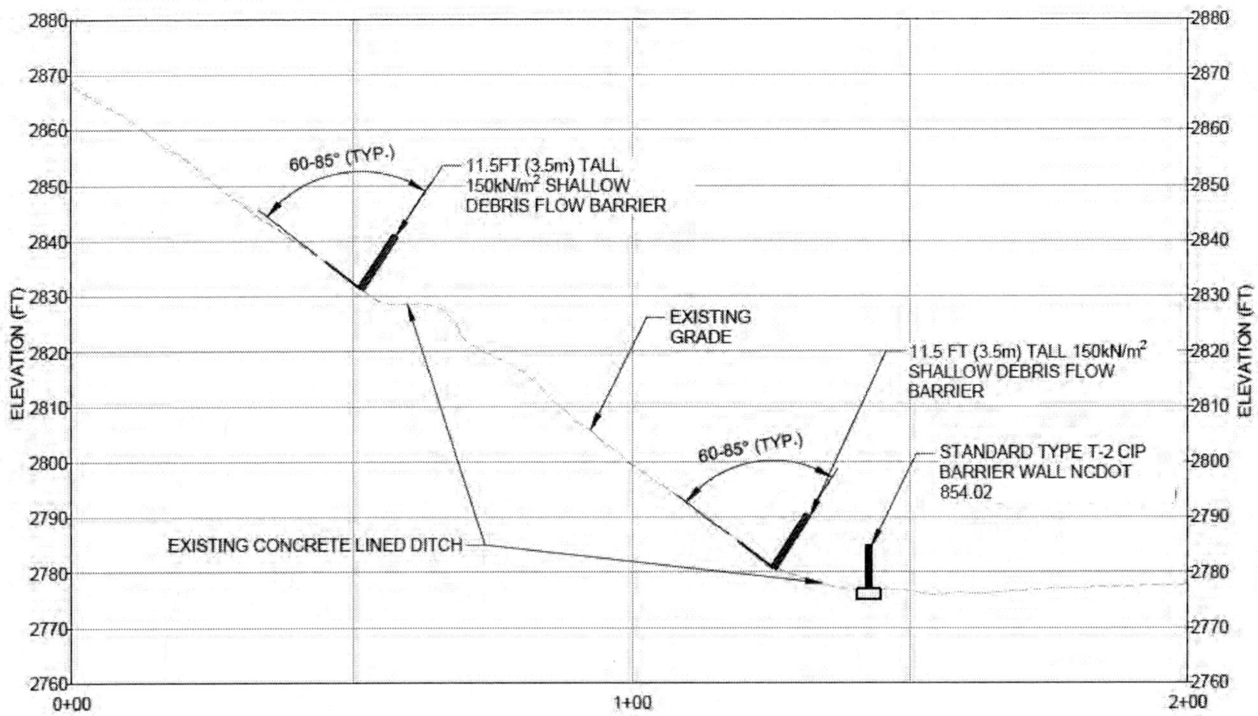

Figure 11: Cross section of the double barrier system.

Barrier Anchor Design

Once the barrier was sized, the anchors for the barriers were designed. We proposed micropiles beneath the posts and tie-back anchors. The highly variable nature of the colluvial soils and saprolite created a challenge in that published anchor bond strengths in saprolitic soils are rare. We determined the design bond strengths for the micropile and tie-back anchor designs on a literature search that included Aydin (2006), Deere and Patton (1971) and Hunt (2005) and results of the field geotechnical investigation. These are reported in Table 4 as the ultimate bond strength and the design bond strength based on FS = 1.5. The design bond strengths were verified using sacrificial anchors installed and pull-tested at the start of construction. These measured bond strengths are also reported in Table 4, which show the assumed design bond strengths used for design were greater than the ultimate bond strengths, and thus conservative.

Table 4. Grount-Ground Bond Strengths

Soil Layer	Design (Working) Bond Strength[1] (psi)	Ultimate Bond Strength (psi)	Measured Bond Strength[2] (psi)
Colluvium	0	n/a	n/a
Saprolite	25	37.5	37.8
Weathered Bedrock	50	75	>152

Note: [1]using Factor of Safety, FS = 1.5; [2]based on drilling resistance encountered during installation.

We additionally designed and sized the anchor connections, post foundations, and anchor lengths to satisfy the loading demands on the posts and tie-backs for the system per the dimensioning provided in Geobrugg (2019b) and design guidance from ACI 318-14 Section 22.6. Table 5 presents the design loading for each element with FS = 1.5. Note, each post location is considered an anchor system and was evaluated for each of the anchor section (i.e., the post foundation tension and compression, along with the uphill anchor tension, support rope, and downhill anchor tension). A total of 10 upper barrier and 12 lower barrier anchor systems were evaluated. Table 5 additionally presents the ranges of total anchor length installed between the upper and lower barrier systems, along with the grouted length for reference. The grouted length is less than the total length, as the anchors are sleeved in the colluvium. All anchor load is transferred to the saprolite and weathered bedrock.

Table 5: Barrier Anchor Sections with Design Loads and Lengths.

Anchor Section[1]	**Design Load[2] (kips)**	**Design Total Length[3] (ft)**	**Design Grouted Length[4] (ft)**
Uphill Anchor Posts	67.5	15 (*17*), 25 (*3*), 30 (*2*)	11.5 to 22.5
Tie-back Support Rope	84.3	20 (*17*), 30 (*2*)	16.5 to 26.5
Foundation Dowel - Compression	78.8	20 (*17*), 30 (*5*)	11.8 to 25.2
Foundation Dowel - Tension	45.0	20 (*20*), 30 (*2*)	14.0 to 16.0
Downslope Anchor Posts	78.8	20 (*17*), 30 (*2*)	13.1 to 18.5

Notes: [1]Anchors have 4-inch diameter boreholes; [2]Using FS = 1.5; [3]Total length given by the length with the number of anchors at this length in parentheses. Number of anchors not adding to 22 for each category indicates certain elements were not present or necessary in the design; [4]Grouted length is less than the total length, as the anchors are sleeved in the colluvium.

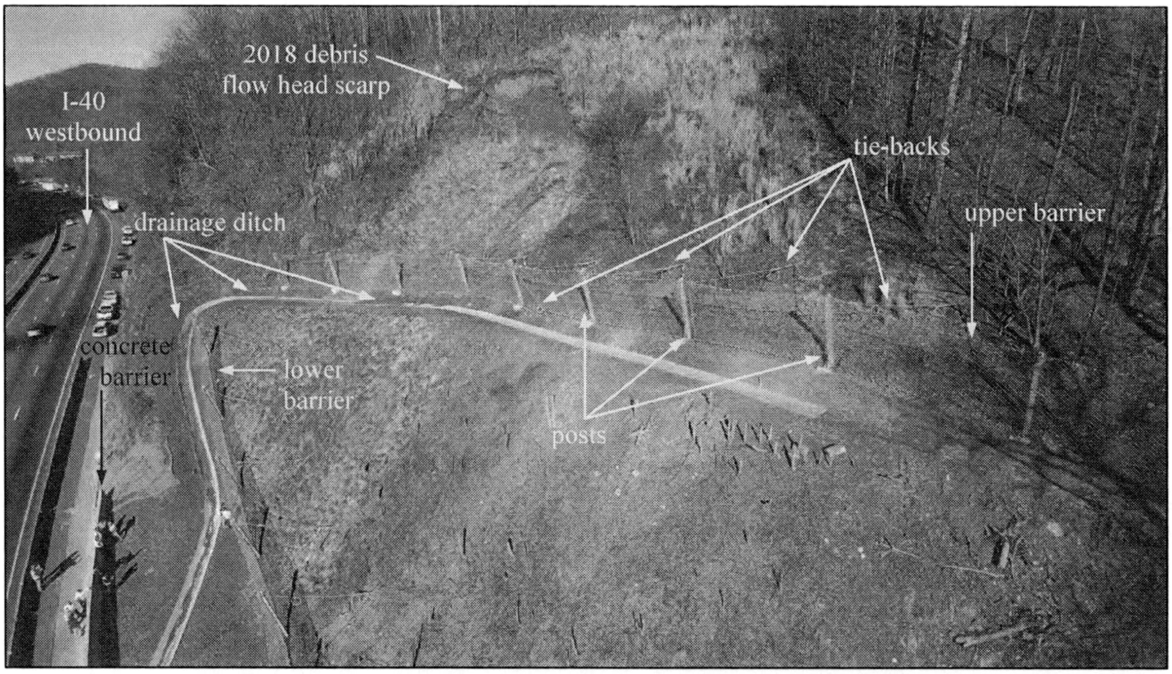

Figure 12: Aerial View to the West of the Barrier System (Drone Image from Fall 2019/Winter 2020).

CONSTRUCTED SYSTEM

The double barrier system was constructed at the site between August and September 2019. Figure 12 illustrates the installed system during colder months when vegetation is sparse. The image shows the major features of the system installed, mainly the upper and lower barriers and the associated mesh, fence, and tie-back anchor lines, as well as the concrete barrier at the base of the slope adjacent to I-40. Figure 13 shows a closeup of the components of the barrier system, mainly the mesh, posts, and lines with breaking element loops to the tie-back anchors.

Figure 13: Completed Debris Flow Barrier System: a) View of Mesh and Post and b) Typical End Post showing Braking Element Loops in the Two Lateral End and Rear Lines to the Tie-back Anchors. (Photographs from April 27, 2020.)

CONCLUSION

Right-of-way limitations, steep slopes, deep saprolitic slopes, and construction constraints hindered the Swannona Gap debris flow barrier design-build project. The viability of an advanced debris flow barrier concept composed of a two-tiered barrier system was verified using 3D debris flow modeling to determine design debris flow geometry, dynamic loading, and volumes. The 3D debris flow modeling using RAMMS::Debris Flow was based on a field investigation of soils, calibration of a model to the 2018 debris flow characteristics and post-event reconnaissance, and anticipated future debris flows determined from slope characteristics and engineering judgement. Careful geologic mapping and geotechnical exploration drilling in the complex weathered saprolite was crucial for design of the anchorage systems for the barriers. The anticipation of a variety of encountered materials, ranging from prior debris flow material, completely weathered saprolite, and weathered and unweathered bedrock assisted in adjusting the bond lengths of the foundation element design to encountered conditions. The true test of the system's effectiveness will be the next debris flow event triggered by heavy rains, which in the current times of climate change, may not be far away.

REFERENCES

ACI (2014). Building Code Requirements for Structural Concrete (ACI 318R-14), American Concrete Institute.

Aydin, A., 2006. Stability of Saprolitic Slopes: Nature and Role of Field Scale Heterogeneities. Natural Hazards and Earth System Sciences, vol. 6, p. 89-96.

Deere, D.U. and Patton, F.D., 1971. Slope Stability in Residual Soils. Proceedings of the Fourth Panamerican Conference on Soil Mechanics and Foundation Engineering, San Juan, Puerto Rico, June 1971, American Society of Civil Engineers, New York, NY, p. 87-170.

Cattanach, B.L., Bozdog, G.N., and Wooten, R.M., 2014. Bedrock Geologic Map of the Black Mountain 7.5-minute Quadrangle, North Carolina. North Carolina Geological Survey Open File Map 2014-03, scale 1:24,000, 1 sheet.

Geobrugg, 2019a. Shallslide Online Tool for Dimensioning of Flexible Shallow Landslides. Version 1.0. https://www.geobrugg.com/shallslide_en.html#/design.

Geobrugg, 2019b. Shallow Landslide System SPIDER SL-150 Product Manual. https://www.geobrugg.com/file-34191/downloadcenter/level2-product-manuals/SL-barriers/L2_SPIDER-SL-150-manual-e-14_170831.pdf

Eidgenössiche Technische Hochschule (ETH), 2019, WSL Institute for Snow and Avalanche Research SLF. RAMMS – Rapid Mass Movement Simulation, Swiss Federal Institute for Forest, Snow and Landscape Research, Zurich, Vers. 1.7.0.

Hatcher, R.D., Jr., and Goldberg, S.A., 1991. Chapter 2. The Blue Ridge Geologic Province, in: Horton, J.W., Jr., and Zullo, V.A. (eds.), The Geology of the Carolinas, Carolina Geological Society, Fiftieth Anniversary Volume, University of Tennessee Press, Knoxville.

Hunt, R.E., 2005. Geotechnical Engineering Investigation Handbook. Taylor and Francis, Boca Raton, FL, 1,066 p.

North Carolina Department of Environmental Quality (NCDEQ), September 29, 2015. Physiographic Provinces of North Carolina. https://ncdenr.maps.arcgis.com/apps/MapSeries/index.html. Accessed March 14, 2022.

United States Geological Survey (USGS), 2016a. Black Mountain Quadrangle, North Carolina, 7.5-minute series, scale 1:24,000, 1 sheet.

United States Geological Survey (USGS), 2016b. South Atlantic Water Science Center – North Carolina Office, Physiographic Regions, last updated December 5, 2016. https://nc.water.usgs.gov/projects/index_physio.html. Accessed March 10, 2022.

Geographic Information System (GIS) and Interpretation of Relative Geologic and Geotechnical Risk Susceptibility For Proposed Roadway Alignments Through Gates of the Arctic National Park, Alaska

Orion George
Federal Highway Administration
Western Federal Lands Division
610 East Fifth Street
Vancouver, Washington 98661
(360) 619-7634
Orion.George@dot.gov

Douglas A. Anderson
Federal Highway Administration
Western Federal Lands Division
610 East Fifth Street
Vancouver, Washington 98661
(360) 619-7958
Douglas.A.Anderson@dot.gov

Prepared for the 71st Highway Geology Symposium, May 2022

Acknowledgements

The authors would like to thank the many individuals who contributed in our portion of the project. The following individuals' contributions were particularly integral for the work described (in alphabetical order):

Acknowledge
Brian Collins, Senior Geotechnical Engineer, (formerly of) Federal Highway Administration
Betty Chon, Project Manager (retired), Federal Highway Administration
Jeff Currey, Materials Engineer, Alaska Department of Transportation and Public Facilities
Joe Durenberger, Project Manager/Engineer (retired), Gates of the Arctic National Park and Preserve
Chad Hults, Regional Geologist, National Park Service - Alaska Region
Jeff Rasic, Chief of Resources, Gates of the Arctic National Park and Preserve
Dave Swanson, Ecologist, Gates of the Arctic National Park and Preserve

Disclaimer

Statements and views presented in this paper are strictly those of the authors, and do not necessarily reflect positions held by their affiliations, the Highway Geology Symposium (HGS), or others acknowledged above. The mention of trade names for commercial products does not imply the approval or endorsement by HGS

Copyright

ABSTRACT

The Federal Highway Administration's, Western Federal Lands Highway Division (FHWA) was requested by the National Park Service (NPS) to assist with geotechnical and engineering considerations for portions of the Ambler Mining District's Industrial Access Project (AMDIAP). The Alaska Industrial Development and Export Authority (AIDEA) proposes a 211-mile industrial gravel road connecting the Dalton Highway with the Ambler Mining District, in northern Alaska. Gates of the Arctic National Park (GAAR) reviewed two alternative alignment options to comply with the 1980 Alaska National Interest Lands Conservation Act (ANILCA). The two proposed alignments traverse GAAR managed lands along a 45-mile northern alignment or a 62-mile southern alignment. As part of this work, FHWA was requested by NPS to provide a desktop geologic and geotechnical evaluation of these two road corridor alternatives in 2018. The FHWA developed a process utilizing available data and a Geographic Information System (GIS) to remotely map geological hazards with available data, assess those hazard layers as it relates to the relative geologic and geotechnical risk, spatially aggregate the relative risk, and compare the two proposed alignments by their total associated relative geological and geotechnical risk susceptibility. This iterative, spatial, geological risk analysis process, tool, and final work product assisted GAAR's interdisciplinary team with development of an Environmental and Economic Analysis (EEA) and was used to inform their evaluation and decision of a preferred alignment for permitting the project through GAAR by the Department of Interior. In the end, FHWA's analyses associated a higher total relative geologic and geotechnical risk susceptibility with the southern alignment versus the northern alignment. When all other discipline impacts were considered, the northern alignment was preferred for permitting road design, construction, and maintenance through GAAR. This project serves as an example of how leveraging available geospatial data sets in GIS and providing good communication with a knowledgeable interdisciplinary team on a complicated problem can inform a complex decision.

INTRODUCTION

On December 2, 1980 President Carter signed into law the Alaska National Interest Lands Conservation Act (ANILCA). In Alaska this law created Gates of the Arctic National Park and Preserve (GAAR), including most other national parklands, national wildlife refuges, national monuments, wild and scenic rivers, recreational areas, national forests, and conservation areas in the state. With 103 million acres of land, it is the single largest expansion of protected lands in United States history. However, the act, considered a Great Compromise, also established many exceptions to balance preservation with development. One compromise in the ANILCA directed the National Park Service (NPS) to determine a preferred alignment through GAAR to access the Ambler Mining District (AMD) and develop appropriate terms and conditions for a right-of-way permit in an Environmental and Economic Analysis (EEA) (*1*).

Currently, the Alaska Industrial Development and Export Authority (AIDEA), a public corporation of the State of Alaska, proposes a 211-mile controlled-access industrial road along the southern Brooks Range that would connect the Dalton Highway to the AMD in interior Alaska (Figure 1). This joint public-private venture is the Ambler Mining District's Industrial Access Project (AMDIAP) and is modeled after the 52-mile DeLong Mountain Transportation System accessing the Red Dog Mine with Kotzebue, Alaska. The proposed road will provide surface transportation access to the mining district to allow for expanded exploration, mine development, and associated operations.

At the request of NPS, AIDEA evaluated two alignments through GAAR. In 2010 the Alaska Department of Transportation and Public Facilities (ADOT&PF) started to evaluate multiple access routes to the AMD. The ADOT&PF developed two potential routes, a north route and a south route, across GAAR, which also includes the Kobuk Wild and Scenic River (Figure 2). The locations where the proposed southern route leaves the proposed northern alignment are referred to as the "alignment junctions". Considered side by side the northern alignment is a fairly straight stretch with approximately 26 miles within GAAR. The proposed southern alignment branches off of the original alignment outside the boundaries of GAAR and extends approximately 18 miles through the park. However, from junction to junction the northern proposed alignment is approximately 45 miles long and the southern proposed route is about 62 miles long, (Figure 2).

These two proposed alignments led to a request by NPS to have the Federal Highway Administration's Western Federal Lands Division (FHWA) review permit application documents along with available geotechnical data and reports to develop a geologic and geotechnical hazard and relative risk model to help NPS evaluate potential impacts to resources along the north and south proposed road corridors. The geologic and geotechnical hazard and relative risk model was intended to be an analysis tool used by NPS's interdisciplinary team for preparation of the EEA. The EEA provided data for evaluation and selection of NPS's preferred alignment across GAAR and supported development of permit terms and conditions, to avoid or minimize resource damage anticipated from proposed, staged road construction and maintenance operations within the park and preserve (*2*).

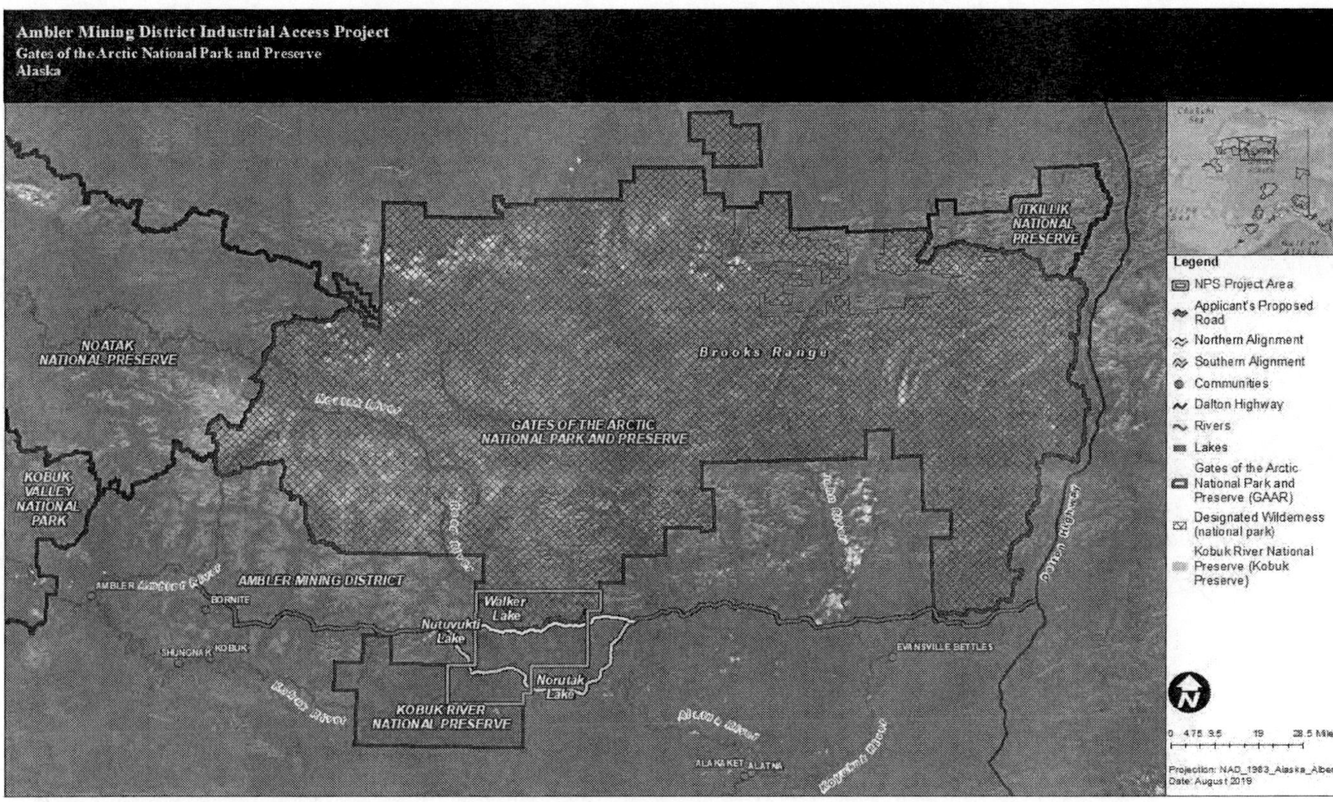

Figure 1 - Ambler Mining District Industrial Access Road project overview. The map is from the final NPS Ambler Mining District Industrial Access Project Economic and Environmental Analysis (*2*).

Figure 2 - Two alternative alignments through Gates of the Arctic National Park and Preserve; the north and south routes. The map is from the final NPS Ambler Mining District Industrial Access Project Economic and Environmental Analysis (*2*).

PROJECT DEVELOPMENT

The NPS requested FHWA interpretation of relative geologic and geotechnical risk susceptibility along the two proposed alignments, in relation to staged construction and long-term maintenance of an industrial gravel road with associated material sources, airstrips, and access roads. It was developed and mapped from the office as a planning level project without on-site observation or subsurface investigation by FHWA. The following provides the iterative scope of work that was requested by NPS to assist them with selection of their preferred route, development of their EEA documentation, and considerations for development of permit terms and conditions for design, construction, and ongoing maintenance operations of the selected route through GAAR.

The NPS initially requested FHWA to provide geologic and geotechnical hazard and relative risk susceptibility modeling for both proposed alignments within the boundaries of GAAR, considered *Iteration 1*. A second iteration (*Iteration 2*) of work, requested by NPS, extended the same modeling process to the proposed northern and southern alignment areas outside of GAAR to the eastern and western junctions of the north and south proposed alignments (Figure 2). A third iteration (*Iteration 3*) of mapping and data analyses was requested by NPS to refocus relative geologic and geotechnical risk susceptibility interpretation within GAAR boundaries and concentrate on effects of the proposed Phase I construction of a pioneer road.

This paper documents a description of the three iterations, separate levels of spatial analyses, and the overall process used to develop the geologic and geotechnical hazard and relative risk susceptibility maps for NPS's decision making process and citation in their EEA document.

GEOLOGIC AND GEOTECHNICAL DATA

Multiple geospatial datasets were consulted and incorporated for Geographic Information System (GIS) based geologic and geotechnical hazard mapping and ranking of relative geologic and geotechnical risk susceptibility. Datasets used are cited below.

Geologic and related geotechnical hazards were interpreted from the geospatial datasets and mapped by FHWA along an approximate half mile wide corridor for the two proposed alignments. The corridor width is the bulk area mapped as this was the area with available Light Detection and Ranging (lidar) data acquired in 2012 by AIDEA for the project. Some areas outside of the half mile corridor of available lidar data were mapped as well, such as potential material sources, airstrips, and their associated access roads.

More data was available within GAAR boundaries at a larger scale and higher resolution than areas outside of GAAR's boundaries. This is due to generally higher interest and investment in scientific studies, on-the-ground investigation, and documentation within GAAR boundaries. This increased resolution facilitated more robust analyses and interpretation within GAAR boundaries versus outside this management unit. In addition, some ADOT&PF test borings, soils, and geomorphology mapping combined with personal communication with GAAR employees, also allowed for a better understanding of geologic materials and their respective conditions on-the-ground as well as their potential geotechnical challenges within the GAAR boundaries. For this reason, some data within GAAR boundaries was used to extrapolate interpretations outside of GAAR to the junction areas.

Within boundaries of GAAR, the following data sets were utilized by FHWA for GIS mapping:

- NPS mapped Surficial Materials and permafrost potential (unpublished by NPS),
- Orthorectified aerial (1-foot resolution) (privately acquired in 2012 by AIDEA),
- IKONOS Satellite imagery (15 feet resolution) (provided by NPS),
- Publicly available Google Earth satellite imagery (*3*),
- Hamilton and Labay (*4*) surficial map of GAAR;
- Wilson et al. (*5*) Geologic Map of Alaska (1:250,000 scale mapping in the area of interest);
- Swanson (*6*) landscape ecosystem map;
- Test boring and geotechnical information from Speeter (*7*) (*8*) (*9*) Alaska Department of Transportation (ADOT&PF) geotechnical investigation,
- Interferometric synthetic aperture radar (IfSAR) derived hillshade (15 feet resolution) (provided by NPS), and
- Lidar data (3-foot resolution) (privately acquired in 2012 by AIDEA).

Outside boundaries of GAAR, the following additional data sets were utilized by FHWA for GIS mapping:

- Brown et al. (*10*) circum-Arctic map of permafrost and ground-ice conditions
- Permafrost database development, characterization, and mapping for northern Alaska (*11*) (*12*),
- DOWL HKM geotechnical (*13*) and preliminary hydrology (*14*) memorandums.

From data sets presented above, the following geologic and geotechnical hazard layers were developed and mapped by FHWA:

- **Surficial Geology/Materials** (mapped by Chad Hults, NPS Alaska Regional Geologist within GAAR boundaries; mapped by FHWA outside of GAAR boundaries)
    - Permafrost potential as an attribute assigned to Surficial Materials,
- **Muskeg** (areas not captured in surficial geology/materials data),
- **Permafrost Landforms** (areas not captured in permafrost potential from surficial geology/materials data; mapped inside and outside GAAR boundaries by FHWA),
- **Mass Wasting** (landslide areas; mapped inside and outside GAAR boundaries by FHWA),
- **Flooding and Erosion** (mapped inside and outside GAAR boundaries by FHWA), and
- **Slope Gradient** (mapped inside and outside GAAR boundaries within lidar coverage by FHWA).

Based on our understanding of geomorphic and geologic materials interaction with anticipated natural processes, staged construction, and long-term maintenance of the proposed transportation corridor, we assigned a relative risk rank ranging from zero (0) to three (3) for features within the mapped geologic and geotechnical hazard layers. A relative risk rank of zero (0) would suggest that a particular geologic and geotechnical hazard has a relatively low risk of affecting resources from road construction and maintenance, whereas a relative risk rank of three (3) would be considered a relatively high risk of that geologic and geotechnical hazard affecting resources due to construction and maintenance of the proposed road within a given corridor. The Surficial

Geology/Materials layer also received a relative risk rating of 0 – 3 based on the materials anticipated probability to contain significant permafrost as well. Table 1 lists all geologic and geotechnical hazard layers, their associated units, and the units' assigned relative risk rankings.

Table 1 - Mapped geologic – geotechnical hazard layers, units, and relative risk rankings.

Geologic/Geotechnical Hazard Layer Unit	**Relative Risk Ranking**	**Associated Permafrost (PF) Probability**	**Added PF Relative Risk Ranking**	**Total Relative Risk Ranking**
Surficial Materials Layer				
Piedmont gravel	1	Low	0	1
Muskeg	3	High	3	6
Glacial lacustrine deposits	3	High	3	6
Glacial outwash	1	Low	0	1
Glacial outwash (reworked)	2.5	Variable	2.5	5
Glacial drift (subdued)	2	Moderate-High	2	4
Glacial drift (kame)	1	Low-Moderate	1	2
Alluvium	1	Low	0	1
Colluvium over unconsolidated deposits	1	Variable	2.5	3.5
Colluvium - shallow bedrock	0	Low	0	0
Colluvium - deep bedrock	2	High	3	5
Bedrock	0	Low	0	0
Alluvial terrace deposits	0	Variable	2.5	2.5
Permafrost Landforms Layer				
No evidence of permafrost	0	-	-	0
Evidence of permafrost	1.5	-	-	1.5
Mass Wasting Layer				
Deep-seated landslide	3	-	-	3
Debris flow	2	-	-	2
Valley wall	1.5	-	-	1.5
Flooding and Erosion Layer				
Major drainages	1.5	-	-	1.5
Minor drainages	0.5	-	-	0.5
Slope Gradient Layer				
0 - 30 degrees	0	-	-	0
30 - 40 degrees	2	-	-	2
> 40 degrees	3	-	-	3

Surficial Geology/Materials Layer

Within the boundaries of GAAR, this layer was mapped at approximately 1:5,000 scale by Chad Hults (*15*), NPS - Alaska Regional Geologist, by interpreting lidar data and consulting Hamilton and Labay (*13*), Wilson et al. (*5*), Swanson (*6*), and Speeter (*9*). The original mapping was completed for areas within boundaries of GAAR. Subsequent mapping of surficial materials was completed by FHWA for areas outside of GAAR's boundaries using similar techniques, data sets, and methodologies.

Units within this layer are landforms and geological units that suggest certain types of materials are present. Landform units were used to estimate probability of permafrost, based on material types common with the associated landforms (*11*) (*12*). This layer has two separate relative risk rankings attached to it by FHWA. One for the risk associated with anticipated hazards with relation to engineering geological and geotechnical material behaviors and another for the relative risk associated with the probability of permafrost within these materials.

Hazardous geological conditions assumed for the relative risk rankings of surficial materials were the layer's interpreted susceptibility to slope instability, settlement, and overall poor foundation performance. The relative risk of a materials susceptibility to permafrost was estimated based on type of materials and their ability to develop and sustain permafrost, their estimated hydraulic conductivity, personal communication of field observations from GAAR employees, and our observations of similar geologic materials permafrost susceptibility and performance in Alaska and other cold regions.

Table 1 lists surficial material units mapped by Hults and the probability of permafrost attributed to those material units. The FHWA assigned geologic and geotechnical relative risk rankings are also included for each of the surficial materials and their associated permafrost probability.

Muskeg Layer

This layer was mapped by FHWA to capture areas likely to have muskeg present, but is not captured in the Surficial Materials layer described above. The Muskeg layer is only supplemental to the Surficial Materials Layer within GAAR's boundaries, where the original Surficial Materials mapping was completed. Muskeg areas outside of GAAR's boundaries were captured in the Surficial Materials mapping done by FHWA to the junctions outside of GAAR's boundaries. Where the Muskeg layer overlaps the Surficial Materials layer within GAAR, the aggregated relative risk ranking is higher. A risk ranking of three (3) was assigned to features within this layer because it is anticipated areas of muskeg would exhibit instability and settlement during construction and likely present problems for long term maintenance of a proposed roadway (Table 1).

Permafrost Landforms Layer

This layer was mapped within the GAAR boundaries by FHWA where observations of thermokarst and polygonal landforms suggest permafrost is likely. In some areas, our observations were confirmed by ADOT&PF (*8*) borings that encountered permafrost or through personal communication validating these field observations by GAAR employees. Thermokarst and patterned ground topography are periglacial landforms formed via geomorphic processes resulting from seasonal freezing and thawing of ground in permafrost of previously glaciated areas.

This layer is also supplemental to the Surficial Materials layer within GAAR boundaries. When thermokarst, patterned ground, and subsurface ice were observed in borings, we mapped the area as a feature in the Permafrost Landforms layer and assigned an additional relative risk rank of 1.5 to the area (Table 1).

As in the Muskeg layer, the Permafrost Landforms layer overlaps units in the Surficial Materials layer and the aggregated relative risk ranking are higher in those overlapping instances. We felt the strong evidence of permafrost, the likelihood of climate induced permafrost degradation over the 50-year design life of the road, and related geotechnical road building and maintenance issues justified increasing the overall risk associated with areas identified in this layer.

Mass Wasting Layer

This layer was mapped by FHWA to capture areas with map-level evidence of landslide morphology inside and outside of GAAR's boundaries from junction to junction. Mass wasting is an inclusive term for all types of slope movement such as debris flow, landslides, slow moving creep, and solifluction landforms. Common topographic characteristics associated with mass wasting include, but are not limited to, convergent and concave topography, more landscape surface roughness (in the form of hummocks and localized depressions), arcuate scarps, and bulging areas.

Three features were mapped for this layer, deep-seated landslides, debris flows, and valley walls. Relative risk ranking associated with each feature is based on anticipated difficulty and investment needed to design and construct mitigation for these potential landforms and long-term maintenance investment that may be needed for these sections of the proposed road corridor. Table 1 lists features and associated relative risk ranking attributed to the mass wasting feature units in this layer.

Flooding and Erosion Layer

This layer was mapped inside and outside GAAR boundaries by FHWA to capture potential risk associated with flooding and erosion hazards from high flow events along streams and rivers. The scale of mapping and available hydrologic and climatic data made smaller drainages difficult to assess for this evaluation. For this reason, two features were mapped within the project area, major drainages with an assigned relative risk rank of 1.5 and minor drainages with a relative risk rank of 0.5 (Table 1).

Slope Gradient Layer

This layer was created from a lidar derived digital elevation model (DEM) with a resolution of 3 feet. The lidar DEM was resampled to a lower resolution (13.72 feet) to decrease complexity of the final slope gradient hazard layer. A slope map was calculated in degrees from the DEM and FHWA assigned relative risk ranking at the following slope gradient breaks to highlight areas where slope instability is more likely to occur, especially in a landscape with anticipated permafrost degradation over the course of the 50-year permit life of the road: 0 to 30 degrees, 30 to 40 degrees, and greater than 40 degrees. Table 1 lists relative risk rankings of the slope classes for this layer.

This calculation was only done for areas of lidar coverage, inside and outside of GAAR's boundaries. At the time of mapping an IfSAR DEM was not available for developing the Slope Gradient layer. As such, the Slope Gradient layer was not developed for potential access roads, airstrips, and material source areas outside of lidar coverage.

GEOGRAPHIC INFORMATION SYSTEM (GIS) SPATIAL ANALYSES AND RESULTS

Features within the geologic and geotechnical hazard layers were given relative rankings of geologic and geotechnical risk and permafrost susceptibility (0 – 3) based on their expected geologic and geotechnical risk relative to the staged construction and maintenance of the industrial roadway proposal submitted by the permittee. An aggregation of relative geologic and geotechnical risk ranking was then calculated by making a spatial union with the Union geoprocessing tool of all geologic/geotechnical hazard layers into a single layer. The Field Calculator tool was utilized to sum the individual risk ranks into a total overall relative geologic and geotechnical risk susceptibility ranking, as illustrated in Figure 2A. This process yielded an overall aggregated relative geologic and geotechnical risk susceptibility rank of the spatially overlapping areas along the mapped corridor.

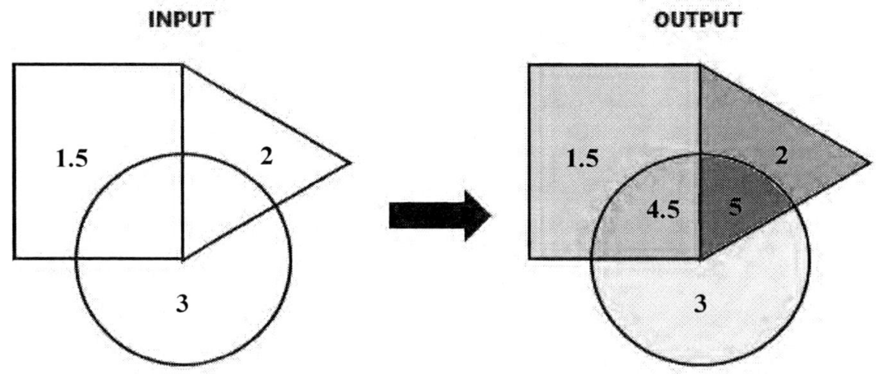

Figure 3 – Schematic diagram of the GIS union tool and Field Calculator process.

Iteration 1

The first work product requested by NPS included using existing and FHWA mapped geologic and geotechnical hazard layers within the boundaries of GAAR: the Surficial Materials, Flooding and Erosion, Mass Wasting, Muskeg, and Permafrost Landforms layers. Geohazard mapping was used to assign a Low, Moderate, or High relative risk to portions of the alignments. This assisted NPS with understanding geologic and geotechnical hazards and relative risks associated with the proposed alignments to compare with other interdisciplinary team data to select a preferred alignment through GAAR.

Aggregation of the relative risk rankings were considered the overall relative geologic and geotechnical risk susceptibility within the half mile width near the proposed road corridors mapped inside GAAR's boundaries. The aggregated relative geologic and geotechnical risk susceptibility scale ranged from 0 to 13.5 points for Iteration 1.

A total of three relative geologic and geotechnical risk susceptibility categories: Low, Moderate, and High, was used to visualize the risk. Categories were selected on natural, numerical breaks of aggregated relative risk rank as follows:

- Low = 0 to 3
- Moderate = 3 to 6.5

- High = greater than 6.5

Iteration 1 Results

Results of the first iteration of geologic and geotechnical hazard and relative risk susceptibility mapping, considered by length of proposed alignment and area over the half mile corridor suggested the north route had lower high relative geologic and geotechnical risk susceptibility, but more moderate risk and less low risk than the southern route. Table 2 lists relative geologic and geotechnical risk susceptibility category results of Iteration 1 of each proposed alignment by percent area of the entire half mile width corridor. Results by proposed length were similar, but are not included here.

Table 2 - Iteration 1 results: Relative geologic and geotechnical risk within Gates of the Arctic National Park and Preserve boundaries.

Relative Geologic - Geotechnical Risk Susceptibility Category[1]	North Route	South Route
	Percent Area	Percent Area
Low	38%	46%
Moderate	58%	43%
High	4%	11%

Notes:

1. Aggregated relative risk rank range: Low = 0 - 3.0; Moderate = 3.0 - 6.5; High = greater than 6.5.

Iteration 2

A second iteration of geologic and geotechnical hazard and relative risk susceptibility mapping was requested by NPS, after delivery of the first iteration of mapping results. The NPS requested FHWA to:

- Conduct the mapping method to areas outside of GAAR's boundaries to the eastern and western junctions of the northern and southern alignments.
- Consider slope gradient as a geologic/geotechnical hazard layer.
- Map geologic and geotechnical hazards for airstrips, source material, and access road areas.
- Add a relative geologic/geotechnical risk category; bringing the number of categories to four: Low, Moderate, Moderate-high, and High.

Geologic and geotechnical hazard mapping and risk analyses outside of GAAR's boundaries to the west and east junctions was requested by NPS to better understand potential resource impacts that could result from their decision between the proposed northern or southern routes.

As part of the second iteration the Slope Gradient hazard layer, as described above in the Geologic and Geotechnical Data Section, was developed and incorporated into the relative risk susceptibility mapping and a fourth relative risk susceptibility category was added. These were both requested by NPS in an effort to highlight areas that were on the boundary of moderate and high risk in the first iteration of mapping.

The aggregated relative geologic and geotechnical risk susceptibility scale ranged from 0 to 13.5 points in Iteration 2. The four relative risk rank susceptibility categories were selected on natural, numerical breaks of the summed relative risk rank as follows:

- Low = 0 to 2
- Moderate = 2 to 4.5
- Moderate-high = 4.5 to 7
- High = greater than 7

To gain a better understanding of the relative geologic and geotechnical risk along the permittee's proposed alignment, we clipped the spatial footprint of the permittee provided proposed project impact area, or "daylight limits", of the proposed northern and southern alignments from Iteration 2's Union output layer. Daylight limits are the anticipated limits of cuts and fills that the permittee provided as a GIS polygon for both the northern and southern alignments. The Clip geoprocessing tool was used to cut the spatial footprint and develop a new layer of the daylight limits extent out of the Union output layer (Figure 4).

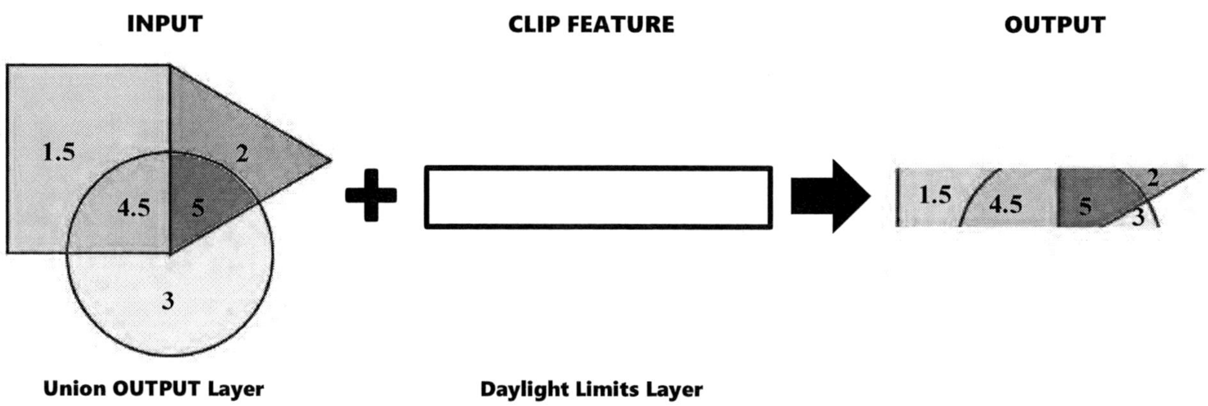

Figure 4 – Schematic diagram illustrating the GIS clip geoprocessing tool.

As part of the second iteration, FHWA also mapped geologic and geotechnical hazards for airstrips, source material areas, and access roads with available data. Many of these areas were outside lidar data coverage. IfSAR derived hillshades, satellite imagery, and aerial photographs were utilized instead to interpret geologic and geotechnical hazard maps. Unfortunately, IfSAR DEMs were not available until after mapping was completed so IfSAR derived slope classes were not added to the Slope Gradient layer.

Iteration 2 Results

Results of the second iteration of geologic and geotechnical hazard and relative risk susceptibility mapping, considered by length of proposed alignment and daylight limit area along the proposed alignments suggested the north route again had lower high relative geologic and geotechnical risk susceptibility inside GAAR's boundaries, but slightly more high-risk length and area outside of GAAR's boundaries. When the routes were considered from junction to junction: the north route had less high-risk areas, more moderate-high risk, and less moderate and low risk areas than the south route. Table 3 lists relative geologic and geotechnical risk susceptibility category results of Iteration 2 by percent daylight limit area of proposed alignments of the north and south corridors. Again, results by proposed length were similar, but not included here.

Table 3 - Iteration 2 results: Comparison of relative geologic and geotechnical risk by daylight limits area: junction to junction, within and outside Gates of the Arctic National Park and Preserve boundaries.

Relative Geologic – Geotechnical Risk Susceptibility Category[1]	Junction to Junction[2]		Within GAAR Boundaries[3]		Outside GAAR Boundaries[4]	
	North Route	South Route	North Route	South Route	North Route	South Route
	Percent Area	Percent Area	Percent Area	Percent Area	Percent Area	Percent Area
Low	41%	43%	39%	33%	43%	47%
Moderate	24%	37%	15%	26%	36%	42%
Moderate-high	33%	16%	43%	29%	19%	11%
High	2%	4%	3%	12%	1%	0%

Notes:

1. Aggregated relative risk rank range: Low = 0 - 2.0; Moderate = 2.0 - 4.5; Moderate to high = 4.5 - 7.0; High = greater than 7.0.
2. Area calculated from the daylight limits along the proposed northern and southern alignments from the eastern junction of the two proposed alignments to the western junction with the two proposed alignments.
3. Area calculated from the daylight limits along the proposed northern and southern alignments within GAAR's boundaries.
4. Area calculated by subtracting the "Within GAAR's Boundaries" area from the "Junction to Junction" area.

Statistics reported in Table 3 were normalized by daylight limit area along each proposed alignment from junction to junction of the proposed northern and southern alignments, within GAAR's boundaries, and outside GAAR's boundaries. It must be stressed the second iteration of geologic and geotechnical hazard and relative risk susceptibility analyses was only calculated based on daylight limit area provided by the permittee, and it is important to note again that the northern alignment has a longer alignment length and larger daylight limit area within GAAR's boundaries, but an overall shorter length and smaller daylight limit area from junction to junction when compared to the proposed southern alignment.

Iteration 3

A third iteration of geologic and geotechnical hazard and relative risk susceptibility mapping was requested by NPS to help them assess phased construction of the proposed road. In particular, they wanted a better understanding of how relative geologic and geotechnical risk susceptibility mapping could inform them about the permittees anticipated phased construction of the proposed alignments and what impacts there may be on GAAR's resources.

The permittee proposed phased construction of the selected alignment would begin with an initial pioneer road stage with river crossings and large stream crossings being constructed to full road build-out specifications. The NPS wanted to utilize the geologic and geotechnical hazard and relative risk susceptibility mapping in the third iteration to help determine roadway sections that would likely be susceptible to environmental and operational impacts from the staged construction proposal. This would also support the permit's terms and conditions for the preferred alignment selected by NPS through the EEA process.

FHWA developed assumptions of a pioneering stage of construction over good, fair, and poor geologic conditions, highlighting potential environmental impacts if permit terms and conditions were not thoroughly considered for the design, construction, and maintenance of the preferred alignment. The following list was shared and discussed about the pioneer stage of construction:

- Little to no maintenance should be expected.
- The roadway will be built at the lowest cost possible.
- The project could be stopped due to economic viability of the mineral deposits.
- The Tanana Road, a pioneer road completed in 2016 in interior Alaska connecting the village of Tanana with Manley Hot Springs on the Yukon River, was used as an analogous example.

A list of key indicator geologic and geotechnical hazard layers were developed by FHWA to help focus relative geologic and geotechnical risk susceptibility mapping for a proposed pioneer stage of construction and maintenance. It was determined that: surficial materials, permafrost probability, muskeg, and slope gradient were the four hazards anticipated to have the largest impact along proposed alignments for a pioneering stage of construction and maintenance.

The Mass Wasting and Flooding and Erosion hazard layers were removed for the third iteration's analyses. It was counterintuitive for the Mass Wasting layer to be removed, but this layer affected relatively small areas along both proposed alignments, and it was felt the Slope Gradient layer would capture mass wasting risk because steeper slopes are typically prone to instability in this geologic setting.

The Flooding and Erosion hazard layer was also removed because the road would bridge over the major rivers and large culverts would span major stream crossings with full road build out specifications during the pioneering stage of construction. It was anticipated standard practices of geologic and engineering investigation for appropriate design and construction would be completed for these structures. In addition, as noted above, hazards and risks associated with small drainages were also difficult to capture at the scale of available data for our mapping.

The third iteration of analyses subsequently changed the relative geologic and geotechnical risk susceptibility category ranges. Relative geologic and geotechnical risk susceptibility categories were again selected on natural, numerical breaks:

- Low = 0 to 1.5
- Moderate = 1.5 to 3.5
- Moderate-high = 3.5 to 5.5
- High = greater than 5.5

For Iteration 3 the aggregated relative geologic and geotechnical risk susceptibility scale ranged from 0 to 12 points.

Iteration 3 Results

Results of the third iteration of geologic and geotechnical hazard and relative risk susceptibility mapping, considered by length of proposed alignment and daylight limit area along the proposed alignments suggested the north route had higher relative geologic and geotechnical risk susceptibility than the south route within and outside of GAAR's boundaries. However, the north route had significantly less area categorized as moderate-high and more area categorized as moderate and low relative geologic and geotechnical risk susceptibility. When considered from junction to junction:

- the north route had
  - approximately 60% of daylight limit area categorized as low to moderate risk and
  - about 40% categorized as moderate-high to high risk;
- the south route had
  - approximately 48% daylight limit area categorized as low to moderate risk and
  - about 52% categorized as moderate-high to high risk.

Table 4 lists relative geologic and geotechnical risk susceptibility category results of Iteration 3 by percent daylight limit area of proposed alignments for the north and south corridors. Figure 5 displays the resultant relative geologic and geotechnical risk susceptibility GIS analyses and mapping over the daylight limit area. Again, results by proposed length were similar, but not included.

Table 4 - Iteration 3: Comparison of relative geologic and geotechnical risk by daylight limits area: junction to junction, within Gates of the Arctic National Park and Preserve, and junction to junction outside of GAAR's boundaries.

Relative Geologic – Geotechnical Risk Susceptibility Category[1]	Junction to Junction[2]		Within GAAR Boundaries[3]		Outside GAAR Boundaries[4]	
	North Route	South Route	North Route	South Route	North Route	South Route
	Percent Area	Percent Area	Percent Area	Percent Area	Percent Area	Percent Area
Low	31%	25%	31%	19%	31%	28%
Moderate	29%	23%	26%	23%	32%	24%
Moderate-high	23%	42%	19%	37%	29%	44%
High	17%	9%	24%	21%	8%	4%

Notes:

1. Aggregated relative risk rank range: Low = 0 - 1.5; Moderate = 1.5 - 3.5; Moderate to high = 3.5 - 5.5; High = greater than 5.5.

2. Area calculated from the daylight limits along the proposed northern and southern alignments from the eastern junction of the two proposed alignments to the western junction with the two proposed alignments.

3. Area calculated from the daylight limits along the proposed northern and southern alignments within GAAR's boundaries.

4. Area calculated by subtracting the "Within GAAR's Boundaries" area from the "Junction to Junction" area.

Statistics reported in Table 4 and on Figure 5 were normalized by daylight limit area along each proposed alignment from junction to junction of the proposed northern and southern alignments, within GAAR's boundaries, and outside GAAR's boundaries. It must be stressed the third iteration of geologic and geotechnical hazard and relative risk susceptibility analyses was only calculated based on daylight limit area provided by the permittee.

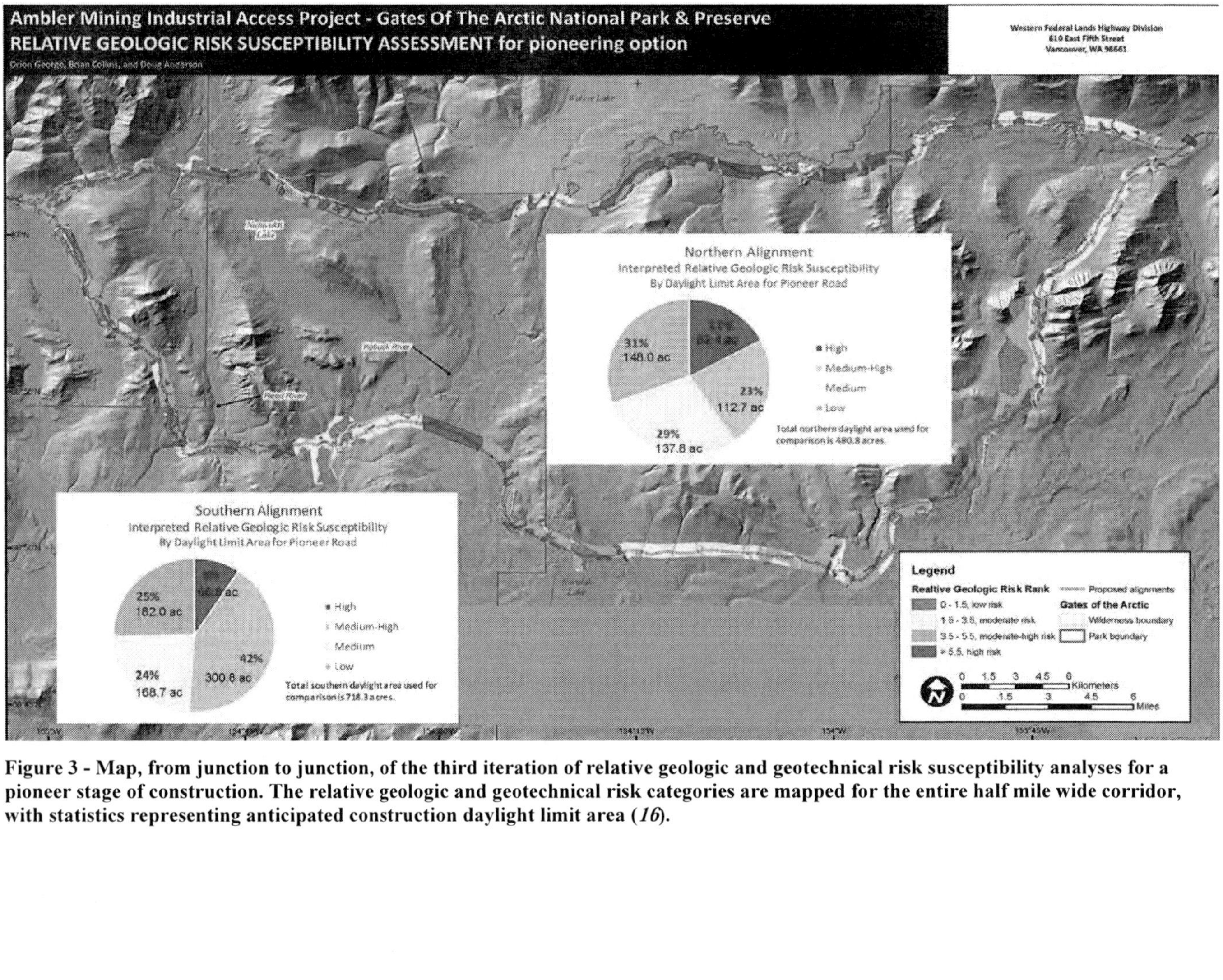

Figure 3 - Map, from junction to junction, of the third iteration of relative geologic and geotechnical risk susceptibility analyses for a pioneer stage of construction. The relative geologic and geotechnical risk categories are mapped for the entire half mile wide corridor, with statistics representing anticipated construction daylight limit area (*16*).

CONCLUSIONS

Approximately 65 acres, or 24% of the area of the northern alignment within GAAR, is at a relative high risk of having negative impacts on natural resources as a result of geologic and geotechnical hazards and risks associated with proposed roadway construction and long-term maintenance (Table 4, Figure 5). Approximately 53 acres, or 19%, of the area of the northern alignment within GAAR is at a relative moderate-high risk. Approximately 45 acres, or 21% of the area of the southern alignment within GAAR, is at a relative high risk and 78 acres or 37% is at a relative moderate-high risk. Sections of the alignment ranked moderate-high or high would likely be at risk for significant changes to the physical resources, which could result in adverse impacts to local hydrology and permafrost as a result of the proposed road construction and long-term maintenance.

With data presented above and considering potential impacts to other resources: subsistence, hydrology, wetlands, water quality, fish, wildlife, visitors, socioeconomic, and others, the NPS completed their EEA in July 2020 with the northern rout the preferred alignment. A final decision by the Department of Interior was issued soon afterwards with the northern route being chosen for right-of-way permitting. A 50-year right-of-way permit along the full length of the Ambler Road was signed by NPS, BLM, and AIDEA on January 6, 2021. Numerous terms and conditions considering surface water drainage, culverts, cut and fill slopes, permafrost protection, road foundation stability, slope stability, erosion, bridge spans, creek and river crossings, dust abatement, among others were included with FHWA consultation in the final NPS decision document.

Permits were approved and AIDEA dedicated $60,000,000 for investigation work to begin towards construction of the AMDIAP in the 2022 field season. However, as of the end of February 2022, the permitting for the project and this coming season's investigation work is now on hold to address public concerns with the permitting process and documentation.

We presented this methodology as a successful, iterative process and tool which helped inform the NPS in a challenging decision-making process. We hope methodologies presented above can be used in future projects for a data driven approach to cost-effective geologic and geotechnical hazard evaluation informing a relative risk susceptibility assessment. This process teamed with good interdisciplinary communication provided a means to assist where numerous challenges interact, impact, and affect management decisions of proposed work.

REFERENCES

1. H.R. 39 – 96th Congress (1979 – 1981): Alaska National Interest Lands Conservation Act (ANILCA), 1980, Public Law 96-487, 94 Stat. 2371-2551 [https://www.congress.gov/96/statute/STATUTE-94/STATUTE-94-Pg2371.pdf]

2. National Park Service, Gates of the Arctic National Park and Preserve, 2021, Ambler Mining District Industrial Access Project EEA: https://www.nps.gov/gaar/learn/management/ambler-row.htm (accessed March 1, 2022).

3. Google Earth 7.3.1 (2018), Satellite imagery, dated August 8, 2009, centered around approximate latitude 66.9143, longitude -154.4707, [Online], available at https://earth.google.com/web/, accessed 2017 through 2018.

4. Hamilton, D.T. and K.A. Labay, 2011, Surficial geologic map of the Gates of the Arctic National Park and Preserve, Alaska: U.S. Geological Survey Scientific Investigations Map 3125, pamphlet 19 p., scale 1:300,000, [http://pubs.usgs.gov/sim/3125/].

5. Wilson, F.H., C.P. Hults, C.G. Mull, and S.M. Karl, compilers, 2015, Geologic map of Alaska: U.S. Geological Survey Scientific Investigations Map 3340, pamphlet 197 p. 2 sheets, scale 1:1,584,000, [http://dx.doi.org/10.3133/sim3340].

6. Swanson, D.K., 1995. Landscape ecosystems of the Kobuk Preserve Unit: Gates of the Arctic National Park, Alaska. Technical Report, NPS/ARRNR/NRTR-95/22U.S. National Park Service. Alaska Regional Office, Anchorage, AK. 291 pp.

7. Speeter, G., 2013, Reconnaissance material site report, Ambler Mining District Access, AKSAS 63812, geotechnical investigations report: State of Alaska Department of Transportation and Public Facilities, 243 p.

8. Speeter, G., 2014, Material site report, Ambler Mining District Access phase 1, AKSAS 63812: State of Alaska Department of Transportation and Public Facilities, 122 p.

9. Speeter, G., 2015, Geotechnical investigation, Ambler Mining District Access phase 2, Gates of the Arctic National Park and Jim River landslides AKSAS 63812: State of Alaska Department of Transportation and Public Facilities, 198 p.

10. Brown, J., O. Ferrians, J.A. Heginbottom, and E. Melnikov, 2002, Circum-Arctic map of permafrost and ground-ice conditions, version 2, Boulder, Colorado, USA, National Snow and Ice Data Center, accessed November, 2017, [http://alaska.portal.gina.alaska.edu/catalogs/305-circum-arctic-map-of-permafrost-and-ground-ice].

11. Jorgenson, M.T., K. Yoshikawa, M. Kanevskiy, Y. Shur, V. Romanovsky, S. Marchenko, G. Grosse, J. Brown, and B. Jones, 2008, Permafrost Characteristics of Alaska, Institute of Northern Engineering, University of Alaska Fairbanks, 2 sheets.

12. Jorgenson, M.T., M. Kanecskiy, Y. Shur, J. Grunblatt, C.L. Ping, G. Michaelson, 2015, Permafrost database development, characterization, and mapping for northern Alaska, prepared for US Fish and Wildlife, Arctic Landscape Conservation Cooperative, 41 p.

13. DOWL HKM, 2011, Ambler Mining District access geotechnical memorandum, prepared for State of Alaska Department of Transportation and Public Facilities, 74 p.

14. DOWL HKM, 2011, Ambler Mining District access preliminary hydrology reconnaissance memorandum, prepared for State of Alaska Department of Transportation and Public Facilities, 170 p.

15. Hults, C.P., National Park Service Alaska Regional Geologist, personal communication, September, 2017.

16. Federal Highway Administration (FHWA), 2019, Geotechnical memorandum 10-19: Ambler Mining District Industrial Access Project, Federal Highways Administration, Western Federal Lands Highway Division, February 26, 2019.

Shallow Foundation Load-Settlement Behavior Assessed from Surface Geophysical Data

Gary Norris
Emeritus Professor
University of Nevada Reno
1664 N. Virginia St, MS258
Reno, NV 89557
(775) 331-5582
norris@unr.edu

Sherif Elfass
Research Associate Professor
University of Nevada Reno
1664 N. Virginia St, MS258
Reno, NV 89557
(775) 331-5582
elfass@unr.edu

Horng-Jyh (Tigra) Yang
Associate Professor
West Virginia University Institute of Technology
410 Neville Street
Beckley, WV 25801
(304) 929-1640
Horng-Jyh.Yang@mail.wvu.edu

Prepared for the 71st Highway Geology Symposium, May 2022

Disclaimer

Copyright Notice

ABSTRACT

Given soil data from the Soil Conservation Service (USDA NRCS) and a shallow geophysical test shear or P wave record, the following method and spreadsheet provide a means for undertaking a preliminary evaluation of the load-settlement response of a shallow foundation at a prospective site. The method follows the stress-strain formulation currently used in laterally loaded pile/shaft response evaluation recognized by AASHTO for large diameter drilled shafts.

INTRODUCTION

A method for the assessment of the bearing capacity and load-settlement response of a footing based on geophysical shear or compressional/primary wave velocity (V_s or V_p) of the supporting soil is presented. From the shear wave velocity (V_s), an initial shear modulus (G_o) and an initial Young's modulus (E_i) at the level of geophysical test field strain (1 x 10^{-6}) are assessed. Alternatively, E_i can be assessed directly from the primary wave velocity (V_p) if that is the geophysical method employed. The Young's modulus (E) at a specified stress level (SL) is then determined from a modulus reduction relationship after Ashour and Norris (1999). From the Schmertmann et al. (1978) relationship between Young's modulus E (at, say, 50% stress level, SL) and the cone penetration test point resistance, q_c ($E_{50} = E = 2.5q_c$ for a square foundation), and the Robertson and Campanella (1983) relationship [$q_c/N_{60} = f(D_{50})$], a function of the soil's D_{50} particle size, the blow count, N_{60}, is determined. From the corrected blow count, $N_{1,60}$, the soil friction angle (ϕ) is obtained from the Florida DOT (2004) modified Peck et al. (1974) curve. The deviatoric strength (σ_{df}) of the circle tangent to the Mohr-Coulomb (ϕ) envelope of failure is then determined. The stress difference at 50% of this failure value, $\sigma_{d,50}$, is used to assess the corresponding strain ($\varepsilon_{50} = \sigma_{d,50}/ E_{50}$). A nonlinear stress-strain relationship is used to assess Young's Modulus (E) and strain (ε) as a function of stress level, SL ($= \sigma_d/\sigma_{df}$).

The net bearing capacity, q_{net}, is assessed knowing width (B), embedment depth (D), ϕ and the soil's effective unit weight. The mobilized bearing pressure, $q_{net,m}$, and the strain ($\varepsilon = SLe^{3.707SL}\ \varepsilon_{50}/\lambda$) at the specified stress level (SL) are assessed along with foundation settlement (= ε B, the area of the Schmertmann triangle of strain, $\varepsilon = \sigma_d/E$, for a square footing). The preceding method is for a c-ϕ soil with cohesion, c, that is a user assigned value or taken conservatively as zero. A separate method is provided for the assessment of the (immediate) load-settlement response of a purely cohesive (c) soil (the undrained response of a saturated clay).

METHODOLOGY FOR A c-ϕ SOIL

Given that publicly available Soil Conservation Service (USDA NRCS) reports give a wealth of information (depth to groundwater, soil classification, grain size data, liquid and plastic limits of soil to a depth of five feet), a quickly performed geophysical survey at the surface of a prospective site may be enough to establish a preliminary assessment of the load-settlement response and bearing capacity of a shallow foundation using appropriate analytical analysis. The following is an effort to provide a tool toward that end that can be readily presented in the form of a spreadsheet. Such formulation is intended for a c-ϕ soil under drained loading. In that case, the cohesion (c) may be the result of capillary tension/soil suction, cementation or other source or conservatively taken as zero. Cohesion is not the result of undrained loading of a saturated soil such as a saturated clay. The methodology for such soil's (c only) load-settlement response evaluation is presented in the next section.

From the geophysical field test's shear or primary wave velocity (V_s or V_p), the initial shear (G_o) or Young's (E_i) modulus is assessed corresponding to a field shear strain of 1 x 10^{-6}.

$$G_o = (\gamma_{eff}/g)V_s^2 \qquad E_i = 2(1+\nu_i)\, G_o \quad \text{or} \quad E_i = (\gamma_{eff}/g)V_p^2 \qquad (1)$$

where g is the value of gravity, 32.2 ft/sec^2, and γ_{eff} is the effective unit weight (equal to the vertical effective stress, $\sigma_3' = D\,\gamma_x + 0.5\,B\,\gamma_y$, divided by depth, D + B/2); γ_x is the total or buoyant unit weight (depending on the water table location) over embedment depth (D) of the intended footing and γ_y is the (total or buoyant) unit weight of the soil within half the footing width (B) below foundation base. (ν_i is taken equal to zero at the field shear strain of 1 x 10^{-6}.)

Based on the established stress-strain relationship (Ashour and Norris, 1999; Elfass et al. 2007; Norris, et al. 2011; Nimeri et al. 2017)

$$\varepsilon = SL\, e^{3.707\,SL}\, \varepsilon_{50}/\lambda \qquad \lambda = 3.19 \quad \text{for } SL <= 0.50 \qquad (2)$$

$$\lambda = -7.121\, SL^2 + 7.0592\, SL + 1.4403 \quad \text{for } SL > 0.50$$

where ε is the axial strain in the standard drained triaxial test; SL (= σ_d/σ_{df}) is the stress level, equal to the ratio of the current to failing deviator stress; ε_{50} is the strain at SL = 0.5 and λ is the fitting parameter that varies with stress level (SL). From this relationship it follows that the Young's modulus at any stress level is

$$E = \sigma_d/\varepsilon = E_i\, e^{-3.707\,SL}\,(\lambda/3.19) \qquad E_{50} = E_i/6.38 \text{ at } SL = 0.5 \qquad (3)$$

From the Schmertmann et al. (1978) relationship between Young's modulus E (at, say, SL = 50%) and the cone penetration test (CPT) point resistance, q_c,

$$E = 2.5\, q_c \text{ (tons/ft}^2\text{, tsf)} \qquad \text{or } = 5\, q_c \text{ (kips/ ft}^2\text{, ksf)} \quad \text{for a square foundation} \qquad (4)$$

and the Robertson and Campanella (1983) relationship, $q_c/N_{60} = f(D_{50})$, of Fig. 1, a function of the soil's mean particle size (D_{50}), the standard penetration test (SPT) blow count N_{60} (blows/ft) is determined from Eq. 5 as follows:

$$E = 5\, q_c = 5\,(q_c/N_{60})\, N_{60}$$

$$N_{60} = E/(q_c/N_{60}) \qquad \text{upon converting } (q_c/N_{60}) \text{ of Fig. 1 (in bars) to ksf} \qquad (5)$$

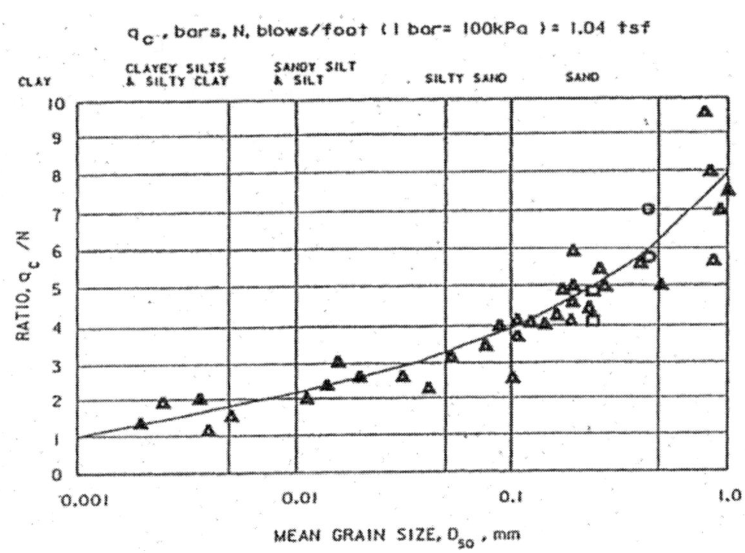

Figure 1 – q_c/N vs D50 after Robertson and Campanella 1983

The standard penetration test blow count at 60 % energy ratio, N_{60}, is then corrected with factor C_N,

$$C_N = (2/\sigma_3')^{0.5} \quad \text{less than or equal to 2} \qquad \text{for } \sigma_3' \text{ in ksf} \qquad (6)$$

to obtain $N_{1,60}$, the N_{60} at an effective overburden pressure of one ton/ft^2. σ_3' is the effective vertical pressure at the depth one-half the foundation width (B) below the intended footing depth (D), i.e. σ_3, plus any assigned capillary/soil suction (c/tan ϕ) or other equivalent cohesional component of effective stress increase ($\sigma_3' = \sigma_3 + c/\tan\phi$).

The value of $N_{1,60}$ is used with Florida DOT's (1994) modified Peck, Hanson and Thornburn (1974) curve to establish the friction angle (ϕ) of the soil. See Fig. 2.

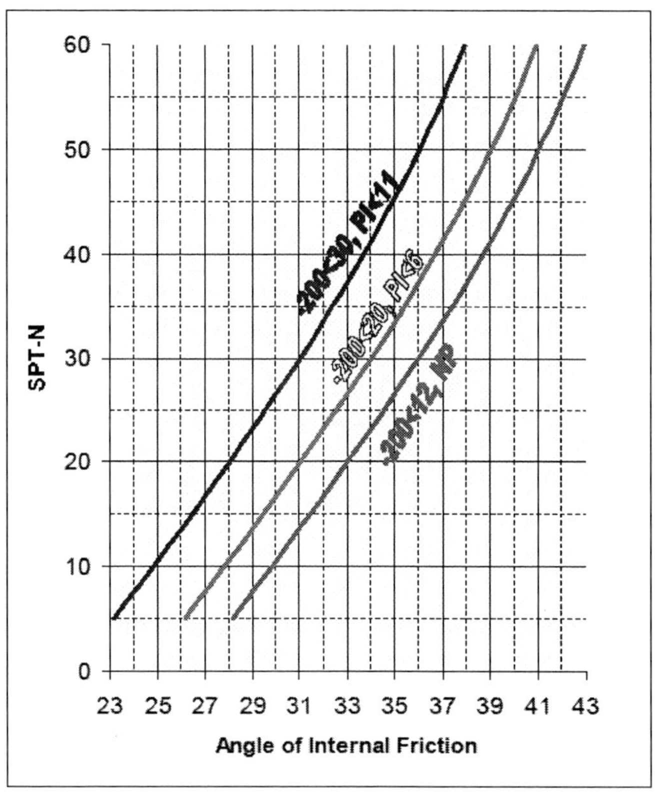

Figure 17 - Angle of Internal Friction vs. SPT-N (After Peck, 1974)

Figure 2 – Friction Angle vs SPT from Florida DOT 2004

The deviatoric stress of failure (σ_{df}), the diameter of the Mohr circle tangent to the Mohr-Coulomb ϕ envelope of failure as pictured in Fig. 3 is equal to

$$\sigma_{df} = \sigma_3' A \qquad A = [\tan^2(45+\phi/2)-1] \quad \text{or} \quad = 2\sin\phi/(1-\sin\phi) \qquad (7)$$

from which $\sigma_{d50} = \frac{1}{2}\sigma_{df}$ and the associated strain, ε_{50}, used in Eq. 2 is

$$\varepsilon_{50} = \tfrac{1}{2} A \, \sigma_3'/E_{50} \qquad (8)$$

Note that using σ_3'taken from the shifted origin O', effectively converts a c-ϕ relationship relative to the origin at O, to a purely ϕ relationship relative to O'. For instance, soil suction (u_s) due to capillary rise (h), $u_s = S\,h\,\gamma_w$ (taken equal to c/tan ϕ) is the source of the apparent cohesion (c) of the c-ϕ envelope relative to origin O. (S is the degree of saturation of the soil relative to rise, h.)

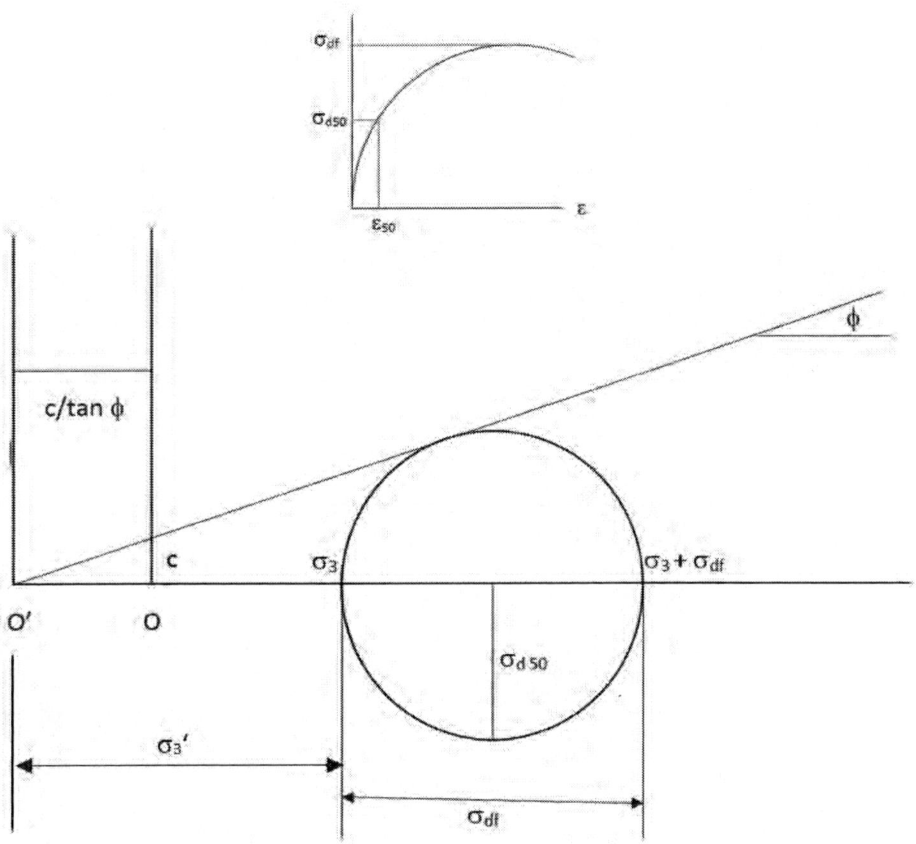

Figure 3 – Mohr Circle of Failure Tangent to Original (c-ϕ) and Shifted (ϕ only) Mohr-Coulomb Failure Envelopes

As shown in Fig. 4 of the envisioned foundation failure, the net ultimate bearing capacity (ultimate bearing capacity less the effective overburden pressure at foundation base, $D\gamma_x$) as given by Elfass et al. (2007) is

$$q_{net} = P_0^*(\tan^6\alpha_f - 1) \qquad \alpha_f = 45+\phi/2 \qquad (9)$$

which equals the horizontal distance (the difference in normal stress) between the upper end of the last circle (major principle stress in Zone III) and the lower end (minor principle stress of P_0) of the first circle (corresponding to Zone I). Note that P_0^* is P_0 (= $D\,\gamma_x + 0.5\,B\,j\,\gamma_y$; $j = 1.5 \tan\phi$)

plus the offset between the origin at O and the shifted origin O', c/tanϕ, to the left of O. Based on origin O', the equation for q_{net} becomes a very simple and straightforward one (Eq. 9).

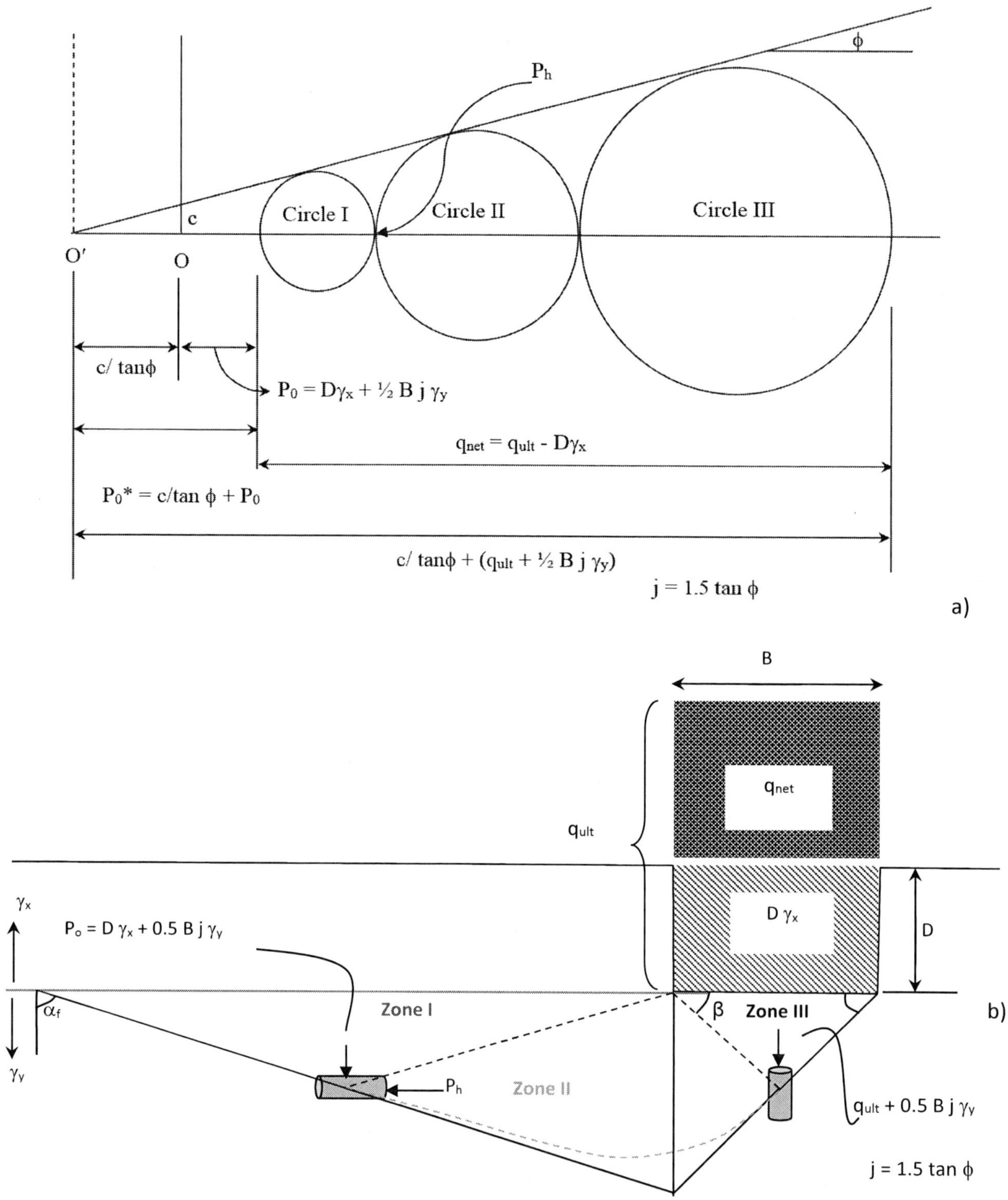

Figure 4 – a) Mohr Circles for b) Envisioned Three Zone Failure Mass

q_{net} represents a stress level of one (SL = 1) for the three circles/zones pictured in Fig. 4 corresponding to tangency to the failure envelope. At a SL less than one, the three circles emanating from P_0* relative O' (or P_0 relative to O) are tangent to a mobilized friction angle, ϕ_m (from O'), related to SL in the soil (Zones I-III) as

$$\phi_m = \sin^{-1} [SL \cdot A / (SL \cdot A + 2)] \qquad (10)$$

See Fig. 5. The associated mobilized net pressure (the distance between the upper end of the last circle and the lower end of the first circle of the three circles tangent to the ϕ_m envelope emanating from O') is $q_{net,m}$ which is given by the equation

$$q_{net,m} = P_0^*(\tan^6\alpha_m - 1) \qquad \alpha_f = 45+\phi_m/2 \qquad (11)$$

Note that the traditional safety factor (SF) relative to bearing capacity failure is given by the ratio of pressures, net ultimate to the applied/mobilized pressure.

$$SF = \frac{q_{net}}{q_{net,m}} \qquad (12)$$

By contrast, a safety factor in terms of strength (similar to the safety factor employed in slope stability analysis) would be

$$SF = \tan\phi/\tan\phi_m \qquad (13)$$

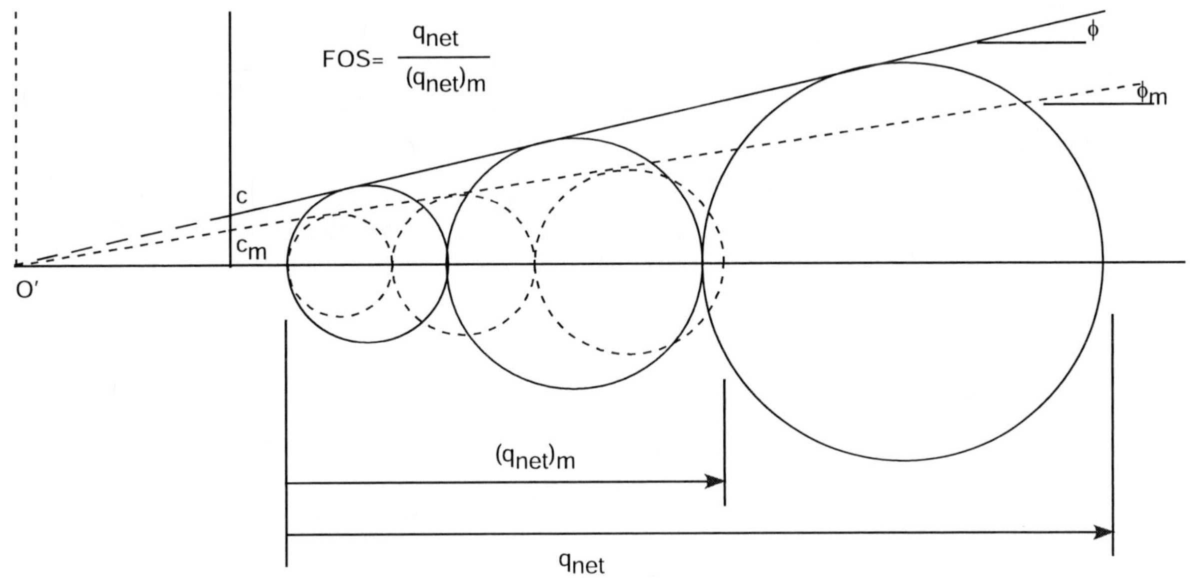

Figure 5 – Mobilized Mohr Circles (SL < 1) vs Failure Mohr Circles (SL = 1)

The reciprocal of the bearing capacity safety factor would be pressure level (PL = $q_{net,m}/q_{net}$) which is different from the soil's stress level (SL) in the case of a ϕ soil. (By contrast, in the case of a purely c soil discussed in the next section, they are one and the same.)

The associated settlement (ρ_i) of a square foundation is the area of the Schmertmann Zone III deviatoric stress triangle ($q_{net,m}$ $I_z = \sigma_{d\,III}$ in Fig. 6) that, when divided by the current Young's modulus (E), yields the triangle of strain with ε (for E at the given SL) at its peak.

$$\rho_i = \varepsilon B \qquad (14)$$

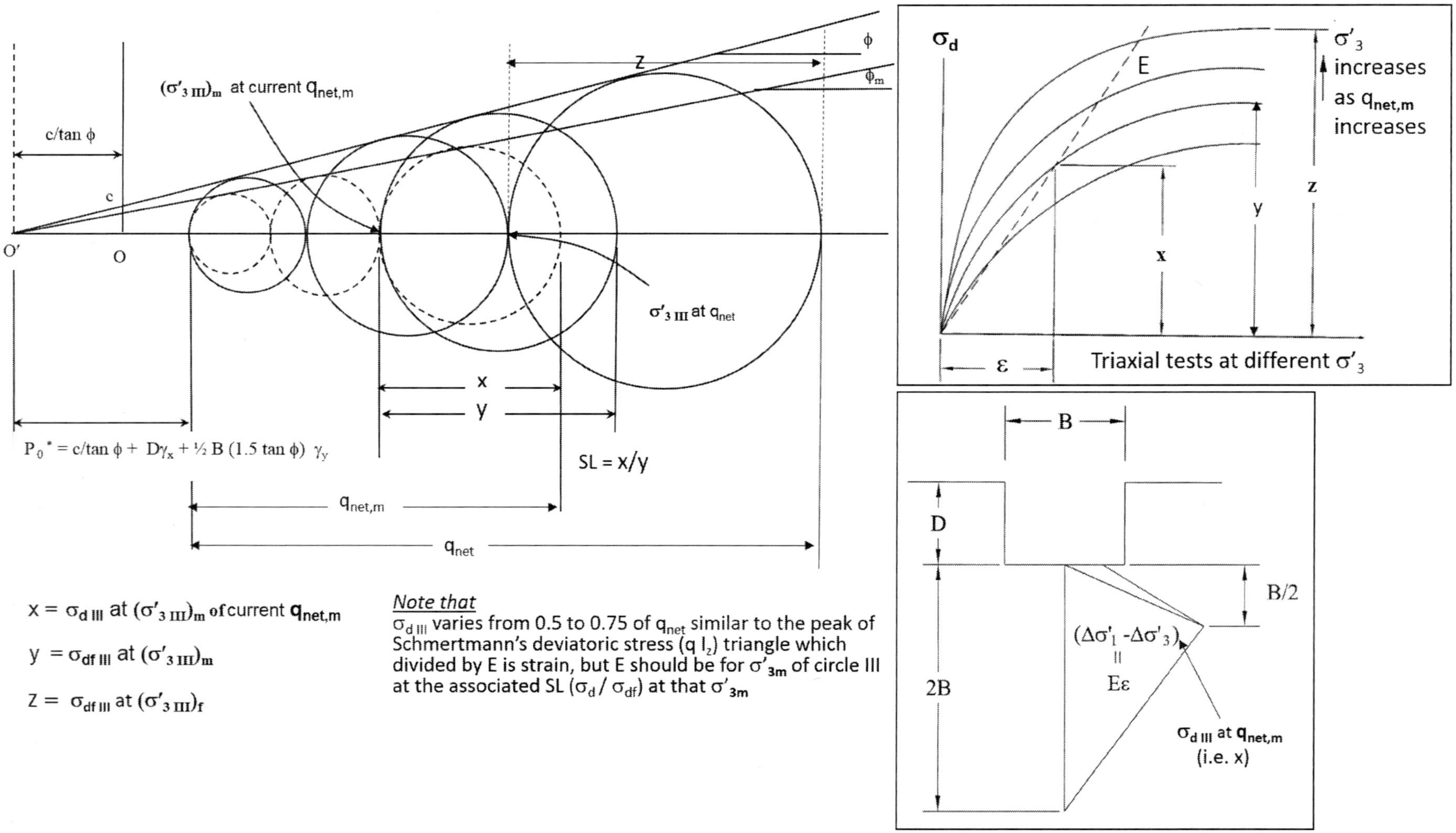

Figure 6 – Relation Between Zone III Stress State and Associated Strain and Resulting Immediate Settlement

Note that the SL for ε is the diameter $\sigma_{d\,III}$ (distance labelled x in Fig. 6) relative to σ_{df} (distance labelled y) at the same mobilized confining pressure of the two circles anchored at $(\sigma'_{3III})_m$. The strain triangle of Zone III corresponds to the soil immediately below the foundation (see Fig. 4b). Strain ε of Zone III jumps from one drained triaxial test stress-strain curve of constant σ'_3 (as pictured in Fig. 6) to another as $q_{net,m}$ and therefore $(\sigma'_{3III})_m$ increases.

The accompanying spreadsheet (Fig. 7) carries out the preceding calculations for a set of SL's (cells B16—B26) for the specified shear wave velocity (cell D9). Based on this V_s, Ei of cell C34 is obtained from Eq. 1 and E_{50} of cell C35 from Eq. 3. Other designated input appears as cells highlighted in yellow. Cell D4 requires the value of q_c/N obtained from Fig. 1, for soil below the anticipated foundation base, based on the soil's mean grain size (D_{50}). D_{50} can be judged from grain size data from the Soil Conservation Service report for the site. Cells D6 and D7 require values of effective unit weight (total or buoyant depending on the location of the water table) of the soil above and below foundation base (see Fig. 4b). ε_{50} in cell D10 is based on Eq. 8. N_{60} in cell H7 is based on Eq. 5 using E from cell C35; while C_N in cell H8 is from Eq. 6. The $N_{1,60}$ value of cell H9 is $C_N N_{60}$. The $N_{1,60}$ is used in Fig. 2 to establish the value of friction angle (ϕ) to input to cell H10. Alternatively, ϕ in cell H10 is established from Fig. 3 in the spreadsheet (Fig. 2 with switched axes) to which equations have been supplied to the (PI<, and -#200<) lines and lines between, so that a specified PI< in cell R5 (and its linked -#200< value in cell R4) yields the required ϕ value in cell H10. The Soil Conservation Service report will provide the values of the soil's fines (-#200) and plasticity index (PI) needed for the spreadsheet Fig. 2 ϕ determination.

Cell H11 provides the user the ability to assign a value of cohesion, c, which is initially set conservatively equal to zero. (The corresponding capillary rise, h, is shown in cell N13 if c is to be taken due to soil suction for an assigned value of degree of saturation in cell N12.) The value of γ_{eff} in cell C 38 (and cell H6) is used to establish E_i in cell C34 based on Eq. 1. C_N in cell H8 is based on Eq. 6 using σ_3' from cell C37 (which in turn depends upon σ_3 in cell H5 and ϕ in cell H 10).

The spreadsheet provides the associated values of q_{net} (in cell G14 from Eq. 9 based on P_0* in cell O6), and successive values of $q_{net,m}$ (Eq. 11), SF (Eq. 12), ρ_i (Eq. 14) and column load (= $B^2 \cdot q_{net,m}$) in cells G16-J26 corresponding to the SL's of cells B16-26. Corresponding values of ϕ_m (°) and α_m used to calculate $q_{net,m}$ and σ'_{3III} (and ε_{50III} to assess an adjusted ε in Zone III for ρ_i) appear in cells M16-P26. Plots of $q_{net,m}$ versus ρ_i and SF versus ρ_i, as shown in Fig. 8, are easily generated from such data.

The spreadsheet also includes a Fig. 9 (from Ashour et al. 1998, Norris et al. 2011, or Nimeri et al. 2017) that relates ε_{50} (%) to void ratio, e, as a function of uniformity coefficient, C_u. Equations have been fitted to the different curves, and those between, so that with the value of ε_{50} from cell D10 entered automatically in percent into cells U4 and W4, the value of e is assessed in cells U5 and W5 for separate specified values of C_u (C_u from 1 to 4 in cell T4 and C_u >4 in cell V4). From that, various unit weights (dry, saturated, buoyant and moist at a specified water content, w) are calculated, from which chosen values can be substituted for previously assumed values in cells D6 and D7.

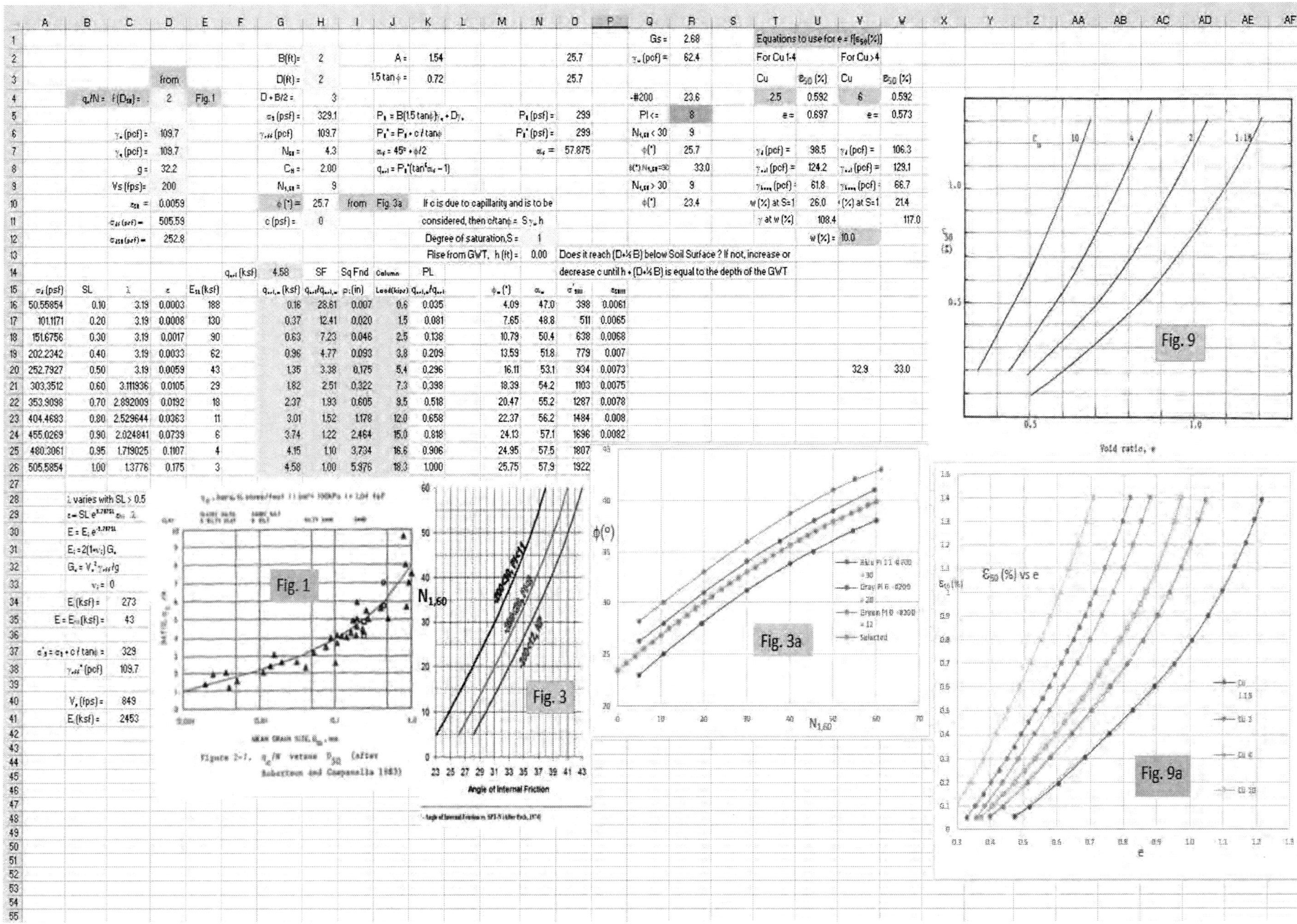

Figure 7 – Spreadsheet for Load-Settlement Assessment of Square Footing on c–ϕ Soil

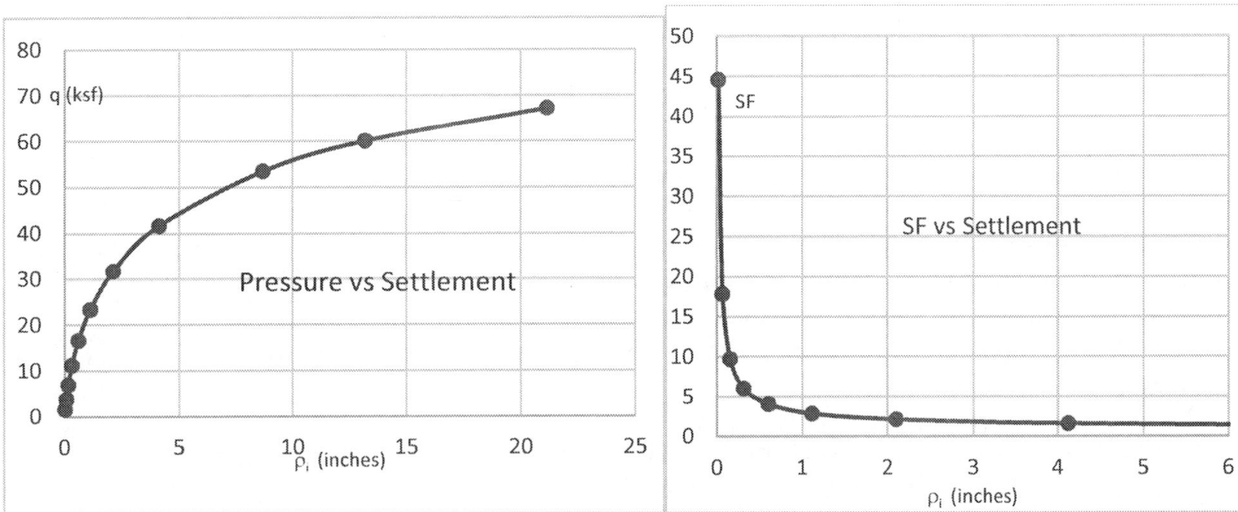

Figure 8 – Pressure vs Settlement and SF vs Settlement Responses from Spreadsheet

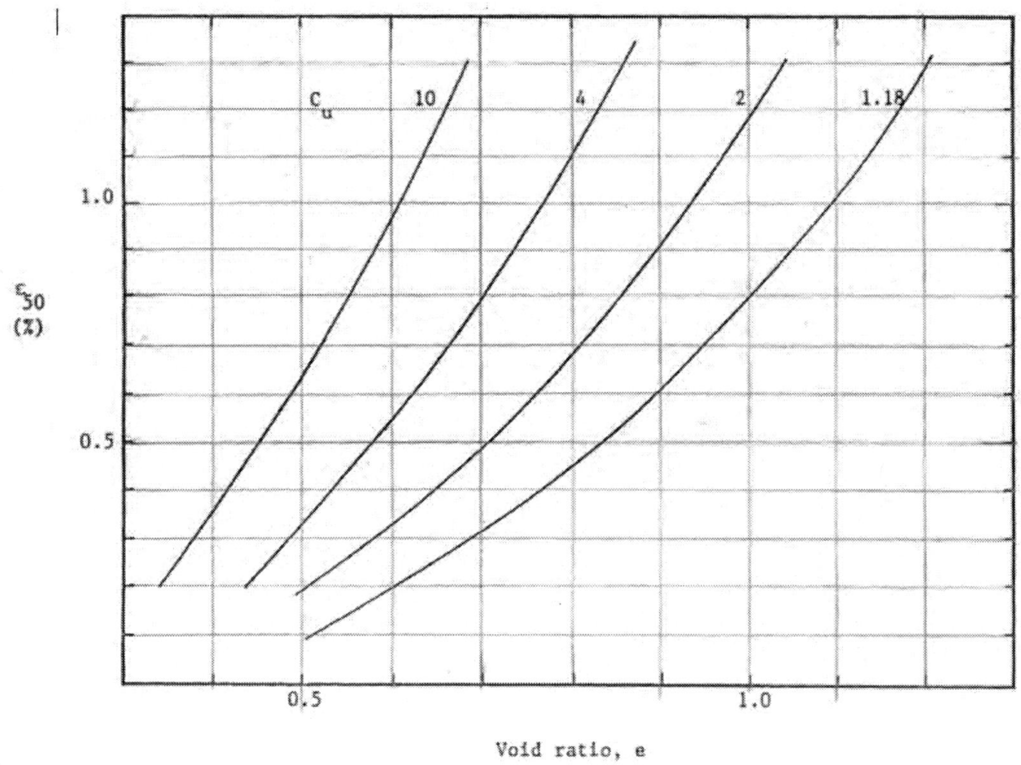

Figure 9 - ε_{50} (%) vs Void Ratio, e, as a Function of Uniformity Coefficient, C_u

The spreadsheet can be used with input in terms of a primary wave velocity (V_p) instead of the shear wave velocity (V_s) by entering the value of V_p in fps in cell C40 which will calculate E_i in ksf in cell C41 that should then be copied as a value into cell C34. However, be aware that in the geophysical field test, once the water table is encountered, V_p values become 5000 fps of the water, masking the P wave velocity of the skeletal structure of the soil.

METHODOLOGY FOR A PURELY c ($\phi = 0$) SOIL

Undrained or short-term loading of saturated soil, clay the most common case, results in a Mohr-Coulomb failure envelope that is horizontal, i.e. $\phi = 0$. The lack of a frictional (ϕ) contribution to strength is the result of the developing excess porewater pressure under load whereby the effective stress remains unchanged such that no increase in strength results from greater confinement.

The c-ϕ methodology of the previous section can be modified to account for the loss of ϕ resistance through the assignment of a very low value of ϕ (say 0.001 degrees) resulting in the same net bearing capacity (q_{net}) for a surface footing as the classical equation, $q_{net} = c\ N_c$, where N_c is 6 for a square footing. Six times cohesion (6c) corresponds to three circles of radius c tangent to the horizontal Mohr- Coulomb envelope of height c. See Fig. 10. However, it is much simpler to assess the corresponding mobilized pressure, $q_{net,m} = c_m\ N_c$, where c_m = SLc, or $q_{net,m}$ = SL q_{net}, compared to employing Eq. 11 in the c-ϕ analysis procedure to get the same $q_{net,m}$.

Treatment of embedment (D) requires adjustment of N_c from 6 at D/B = 0 to N_c = 9 at D/B = 4 based on Fig. 18.2 of Peck, Hanson and Thornburn (1974). See Fig. 11a. An Embedment Factor, or $(D/B)_{factor}$ (= $N_c/6$) as a function of relative embedment (D/B) can be expressed by the equation,

$$(D/B)_{factor} = 0.0103\ (D/B)^3 - 0.1013\ (D/B)^2 + 0.3658\ (D/B) + 1.0014 \qquad (16)$$

as shown in Fig. 11b.

What changes for saturated clay in the spreadsheet is that q_c/N =1 in Fig. 1 (while Figs. 2, 3 and 9 no longer apply). Equation 5 is no longer used since it derives from Schmertmann's treatment of the settlement of cohesionless material, not the immediate undrained settlement of saturated clay. Instead, the relationship of N_{60} to shear wave velocity is employed. Bellana (2009) and Farrokhzad and Choobbasti (2016) list relationships for clay by various researchers which are plotted as shown in Fig. 12. An average for all 15 curves yields the following reverse relationship,

$$N_{60} = 5x10^{-8} Vs^{2.953} \qquad (17a)$$

where Vs is in ft/sec, or

$$N_{60} = 4x10^{-9} Vs^{3.3285} \qquad (17b)$$

if three curves from Fig. 12 that do not follow the general trend of the others are omitted.

Cohesion, c, in ksf is obtained from N_{60} as follows,

$$c = N_{60} / x \qquad (18)$$

where x varies with plasticity as shown on page 7.1-88 of DM 7.1 (1986). Instead of the Terzaghi and Peck line of an x value 7.5, the authors provide Fig. 13 which shows a variation in x with plasticity index (PI) reflecting the Sowers characterization in the DM 7.1 figure.

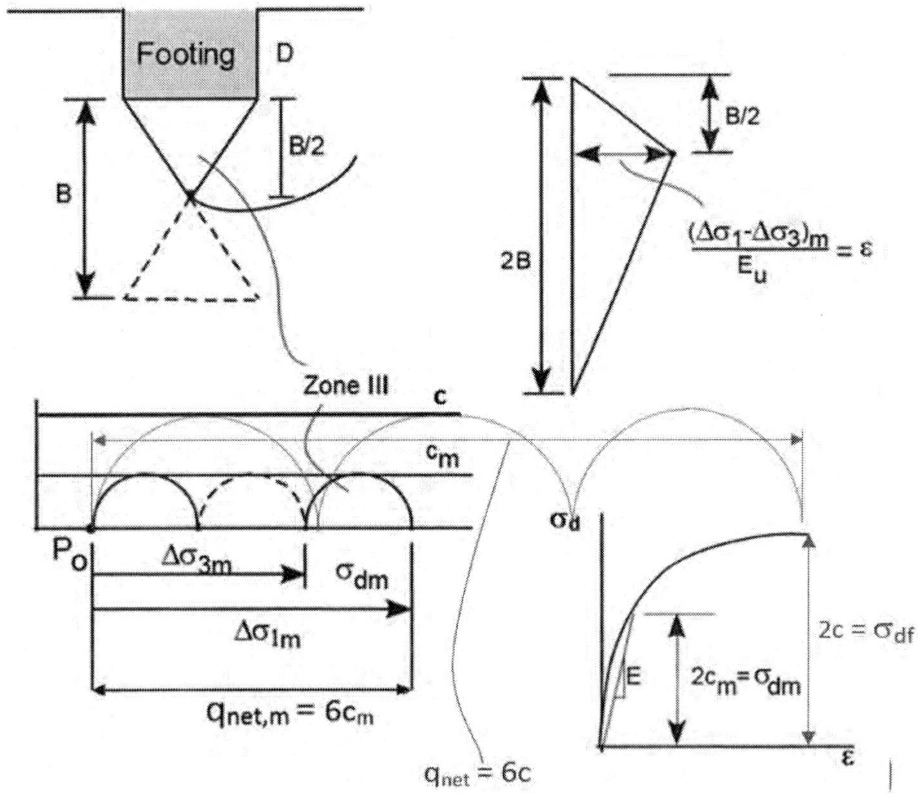

Figure 10 – Relationship Between/Among Mohr Circles of Stress, Stress-Strain Response and (Immediate) Strain Triangle for Saturated Clay (c =0 Soil)

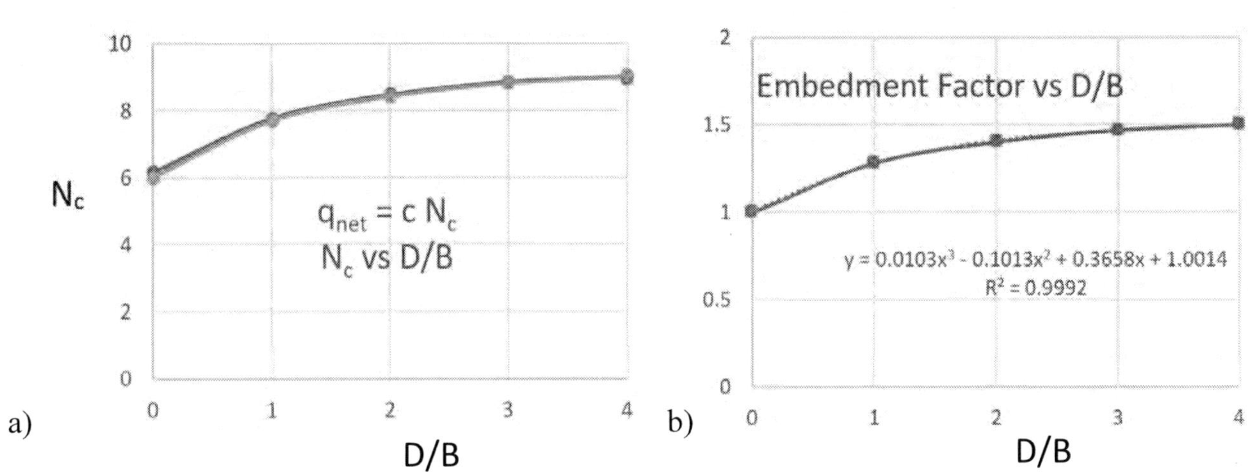

Figure 11 – Nc and Embedment Factor vs D/B

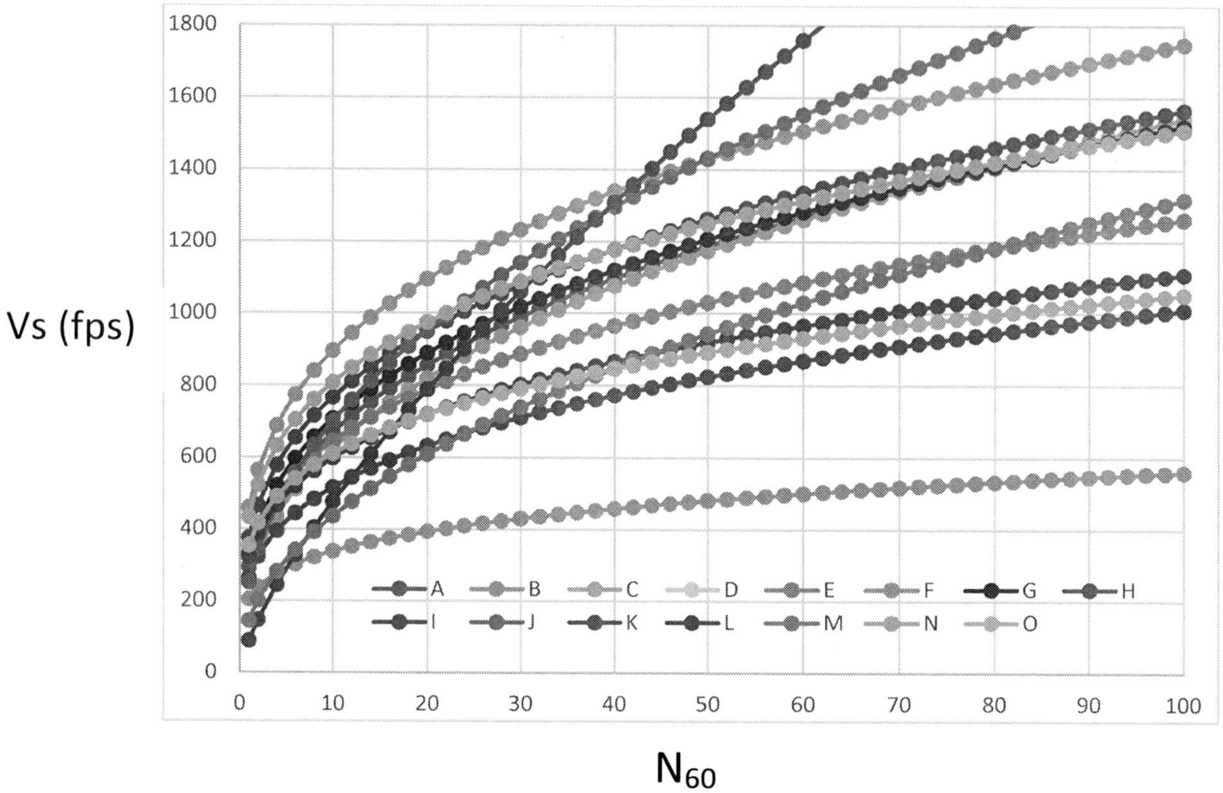

Figure 12 – Various Relationships for Vs vs N_{60} for Clay

Finally, immediate settlement (ρ_i) is still calculated from Eq. 14 though ε must be tied to an ε_{50} that is specifically for clay. Figure 14a is from Evans and Duncan (after Reese) as presented in Ashour et al. (1998). Using midpoint values from Fig. 14a, ε_{50} as a function of S_u or c is shown in Fig.14b. The resulting best fit equation to said curve is

$$\varepsilon_{50} = 0.6175\ c^{-0.61} \qquad \text{with c expressed in psf} \qquad (19)$$

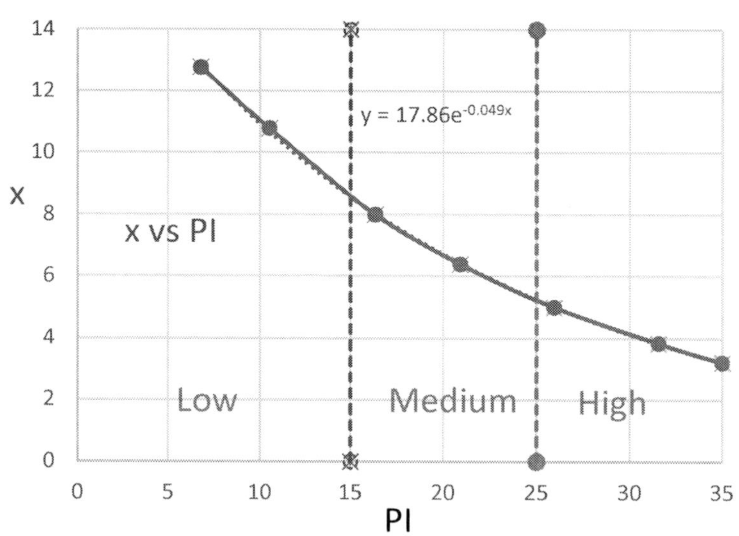

Figure 13 – Variation in Factor x with PI

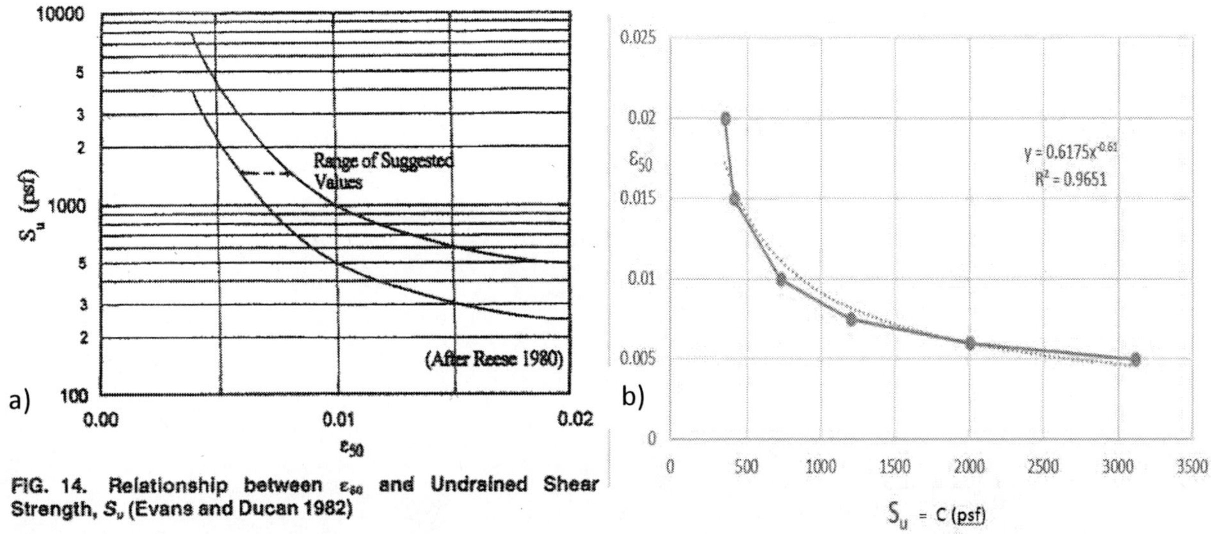

Figure 14 – a) Relationship Between ε_{50} and Undrained Shear Strength (S_u or c) as Given by Evans and Duncan 1982 (after Reese 1980) and b) Best-Fit Equation to Average Line

Figure 15 shows the appropriately modified spreadsheet for such c soil based on shear wave velocity (V_s) input. It should be noted that there is considerable deviation in the pressure versus settlement curves at low and high shear wave velocities derived using Eq. 17a versus 17b. Since the clay is saturated, and V_p would register as 5000 fps of the water, there is no equivalent modification that would apply for P wave analysis.

SUMMARY/DISCUSSION

The preceding presentation has provided a method for assessing a preliminary load-settlement response of a shallow (square) foundation based on surface geophysical measurements undertaken in the exploratory phase of investigation. Input will likely require data obtained from the Soil Conservation Service report for the site.

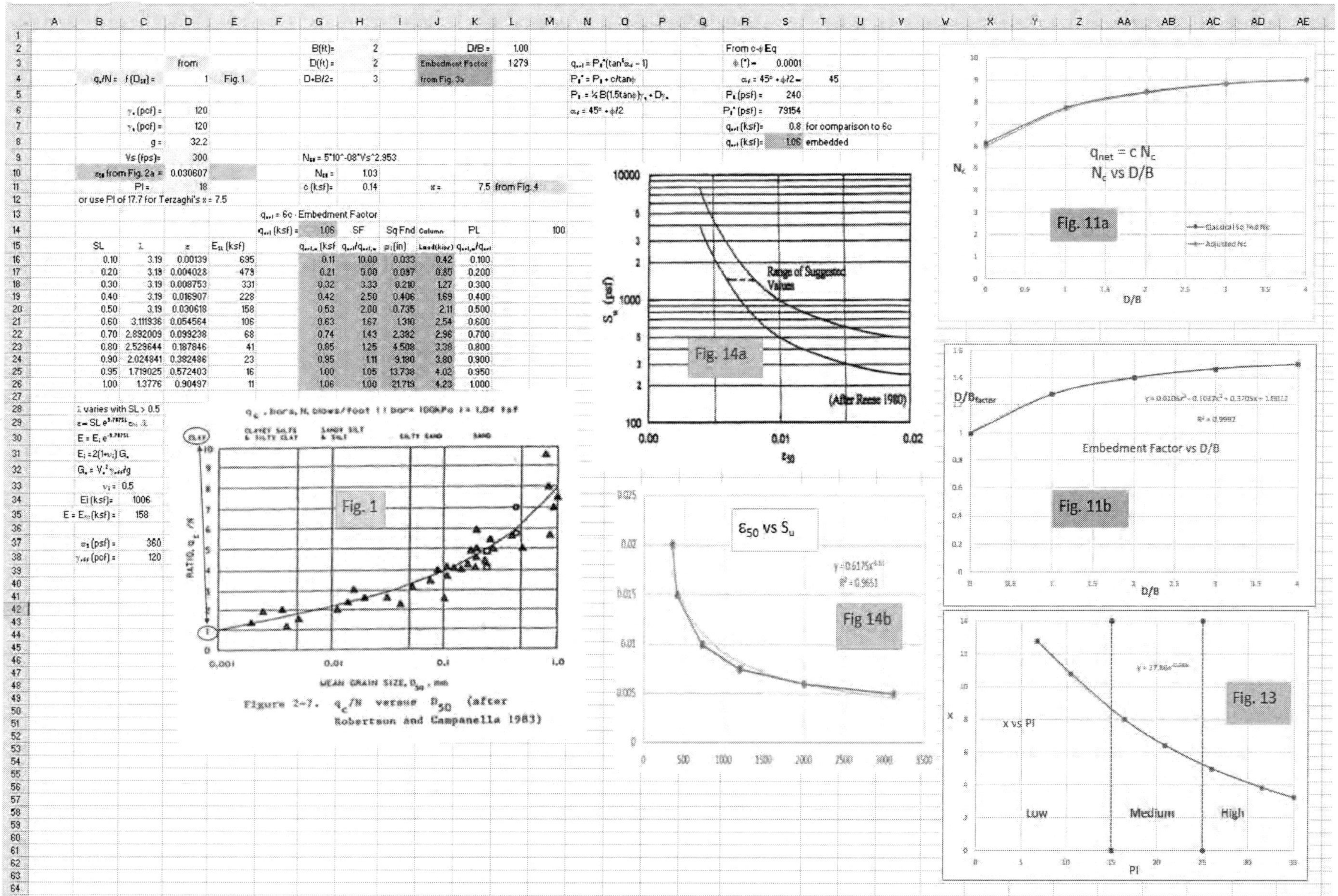

Figure 15 – Spreadsheet for Load-Settlement Assessment of Square Footing on c Soil

REFERENCES

Ashour, M., Norris, G. and Pilling, P. (1998) Lateral Loading of a Pile in Layered Soil Using the Strain Wedge Model, Journal of Geotechnical and Geoenvironmental Engineering, ASCE, Vol. 124, No. 4, pp. 303-315.

Ashour, M. and Norris, G., (1999) Liquefaction and Undrained Response Evaluation from Drained Formulation. Journal of Geotechnical and Geoenvironmental Engineering, ASCE, Vol. 125, No. 8, pp. 649 -658.

Bellana, N. (2009) Shear Wave Velocity as Function of SPT Penetration Resistance and Vertical Effective Stress at California Bridge Sites, M.S. Thesis, UCLA, 67 pp.

Elfass S., Norris G., Vimalaraj, P. (2007) A Simple Bearing Capacity Equation. GeoDenver 2007, ASCE, New Peaks in Geotechnics. In: Advances in Shallow Foundations, GSP, Vol. 171, pp 1–10.

Evans Jr., L. and Duncan, G. (1982) Simplified Analysis of Laterally Loaded Piles. University of California, Berkeley Report Number USB/GT/82-04.

Farrokhzad, T. and Choobbasti, A. (2016) Empirical Correlations of Shear Wave Velocity and Standard Penetration Resistance Based on Soil Type in Baboil City, Indian Journal of Geo Marine Sciences, Vol. 45 (11), pp. 1556-1577.

Florida Department of Transportation. (2004). Soils and Foundation Handbook.

NAVFAC (Naval Facilities Engineering Command) (1986, updated from 1982). DM 7.1 Design Manual: Soil Mechanics.

Nimeri, M., Elfass, S. and Norris, G. (2017) Load–settlement Response of Shallow Foundations Resting on Granular Soil. Innovative Infrastructure Solutions, 2:33 DOI 10.1007/s41062-017-0080-9

Norris, G., Elfass, S., Vimalaraj, P. and Lofty, A. (2011) A Simple Method for Assessing Load vs. Settlement of a Shallow Foundation up to Bearing Capacity Failure. Ist Congress on Transportation Infrastructure 1st CITRANS, Costa Rica.

Peck, R., Hanson,W. and Thornburn, T. (1974). Foundation Engineering. New York, John Wiley & Sons.

Robertson, P. and Campanella, R. (1983) Interpretation of Cone Penetration Tests. Part I: Sand. Canadian Geotechnical Journal, Vol. 20, No. 4, pp.718-733.

Schmertmann, J. Hartman, J. and Brown, P. (1978) Improved Strain Influence Factor Diagrams. Journal of Geotechnical Engineering, ASCE, Vol. 104, No. GT8, pp. 1131-1135.

Back Calculation from a Plate Load Test on Cohesionless Soil

Horng-Jyh Yang
West Virginia University Institute of Technology
410 Neville St.
Beckley, WV 25801
(304) 929-1640
hoyang@mail.wvu.edu

Gary Norris
University of Nevada Reno
1664 N. Virginia St, MS258
Reno, NV 89557
(775) 331-5582
norris@unr.edu

Sherif Elfass
Research Associate Professor
University of Nevada Reno
1664 N. Virginia St, MS258
Reno, NV 89557
(775) 331-5582
elfass@unr.edu

Prepared for the 71st Highway Geology Symposium, May, 2022

Disclaimer

Statements and views presented in this paper are strictly those of the author(s), and do not necessarily reflect positions held by their affiliations, the Highway Geology Symposium (HGS), or others acknowledged above. The mention of trade names for commercial products does not imply the approval or endorsement by HGS.

Copyright Notice

ABSTRACT

Pressure versus settlement data from a plate load test on sand can be used, with available formulation, to back calculate, in order, the increasing strain, the mobilized friction angle, the corresponding stress level, the deviatoric stress and the secant Young's modulus (first in the sand in the zone immediately beneath the plate, and subsequently, in the sand adjacent to the plate). A separate assessment of the volume change curve and the nonlinear variation in secant Poisson's ratio requires an assumption of the characteristic friction angle. Using a modified version of Bolton's equation, the log change in friction angle with confining pressure can be assessed and iteratively used to evaluate the same responses for a curved mobilized friction envelope that matches the mobilized load-settlement response. Such evaluation is presented for a plate load test on dense sand taken from the literature.

INTRODUCTION

A methodology for evaluating the load-settlement behavior of a foundation in soil with combined cohesive and frictional (c-ϕ) resistance has been presented by Elfass and Norris (2007, 2011, 2012 and 2017 with co-authors Vimalaraj, Lofty and Nemeri). The drained stress-strain characterization originally presented by Ashour and Norris (1999) has been upgraded and recently extended to include cemented soils (Elfass, et al. 2019). The characteristic friction angle and its use relative to the evaluation of the volume change curve and the nonlinear variation in Poisson's ratio has been established by Norris (2019). The modified Bolton equation used to assess the log cycle change in friction angle relative to the curved strength envelope is presented by Elfass and Norris (2012). All such background required in the context of the present objective, interpretation of the plate load test response described above, is summarized as needed.

LOAD-SETTLEMENT SOIL STRESS STATE MODEL

The model for the developing stress state in the soil under Nd around a shallow foundation upon loading can be visualized by what transpires in the three zones (or wedges) shown in Fig. 1. The interdependent stress state of the three zones, and Mohr–Coulomb failure envelope is illustrated in Fig. 2. The minor principal stress of an average element in zone I is the effective overburden pressure, Po, equal to embedment depth (D) multiplied by the effective unit weight of the soil above foundation base (γ_x) , plus one-half the foundation width (B) times the effective unit weight of the soil below the base of the foundation (γ_y), multiplied by a factor (j) (after Hansen 1961 and in ASCE 1993) equal to 1.5 times the tangent of the peak friction angle (ϕ) of the sand.

$$Po = D\,\gamma_x + 0.5\,B\,j\,\gamma_y \qquad j = 1.5 \tan\phi \qquad \text{(1a \& b)}$$

The vertical, or major principal stress, of zone III at the same depth, is $q_{ult} + 0.5\,B\,j\,\gamma_y$. Zone II of Fig. 1 (represented by a dashed Mohr circle II of Fig. 2) is the classical radial shear zone over which stress state is continuously varying from that of the boundary of zone I to that of zone III.

Effective horizontal pressure, P_h, the major principal stress of zone I, is also the minor principal stress of zone II. Likewise, the major principal stress of the dashed Mohr circle of zone II is the minor principal stress of zone III. A new origin, O', at the distance c/tan ϕ from O is introduced to convert the c–ϕ analysis to that of a purely frictional ϕ material. Based on the new origin, the c–ϕ envelope relative to O becomes a ϕ envelope relative to the transformed origin O'. Hence, the effective overburden pressure of zone I relative to O' is

$$Po^* = Po + c/\tan\phi = D\,\gamma_x + 0.5\,B\,j\,\gamma_y + c/\tan\phi \qquad (2)$$

Note that the horizontal distance between the lower end or minor principal stress of circle I and the upper end of the major principal stress of circle III is the net ultimate bearing pressure, q_{net}, while q_{ult} is the ultimate bearing capacity or the gross pressure applied at the base of the foundation at failure, as shown in Fig. 2. The net pressure is the gross pressure at the foundation base minus the overburden pressure due to base embedment, i.e., D γ_x.

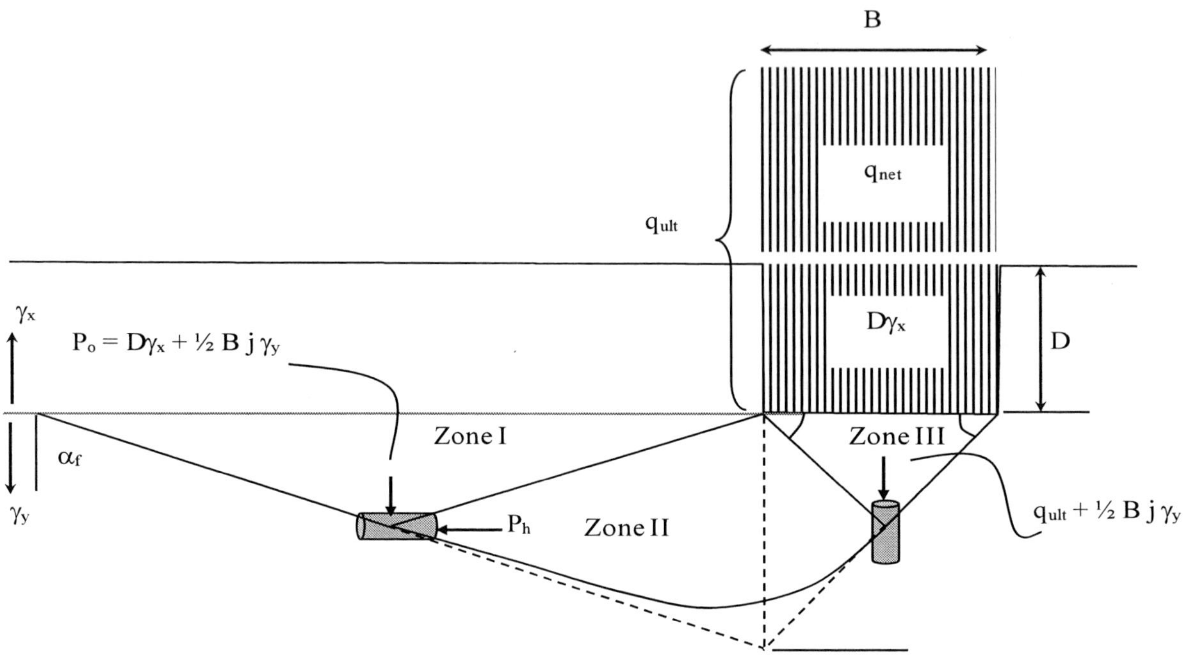

Figure 1 - Three Zone/Wedge Model of the Developing Failure Mass of a Shallow Foundation

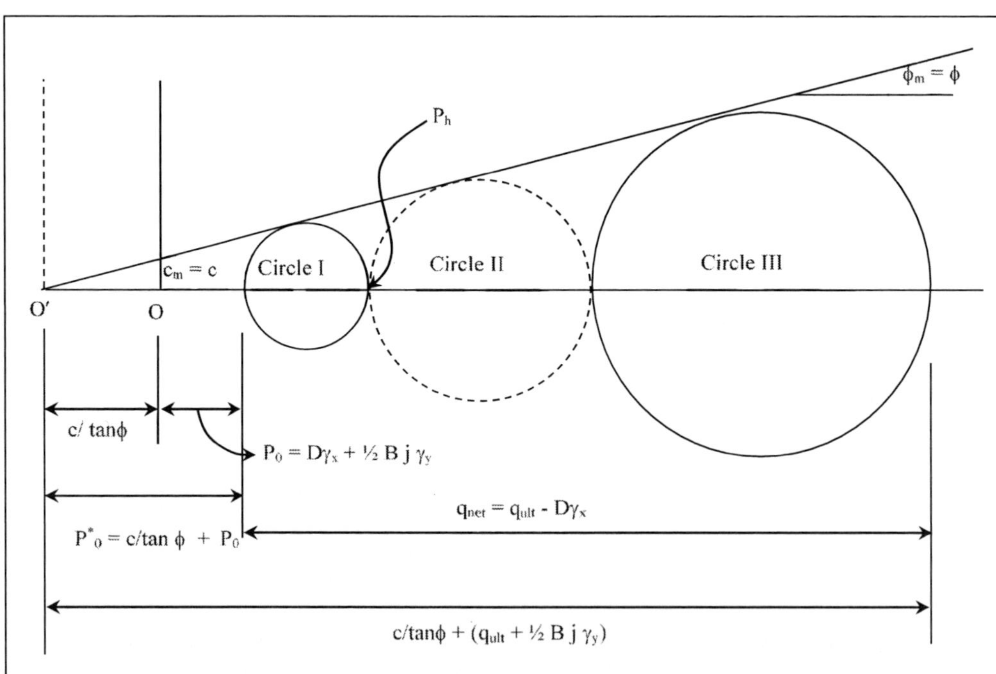

Figure 2 - Mohr Circle Representation of the Three Zones

$q_{net} = q_{ult} - D\,\gamma_x$ (3)

While Figures 1 and 2 characterize failure conditions, at some mobilized friction angle, ϕ_m, and mobilized cohesion, c_m, the distance noted as q_{net} would instead be a net mobilized pressure, $q_{net,m}$, or simply q_m. The net pressure applied at the foundation base can be visualized as the horizontal distance (a normal pressure) between the lower end of circle I and the upper end of circle III, as shown in Fig. 3. In fact, the traditionally defined factor of safety against (net) bearing capacity failure is the ratio q_{net} / q_m, while its reciprocal, q_m / q_{net}, is the pressure level, PL, both of which are pictured in Fig. 3. Alternatively, a factor of safety based on shear strength (as employed, for instance, in slope stability analysis) is the ratio of the slopes, $\tan\phi / \tan\phi_m$, also pictured in Fig. 3.

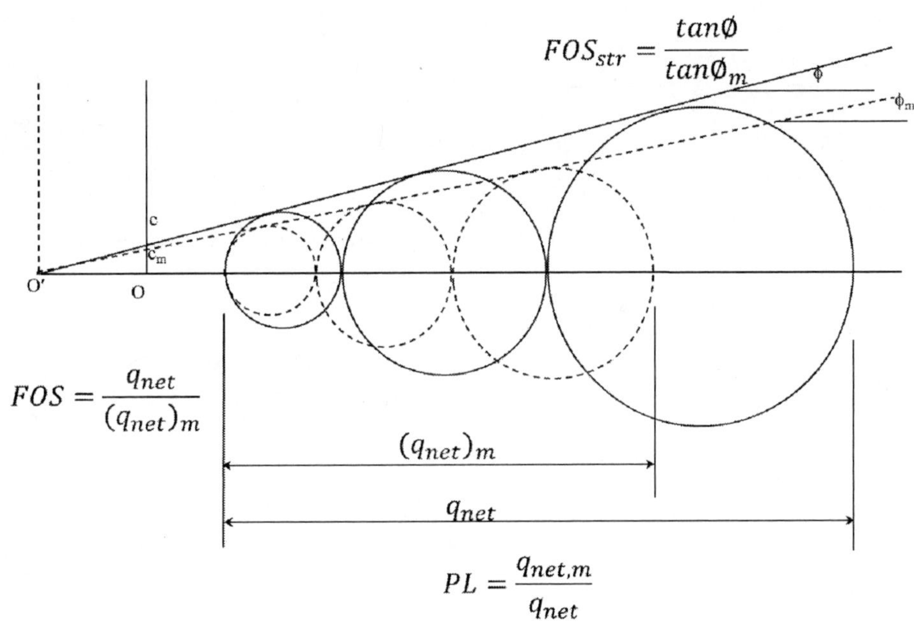

Figure 3 - Factor of Safety Based on Pressure, Its Reciprocal (Pressure Level) and Factor of Safety Based on Shear Strength

Based on the model depicted in Figs. 1 and 2, the resulting (net) ultimate bearing capacity becomes

$q_{net} = Po^* (\tan^6\alpha_f - 1)$ (4a)

where

$\alpha_f = 45 + \phi / 2$ (4b)

while the equation for a given mobilized condition is

$q_m = Po^* (\tan^6\alpha_m - 1)$ $\alpha_m = 45 + \phi_m / 2$ (5a & b)

The proposed model assumes the same stress level (SL) develops in all three zones at a given mobilized condition, though the strain will not be the same in the three zones at this SL.

The effect of soil compressibility on the stress state can be accounted for via a changing secant friction angle as a function of the corresponding current effective confining pressure (σ_{3m}) in each of the three zones, as seen in Fig. 4.

While Fig. 4 illustrates the angles at failure, it can be shown that the corresponding value of mobilized friction angle, in terms of the peak value at the same confining pressure, at the specified stress level (SL) is

$$\sin \phi_m = SL\ A / (SL\ A + 2) \qquad (6)$$

where

$$A = \tan^2 \alpha_f - 1 \quad \text{or} \quad A = 2 \sin \phi / (1 - \sin \phi) \qquad (7a\ \&b)$$

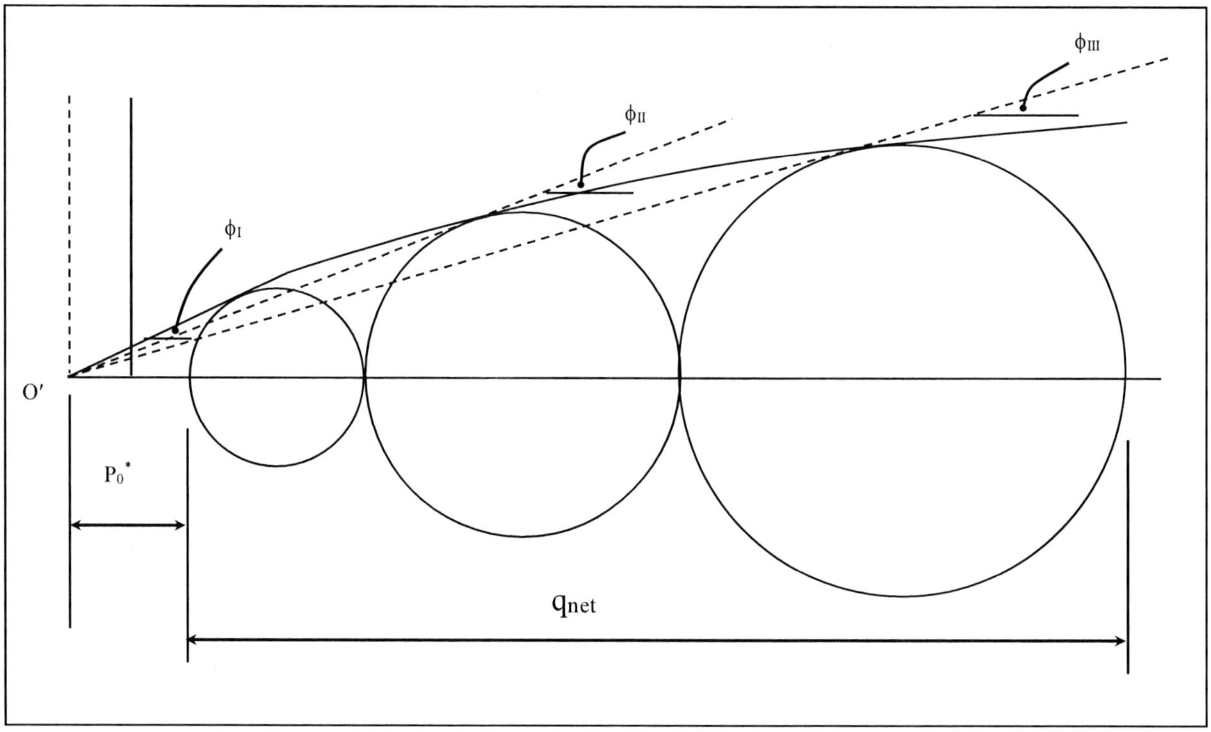

Figure 4 - Change in the Secant Friction Angle from One Zone to Another

Since the model considers a square or circular foundation, the stress state in zones II and III represent conditions in any radial direction (from vertical centerline of the footing). The stress and strain that occurs in zone III of Fig. 1 can be thought of as what occurs in the upper cone of a standard triaxial test (with due consideration for the changing confining pressure of zone III). Since there is full friction between the base and underlying soil of the foundation, this is equivalent to the standard triaxial test with friction between soil and the cap or base at the ends of the soil specimen.

Elfass et al. (2007) provide more details on the load calculations.

SETTLEMENT CALCULATION

Foundation settlement, ρ, is directly related to the peak vertical or major principal strain, ε, of zone III of the Schmertmann et al. (1978) strain triangle over depth 2B (for the square and circular foundation). See Fig. 5. The strain, ε, is the current deviatoric stress of zone III ($\sigma_{dm} = \Delta\sigma_1 - \Delta\sigma_3$) divided by the secant Young's modulus, E, corresponding to σ_{3m} of zone III.

Picture this as a point on a triaxial test stress–strain curve of that confining pressure (σ_3). As q_m increases, so does σ_3 (i.e. σ_{3m}) of zone III, as if the point of concern for zone III jumps from one triaxial test stress–strain curve to another. The settlement, ρ, at any q_m is equal to the area of the current strain triangle or ε B. For the rectangular foundation of length, L, the strain triangle's peak and base move deeper, and a factor (0.9 + 0.1 L/B) is employed such that settlement becomes

$$\rho = \varepsilon B (0.9 + 0.1 L/B) \tag{8}$$

Stress level (SL) represents the ratio of the deviator stress (σ_{dm}) to its failing value (σ_{df}) in zone III as pictured in Fig. 5 (i.e. diameters, R/F in zone III) corresponding to the current confining pressure (σ_{3m}) in that zone (as is the stress level in a standard triaxial test at the current σ_3 of zone III). (Note, also, that the SL in zone I is the same as in zone III.)

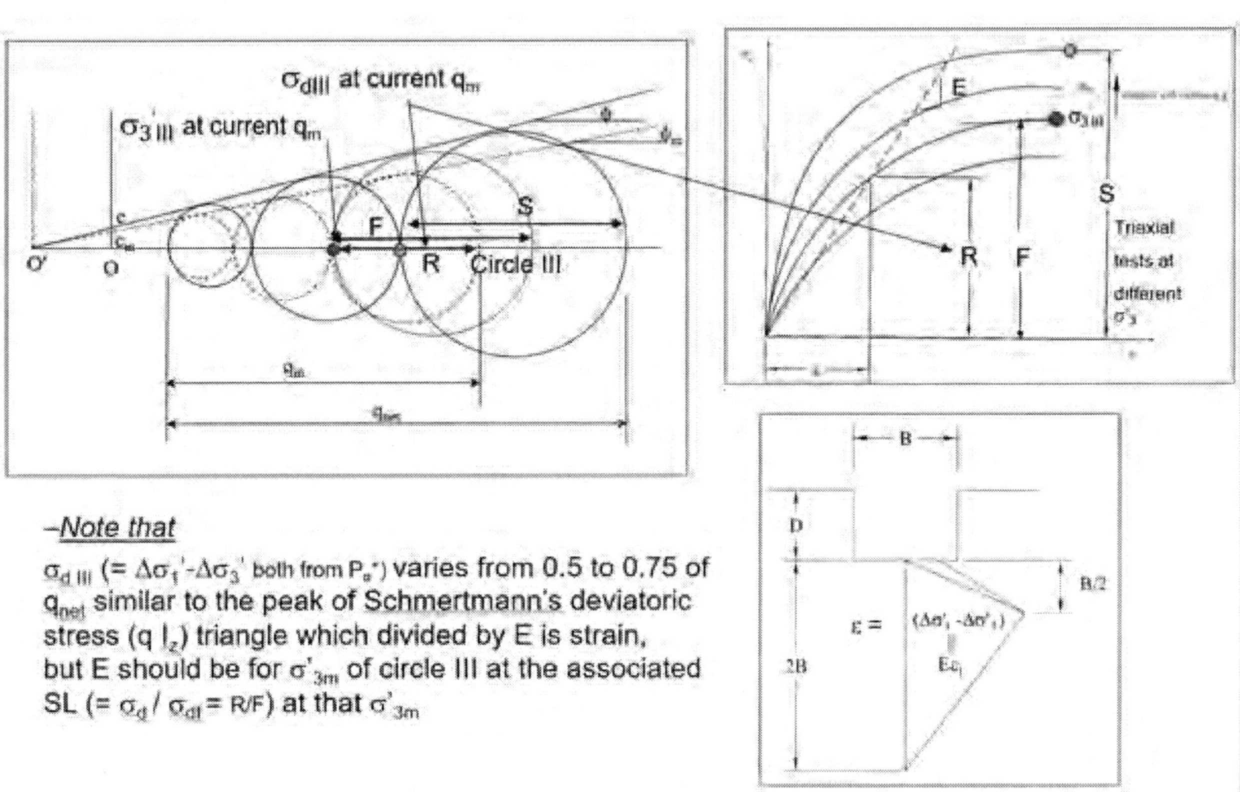

Figure 5 - Deviatoric Stress at Current Confining Pressure of Zone III and the Corresponding Strain at ½ B of the Schmertmann Triangle

Picture this as a point on a triaxial test stress–strain curve of that confining pressure (σ_3). As q_m increases, so does σ_3 (i.e. σ_{3m}) of zone III, as if the point of concern for zone III jumps from one triaxial test stress–strain curve to another. The settlement, ρ, at any q_m is equal to the area of the current strain triangle or ε B. For the rectangular foundation of length, L, the strain triangle's peak and base move deeper, and a factor (0.9 + 0.1 L/B) is employed such that settlement becomes

$$\rho = \varepsilon \, B \, (0.9 + 0.1 \, L/B) \tag{8}$$

Stress level (SL) represents the ratio of the deviator stress (σ_{dm}) to its failing value (σ_{df}) in zone III as pictured in Fig. 5 (i.e. diameters, R/F in zone III) corresponding to the current confining pressure (σ_{3m}) in that zone (as is the stress level in a standard triaxial test at the current σ_3 of zone III). (Note, also, that the SL in zone I is the same as in zone III.)

INTERPRETATION OF THE PLATE LOAD TEST DATA

Given that settlement, ρ, is related to the current vertical or major principal strain in zone III, ε_{III}, can be back-calculated from the recorded settlement (via Eq. 8) as

$$\varepsilon_{III} = \rho \, / \, B \, (0.9 + 0.1 \, L/B) \tag{9}$$

at the corresponding confining pressure, $\sigma_{3m,III}$, i.e.

$$\sigma_{3m,III} = Po^* \tan^4 \alpha_m \tag{10}$$

This strain can be used to establish the major principal strain associated strain in zone I, ε_I, as

$$\varepsilon_I = \varepsilon_{III} \, (Po^* / \, \sigma_{3m,III})^{\,n} \qquad n = 0.2 \tag{11}$$

once $\sigma_{3m,III}$ is established. Equation 11 follows the relationship established relative to the strains at 50% stress level as given by Ashour and Norris (1999) (Note that confining pressure in zone I remains constant at Po*.)

To establish $\sigma_{3m,III}$ in Eq. 11, α_m of Eq. 5b needs to be established. Rearranging Eq. 5a

$$\alpha_m = \tan^{-1}[(q_m/Po^*+1)^{1/6}] \tag{12}$$

whereby

$$\phi_m = 2 \, (\alpha_m - 45) \tag{13}$$

and from ϕ_m, the associated value of SL in all three zones is established from a rearranged Eq. 6, i.e.

$$SL = 2 \, [\sin \phi_m / (1 - \sin \phi_m)] \, / A \tag{14}$$

Note that factor j in Po* and A require knowledge of the peak friction angle, ϕ. This, in turn, requires that the plate load test be carried to net ultimate capacity (unless a value of $q_{net} = q_m$ at some displacement is taken to be "failure"). Initially, a value of ϕ must be assumed to assess initial values of j and A. Using these values of j and A, ϕ_m at q_{net} is assessed and taken as the new value of ϕ leading to updated values of j and A. Such iteration is easily undertaken in a spreadsheet using a circular reference.

EXAMPLE SHOWING THE METHOD AND SEQUENCE OF CALCULATIONS

A carefully conducted lab plate load test by Valore et al. (2017) atop a dense sand (relative density, $D_r = 92\%$ for the void ratio $e_c = 0.622$ between $e_{min} = 0.606$ and $e_{max} = 0.798$) of unit weight $\gamma_y = 16\ kN/m^3$ was used to demonstrate the aforementioned analysis. The rigid rectangular plate was 60 mm by 100 mm for which the shape factor (0.9 + 0.1 L/B) for settlement is 1.067. As indicated by the article's authors, the strength envelope established from triaxial tests (and confirmed from direct shear tests) over the very low confining pressure range encountered in the plate load test was curved. The secant friction angle exceeded 50° at confining pressure < 10 kPa.

Figure 6 is the digitized version of the test figure appearing in the Valore et al. (2017) paper as represented by columns A and C in the spreadsheet of Fig. 7. Given values of B and L in cells B1 and B 2, shape factor (0.9 + 0.1 L/B) is evaluated in cell E2. Given γ_y in cell B3 and an initial value of ϕ in cell B4 / E4, initial values of Po* = Po (for c = 0) in cell B5 from Eqs. 1 and 2 (D=0) and A in cell E5 from Eq. 7b are calculated. Values of α_m and ϕ_m in columns D/E and F are assessed from Eqs. 12 and 13, successively, based on the values of q_m in column C. The maximum value of ϕ_m in column F is then taken equal to ϕ in cell B4 whereby Po* and A are updated. Whether the iterative value of ϕ is reassessed manually or by circular reference in the spreadsheet program, final values of ϕ, Po* and A result. Column G yields the associated values of SL based on Eq. 14. Values of pressure level, PL = q_m / q_{net}, appear in column H though they could have been established earlier after column C given that q_{net} is the maximum value of column C.

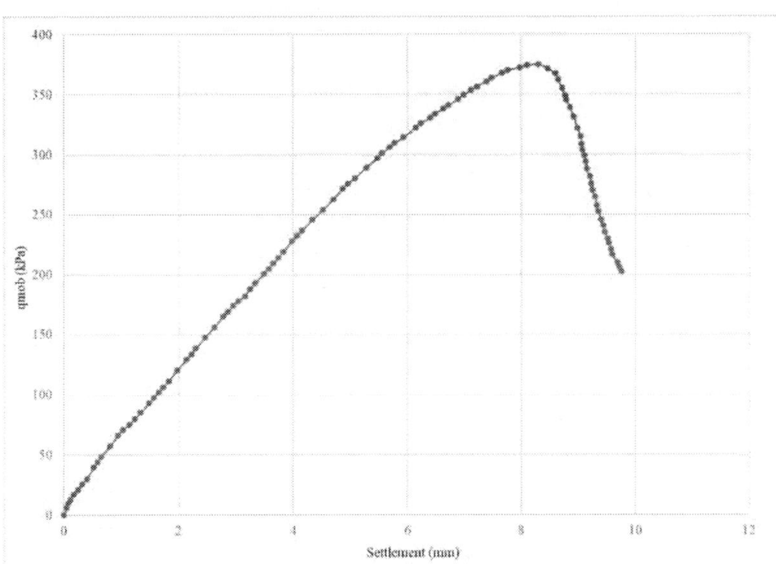

Figure 6 - Applied Pressure (q_m) versus Settlement (ρ) from the Valore et al. (2017) Test

	A	B	C	D	E	F	G	H	I	J	K	L	M	N	O	P	Q	R	S	T	U	W	X
1	B (mm) =	60										e_{10} (%)	1.495										
2	L (mm) =	100		Fac B/L =	1.06667	for Sett						$\sigma_{3III,50}$ =	15.8694										
3	γ_s (kN/m^3) =	16		n =	0.2												ϕ_{pr} (°) =	26					
4	ϕ (°) =	50.093		ϕ (rad) =	0.87429																		
5	Po* (kPa)	0.8609		A =	6.58689					Zone III				Zone I		Zone III, in which σ_{3III} varies			Zone I, in which σ_{3eI} = Po* is const			constant σ_{3III} = σ_3	
6	Sett (mm)	ε_x (%)	q_{mob} (kPa)	α_m (rad)	α_m (deg)	ϕ_m (°)	SL	PL	σ_{3IIIm}	σ_{dIIIm}	σ_{1IIIf}	E (kPa)	σ_{dm}	ε (%)	E (kPa)	$\phi_{m,area}$ (°)	ε_v (%)	ν_{sec}	$\phi_{m,area}$ (°)	ε_v (%)	ν_{sec}	$\phi_{m,area}$ (°)	ν
25	1.6521	2.58	102.199	1.14757	65.751	41.502	0.59641	0.27246	20.9111	82.1491	137.739	3182.34	3.38202	1.36386	247.974	90.9679	-0.91736	0.67769	47.1281	-0.44876	0.66452	52.6282	0.66452
26	1.57094	2.45	97.6221	1.14473	65.5881	41.1762	0.58516	0.26026	20.2873	78.1957	133.63	3185.69	3.31825	1.30474	254.322	85.7256	-0.84255	0.67163	44.6841	-0.41388	0.65861	49.899	0.65861
27	1.73596	2.71	106.362	1.15004	65.8923	41.7845	0.60635	0.28356	21.4705	85.7522	141.424	3161.45	3.43839	1.42554	241.198	96.4208	-0.99606	0.68361	49.695	-0.4858	0.67039	55.4946	0.67039
28	1.82702	2.85	111.296	1.15283	66.052	42.1041	0.61781	0.29671	22.1243	90.033	145.73	3153.84	3.50336	1.49135	234.912	102.389	-1.08332	0.68974	52.4551	-0.52616	0.6764	58.5768	0.6764
29	1.97624	3.09	120.31	1.15758	66.3247	42.6494	0.63789	0.32074	23.2942	97.8763	153.437	3169.7	3.61726	1.59661	226.558	112.269	-1.23018	0.6992	56.916	-0.59246	0.68554	63.5583	0.68554
30	2.13797	3.34	129.346	1.16197	66.5763	43.1525	0.65706	0.34483	24.4385	105.769	160.973	3166.18	3.72593	1.71079	217.79	123.111	-1.39445	0.70871	61.8143	-0.66668	0.69485	69.0283	0.69485
31	2.29313	3.58	138.392	1.16604	66.8093	43.6186	0.67537	0.36895	25.5575	113.695	168.345	3173.16	3.82978	1.81859	210.59	133.629	-1.55656	0.71721	66.4914	-0.73877	0.70311	74.2512	0.70311
32	2.22119	3.47	133.634	1.16394	66.6889	43.3778	0.66584	0.35626	24.9721	109.523	164.488	3155.73	3.77574	1.76972	213.352	128.739	-1.48091	0.71335	64.3655	-0.70587	0.69343	71.8772	0.69943
33	2.45672	3.84	147.508	1.16985	67.0277	44.0554	0.69304	0.39325	26.6611	121.708	175.614	3170.6	3.92998	1.93193	203.423	144.828	-1.73168	0.72556	71.4566	-0.8164	0.71129	79.7958	0.71129
34	2.62052	4.09	155.925	1.17315	67.2164	44.4329	0.70872	0.41569	27.6602	129.126	182.195	3153.6	4.01892	2.04563	196.464	156.151	-1.91126	0.73339	76.4871	-0.89619	0.71905	85.4134	0.71905
35	2.77472	4.34	165.152	1.17654	67.4108	44.8215	0.72529	0.44029	28.7351	137.278	189.275	3166.38	4.11283	2.14955	191.335	166.904	-2.08388	0.74033	81.1248	-0.97064	0.72578	90.5924	0.72578
36	2.9481	4.61	173.857	1.17955	67.5833	45.1666	0.74036	0.4635	29.731	144.987	195.835	3147.51	4.19828	2.26836	185.081	179.093	-2.28179	0.74768	86.4705	-1.05743	0.73308	96.5619	0.73308
37	2.84839	4.45	169.045	1.17791	67.4891	44.9783	0.73209	0.45067	29.1825	140.723	192.222	3161.89	4.1514	2.19981	188.716	172.071	-2.1675	0.74351	83.3809	-1.00715	0.72892	93.1117	0.72892
38	3.03617	4.74	178.273	1.18102	67.6672	45.3344	0.74781	0.47527	30.2298	148.904	199.12	3138.77	4.24055	2.32836	182.126	185.32	-2.38368	0.75123	89.1857	-1.10186	0.73662	99.594	0.73662
39	3.15006	4.92	182.382	1.18234	67.7432	45.4864	0.75463	0.48622	30.6903	152.552	202.154	3099.41	4.27926	2.4084	177.68	193.401	-2.51654	0.75564	92.8206	-1.16162	0.74116	103.653	0.74116
40	3.24083	5.06	188.013	1.18411	67.8444	45.6887	0.76383	0.50123	31.3159	157.558	206.275	3111.46	4.33138	2.46782	175.514	199.867	-2.62338	0.75903	95.5293	-1.20638	0.74442	106.678	0.74442
41	3.48182	5.44	200.607	1.18785	68.0588	46.1177	0.78374	0.53481	32.693	168.775	215.345	3102.28	4.44431	2.62861	169.075	217.152	-2.91164	0.7676	102.91	-1.32947	0.75288	114.92	0.75288
42	3.32611	5.20	193.125	1.18566	67.9333	45.8666	0.77201	0.51486	31.8784	162.107	209.98	3119.22	4.37781	2.52376	173.464	205.962	-2.72455	0.76213	98.0876	-1.24884	0.74742	109.535	0.74742
43	3.56329	5.57	204.87	1.18906	68.1281	46.2561	0.7903	0.54618	33.1526	172.579	218.372	3099.67	4.48147	2.68261	167.056	223.031	-3.0105	0.77036	105.405	-1.37141	0.75561	117.706	0.75561
44	3.64789	5.70	209.454	1.19033	68.2007	46.4014	0.79724	0.5584	33.6432	176.672	221.604	3099.6	4.52086	2.73824	165.101	229.156	-3.11385	0.77315	107.982	-1.41491	0.75836	120.584	0.75836
45	3.7294	5.83	214.047	1.19157	68.2718	46.5435	0.8041	0.57064	34.1313	180.777	224.819	3102.31	4.55976	2.79138	163.352	235.074	-3.21413	0.77579	110.451	-1.45675	0.76094	123.341	0.76094
46	3.81976	5.97	218.76	1.19281	68.3429	46.6858	0.81104	0.5832	34.6284	184.992	228.094	3099.54	4.59909	2.85076	161.329	241.656	-3.32609	0.77864	113.219	-1.50383	0.76376	126.432	0.76376
47	3.9702	6.20	227.893	1.19513	68.476	46.952	0.8242	0.60755	35.5819	193.172	234.374	3113.95	4.67375	2.94698	158.595	252.661	-3.51431	0.78325	117.724	-1.58088	0.76827	131.463	0.76822
48	4.06242	6.35	232.721	1.19632	68.544	47.088	0.83102	0.62042	36.0808	197.501	237.66	3111.46	4.71242	3.00704	156.713	259.436	-3.63079	0.786	120.548	-1.62944	0.77094	134.617	0.77094
49	4.14957	6.48	236.825	1.19731	68.6006	47.2011	0.83674	0.63136	36.5022	201.184	240.436	3102.91	4.74487	3.06443	154.837	265.856	-3.74154	0.78853	123.254	-1.6761	0.77348	137.638	0.77348
50	4.33368	6.77	245.735	1.19938	68.7197	47.4394	0.84895	0.65512	37.4088	209.187	246.408	3089.28	4.81406	3.18473	151.161	279.469	-3.97743	0.79369	128.947	-1.77475	0.77863	143.995	0.77863
51	4.50958	7.05	253.791	1.20119	68.8233	47.6466	0.85973	0.6766	38.2192	216.433	251.746	3071.62	4.8752	3.29981	147.742	292.536	-4.20515	0.7984	134.418	-1.87011	0.78337	150.105	0.78337
52	4.69511	7.34	262.593	1.2031	68.9324	47.8647	0.87125	0.70006	39.0949	224.359	257.514	3058.28	4.94054	3.42005	144.458	306.38	-4.44773	0.80314	140.16	-1.97072	0.78811	156.517	0.78811
53	4.86081	7.60	271.66	1.20498	69.0405	48.0811	0.88285	0.72423	39.9868	232.534	263.389	3061.67	5.00635	3.52481	142.032	318.8	-4.66653	0.80721	145.186	-2.05925	0.79211	162.129	0.79211
54	4.94835	7.73	275.864	1.20564	69.0893	48.1786	0.88815	0.73544	40.397	236.328	266.091	3056.57	5.03636	3.58097	140.642	325.383	-4.78295	0.8093	147.889	-2.10705	0.7942	165.148	0.7942
55	5.06919	7.92	280.316	1.20672	69.1401	48.2801	0.89369	0.74731	40.8291	240.347	268.937	3034.46	5.06782	3.66062	138.442	334.489	-4.94438	0.81212	151.73	-2.17515	0.7971	169.437	0.7971
56	5.27463	8.24	288.769	1.20836	69.234	48.468	0.90407	0.76984	41.6433	247.986	274.3	3008.95	5.12664	3.79396	135.126	350.018	-5.22062	0.81672	158.18	-2.2899	0.80178	176.641	0.80178
57	5.46684	8.54	297.108	1.20993	69.3237	48.6474	0.91411	0.79208	42.4389	255.53	279.541	2991.48	5.18357	3.91736	132.323	364.601	-5.48118	0.82084	164.172	-2.39696	0.80594	183.332	0.80594
58	5.54741	8.67	301.362	1.21071	69.3684	48.7368	0.91916	0.80342	42.8418	259.381	282.195	2992.45	5.21219	3.96759	131.369	370.731	-5.59105	0.82252	166.618	-2.4408	0.80759	186.063	0.80759
59	5.67983	8.87	305.96	1.21154	69.4159	48.8318	0.92456	0.81567	43.2753	263.545	285.05	2969.61	5.24284	4.05413	129.321	380.825	-5.77238	0.82521	170.84	-2.51664	0.81038	190.778	0.81038
60	5.77056	9.02	309.706	1.2122	69.454	48.908	0.92892	0.82566	43.6268	266.94	287.365	2960.57	5.26758	4.11223	128.095	387.753	-5.89708	0.82702	173.679	-2.56774	0.81221	193.948	0.81221
61	5.92177	9.25	314.168	1.21298	69.4987	48.9975	0.93407	0.83756	44.0437	270.985	290.111	2928.7	5.29679	4.21197	125.756	399.319	-6.10565	0.82994	178.562	-2.65579	0.81527	199.4	0.81527
62	6.1415	9.60	322.386	1.21439	69.5793	49.1586	0.94343	0.85947	44.8063	278.44	295.135	2901.6	5.34987	4.35328	122.893	416.168	-6.41039	0.83401	185.497	-2.78122	0.81944	207.145	0.81944
63	6.23172	9.74	326.105	1.21501	69.615	49.23	0.94762	0.86938	45.1494	281.817	297.394	2894.27	5.3736	4.4105	121.837	423.103	-6.53614	0.83563	188.312	-2.83226	0.82108	210.288	0.82108
64	6.39093	9.99	330.536	1.21574	69.6569	49.3138	0.95256	0.88119	45.5564	285.84	300.075	2862.46	5.40164	4.51507	119.636	435.361	-6.75882	0.83842	193.464	-2.92587	0.82401	216.042	0.82401
65	6.48159	10.13	333.931	1.2163	69.6886	49.3772	0.95632	0.89024	45.867	288.925	302.121	2852.88	5.42295	4.5729	118.589	442.35	-6.886	0.83997	196.318	-2.97779	0.82559	219.229	0.82559
66	6.62988	10.36	338.474	1.21703	69.7305	49.4609	0.96131	0.90236	46.281	293.054	304.848	2828.92	5.45124	4.66913	116.751	453.801	-7.09471	0.84244	201.073	-3.06446	0.82816	224.539	0.82816
67	6.71756	10.50	341.176	1.21746	69.7551	49.5102	0.96426	0.90956	46.5263	295.51	306.464	2815.41	5.46796	4.72587	115.703	460.58	-7.21845	0.84386	203.881	-3.11577	0.82964	227.675	0.82964
68	6.88245	10.75	345.957	1.21821	69.7981	49.5961	0.96943	0.92231	46.9589	299.859	309.313	2788.39	5.49731	4.83292	113.747	473.348	-7.45185	0.84647	209.186	-3.2127	0.83238	233.599	0.83238
69	6.98142	10.91	349.621	1.21877	69.8306	49.6612	0.97337	0.93207	47.2891	303.193	311.488	2779.43	5.51962	4.89556	112.748	481.023	-7.59239	0.848	212.295	-3.26962	0.83394	237.07	0.83394
70	7.12074	11.13	353.774	1.21941	69.867	49.7339	0.9778	0.94315	47.6619	306.973	313.944	2759.02	5.54473	4.98541	111.219	491.841	-7.7908	0.85011	216.76	-3.35152	0.83613	242.057	0.83613
71	7.22517	11.29	356.72	1.21985	69.8925	49.7849	0.98092	0.951	47.9255	309.655	315.68	2742.9	5.56241	5.05295	110.083	499.96	-7.93891	0.85166	220.121	-3.41323	0.83775	245.81	0.83775
72	7.38781	11.54	360.797	1.22046	69.9274	49.8548	0.9852	0.96187	48.2891	313.369	318.075	2714.69	5.58673	5.15889	108.293	512.621	-8.17273	0.854	225.399	-3.51029	0.84022	251.704	0.84022
73	7.4772	11.68	363.688	1.22089	69.9519	49.9038	0.98823	0.96957	48.5[illegible]	[illegible]	319.768	2704.78	5.60386	5.21577	107.441	519.587	-8.301	0.85526	228.236	-3.56253	0.84152	254.872	0.84152
74	7.66236	11.97	368.039	1.22153	69.9884	49.9767	0.99274	0.98118	48.9316	[illegible]	322.307	2672.54	5.62948	5.33648	105.491	534.036	-8.5674	0.8578	234.264	-3.67368	0.8442	261.604	0.8442
75	7.75438	12.12	369.989	1.22181	70.0045	50.0091	0.99476	0.98637	49.1039	321.746	323.442	2655.5	5.6409	5.39677	104.524	541.224	-8.70008	0.85903	237.278	-3.72932	0.84551	264.97	0.84551
76	7.96848	12.45	372.511	1.22217	70.0253	50.0506	0.99735	0.9931	49.3262	324.045	324.907	2602.62	5.6556	5.54077	102.073	557.96	-9.00926	0.8618	244.482	-3.8624	0.84854	273.014	0.84854
77	8.09503	12.65	374.293	1.22243	70.0399	50.0798	0.99918	0.99785	49.4831	325.671	325.94	2574.78	5.66596	5.62519	100.725	567.86	-9.19228	0.86337	248.709	-3.94054	0.85026	277.734	0.85026
78	8.29	12.95	375.1	1.22254	70.0465	50.093	1	1	49.554	326.407	326.407	2519.91	5.67063	5.75903	98.4652	583.118	-9.4745	0.86572	255.412	-4.06453	0.85288	285.22	0.85288
79	8.45282	13.21	371.6	1.22204	70.0178	50.0357	0.99641	0.99067	49.246	323.215	324.378	2447.2	5.6503	5.87946	96.1024	595.855	-9.70997	0.86759	261.442	-4.176	0.85513	291.953	0.85513
80	8.58546	13.41	367.247	1.22141	69.9818	49.9635	0.99192	0.97906	48.8615	319.246	321.845	2379.81	5.62483	5.98109	94.0436	606.218	-9.90128	0.86904	266.523	-4.26981	0.85694	297.628	0.85694
81	8.63628	13.49	362.322	1.22069	69.9403	49.8807	0.9868	0.96593	48.4247	314.758	318.968	2332.54	5.59578	6.02731	92.8404	610.182	-9.97433	0.86958	268.831	-4.31233	0.85773	300.204	0.85773
82	8.76092	13.69	349.361	1.21873	69.8283	49.6566	0.97309	0.93138	47.2657	302.956	311.334	2213.15	5.51804	6.14399	89.812	619.874	-10.1524	0.87082	274.638	-4.419	0.85962	306.689	0.85962
83	8.70932	13.61	355.151	1.21962	69.8789	49.7578	0.97926	0.94682	47.7852	308.227	314.756	2264.99	5.55301	6.09447	91.1155	615.866	-10.0789	0.87032	272.176	-4.37384	0.85884	303.94	0.85884
84	8.77718	13.71	345.624	1.21815	69.7951	49.5902	0.96908	0.92142	46.9289	299.556	309.115	2184.25	5.49527	6.16421	89.1481	621.133	-10.1754	0.87098	275.64	-4.43734	0.85993	307.809	0.85993
85	8.84207	13.82	339.311	1.21716	69.7381	49.4762	0.96223	0.90459	46.3571	293.815	305.349	2126.67	5.45643	6.22502	87.6532	626.155	-10.2672	0.87158	278.653	-4.49239	0.86083	311.173	0.86083
86	8.91357	13.93	331.421	1.21589	69.6652	49.3304	0.95355	0.88356	45.6375	286.645	300.609	2058.13	5.40721	6.29502	85.8966	631.675	-10.3677	0.8722	282.111	-4.5554	0.86183	315.034	0.86183
87	8.97869	14.03	321.953	1.21431	69.5751	49.1502	0.94295	0.85831	44.7664	278.048	294.871	1981.92	5.3471	6.3655	84.0012	636.685	-10.4587	0.87275	285.581	-4.6184	0.86277	318.91	0.86277
88	9.03625	14.12	315.105	1.21314	69.508	49.0161	0.93515	0.84006	44.131	271.835	290.686	1925.3	5.30289	6.42465	82.5397	641.1	-10.5385	0.8732	288.485	-4.67091	0.86351	322.152	0.86351
89	9.07091	14.17	303.693	1.21113	69.3926	48.7852	0.9219	0.80963	43.0619	261.492	283.644	1844.96	5.22777	6.48101	80.6629	643.748	-10.5862	0.87346	291.24	-4.72055	0.86418	325.229	0.86418
90	9.10569	14.23	299.496	1.21037	69.3489	48.6978	0.91695	0.79844	42.6653	257.691	281.032	1811.2	5.19967	6.51791	79.7751	646.397	-10.6338	0.8737	293.039	-4.75282	0.8646	327.238	0.8646
91	9.05238	14.14	308.919	1.21206	69.4461	48.8921	0.92801	0.82356	43.5531	266.227	286.88	1882.22	5.2624	6.45311	81.5483	642.332	-10.5607	0.87332	289.877	-4.69601	0.86386	323.707	0.86386
92	9.12972	14.27	294.075	1.20936	69.2914	48.5829	0.91048	0.78399	42.1505	252.786	277.641	1772.05	5.16299	6.55099	78.8123	648.222	-10.6664	0.87386	294.648	-4.78161	0.86495	329.034	0.86495
93	9.14075	14.28	288.119	1.20824	69.2269	48.4538	0.90328	0.76811	41.581	247.399	273.89	1732.19	5.12216	6.57677	77.8826	649.058	-10.6813	0.87393	295.899	-4.80394	0.86522	330.431	0.86522
94	9.22451	14.41	275.275	1.20572	69.0825	48.1651	0.88741	0.73367	40.3397	235.796	265.713	1635.96	5.03217	6.6774	75.3613	655.38	-10.7936	0.87443	300.76	-4.89028	0.86618	335.859	0.86618
95	9.20273	14.38	281.547	1.20696	69.154	48.3079	0.89522	0.75059	40.9482	241.46	269.722	1679.22	5.07646	6.64171	76.4331	653.739	-10.7645	0.87431	299.038	-4.85976	0.86585	333.937	0.86585
96	9.24431	14.44	270.249	1.2047	69.024	48.0479	0.88107	0.72047	39.8486	231.261	262.479	1601.06	4.9962	6.70814	74.4796	656.869	-10.82	0.87454	302.239	-4.91643	0.86645	337.511	0.86645
97	9.293	14.52	264.803	1.20356	68.9591	47.9182	0.8741	0.70595	39.3132	226.351	258.952	1558.86	4.95672	6.76174	73.3053	660.519	-10.8843	0.87479	304.811	-4.96175	0.8669	340.383	0.8669
98	9.31982	14.56	257.34	1.20197	68.8678	47.7355	0.86441	0.68606	38.5735	219.628	254.08	1508.2	4.90173	6.80707	72.0094	662.524	-10.9195	0.87492	306.978	-4.9998	0.86725	342.804	0.86725
99	9.34854	14.61	252.743	1.20096	68.81	47.62	0.85834	0.6738	38.1143	215.49	251.055	1475.24	4.86732	6.84442	71.1137	664.663	-10.9569	0.87505	308.759	-5.03094	0.86752	344.793	0.86752
100	9.43634	14.74	240.843	1.19825	68.6549	47.3098	0.84228	0.64208	36.9125	204.792	243.138	1388.96	4.77628	6.95311	68.6928	671.175	-11.0701	0.8754	313.918	-5.12067	0.86823	350.554	0.86823
101	9.3928	14.68	245.555	1.19934	68.7173	47.4346	0.8487	0.65464	37.3906	209.025	246.288	1424.24	4.81268	6.90324	69.7163	667.952	-11.0142	0.87524	311.556	-5.07968	0.86792	347.916	0.86792
102	9.46389	14.79	235.436	1.19697	68.5815	47.1631	0.83482	0.62766	36.3599	199.937	239.499	1352.08	4.73393	6.99448	67.6809	673.206	-11.1052	0.8755	315.872	-5.15442	0.86846	352.735	0.86846
103	9.51296	14.86	229.963	1.19564	68.5054	47.0107	0.82714	0.61307	35.7963	195.028	235.786	1312.08	4.6904	7.05275	66.5046	676.816	-11.1674	0.87565	318.615	-5.20168	0.86877	355.799	0.86877
104	9.53552	14.90	226.042	1.19467	68.4495	46.899	0.82156	0.60262	35.3897	191.513	233.108	1285.39	4.65879	7.08564	65.7497	678.471	-11.1958	0.87572	320.16	-5.22819	0.86893	357.524	0.86893
105	9.57315	14.96	220.865	1.19335	68.3741	46.7482	0.8141	0.58882	34.8493	186.876	229.549	1249.34	4.61648	7.13553	64.6971	681.224	-11.2429	0.87581	322.495	-5.26814	0.86915	360.132	0.86915
106	9.59214	14.99	216.674	1.19226	68.3116	46.6232	0.80798	0.57764	34.4088	183.126	226.647	1221.84	4.58175	7.1679	63.9205	682.61	-11.2665	0.87586	324.007	-5.2939	0.86928	361.82	0.86928
107	9.68156	15.13	209.772	1.19041	68.2057	46.4113	0.79772	0.55924	33.677	176.955	221.827	1169.77	4.52357	7.26589	62.2576	689.109	-11.3767	0.87603	328.565	-5.37122	0.86962	366.91	0.86962
108	9.71707	15.18	206.141	1.18941	68.1484	46.2968	0.79223	0.54956	33.289	173.713	219.271	1144.14	4.49246	7.30946	61.4608	691.68	-11.4202	0.87609	330.585	-5.40533	0.86975	369.165	0.86975
109	9.75757	15.25	202.642	1.18843	68.0921	46.1842	0.78688	0.54024	32.9128	170.59	216.793	1118.9	4.46212	7.35663	60.6544	694.607	-11.4694	0.87614	332.766	-5.44206	0.86987	371.601	0.86987
110																							
111			375.1			50.093																	

Figure 7 – Spreadsheet for Plate Load Test

While confining pressure in zone I is constant at Po*, the corresponding pressure in zone III, $\sigma_{3m,III}$, changes and is given by Eq. 10 used to calculate the values shown in column I. The current diameter of circle III or the deviator stress in zone III, $\sigma_{dm,III}$, is equal to

$$\sigma_{dm,III} = SL\ \sigma_{3m,III}\ A \qquad \text{or} \qquad = Po^*\ (\tan^6\alpha_m - \tan^4\alpha_m) \tag{15a}$$

as compared to the diameter at failure if the confining pressure were held constant ($\sigma_{3m,III}$) equal to

$$\sigma_{df,III} = \sigma_{3m,III}\ A \qquad \text{or} \qquad = Po^*\ (\tan^6\alpha_f - \tan^4\alpha_f) \tag{15b}$$

Values of $\sigma_{dm,III}$ and $\sigma_{df,III}$ appear in columns J and K, respectively. Figure 8 is a plot of the deviator stress, $\sigma_{dm,III}$ (column J) versus ε (column B) of zone III. Figure 9 is a plot of $\sigma_{dm,III}$ divided by its $\sigma_{df,III}$ (column K), i.e. SL (column G), versus ε (column B) of zone III.

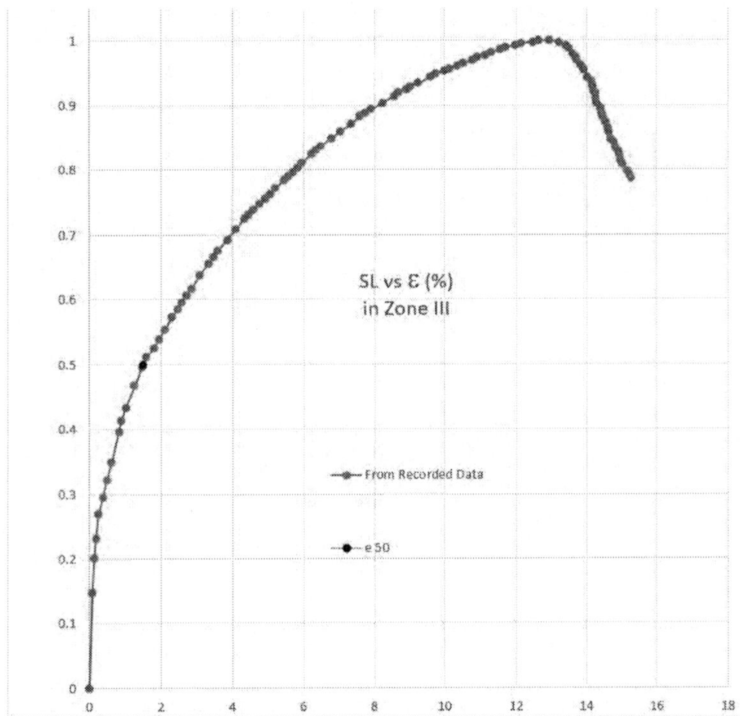

Figure 8 - Stress Level SL (= $\sigma_{d,III}$ /($\sigma_{df,III}$) versus Strain (ε) in Zone III

The developing Young's modulus (E_{III}) in zone III in column L,

$$E_{III} = \sigma_{dm,III} / \varepsilon \tag{16}$$

is simply the value in column J divided by the value in column B. Figure 10 provides the plot of E_{III} vs ε in zone III.

To establish principal strain, ε_I, in zone I, the strain in zone III, which varies with its changing confining pressure, $\sigma_{3m,III}$, is adjusted for the constant confining pressure Po* of zone I as given by Eq. 11. Column N gives the values of ε_I so evaluated. (Note that this major principal strain is in the horizontal direction.) The variation of Young's modulus, E_I, in zone I is simply the value of $\sigma_{dm,I}$ (i.e. with Po* substituting for $\sigma_{3m,III}$ in Eq 15a) of column M, divided by the strain of column N as shown in column O. The E_I vs ε_I curve is provided in Fig. 10 for comparison with the curve for zone III.

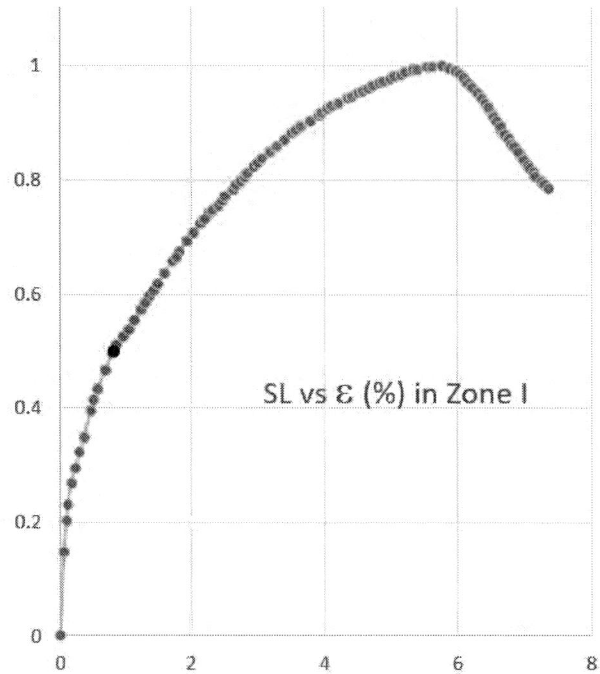

Figure 9 - Stress Level SL versus Strain (ε) in Zone I

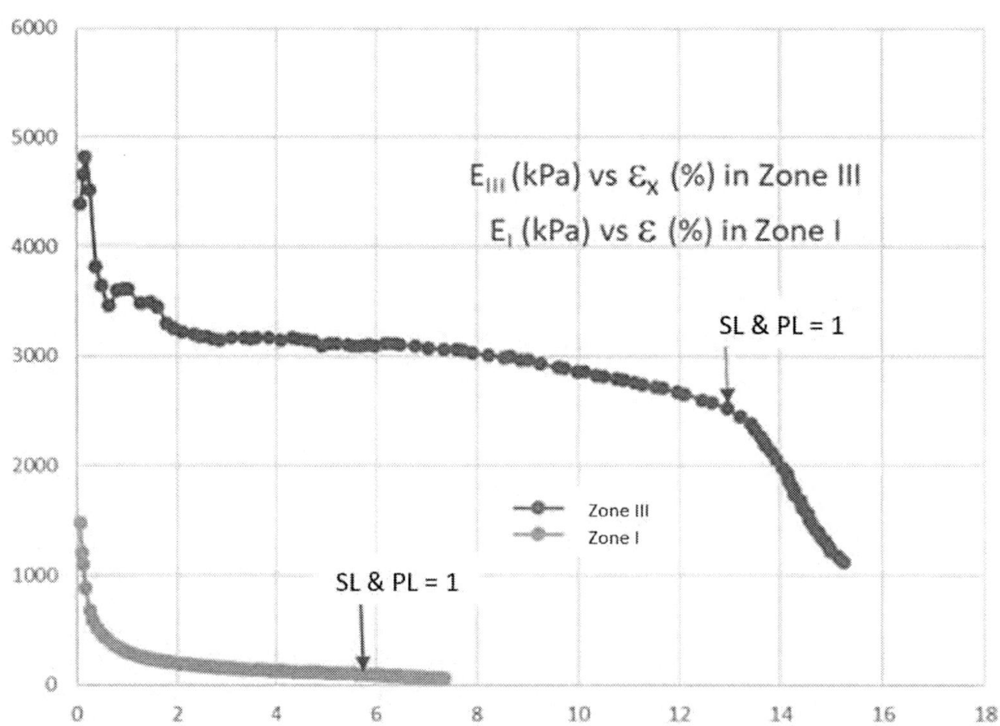

Figure 10 - Secant Young's Modulus (E) versus Strain (ε) in Zones I and III

Figure 11 provides the plots of SL vs strain in zones I and III along with the plots of PL and $\sigma_{dm,III} / \sigma_{dm,IIImax}$ vs zone III strain.

One should note the difference in strain between zones I and III and the likely gradual variation that would develop through radial shear zone II. Also of note is the much more linear variation of PL and the deviatoric stress of zone III normalized by its peak value (which occurs at SL and PL =1) versus the strain of zone III (and therefore settlement, which is proportional to zone III strain).

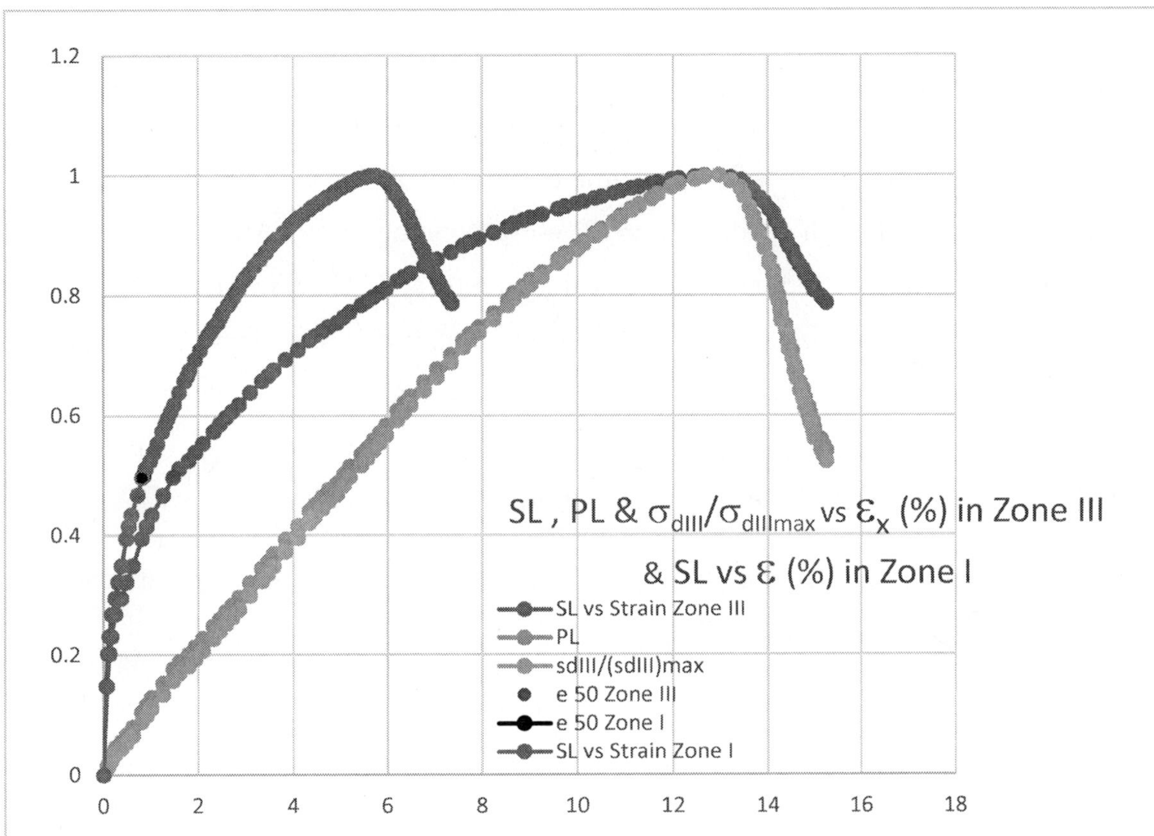

Figure 11 – SL, PL and $\sigma_{dm,III}/\sigma_{dm,IIImax}$ vs Strain in Zone III and SL vs Strain in Zone I

DERIVED VOLUME CHANGE CURVE AND POISSON'S RATIO VARIATION

While not part of the results directly obtained from the recorded data, if the characteristic friction angle were to be approximated, additional analysis could be performed yielding the volume change curves in zones I and III as well as the Poisson's ratio variations in each zone. As presented by (Norris 2019), the slope of the volume change curve (ε_v versus ε_1) is related to the mobilized (ϕ_m) and characteristic (ϕ_{mc}) friction angles as given by the equation

$$d\varepsilon_v/d\varepsilon_1 = 1 - \phi_m/\phi_c \qquad (17)$$

Equation 17 can be used to evaluate the volumetric strain (ε_v) as a function of the axial strain (ε_1), i.e.

$$\varepsilon_v = \varepsilon_1 - \int (d\varepsilon_v/d\varepsilon_1)\, d\varepsilon_1 \quad (18)$$

and with $d\varepsilon_v/d\varepsilon_1$ from Eq. 17

$$\varepsilon_v = \varepsilon_1 - 1//\phi_c \int \phi_m d\varepsilon_1 \quad (19)$$

The second term of Eq. 19, the area under the ϕ_m vs ε_1 curve at ε_1, divided by ϕ_c, is the vertical offset at ε_1 from a 1:1 ε_V vs ε_1 line as pictured in Fig. 12. Column P is the numerical integration of the area under the mobilized friction curve (with ε_1) up to the corresponding value of ε_1, in this case using values of ε_1 from column B corresponding to zone III. Column Q gives the values of ε_v based on Eq. 19 for an assumed value of ϕ_c of 42°. The plot of ε_v, from column Q, versus ε_1, from column B, is shown in Fig. 13. Alternatively, column S is the numerical integration of the area under the mobilized friction curve (with ε_1 from zone I) up to the corresponding value of ε_1 from column N. The corresponding volume change (in column T) versus strain (column N) for zone I is also shown in Fig. 13.

In the standard drained axial compression test, as envisioned for average elements in zones I and III, ε_V is

$$\varepsilon_V = \varepsilon_1 + 2\varepsilon_3 \qquad \text{so that} \qquad -\varepsilon_3 = \tfrac{1}{2}(\varepsilon_1 - \varepsilon_V) \quad (20\text{ a \& b})$$

With $-\varepsilon_3$ from Eq. 20 b

$$\nu_{sec} = -\varepsilon_3/\varepsilon_1 = \tfrac{1}{2}(\varepsilon_1 - \varepsilon_V)/\varepsilon_1 = \tfrac{1}{2}(1 - \varepsilon_V/\varepsilon_1) \quad (21)$$

Dividing Eq. 19 by ε_1 and substituting for $\varepsilon_V/\varepsilon_1$ in Eq. 21, the secant Poisson's ratio becomes

$$\nu_{sec} = \tfrac{1}{2}\left(\int \phi_m d\varepsilon_1/\phi_c\right)/\varepsilon_1 = \tfrac{1}{2}\,\phi_{m,ave}/\phi_c \quad (22)$$

where $\phi_{m,ave}$ is the average value of ϕ_m under the curve of ϕ_m versus ε_1, i.e. $\phi_{m,area}/\varepsilon_1$, up to the value of ε_1 in question. ν_{sec} for zone III in column R uses values of $\phi_{m,area}$ in column P and ε_1 in column B, while ν_{sec} for zone I in column U uses values of $\phi_{m,area}$ in column S and ε_1 in column N.

Figure 14 is a plot of ν_{sec} vs ε_1 in each zone. Note that ν_{sec} exceeds the elastic limit of one-half due to dilatancy of this very dense sand. Furthermore, while ε_V is negative and ν_{sec} exceeds ½, the sand is bulging laterally in zone III and vertically in zone I.

While Figs. 13 and 14 depend upon the choice of the characteristic friction angle. A value of 42° was chosen based on a procedure of matching the assessed isotropic rebound curve (Ashour and Norris 1999) and one based on knowledge of the characteristic friction angle (Norris 2019) as explained in an upcoming paper.

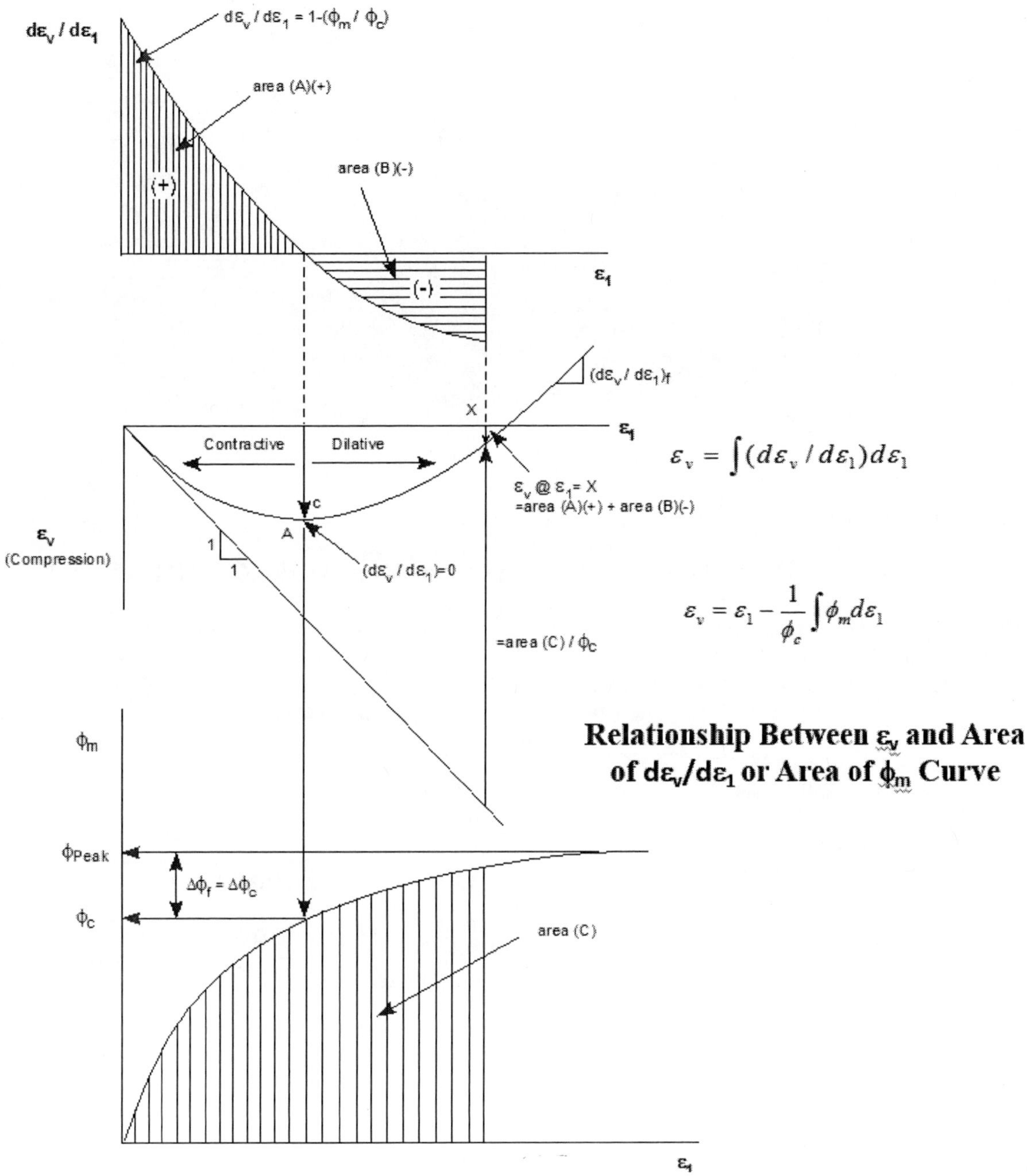

Figure 12 - Relationship Linking Stress-Strain and Volume Change Behavior: $d\varepsilon_v/d\varepsilon_1 = 1 - \phi_m/\phi_c$

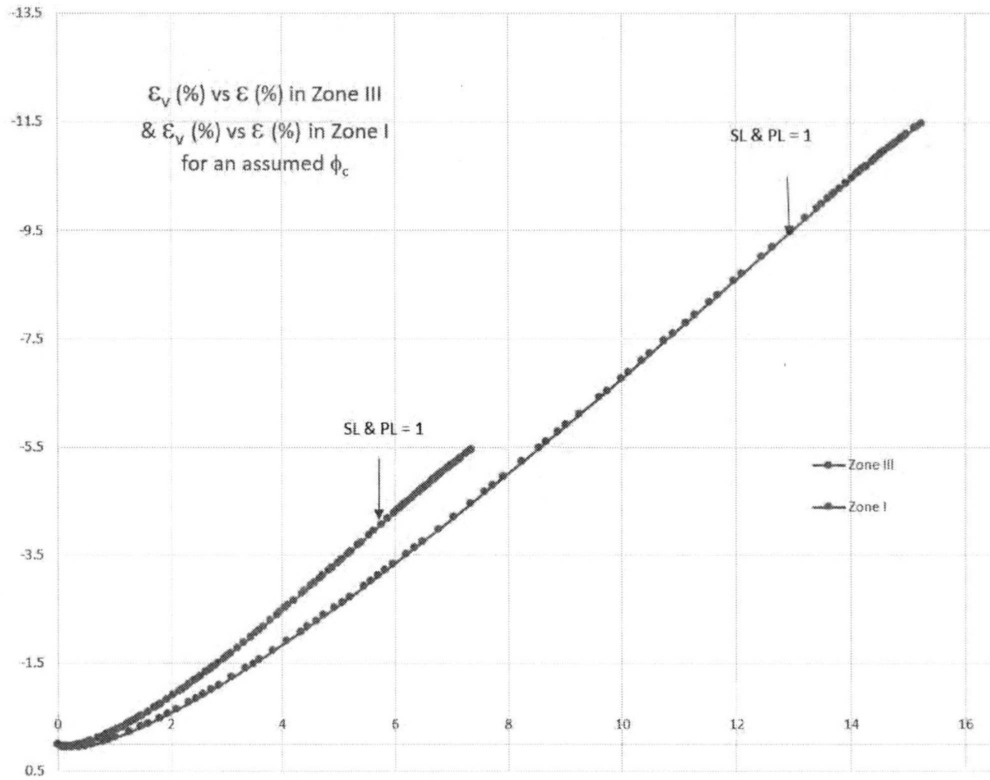

Figure 13 – Volume Change Curves for Zone I and Zone III

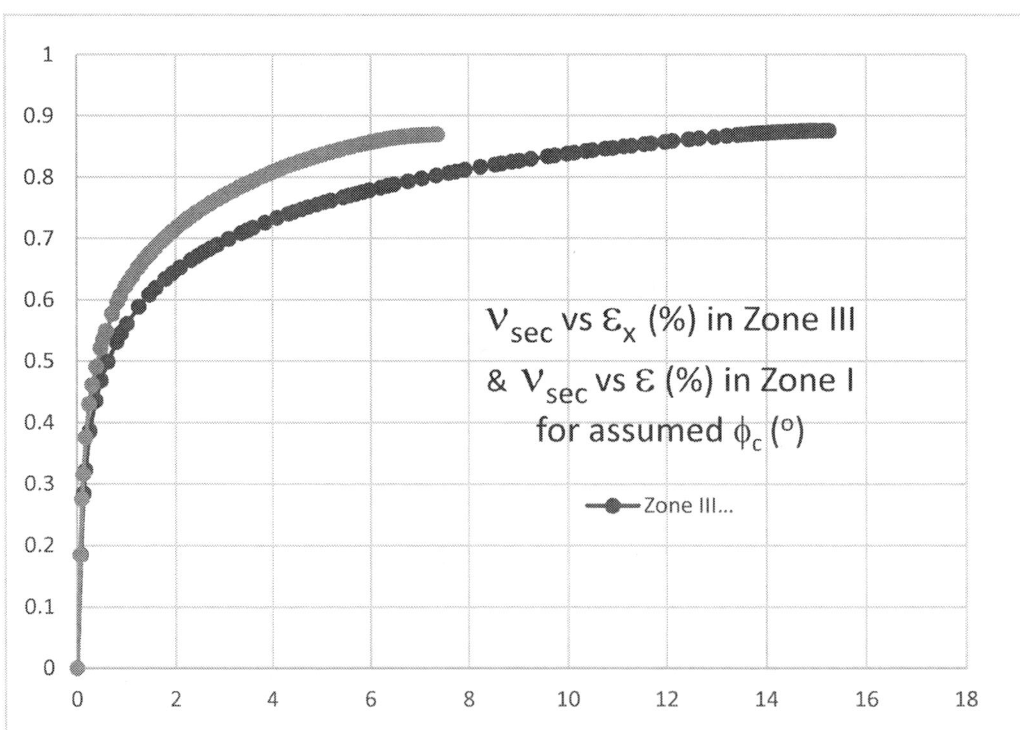

Figure 14 – Poisson's Ratio vs Strain in Zones I and III

DEVELOPING A CURVED MOBILIZED ENVELOPE

Up to now, the developing mobilized envelope has been linear employing a single ϕ_m over circles I, II and III. In Fig. 7, an assumed initial value of ϕ of 50° was employed in cell B4 after which cell B4 was set equal to the maximum value in column F that was assessed in cell B111. As it turned out, over only a few automatic iterations, convergence to a ϕ of 50.093° resulted.

As shown in Fig. 4, the current method can easily handle a curved envelope, both mobilized and at failure. Figure 15 shows a spreadsheet in which this is attempted. Column C provides the SL values, in this case, chosen to be those from Fig. 7 for the single ϕ_m envelope solution. The corresponding values of the settlement are the same as before and are not duplicated in Fig. 15. It is the task here to see what combination of ϕ for zone I, with a chosen $\Delta\phi$, the log cycle change in ϕ with confining pressure, yields q_m values that match the recorded values of q_m in the spreadsheet in Fig. 7.

With an assumed value of ϕ for zone I and the $\Delta\phi$ obtained from the modified form of Bolton's equation (explained later), column G assesses the variation of ϕ_m in zone I with SL values of column C based on Eq. 6, i.e.

$$\phi_m = \sin^{-1}(SL\ A/\ (SL\ A + 2)) \tag{6}$$

where A for zone I in cell F10 ($A_{zone\ I}$) is based on Eq. 7b. Values of α_m in column H/I for the ϕ_m in column G follow from Eq. 5b.

Using values of α_m in column H/I, the values of confining pressure, $\sigma_{3m,II}$, of the mobilized circle II of zone II in column K are obtained.

$$\sigma_{3m,II} = Po^*\ \tan^2 \alpha_m \tag{23}$$

The peak secant friction angle in column L for each value of $\sigma_{3m,II}$ of column K is calculated from

$$\phi_{II} = \phi_I - \Delta\phi \log (\sigma_{3m,II} / Po^*)$$

where ϕ_I is the value from zone I in cell B2. Values of A in zone II (i.e. $A_{zone\ II}$) in column N follow from Eq. 7b based on the peak friction values of column L. Then the mobilized values of friction, ϕ_m, based Eq. 7b, to which the mobilized circles of zone II are tangent, appear in column O. Columns S through Y follow the same pattern employed in tabulating columns K through Q.

The values of mobilized major principal stress of circles in zone III in column Z are then tabulated, i.e.

$$\sigma_{1m,III} = \sigma_{3m,III} \tan^2 \alpha_m \tag{24}$$

from values of $\sigma_{3m,III}$ of column S and α_m of column X/Y.

Row	A	B	C	D	E	F
1	B (mm) =	60	L (mm) =	100		
2	ϕ (°) =	54.31		Fac B/L	1.06667	for Sett
3	ϕ (rad) =	0.94789				
4	Po* (kPa)	1.00236				
5			γ_t (kN/m³	16		
6			n	0.2		
7			$\Delta\phi$ (°)	5.7		
8						
9	Zone I	0	0.5			
10	ε_{50} (%)	0.84	0.5		$A_{Zone\ I}$ =	8.6488
11						
12						
13						

Row	A	B	C	E	F	G	H	I
14	Zone III Single ϕ			Zone I				
15	σ_{3IIIm}	ε_1 (%)	SL	σ_{3Im}	ε (%)	ϕ_m (°)	α_m (deg)	α_m (rad)
16	0.8609	0	0	0	0	0	45	0.7854
17	3.36881	0.07504	0.1485	1.28739	0.05889	23.0201	56.51	0.98629
18	4.67991	0.13363	0.20215	1.75247	0.09819	27.803	58.9015	1.02802
19	5.47895	0.17311	0.23118	2.00412	0.12325	29.9951	59.9976	1.04715
20	6.60347	0.25848	0.26865	2.32896	0.17729	32.5075	61.2538	1.06908
21	7.4574	0.37976	0.29501	2.55748	0.25421	34.096	62.048	1.08294
22	8.39105	0.48823	0.32215	2.79281	0.3192	35.6009	62.8005	1.09607
23	9.39045	0.6245	0.34959	3.03062	0.39921	37.004	63.502	1.10832
24	11.1694	0.80705	0.39502	3.4245	0.49831	39.1058	64.5529	1.12666
25	12.0061	0.90808	0.41513	3.59886	0.55265	39.9594	64.9797	1.13411
26	12.8121	1.0146	0.43385	3.76115	0.6095	40.7163	65.3581	1.14071
27	14.2961	1.26139	0.46664	4.04715	0.74133	41.9703	65.9851	1.15166
28	15.7016	1.46865	0.49654	4.30461	0.8471	43.0206	66.5103	1.16082
29	16.4266	1.60128	0.51134	4.43291	0.9153	43.519	66.7595	1.16517
30	17.115	1.7948	0.5251	4.55214	1.01752	43.968	66.984	1.16909
31	17.8112	1.93896	0.53873	4.67031	1.09052	44.4005	67.2003	1.17287
32	18.5619	2.09534	0.55313	4.79517	1.16879	44.8444	67.4222	1.17674
33	19.6465	2.3198	0.57343	4.97117	1.27937	45.4487	67.7243	1.18201
34	20.9111	2.5814	0.59641	5.17037	1.406	46.1041	68.0521	1.18773
35	20.2873	2.45459	0.58516	5.07289	1.34505	45.787	67.8935	1.18497
36	21.4705	2.71243	0.60635	5.25655	1.46958	46.3788	68.1894	1.19013
37	22.1243	2.85471	0.61781	5.35587	1.53742	46.6891	68.3446	1.19284
38	23.2942	3.08787	0.63789	5.53001	1.64594	47.2175	68.6087	1.19745
39	24.4385	3.34058	0.65706	5.69614	1.76365	47.7039	68.8519	1.20169
40	25.5575	3.58302	0.67537	5.8549	1.87478	48.1535	69.0768	1.20562
41	24.9721	3.47061	0.66584	5.77228	1.8244	47.9213	68.9607	1.20359
42	26.6611	3.83863	0.69304	6.00808	1.99161	48.574	69.287	1.20929
43	27.6602	4.09456	0.70872	6.14405	2.10882	48.9368	69.4684	1.21245
44	28.7351	4.3355	0.72529	6.28762	2.21596	49.3097	69.6549	1.21571
45	29.731	4.60641	0.74036	6.41826	2.33843	49.6404	69.8202	1.21859
46	29.1825	4.4506	0.73209	6.34659	2.26777	49.46	69.73	1.21702
47	30.2298	4.74402	0.74781	6.48287	2.40029	49.8009	69.9005	1.21999
48	30.6903	4.92197	0.75463	6.54205	2.48281	49.9463	69.9732	1.22126
49	31.3159	5.0658	0.76383	6.62175	2.54406	50.1397	70.0698	1.22295
50	32.693	5.44035	0.78374	6.79439	2.70982	50.549	70.2745	1.22652
51	31.8784	5.19705	0.77201	6.69272	2.60173	50.3095	70.1547	1.22443
52	33.1526	5.56764	0.7903	6.8512	2.76549	50.681	70.3405	1.22767
53	33.6432	5.69982	0.79724	6.91142	2.82284	50.8195	70.4097	1.22888
54	34.1313	5.82718	0.8041	6.97088	2.87761	50.9547	70.4774	1.23006
55	34.6284	5.96838	0.81104	7.03102	2.93883	51.0901	70.5451	1.23124
56	35.5819	6.20344	0.8242	7.14515	3.03802	51.3433	70.6717	1.23345
57	36.0808	6.34752	0.83102	7.20426	3.09994	51.4725	70.7362	1.23458

Row	K	L	M	N	O	P	Q
14	Zone II						
15	σ_{3IIm}	ϕ (°)	ϕ (rad)	$A_{Zone\ II}$	ϕ_m (°)	α_m (deg)	α_m (rad)
16	1.00236	54.31	0.94789	8.6488	0	45	0.7854
17	2.28974	52.265	0.9122	7.56253	21.0756	55.5378	0.96932
18	2.75483	51.8073	0.90421	7.34298	25.2146	57.6073	1.00544
19	3.00647	51.5909	0.90043	7.24192	27.1074	58.5537	1.02195
20	3.33131	51.3369	0.896	7.12546	29.2779	59.6389	1.0409
21	3.55983	51.1727	0.89313	7.05137	30.6525	60.3262	1.05289
22	3.79517	51.0142	0.89037	6.98077	31.9574	60.9787	1.06428
23	4.03298	50.8638	0.88774	6.91453	33.177	61.5885	1.07492
24	4.42686	50.6331	0.88371	6.81445	35.0107	62.5053	1.09092
25	4.60121	50.5375	0.88204	6.77348	35.758	62.879	1.09745
26	4.76351	50.4516	0.88055	6.73696	36.4223	63.2111	1.10324
27	5.04951	50.3073	0.87803	6.67607	37.5261	63.763	1.11287
28	5.30696	50.1842	0.87588	6.62467	38.4541	64.227	1.12097
29	5.43527	50.1251	0.87485	6.60014	38.8955	64.4478	1.12483
30	5.55449	50.0713	0.87391	6.57796	39.294	64.647	1.1283
31	5.67267	50.0192	0.873	6.55652	39.6785	64.8392	1.13166
32	5.79752	49.9655	0.87206	6.53444	40.0757	65.0369	1.13511
33	5.97352	49.8913	0.87077	6.50426	40.6128	65.3064	1.13981
34	6.17273	49.8101	0.86935	6.47134	41.1991	65.5996	1.14493
35	6.07524	49.8495	0.87004	6.48729	40.9153	65.4576	1.14245
36	6.2589	49.7758	0.86875	6.45749	41.4453	65.7227	1.14708
37	6.35822	49.7368	0.86807	6.4418	41.7238	65.8619	1.14951
38	6.53237	49.6699	0.8669	6.41498	42.1988	66.0994	1.15365
39	6.69849	49.6078	0.86582	6.39018	42.6371	66.3185	1.15748
40	6.85725	49.5498	0.86481	6.36714	43.0431	66.5216	1.16102
41	6.77464	49.5796	0.86533	6.37905	42.8354	66.4167	1.15919
42	7.01044	49.4951	0.86385	6.34551	43.4236	66.7118	1.16434
43	7.14641	49.4475	0.86302	6.32677	43.7526	66.8763	1.16721
44	7.28997	49.3983	0.86216	6.30744	44.0913	67.0456	1.17017
45	7.42062	49.3543	0.8614	6.29023	44.3921	67.196	1.17279
46	7.34894	49.3783	0.86181	6.29963	44.2279	67.1139	1.17136
47	7.48523	49.3329	0.86102	6.28185	44.5383	67.2692	1.17407
48	7.54441	49.3134	0.86068	6.27425	44.6709	67.3355	1.17523
49	7.6241	49.2873	0.86023	6.26413	44.8473	67.4236	1.17676
50	7.79674	49.2319	0.85926	6.24263	45.2214	67.6107	1.18003
51	7.69507	49.2644	0.85983	6.25522	45.0024	67.5012	1.17812
52	7.85356	49.2139	0.85895	6.23567	45.3422	67.6711	1.18108
53	7.91377	49.195	0.85862	6.22837	45.469	67.7345	1.18219
54	7.97324	49.1765	0.85829	6.22122	45.593	67.7965	1.18327
55	8.03337	49.1579	0.85797	6.21405	45.7172	67.8586	1.18436
56	8.14751	49.123	0.85736	6.20062	45.9496	67.9748	1.18638
57	8.20662	49.1051	0.85705	6.19375	46.0683	68.0342	1.18742

Row	S	T	U	V	W	X	Y	Z	AA
14	Zone III based on a Curved ϕ Envelope								
15	σ_{3IIIm}	ϕ (°)	ϕ (rad)	$A_{Zone\ III}$	ϕ_m (°)	α_m (deg)	α_m (rad)	σ_{1IIIm}	qmob (kPa)
16	1.00236	54.31	0.94789	8.6488	0	45	0.7854	1.00236	0
17	4.86123	50.4014	0.87967	6.71568	19.4346	54.7173	0.955	9.7093	8.7069408
18	6.84405	49.5545	0.86489	6.36903	23.0563	56.5281	0.9866	15.6558	14.653428
19	8.03983	49.1559	0.85793	6.21329	24.7078	57.3539	1.00101	19.588	18.585664
20	9.70827	48.6891	0.84979	6.03661	26.6011	58.3006	1.01754	25.4524	24.450053
21	10.9651	48.3878	0.84453	5.9257	27.8009	58.9005	1.02801	30.1334	29.131048
22	12.3301	48.0973	0.83946	5.82106	28.941	59.4705	1.03796	35.4524	34.450081
23	13.7816	47.8218	0.83465	5.72381	30.008	60.004	1.04727	41.3581	40.355779
24	16.3433	47.3998	0.82728	5.57847	31.6157	60.8078	1.0613	52.3576	51.355263
25	17.5393	47.2249	0.82423	5.51952	32.2724	61.1362	1.06703	57.7279	56.725498
26	18.6865	47.0681	0.82149	5.46725	32.8569	61.4284	1.07213	63.0108	62.008467
27	20.7872	46.8044	0.81689	5.38064	33.83	61.915	1.08062	73.0032	72.00089
28	22.7638	46.5795	0.81297	5.30805	34.6501	62.325	1.08778	82.7617	81.759351
29	23.7789	46.4715	0.81108	5.27358	35.0409	62.5204	1.09119	87.9014	86.899022
30	24.74	46.3734	0.80937	5.2425	35.394	62.697	1.09427	92.8446	91.842243
31	25.7095	46.2783	0.80771	5.21254	35.7351	62.8675	1.09725	97.9054	96.90306
32	26.752	46.1799	0.80599	5.18177	36.0861	63.0431	1.10031	103.428	102.426
33	28.2532	46.0447	0.80363	5.13965	36.5656	63.2828	1.10449	111.525	110.52303
34	29.9968	45.8965	0.80104	5.09431	37.0879	63.544	1.10905	121.136	120.1334
35	29.1376	45.9684	0.8023	5.11635	36.8349	63.4175	1.10684	116.373	115.37061
36	30.7656	45.8338	0.79995	5.0752	37.3076	63.6538	1.11097	125.442	124.43978
37	31.6626	45.7627	0.79871	5.0536	37.5561	63.7781	1.11314	130.518	129.5155
38	33.2633	45.6406	0.79658	5.01677	37.9808	63.9904	1.11684	139.712	138.70919
39	34.8235	45.5271	0.7946	4.98281	38.3732	64.1866	1.12027	148.836	147.83319
40	36.3446	45.4213	0.79275	4.95138	38.7372	64.3686	1.12344	157.882	156.8792
41	35.5495	45.4761	0.79371	4.96761	38.5491	64.2745	1.1218	153.134	152.13193
42	37.8402	45.3215	0.79101	4.92193	39.0788	64.5394	1.12643	166.917	165.91435
43	39.1905	45.2347	0.78949	4.89649	39.3745	64.6873	1.12901	175.192	174.1893
44	40.6393	45.1448	0.78793	4.8703	39.6793	64.8397	1.13167	184.192	183.18966
45	41.9785	45.0646	0.78653	4.84705	39.9504	64.9752	1.13403	192.62	191.61749
46	41.2413	45.1084	0.78729	4.85974	39.8024	64.9012	1.13274	187.968	186.9654
47	42.648	45.0254	0.78584	4.83574	40.0823	65.0412	1.13518	196.872	195.8696
48	43.2654	44.9898	0.78522	4.8255	40.2019	65.101	1.13623	200.816	199.81573
49	44.1032	44.9423	0.78439	4.81187	40.3612	65.1806	1.13762	206.202	205.19959
50	45.9432	44.8412	0.78263	4.78297	40.6994	65.3497	1.14057	218.166	217.16397
51	44.8555	44.9005	0.78366	4.79989	40.5013	65.2507	1.13884	211.071	210.0687
52	46.5561	44.8084	0.78205	4.77364	40.8086	65.4043	1.14152	222.193	221.19038
53	47.2097	44.7738	0.78145	4.76385	40.9234	65.4617	1.14252	226.509	225.50667
54	47.8592	44.74	0.78086	4.75427	41.0357	65.5178	1.1435	230.821	229.81837
55	48.5202	44.7061	0.78027	4.74468	41.1482	65.5741	1.14448	235.231	234.22873
56	49.7859	44.6423	0.77916	4.72673	41.359	65.6795	1.14632	243.741	242.7389
57	50.4472	44.6097	0.77859	4.71756	41.4667	65.7334	1.14726	248.22	247.21797

Figure 15 Spreadsheet for Curved Envelope

The difference between values of $\sigma_{1m,III}$ of column S and Po* are the values of mobilized net pressure, q_m, at each SL. Thus, each line across at a given stress level represents the corresponding construction of the curved mobilized envelope.

What remains besides the iteration involved in choosing the right peak ϕ of zone I (in cell B2) is the choice of $\Delta\phi$ for which a modified version of Bolton's equation provides guidance. $\Delta\phi$ (in degrees) is the decrease in the secant ϕ for a 10-fold increase in confining pressure, that is assessed from Bolton's (1986) equation of relative density index (I_R), rearranged (Elfass and Norris 2012), i.e.

$$\Delta\phi = 3(I_{R,ref} - I_{R,10ref}) \tag{25}$$

where

$$I_{R,ref} = D_r\,[10 - \ln(Po^*\,(3 + A)/3) - 1] \tag{26a}$$

$$I_{R,10ref} = D_r\,[10 - \ln(10\ Po^*\,(3 + A)/3) - 1] \tag{26b}$$

Equation 25 requires iterative solution: calcutate $I_{R,ref}$ based on ϕ at Po*; assume $\Delta\phi$, whereby $\phi_{10ref} = \phi_{ref} - \Delta\phi$ at 10 times Po*; assess a new A and then $I_{R,\ 10ref}$; calculate $\Delta\phi$ from Eq. 25 to compare with the assumed $\Delta\phi$; repeat as needed. Equation 26b requires $\sigma_{3,ref}$' be expressed in kPa and relative density, D_r, in decimal form. Accordingly, $\Delta\phi = 5.7^o$ for $D_r = 92\%$ (inputted in Eqs. 26a and b as 0.92) for the sand of the plate load test.

While the values of $\phi = 54.31^{o}$ in zone I and $\Delta\phi = 5.7^{o}$ yield a close match of q_m vs settlement relative to the curve in Fig. 6, additional iteration of both is required to achieve a near exact match. However, the point of the current exercise was to show how a sequence of curved mobilized envelopes might be used to establish the net pressure vs settlement response.

DISCUSSION / CONCLUSIONS

The authors of the plate load test paper make an important point:

Quote form from Valore et al. 2017 **Numerical simulations, by finite-element analysis, of re the failure mechanism and the ultimate bearing capacity correctly, only if the mean equivalent constant value of the secant angle of shearing resistance used in calculations is selected, taking into account the curvature of the shear strength envelope of the sand within the very low normal stress range existing in the tested models.**

Their reported model plate load test involved only a 60 mm size plate placed at the surface of the sand. For this test, the confining pressure in the developing/mobilizing failure mass (zones I though III) ranged from 0.9 kPa (zone I) to 50 kPa (for the straight line envelope) to 57 kPa (for the curved envelope) in zone III at failure for which the back calculated single/equivalent peak friction angle, ϕ, was found to be 50.1 ° degrees or which varied from a 51.9 ° (zone I) to a 47.5 ° (zone III) degree secant friction angle for the curved failure envelope. These back calculated value(s) from the present analysis agree quite well with the triaxial test results, supplemented by direct shear tests, reported by Valore et al. Had another load test employing a different size plate been undertaken, its analyzed envelope, along with the present one, could have been used to determine the log cycle change in equivalent friction.

While the simple mobilizing bearing capacity analysis employed here has been shown to be quite good in predicting near-full size lab to full size field load test response (Elfass et al. 2007), the present analysis demonstrates its applicability relative to reduced-scale model test results. However, it should be noted that the peak friction angle assessed from a plate load test at the surface of a layer in the field (with due regard to any apparent cohesion) would need to be adjusted via Eq. 23 to reflect the friction angle at depth below a footing in the same soil. The present analysis requires only a limited amount of input and is easily undertaken in a spreadsheet. Besides the friction angle, the analysis provides the stress-strain curves of the material where confining pressure is increasing (zone III) and where it is constant (= Po* in zone I). The Young's modulus variation in both zones can be plotted versus strain or, alternatively, versus stress level, SL (not shown here but easily constructed from the data of Fig.7).

With an additional piece of information, namely the characteristic friction angle, the volume change curves as well as the Poisson's ratio variation with strain can be assessed for both zones.

Given the volume change curve, such analysis can be extended to undrained response analysis (Ashour and Norris 1999).

Finally, while the present analysis has been carried out for a purely frictional material, it is also applicable to a c-ϕ material, by converting it to a ϕ material with Po* taken from a shifted origin as shown in Figs. 2 through 5.

REFERENCES:

1. Ashour, M. and Norris, G. Liquefaction and Undrained Response Evaluation from Drained Formulation. *Journal of Geotechnical and Geoenvironmental Engineering, ASCE* vol. 125 (8), 1999, pp. 649 -658.
2. Bolton, M.D. The Strength and Dilatancy of Sands. *Geotechnique* vol. 36 (1), 1986, pp. 65-78.
3. Elfass S., Norris G., and Vimalaraj, P. A Simple Bearing Capacity Equation. *GeoDenver 2007, ASCE*, New Peaks in Geotechnics. In: Advances in Shallow Foundations, GSP, vol. 171, 2007, pp 1–10.
4. Elfass, S. and Norris, G. A Modified Bolton Equation and Its Application. *Proceedings of the 44th Engineering Geology and Geotechnical Engineering Symposium*, Reno, 2012, pp. 76-95.
5. Elfass, S., Saint Pierre, E., Watters, B. and Norris, G. Modelling of partially Cemented Soils in the Las Vegas Valley. *Modern Concepts in Material Science*, Iris Publishers, 2019, Open Access.
6. Elsayed, A., Elfass,S., Norris, G. and Vimalaraj, P. A New Approach for Non-Linear Load-Settlement Assessment of Shallow Foundations. *Geo-Frontiers Congress 2011*, 2012
7. Nimeri, M., Elfass, S. and Norris, G. Load–settlement Response of Shallow Foundations Resting on Granular Soil. *Innovative Infrastructure Solutions*, 2:33 DOI 10.1007/s41062-017-0080-9, 2017.
8. Norris, G., Elfass, S., Vimalaraj, P. and Lofty, A. A Simple Method for Assessing Load vs. Settlement of a Shallow Foundation up to Bearing Capacity Failure. *1st Congress on Transportation Infrastructure 1st CITRANS*, Costa Rica, 2011.
9. Norris, G. The Characteristic Friction Angle, Its Determination and Use. *Proceedings 70th Highway Geology Symposium*, Portland, 2019.
10. Schmertmann, J. Hartman, J. and Brown, P. Improved Strain Influence Factor Diagrams. *Journal of Geotechnical Engineering, ASCE*, vol. 104 (GT8), 1978, pp. 1131-1135.
11. Valore C., Ziccarelli, M. and Muscolino, S.R. The Bearing Capacity of Footings on Sand with a Weak Layer. *CCE Geotechnical Research*, vol. 4 (1), 2017, pp. 12-29.

Reliability Models for Roads Crossing Slow-Moving Landslides

Michael Porter, P.Eng., LEG
BGC Engineering, Inc.
Suite 500, 980 Howe Street
Vancouver BC, Canada V6Z 0C8100
(604) 684-5900
mporter@bgcengineering.ca

Scott Anderson, Ph.D, P.E.
BGC Engineering, Inc.
701 12th Street, Suite 211
Golden, CO 80401
(720) 617-1873
scanderson@bgcengineering.ca

Mark Vessely, P.E.
BGC Engineering, Inc.
701 12th Street, Suite 211
Golden, CO 80401
(720) 617-1871
mvessely@bgcengineering.ca

Martin Devonald, P.Eng.
BGC Engineering, Inc.
Suite 500, 980 Howe Street
Vancouver BC, Canada V6Z 0C8100
(604) 684-5900
mdevonald@bgcengineering.ca

Prepared for the 71st Highway Geology Symposium, May, 2022

Disclaimer

Statements and views presented in this paper are strictly those of the author(s), and do not necessarily reflect positions held by their affiliations, the Highway Geology Symposium (HGS), or others acknowledged above. The mention of trade names for commercial products does not imply the approval or endorsement by HGS.

ABSTRACT

Roads and other linear infrastructure are often constructed across dormant or normally slow-moving landslides that impact system resilience. The interactions between roads and landslides, in conjunction with an agency's monitoring and maintenance strategies, can be treated as dynamic probabilistic systems. The potential for a deterioration in road condition state or loss of function in response to landslide movement depends on several factors. These include the likelihoods of different landslide velocities being realized, the conditional probabilities that landslide displacements physically impact the roadway, the ability of the roadway infrastructure to accommodate landslide displacements under typical maintenance strategies, and the capability to detect and respond to deteriorating conditions. When a loss of service occurs, site factors such as slope geometry, landslide mechanism, and proximity to watercourses will influence the time and level of effort required to restore service. Each of these factors is difficult to predict but estimating the probabilities of landslide velocity transitions is particularly challenging.

In this paper, we review a conceptual approach to predict landslide velocity and displacement using Markov models that combined geomorphic evidence of long-term landslide behavior with current estimates of landslide velocity. Road performance condition states are defined based on potential escalation from normal roadway maintenance efforts, the level of geotechnical input required for maintenance and mitigation planning, and the frequency and duration of road closures in response to landslide displacements. The annual and cumulative probabilities of road condition states being realized in response to landslide displacement are predicted by defining landslide displacement criteria for each affected road segment and using Monte Carlo Simulation to estimate the likelihood of those criteria being exceeded.

INTRODUCTION

In the highway industry, it has been said that there are landslides you fix and landslides you name. The idea behind this is that it is not always feasible to fix a landslide such that it stops and has a margin of safety (resistance greater than demand) under design conditions. In some cases, the coexistence of landslides and infrastructure is long-lived and familiar. These landslides usually assume a name and an ad-hoc management strategy where the landslide and road coexist, with compromise. Some mitigation is applied to the landslide during periods of disruptive movement rates, and some acceptance of greater cost and/or reduced performance (design speeds, reliability, etc.), and resilience, is realized by the road. For a highway agency, such a management strategy is feasible when movement rates are relatively slow and consistent or when landsliding occurs in an episodic cycle of dormancy or slow movement interrupted by increases in velocity that then returns to historic levels. An undesirable situation is when movement patterns change and result in more movement than historically observed or when velocity increases beyond a rate at which the agency can maintain acceptable levels of service.

The ideas presented here can provide greater ability to recognize which type of landslide is present and confidence for selecting the best management strategies for those landslides that will have names. There are other approaches to doing this. Historically this has been done through the experience and judgment of a few, but as costs and programs get large, resources scarce, impacts on stakeholders significant – both positive and negative, the objectivity of approach is significant. The ideas also capitalize on new technologies that help with understanding of the episodic nature of many types of slope movements.

The interactions between roads and normally slow-moving landslides, in conjunction with an agency's monitoring and maintenance strategies, can be treated as dynamic probabilistic systems. The potential for a deterioration in road condition state or loss of function in response to landslide movement depends on several factors. These include the likelihoods of changes in landslide velocity being realized, the conditional probabilities that landslide displacements physically impact the roadway, the ability of the roadway infrastructure to accommodate landslide displacements under planned maintenance strategies, and the capability to detect and respond to deteriorating conditions. When a loss of service occurs, site factors such as slope geometry, landslide mechanism, water conditions and environmental constraints will influence the time and level of effort required to restore service. Predicting the change in each of these factors is difficult but estimating the probabilities of the transition in landslide velocity is particularly challenging.

In this paper, we review a conceptual approach to predict landslide velocity and displacement using Markov models that combine geomorphic evidence of long-term landslide behavior with current estimates of landslide velocity. Road performance condition states are defined based on potential escalation from normal roadway maintenance efforts, the level of geotechnical input required for maintenance and mitigation planning, and the frequency and duration of road closures in response to landslide displacements. The annual and cumulative probabilities of road condition states being realized in response to landslide displacement are predicted by defining landslide displacement criteria for each affected road segment and using Monte Carlo Simulation to estimate the likelihood of those criteria being exceeded.

CONDITION STATES AND DISPLACEMENT CRITERIA FOR ROADS CROSSING SLOW-MOVING LANDSLIDES

Landslide velocity influences several of the factors used to quantify landslide risk and to model the deterioration of roads crossing pre-existing landslides. Landslide velocity is positively correlated with risk for several reasons. Faster landslides:

- often have greater mobility and potential for retrogression, increasing the spatial probability that infrastructure will be physically impacted by landslide movement;
- develop potentially damaging displacements more quickly and provide less time for avoidance, increasing the temporal probability of impact;
- impose higher impact loads or reduce the time to failure for infrastructure that can accommodate some amount of displacement, increasing infrastructure vulnerability;
- require more intensive, frequent, and costly maintenance interventions to address non-catastrophic, chronic displacements and their effects; and
- complicate efforts to repair infrastructure and restore service following an outage, increasing economic impacts.

Five road condition states are proposed based on potential escalation from normal roadway maintenance efforts, the level of geotechnical input required for maintenance and mitigation planning, and the frequency and duration of road closures in response to landslide displacements. While the actual criteria that will cause a road segment's condition state to deteriorate will be hazard and site-specific, general criteria are proposed based on road design speed and annualized landslide displacement rate. These are illustrated in Table 1.

Table 1 – Road Condition States and Example Annual Displacement Criteria (m)

Condition State	Agency Cost	User Cost	Higher-speed Paved Roads	Lower-speed Paved Roads	Gravel Roads
A No impact	No more than average for that type of road lane mile	None	<0.005	<0.01	<0.02
B Transition between A and C	Routine maintenance activities, but above-average effort	Slight increase in frequency of delays for routine maintenance	>0.005	>0.01	>0.02
C Above average maintenance and repairs	Above-average effort requiring geotechnical input	Occasional lane closures; increased vehicle wear	>0.05	>0.1	>0.2
D Significant damage	Significant emergency response actions and funding required to keep road open	Frequent lane or road closures; increased vehicle wear and accident risk	>0.25	>0.5	>1.0
F Full closure, potential abandonment	Impractical to keep road open. Closures last more than a week, may be permanent	Detours or loss of access; first vehicle encounters face increased accident risk	>1.25	>2.5	>5.0

The future likelihoods of transitioning into the less desirable road condition states, combined with the expected time and effort required to return to a more favorable road condition state, provide a way of quantifying and predicting resiliency. The topics of time and effort are touched on briefly in this paper, but the primary focus is on the challenge of predicting the probabilities of exceeding annual landslide displacement criteria such as those proposed in Table 1, and doing this as efficiently, objectively, and transparently as possible.

LANDSLIDE VELOCITY AND PROPOSED CLASSIFICATION

A proposed landslide velocity classification system is presented in Table 2. It is modified from Cruden and Varnes (1996) who proposed the qualitative descriptions and typical values presented in the second and third column of Table 2. Proposed modifications include: assignment of velocity classes that can be treated as condition states in the Markov models that follow (the first column); subdivision of the Very Slow velocity class; assignment of total annual displacements associated with each velocity class (the fourth column); and, assignment of a left-triangular probability density function to each velocity class, which yields the mean displacement values shown in the fifth column. For purposes of Markov modelling of velocity class distributions for normally slow-moving landslides, all velocity classes Moderate and greater have been combined into Class 4+. The reasons for the proposed modifications are described in the subsections that follow.

Table 2 – Modified Landslide Velocity Classification after Cruden and Varnes (1996)

Class	Description	Typical Velocity	Proposed Annual Displacement Criteria (m)	Proposed Mean Annual Displacement (m)
7	Extremely rapid	>5 m/sec		
6	Very rapid	>3 m/min		
5	Rapid	>1.8 m/hr		
4+	Moderate	>13 m/month	>16	64
3	Slow	>1.6 m/yr	>1.6	6.4
2b	Very slow	>160 mm/yr	>0.16	0.64
2a	Very slow	>16 mm/yr	>0.016	0.064
1	Extremely slow	<16 mm/yr	<0.016	0.005
0	Dormant or relict	0 mm/yr	0	0

Intended Application and Examples

The work presented here is heavily influenced by the authors' experience with normally slow-moving landslides in clay overburden and flat-lying mudstones and shale that are encountered in many regions throughout the world. Common landslide mechanisms include deep-seated compound or translational slides along weak bedding planes in shale and glaciolacustrine clay, rotational slides in till and glaciolacustrine sediments, and earth flows of variable thickness in colluvium and residual soil. Most of these landslides normally move at rates ranging from Extremely Slow to Slow according to the velocity classification of Cruden and Varnes (1996) shown in the second and third columns in Table 2. Rapid to Extremely Rapid slides and flows are less common in these geological conditions but can initiate in till, normally and over-consolidated glaciolacustrine sediments and colluvium, and along over-steepened slopes where a cap of stronger rock overlies weaker shale (e.g., Geertsema et al., 2006). First time slides, retrogression events and the formation of active wedges can result in Rapid to Very Rapid movements which may only persist for a few hours or days (e.g., Krahn et al., 1979; Cruden et al., 2003).

An example of a normally slow-moving landslide that accelerated over part of its width is presented by Anderson et al., (2000). If it were not for the need to maintain access to a dam, the road would have likely closed, but instead it was maintained with great effort, and plans were set in place to re-route the road. Through a facilitated expert-based risk assessment, it was decided that the lowest risk alternative, and the most resilient, as would be described today, was to rebuild across the normally slow-moving landslide, known by the name of the Wells Basin Landslide. Of note in this example, the road is low speed and gravel-surfaced, and relatively easy to maintain and tolerant of deformation.

A more recent example of episodic landslide movement impacting a road is the Last Chance Grade Landslide in northern California. This is in a quite different geologic and climatic setting, and the road is U.S. Highway 101, a higher volume critical corridor that has been managed as it has crossed this landslide for decades (Siel and Anderson, 2017, and Alzamora and Anderson 2018). The long period of road maintenance and observation has provided evidence that areas that were once moving at higher velocity have slowed today, and areas that were moving slowly before are now more active. Once again, an expert-based risk assessment was used to evaluate the risk and resilience of alternatives that stay on alignment versus new alignment alternatives, and the basis for much of the assessment was judgment of the expected velocities of the active and apparently dormant landslides on the alternative alignments, and what those velocities would mean in terms of maintenance requirements and what could be described as the expected road condition states for the alternative alignments. We see the Markov-based methods described here as an improvement to the objectivity of the process of Anderson et al. (2000) and Alzamora and Anderson (2018).

Reasons for Subdivision of the 'Very Slow' Velocity Class

Mansour et al. (2011) compiled examples of damage from slow-moving landslides and demonstrated that the expected degree of damage can be related to the landslide velocity or cumulative displacement. Often minor to no damage is reported for infrastructure impacted by Extremely Slow landslides unless movements continue to accumulate for decades. Expected damage from Very Slow landslides can vary widely, however, ranging from increased maintenance costs at the lower end of the range to complete loss of serviceability or infrastructure collapse at the high end of the range. Consequently, in Table 2 we have subdivided the Very Slow velocity class into Class 2a and 2b to provide greater granularity for hazard and risk assessment and asset deterioration modelling. In the work that follows we reference the velocity class numbers listed in the left column of Table 2.

Reasons for Use of Annual Displacement Criteria

Data and inferences of landslide velocity can come from several sources. Traditionally these included slope inclinometer and survey monument readings, field observations, and comparisons of aerial photographs. These data are typically collected at a frequency of a few times per year or less. Repeat lidar surveys allow for assessment of topographic change and inferred landslide movement rates over wide geographic areas, though often the time between surveys is still several years, and displacements must be annualized to infer average landside velocities. Shape acceleration arrays (SAAs), in-place inclinometers, and satellite-based InSAR and global navigation satellite systems (GNSS) can provide higher frequency or near real-time data on landslide velocity, but such tools are typically only deployed on a small fraction of landslides of interest. Consequently, the actual velocity of many landslides of interest is almost never known.

Landslide velocity often varies seasonally. The slower velocity classes (e.g., 1 and 2a) have velocities that are sometimes maintained year-round, while Velocity Classes 4 and greater rarely persist for more than a few hours or days.

To address ambiguity arising from annual variability in landslide velocity and differing frequencies of displacement observations that might be used to calibrate models of landslide velocity class transition probabilities, we have proposed that velocity classes be associated with the total measured or inferred annual displacements shown in the fourth column of Table 2. Displacements will typically be as recorded at ground surface near to where infrastructure is (or may potentially be) impacted. In some instances, it may also be practical to consider measured displacements on defined shear surfaces for deeper-seated slides.

The proposed boundary between Velocity Class 3 and 4+ is 16 m per year which, as a matter of convenience, is one order of magnitude greater than the proposed boundary between Velocity Class 2b and 3. In our opinion this criterion is reasonable because landslides that move more than 16 m in a given year likely moved at an instantaneous rate exceeding 13 m per month (i.e., Cruden and Varnes' (1996) boundary between Slow and Moderate) for some period of time within that year. Exposure to displacements in excess of 16 m per year are also expected to quickly bring most types of infrastructure to their ultimate limit state, irrespective of whether that displacement occurs over a period of hours, days or weeks.

In the work that follows, we make no attempt to differentiate between the probabilities of occurrence of Velocity Classes 4 to 7, nor their generalized annual displacement criteria. It is expected that other empirical methods (e.g., Glastonbury and Fell, 2008a) and statistical and numerical landslide runout models are much better suited for these types of analysis.

Proposed Mean Annual Displacements for each Velocity Class

Associating landslide velocity classes with mean annual landslide displacements enables the estimation of annual and cumulative displacement over time given assumptions of the distribution of velocity class probabilities. Furthermore, if an appropriate probability density function describing the likely distribution of displacements can be assigned to each velocity class, more insight to the probabilities of exceedance of specified landslide displacement criteria can be gained through Monte Carlo Simulation, which we have done here.

Since within any given inventory of normally slow-moving landslides there will tend to be many more landslides moving at the slower velocity classes than at the higher classes, it is reasonable to assume that within each velocity class more landslides will also be moving at the lower end of the range than at the higher end. Several types of probability density functions can be used to generate a distribution with this characteristic, but the simplest is a triangular distribution. The proposed mean annual displacement values shown in Table 2 are based on an assumed left triangular distribution. For Velocity Class 4+ the mean annual displacement was calculated based on an assumed range extending from 16 m to 160 m.

A MARKOV CHAIN AND MONTE CARLO SIMULATION APPROACH TO ESTIMATING ANNUAL LANDSLIDE DISPLACEMENT PROBABILITIES

States, Transitions and the Markovian Assumption

The Markov process is a probabilistic model useful in analyzing complex systems (Howard, 2007). Within transportation infrastructure systems, the use of Markov models is a well-established practice that is used to forecast future pavement and bridge conditions and develop long-term investment plans for DOT asset management programs. Further discussion on the application of the Markov modeling approach across a number of asset types is described in Transit Cooperative Research Program (TCRP) Report 157: State of Good Repair: Prioritizing the Rehabilitation and Replacement of Existing Capital Assets and Evaluating the Implications for Transit (TRB, 2012).

More recently, the use of Markov models has been incorporated into geotechnical asset management plans for road and railway systems in the United States and United Kingdom. Examples of Markov processes in geotechnical asset management include the National Cooperative Highway Research Program (NCHRP) Research Report 903 – Geotechnical Asset Management for Transportation Agencies (NASEM, 2019); Alaska Department of Transportation and Public Facilities Geotechnical Asset Management Plan (Thompson, 2017); and Network Rail (Power et al., 2016)

In Markov models, the condition of a physical system can be described by a number of state variables. For the physical system comprising a landslide, velocity (or annual displacement) can be treated as a state variable and the velocity classes listed in Table 2 treated as condition states.

In the course of time a system passes from state to state and thus exhibits dynamic behavior. For a landslide, factors such as changes in shear strength, porewater pressure or landslide geometry can cause a change in velocity. Velocity is a continuous variable that can change at any time, but in a simplified Markov model changes in velocity can be treated as transitions occurring at discrete timesteps (years) and between a finite number of velocity classes defined in terms of expected annual landslide displacement (Table 2).

The probabilities of transitioning between velocity classes (or remaining in the current class) are defined by transition probabilities encapsulated in a transition matrix.

The simplifying Markovian assumption is that only the state presently occupied is relevant in determining the future trajectory of the process. For the conceptual landslide models that follow, the Markovian assumption is that only the velocity class (i.e., displacement) experienced in the prior year is relevant in determining the probabilities of the different velocity classes occurring in future years. While there are few physical systems that we would expect to be so memoryless in a strict sense, the Markov process has proven to be extremely useful for shedding insight on the behavior of a wide class of complex systems encountered in engineering, economics, medicine, biology and geology; we conjecture that this can be extended to the velocity of slow-moving landslides.

The changing values of the state vector (the distribution of condition state probabilities) calculated for various timesteps following an observation of the process reflect our changing state of knowledge in the absence of observation (Howard, 2007). If at any time we were able to observe the process, our probability assignment would change so as to assign a probability of 1 to occupying the state actually observed.

A characteristic of these types of Markov models is that after many timesteps without observation our knowledge of the state of the system diminishes to a constant value referred to as the limiting state probability vector, irrespective of the value of the initial state vector. In the case of landslide velocity, the limiting state probability vector can be thought of as the distribution of velocity classes that might be realized over a very long period of observation; (i.e., thousands of years). Alternatively, if one was able to observe the distribution of velocity classes from a large inventory of landslides of a certain type and within a certain geography over a period of a few decades, for example, that distribution also ought to resemble the limiting state probability vector for that type of landslide operating in that type of environment. We made use of this limiting state behavior to develop conceptual Markov models for a range of landslide behavior types.

Landslide Behavior Types, Mean Annual Displacements, and Limiting State Velocity Class Probability Distributions

Markov Chain models (transition matrices) have been developed for five landslide behavior types to help estimate velocity class transition probabilities for the range of normally slow-moving landslides often encountered in our practice.

The five general landslide behavior types and their typical characteristics are shown in Table 3. The Markov Chain models have been 'tuned' to yield specified long-term average outputs including velocity class distributions and mean annual displacements which can be used by a landslide practitioner to help guide the assignment of an appropriate behavior type to each landslide of interest. The underlying premise is that if the models yield appropriate long-term average velocity class distributions and displacements, they might also generate useful insight to potential near-term conditions (over periods of years to decades) which informs maintenance and investment strategies for asset managers and other DOT decision authorities.

Table 3. Behavior Types and Characteristics for Slow-Moving Landslides

Behavior Type	Type A	Type B	Type C	Type D	Type E
Typical mechanism	Translational block slides and spreads	Translational block slides and spreads	Translational block slides and spreads, rotational slides, complex earth slides-earth flows	Translational slides, rotational slides, earth flows, complex earth slides-earth flows	Translational slides, rotational slides, earth flows, complex earth slides-earth flows
Long-term probability of Class 4+ displacements	1 in 20,000	1 in 6,500	1 in 2,000	1 in 650	1 in 200
Assumed limiting state velocity class distribution					
0	0.700	0.500	0.300	0.100	0.005
1	0.285	0.455	0.550	0.449	0.030
2a	0.011	0.032	0.108	0.324	0.540
2b	0.004	0.011	0.036	0.108	0.360
3	0.0006	0.0018	0.0060	0.0180	0.0600
4+	0.00005	0.00015	0.00050	0.00150	0.00500
Mean annual displacement	0.01 m	0.03 m	0.1 m	0.3 m	1.0 m

The transition matrix for each landslide behavior type and its basis is described in Porter et al., (2022), and an example of the matrix developed for Type B landslides is shown in Figure 1.

From/To	0	1	2a	2b	3	4+
0	0.99620	0.00342	0.00034	0.00003	0.000003	0.000000
1	0.00387	0.99376	0.00213	0.00021	0.00002	0.000002
2a	0.00332	0.02991	0.95320	0.01221	0.00122	0.00014
2b	0.00052	0.00467	0.04666	0.92800	0.01814	0.00202
3	0.00015	0.00134	0.01345	0.13446	0.82000	0.03060
4+	0.00007	0.00062	0.03381	0.34500	0.31050	0.31000
Target	0.50	0.455	0.032	0.011	0.0018	0.00015

Figure 1 – Velocity class Probability Transition Matrix for Landslide Behavior Type B and Target Limiting State Vector

Over time, evidence-based calibration of the models enables a geotechnical program to present long-term performance forecasts for a program of many landslides that can adversely impact the operational resilience of the agency. With recent advancements in measuring landslide change at a regional scale through remote sensing methods (Lato et al., 2019), the opportunity now exists to build evidence-based temporal landslide models at statewide scale for a program of several landslides.

The models developed for each proposed landslide behavior type incorporate several important assumptions that have tentatively been assigned based on literature review (e.g., Glastonbury and Fell, 2008b), our experience and judgment, and supported by trial and error. They continue to be tested and will be improved upon as more data for model calibration become available.

The intent is that for a particular landslide, the most applicable behavior type (or types) would be selected based on a review of geomorphic evidence obtained through lidar, aerial photographs, field mapping investigation and monitoring, and potentially radiometric dating or dendrochronology. This evidence would be used to estimate the dominant mechanisms of movement, the age of landslide features such as scarps, sag ponds and debris deposits, and the past occurrence and approximate frequency of more rapid surges of movement (e.g., Dyke et al., 2011). For landslide complexes containing multiple landslides a unique behavior type and initial velocity would be assigned to each individual slide within the complex.

Annual Landslide Displacement Estimates

The Year 1 landslide velocity class probability distribution for a landslide can be estimated by multiplying the initial (Year 0) landslide velocity class state vector (i.e., the probabilities of being in the different landslide velocity classes at Year 0) by the transition matrix for the applicable landslide behavior type.

The initial state vector can be thought of as either a probabilistic estimate of the current landslide velocity (when that velocity is uncertain) or as a means of specifying a precise current velocity when it is known. For example, with reference to the mean annual displacements shown in the fifth column of Table 2, the initial state vector [0, 0.66, 0.34, 0, 0, 0] yields an initial velocity of 25 mm per year.

The state probability vector for any year can be calculated by post-multiplying the state probability vector at the preceding timestep by the transition matrix, or alternatively, the nth state probability vector can be calculated by post-multiplying the initial state vector by the transition matrix raised to the nth power. These calculations are easily completed using a computer spreadsheet or code for as many timesteps as required. For example, the first five years of model outputs using the transition matrix for Landslide Behaviour Type B (Figure 1) and an initial state vector equivalent to 25 mm per year (as per above) yields the landslide velocity class probability distributions shown in Figure 2.

Year	Markov Chain Velocity Class State Vectors					
	Class 0	Class 1	Class 2a	Class 2b	Class 3	Class 4+
0	0.0000	0.6600	0.3400	0.0000	0.0000	0.0000
1	0.0037	0.6660	0.3255	0.0043	0.0004	0.0000
2	0.0073	0.6717	0.3119	0.0082	0.0009	0.0001
3	0.0109	0.6769	0.2991	0.0117	0.0013	0.0001
4	0.0145	0.6817	0.2871	0.0149	0.0017	0.0001
5	0.0181	0.6861	0.2759	0.0177	0.0020	0.0002

Figure 2 – Example Markov Chain Model Outputs for Landslide Behaviour Type B and an Initial State Vector Representing an Initial Velocity of 25 mm per Year

In effect, what the Markov chain model is doing is describing the change in our state of knowledge about the likely annual landslide displacement as we transition from a high degree of knowledge in Year 0, to a condition many years in the future where the current landslide velocity has no predictive power. Many years into the future our best possible prediction is that the landslide will have a velocity class probability distribution equal to the limiting state vector.

The Markov chain state vectors at each timestep can be used to estimate a mean annual displacement each year by multiplying the velocity class probability distribution by the mean displacement associated with each velocity class. However, what is often of greater interest is the probability of exceeding specific landslide displacement criteria, such as the proposed criteria associated with the road condition states summarized in Table 1.

The probabilities of exceeding specified displacement criteria can be determined through Monte Carlo Simulation. Monte Carlo Simulation involves completing thousands of trials for each Markov Chain model timestep. In each trial, a random number is used to select a velocity class from the probability distribution for that timestep, and two additional random numbers are used to select a specific displacement from the velocity class range using a left-triangular probability density function. The number of trials for which the different landslide displacement criteria were exceeded is divided by the total number of trails to obtain estimates of the annual probabilities of criteria exceedances for each timestep.

USE OF ROAD CONDITION STATE PROBABILITIES TO QUANTIFY RESILIENCY AND ESTIMATE LIFECYCLE COST

As outlined above, Markov Chain modelling and Monte Carlo Simulation can be used to estimate the probabilities of the road condition state criteria presented in Table 1 being exceeded. Model inputs include: assignment of the annual landslide displacement criteria associated with each road condition state (e.g. the values presented in Table 1 or other site-specific criteria), the landslide behavior type (Table 3), and the initial landslide velocity.

Figures 3 and 4 provide examples of model output for the following scenario:

- the annual displacement criteria for road condition states are those suggested for lower-speed paved roads in Table 1;
- the landslide behavior type is Type B, with a long-term average mean annual displacement of 0.03 m and the limiting state velocity class probabilities shown in Table 3 and Figure 1; and
- the initial landslide velocity is 0.005 m per year (the mean annual displacement associated with Velocity Class 1 in Table 2).

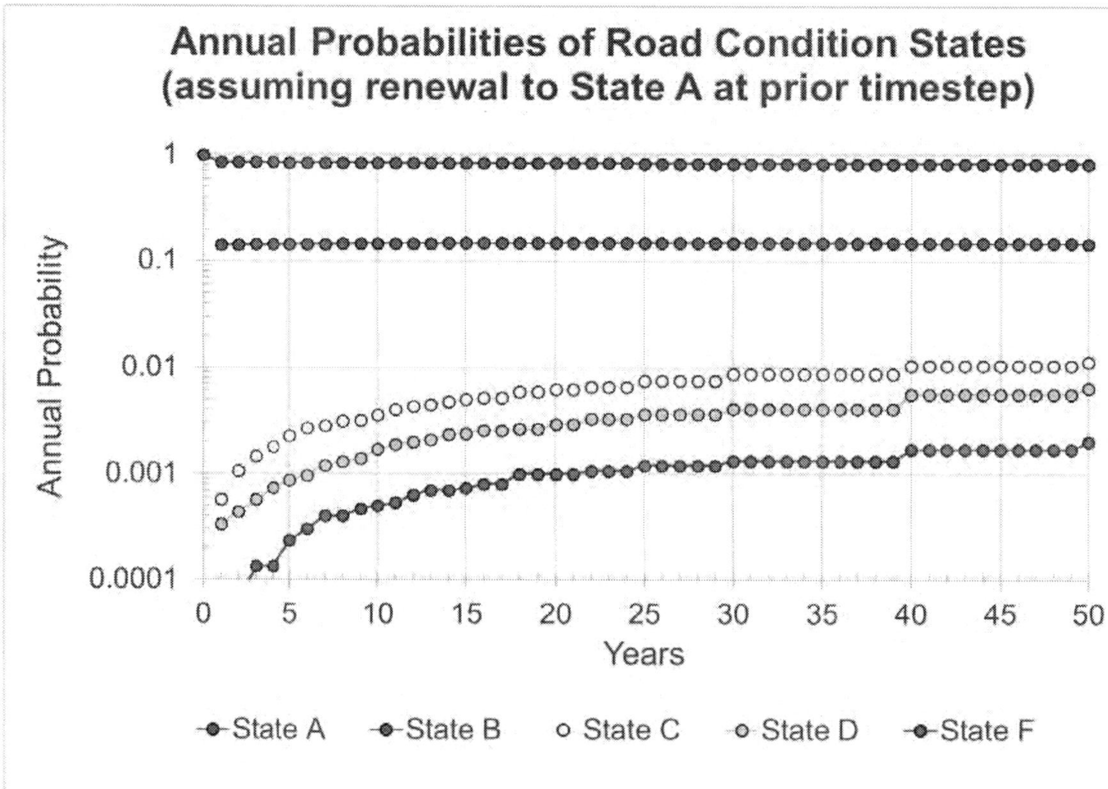

Figure 3 – Example of Annual Probability Distribution of Road Condition States

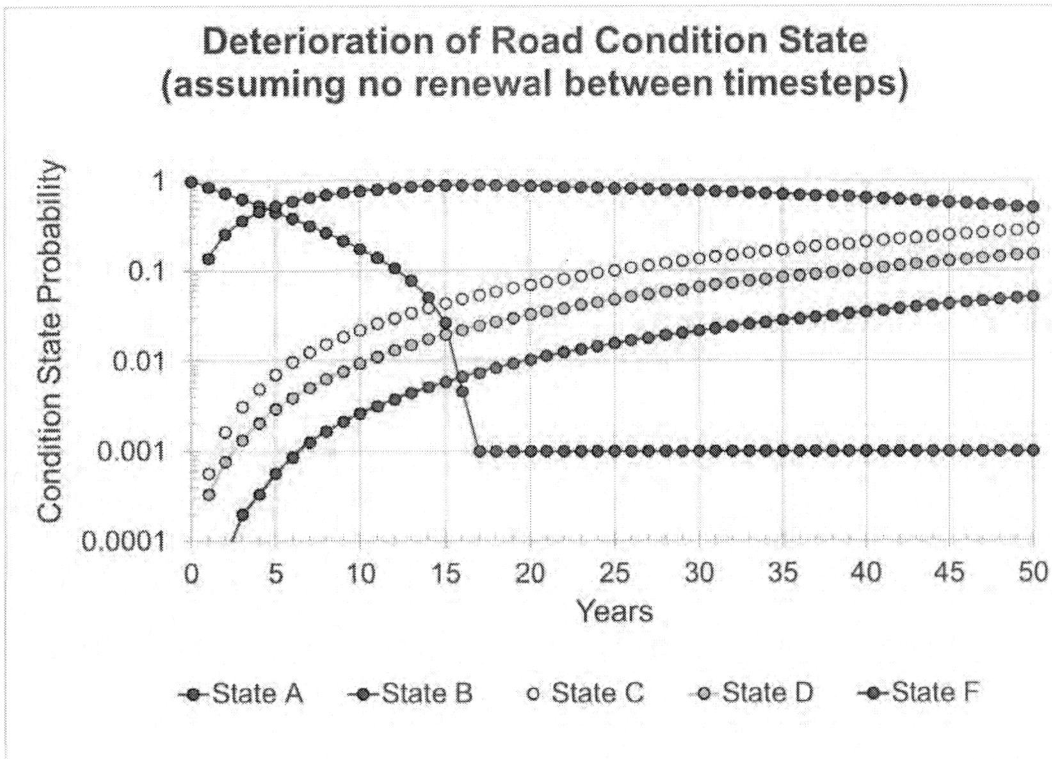

Figure 4 – Example of Cumulative Probability Distribution of Road Condition States

Figure 3 presents the annual probabilities of being in each road condition state. In this representation, the assumption is made that road maintenance and renewal activities transition the road to Condition State A after each timestep, and that the associated cost model includes the required estimated renewal costs. In reality, an Agency would often defer the costs required to transition the road back to Condition State A, but this approach provides a simple way of modelling lifecycle cost to provide for a well-performing roadway on the landslide over 50 years. Note that the condition state probabilities are presented on a semi-log plot. The reasons that the annual probabilities of transitioning to Condition States C, D and F increase over time for this particular example are because the uncertainty in the actual velocity increases with time (thus a small but growing likelihood that the landslide could experience one of the higher velocity classes), and because the initial landslide velocity in this example (0.005 m) was less than the predicted long-term average velocity for the specified landslide behavior type (0.03 m).

Figure 4 presents the same model results shown in Figure 3, but in terms of the cumulative probability of being in the different road condition states after many timesteps assuming that no maintenance or renewal occurs between timesteps. This would be representative of a 'do nothing' asset management treatment option, and can be thought of as the bookend to the representation presented in Figure 3. The cumulative probabilities are calculated by first summing the annual probabilities of being in State F using the binomial equation, and then reducing the probability of remaining in State A such that the total probability of being in each of the condition states remains equal to 1. The process is repeated for the other condition states. When the probability of remaining in State A becomes negligible, it is reduced to and maintained at a value of 1 in 1,000 for all future timesteps (in the example above this occurs in Year 17), and in subsequent timesteps the probability of remaining in State B is reduced such that the total probability of being in each of the condition states remains equal to 1. In the example in Figure 3, State B becomes the most likely road condition state in Year 5. In Year 20 there is about a 1% chance that the road would be in State F and about a 10% chance that it would be in State C. When applied to a life-cycle cost model, the probabilities of each condition state can then be combined with the estimated owner and user costs for that condition state to produce a probabilistic life-cycle cost model. A life-cycle model can be used to complete a site-specific landslide mitigation option trade-off analysis that informs the selection of an optimum management strategy. Alternatively, models from several sites can be aggregated to build an investment need case that enables an agency to build a funding strategy that proactively addresses the risk and resiliency needs across a program of several landslides over a multi-decade period.

In several real-world examples where sufficient road maintenance and performance records are available, we have found that these models yield road condition state probabilities that are reasonably representative of observed performance.

EXAMPLE APPLICATION TO A HISTORICAL SLIDE MITIGATION EFFORT

The purpose of this approach is to provide a systematic and data-driven forecasting tool that informs investment analysis and risk mitigation planning on large landslides, ideally enabling a higher likelihood of selecting the optimum treatment strategy. The consequences of selecting the wrong treatment strategy can range from encumbering funds for a higher than needed level of mitigation to reactively responding after landslide velocity changes have forced an unplanned and unbudgeted response. While an easy solution may be to only execute mitigation projects when funding for complete stabilization is available and continuing to defer maintenance and renewal opportunities in the interim until complete failure forces a response, the total cost of this approach means that the agency will need to fund a significantly and likely unfeasible amount of mitigation projects or transfer risk to system users. When the optimum treatment strategy is selected, the agency can defensively demonstrate good stewardship of public tax revenues and private funds, while also ensuring investments in risk and resiliency can go farther than only a few sites over several decades.

An example of the potential value that exists for considering changes to landslide velocity can be seen in a historical risk management project completed by the Colorado DOT on I-70 near the Eisenhower-Johnson Memorial Tunnel. Per the criteria proposed in Table 1, this section of I-70 would be classified as a "higher speed paved road". For over 20 years and shortly after the original highway construction, a large landslide (Landslide Behavior Type C as per Table 3) at mile marker 212 on I-70 caused several inches of annual settlement to adversely impact the I-70 pavement. This annual landslide displacement (upper end of Velocity Class 2a as per Table 2) generally occurred in the spring and summer months, resulting in an estimated owner cost of around $130,000 per year (current dollars) for pavement overlays and other roadway maintenance. The road condition state (Table 1) alternated between State B and C as a result of the ongoing landslide displacements and maintenance activities. Geotechnical investigations and studies of the landslide generated mitigation options to improve the landslide to above a factor of safety of 1.3; however, the preliminary cost of these options was over $30M (current dollars). This amount of mitigation cost is approximately three times more than the typical annual CDOT Geohazard Program budget and thus not feasible for funding without re-allocating funds from elsewhere in the department.

As an alternative to full stabilization, CDOT developed a roadway settlement mitigation plan that was directed at reducing pavement deformation and the resulting annual maintenance expenses. It was well accepted that the mitigation plan would not change the factor of safety by more than a few percent; however, the opportunity to reduce pavement distress was desirable regardless of the level of improvement in stability. In 2010, CDOT completed a roadway settlement mitigation project involving 135 drilled shafts installed to a maximum depth of 20 feet below the westbound I-70 lanes and backfilled with lightweight cellular concrete. A small scale drilled groundwater drain system was also installed at the base of the slide with a portion of the remaining funds. Based on observed performance improvements, a similar project was performed in 2011 for the eastbound lanes. The cost of these two projects was about 10 to 15 percent of the estimated costs for full stabilization.

The performance data for this slide over a ten-year period suggest the landslide velocity has decreased by approximately a factor of 20 on the slide plane (more than 2 inches per year to approximately 0.1 inches per year, or Velocity Class 1 as per Table 2) (personal communication D. Thomas CDOT Geotechnical Program, 2022). The benefit to CDOT of this velocity change is landslide maintenance expenses over the last decade have reduced to zero (no more recurring overlays) and the slide is viewed as "stable" by management and maintenance teams (Table 1, Road Condition State A). Note, geotechnically the landslide is still at a factor of safety of near unity and thus not geotechnically "stable." By employing this strategy, CDOT was able to reduce landslide velocity, improve roadway performance, and transition the management approach to an optimized life-cycle cost strategy. From an investment perspective, CDOT avoided the need to move over $25M in funds from elsewhere in the department to fund full mitigation or the need to reactively respond to a sudden disruption to the system that impacted the mobility of travelers and resiliency of CDOT. The graph in Figure 5 presents a conceptual life-cycle cost curve for this landslide and estimated options for full stabilization, continuing a do minimum approach, and the selected approach to manage settlement and landslide velocity. As illustrated on the figure, the selected mitigation strategy is approaching parity with the historical annual pavement maintenance approach and is well below the amount needed for full stabilization.

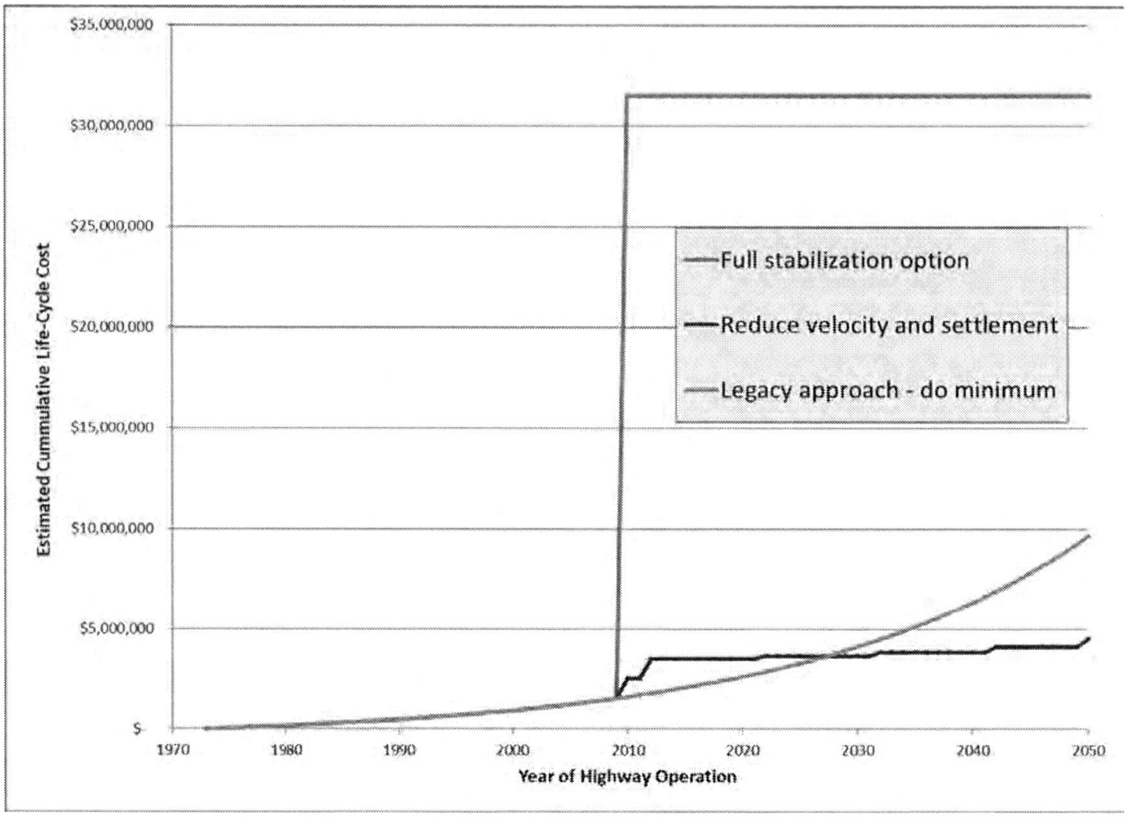

Figure 5 – Conceptual Life-Cycle Benefit from Reducing Landslide Velocity on the CDOT I-70 Mile Marker 212 Landslide.

One of the authors of this paper was involved with the CDOT project over several years, including geological explorations, engineer of record, and resident engineering positions on the project. While the Markov model approach to probabilistic landslide velocity and road condition states presented in this paper was not yet developed for use, the mitigation selection process would have benefited from using this approach in the following ways.

- The uncertainties and risks associated with a potential increase in landslide velocity prior to mitigation could have been more effectively quantified and communicated. For example, the approach proposed here would have estimated the probability of realizing Road Condition States D and F over a 10-year period at 0.35 and 0.09, respectively, in the absence of some form of slope stabilization.
- Subject matter expert input would be considered in a probabilistic approach rather than subjective opinion. For example, if subject matter experts had predicted post-stabilization landslide velocities ranging from about 0.1 to 0.5 inches per year, the approach would have estimated post-mitigation probabilities of realizing Road Condition States D and F over a 10-year period at 0.015 and 0.004 (for 0.1 inches per year), and 0.06 and 0.02 (for 0.5 inches per year).
- The likelihood of success in terms of total life-cycle cost would have been available to executives charged with funding the project. Model outputs for un-mitigated and mitigated scenarios, similar to those presented in Figures 3 and 4, could have been incorporated in life-cycle cost models (similar to Figure 5) and supported risk-cost benefit analyses. These analyses would likely have demonstrated that, in spite of the

uncertainties in slope and highway performance with a partial stabilization option, such an option posed an optimal solution, at least in the interim. It would have enabled the selection of a mitigation approach that is substantially below the typical guidance factor of safety criteria for full stabilization.

Now that the I-70 landslide site has developed a 10-year performance history that demonstrates the value of landslide velocity reductions as a mitigation strategy, future Markov model efforts applied to other sites now have more data to inform probabilistic forecasting of outcomes.

CLOSING REMARKS

Roads crossing large and normally slow-moving landslides can be thought of as dynamic, probabilistic systems. Interpretation of landslide mechanisms and past movement behavior, combined with observations of current landslide velocity, can provide insight to the probabilities of different landslide velocity classes being realized in the future. The potential for accelerated landslide movement is strongly correlated with the potential for a degradation in road condition state.

It is often not practical to fully stabilize large landslides because the needed level investment disproportionally shifts resources from other investment needs. Thus, the owner of a large landslide or a program of assets impacted by several large landslides may be required to manage the operational and safety risks from landsliding through means other than stabilization. The options for managing this operational risk include planning for higher levels of reactive maintenance, increased monitoring, and/or attempting interim measures that may reduce velocity (and risk) by some margin. Even the decision to avoid any action is a management strategy that defers future decisions until landslide impacts force a response.

The individuals charged with managing the risk and resilience impacts from landslides are challenged to make the best decision possible while relying on imperfect information. These decision models can range from 'gut' feelings based on the experience of an individual to reliance on a collective of expert opinions. With time, each new piece of information on a landslide or a finding from similar situation becomes an opportunity to update the decision model that guides the operational risk management of the landslide.

The use of a Markov model process to predict landslide velocity and displacement using existing information and updating these models with new information over time is a tool that a manager of large landslide risk can use to improve the forecasting of long-term landslide behavior. These forecasts of landslide behavior, combined with road condition state criteria linked to landslide displacement rates, can inform ongoing maintenance activities, the likelihood of operational improvements through interim or full mitigation efforts, and probabilistic and risk adjusted life-cycle cost models over a several decade period.

REFERENCES:

Alzamora, D. E., and Anderson, S.A., 2017. The risk assessment of Last Chance Grade. In *Proceedings of the 48th Northwest Geotech Workshop*. August 8, 2018, Golden, Colorado.

Anderson, S.A., Holder, T.S., and Dodd, G. 2000. Rapid reactivation of a large composite earth slide – earth flow. In *Geotechnical Special Publication 101: Slope Stability 2000*. American Society of Civil Engineers, Reston, Virginia: pp1-17.

Cruden, D.M., Martin, C.D. and Soe Moe, K.W. 2003. Stages in the translational sliding of 2 inclined blocks: observations from Edmonton. 56th Canadian Geotechnical Conference, Canadian Geotechnical Society, Winnipeg, Manitoba.

Cruden, D.M. and Varnes D.J. 1996. Landslide types and processes. In: Turner and Schuster (eds) Landslides, investigation and mitigation, Special Report 247, Transportation Research Board, National Research Council. National Academy Press, Washington, USA, 3: 36-75.

Dyke, L.D., Sladen, W.E. and Robertson, L. 2011. Colluvium flows as a hazard to pipelines in northeastern British Columbia. Geological Survey of Canada, Open File 6696.

Geertsema, M., Clague, J., Schwab, J., Evans, S. 2006. An overview of recent large catastrophic landslides in northern British Columbia, Canada. Engineering Geology, 83: 120-143.

Glastonbury, J. and Fell, R. 2008a. A decision analysis framework for the assessment of likely post-failure velocity of translational and compound natural rock slope landslides. Can. Geotech. J. 45: 329-350.

Glastonbury, J. and Fell, R. 2008b. Geotechnical characteristics of large slow, very slow, and extremely slow landslides. Can. Geotech. J. 45: 984-1005.

Howard, R. 2007. Dynamic Probabilistic Systems, Volume 1: Markov Models. Dover Publications, New York.

Krahn, J., Johnson, R.F., Fredlund, D.G., and Clifton, A.W. 1979. A highway cut failure in Cretaceous sediments at Maymont, Saskatchewan. Can. Geotech. J., 16, 703-715.

Lato, M. J., S. Anderson, and M. J. Porter. "Reducing landslide risk using airborne Lidar scanning data." Journal of Geotechnical and Geoenvironmental Engineering 145.9 (2019): 06019004.

Mansour, M., Morgenstern, N., and Martin, D. 2011. Expected damage from displacement of slow-moving slides, Landslides 8:117-131.

National Academies of Sciences, Engineering, and Medicine (NASEM) 2019. *Geotechnical Asset Management for Transportation Agencies, Volume 2: Implementation Manual*. Washington, DC: The National Academies Press. https://doi.org/10.17226/25364.

Porter, M., Quinn, P., and Barlow, P. 2022. Conceptual landslide velocity transition models for a range of landslide behaviour types. Georiques VIII – Proceedings of the 8th Canadian Geohazards Conference, Canadian Geotechnical Society, Quebec City, Quebec, Canada (in Press).

Power, C., J. Mian, T. Spink, S. Abbott, and M. Edwards. 2016. "Development of an Evidence-Based Geotechnical Asset Management Policy for Network Rail, Great Britain." Presented at

Advances in Transportation Geotechnics 3: The 3rd International Conference on Transportation Geotechnics (ICTG 2016), Portugal. In: Procedia Engineering, Vol. 143, pp. 726–733.

Siel, B. D. and Anderson, S.A., 2017. Using event trees to estimate risk on the Last Chance Grade. In *Proceedings of the 47th Northwest Geotech Workshop*. September 12, 2017, Sheridan, Wyoming.

Thomas, D, 2022. Personal communication.

Thompson, P. D. 2017. Geotechnical Asset Management Plan, Technical Report. Report TP000S(802)(B). Prepared for the Alaska Department of Transportation and Public Facilities, Juneau, Alaska.

Transportation Research Board. 2012. State of Good Repair: Prioritizing the Rehabilitation and Replacement of Existing Capital Assets and Evaluating the Implications for Transit. Washington, DC: The National Academies Press. https://doi.org/10.17226/22732

Challenges in Rock Slope Stabilization
SR 209, Section RSM, Rock Slope Stabilization Project
Jim Thorpe, Pennsylvania

Joseph Krupansky, P.G.
Gannett Fleming, Inc.
1010 Adams Avenue
Audubon, PA 19403
610-783-3799
jkrupansky@gfnet.com

Andrew J. Smithmyer, P.G.
Gannett Fleming, Inc.
207 Senate Avenue
Camp Hill, PA 19403
(717) 886-5460
asmithmyer@gfnet.com

Scott M. Cressman, P.E.
Pennsylvania Department of Transportation, Engineering District 5-0
1002 Hamilton Street
Allentown, PA 18101
(610) 871-4520
sccressman@pa.gov

Prepared for the 71st Highway Geology Symposium, May 2022

Acknowledgements

The authors would like to thank PennDOT Engineering District 5-0; Road-Con Inc.; Axis Stabilization, Inc.; Ameritech Slope Constructors; and Gannett Fleming's Valley Forge and Camp Hill offices, for their work on the various aspects of this project.

Disclaimer

Statements and views presented in this paper are strictly those of the author(s), and do not necessarily reflect positions held by their affiliations, the Highway Geology Symposium (HGS), or others acknowledged above. The mention of trade names for commercial products does not imply the approval or endorsement by HGS.

ABSTRACT

U.S. Route 209 (S.R. 209) traverses the southeast side of a narrow, steep-sided valley carved by the Lehigh River just south of the Borough of Jim Thorpe, Pennsylvania. During original roadway construction, a nearly vertical rock cut was required on the uphill side of the roadway. Weathering and erosion from precipitation events, freeze-thaw cycles, and root prying has caused the rock slope to become unstable over time. Consequently, this section of S.R. 209 has experienced regular rockfall events over the past several years, including a significant rockslide in early September 2017 that resulted in temporary closure of the roadway while emergency rock slope repairs were completed.

To remediate this 2,800-foot-long rockfall-hazard-prone section of roadway, PennDOT District 5-0 engaged Gannett Fleming to evaluate the nature of the failures occurring along the exposed rock cut and design a stabilization treatment program to protect the traveling public from future rockslide and rockfall events.

Rock slope failures in the Valley and Ridge physiographic province of Pennsylvania are not unfamiliar to engineers and geologists; however, this site presented a unique set of challenges for stabilization design and construction due to the geometry and proximity of the slope with respect to the active roadway. Challenges included developing a cost effective mitigative solution to protect against multiple modes of potential failure; accounting for non-geological project constraints such as right-of-way limitations, construction access, road closure limitations, protection of public and stakeholder property; and addressing unforeseen adverse slope conditions revealed following initial clearing and scaling operations.

INTRODUCTION

Since the last continental glaciers began to retreat approximately 18,000 years ago, the Lehigh River has carved a meandering course through the ridges and valleys of the Appalachian Mountains as it flows southeast to its confluence with the Delaware River at Easton, Pennsylvania. Just south of Jim Thorpe Borough, the river makes a sweeping horseshoe shaped curve through a narrow pass between Mauch Chunk Ridge and Bear Mountain before turning northeast adjacent to the project area. As the river followed the path of least resistance, generally along underlying geological planes of weakness, valley downcutting exposed the more durable sandstone ridge-building formations along its banks.

The Lehigh Valley Railroad originally established in 1846 *(1)* was the first major mode of transport and industry to take advantage of the Lehigh River corridor as a direct route from the vast anthracite coal regions to the Delaware River Valley and the markets of New York City and Philadelphia. Similarly, following the river was also the most viable and economical land route for vehicular transportation into and out of the region. Formerly Legislative Route 163, this section of S.R. 209 was one of the original highways incorporated into the 1926 U.S. Highway System *(2)*. According to the Pennsylvania Highways website (PAHighways.com), SR 209 in the area of Jim Thorpe was widened in the 1950s to accommodate heavier traffic volumes. Based on field observations of the existing rock face, construction of the road cut required blasting through prominent sandstone formations. Today, S.R. 209 carries approximately 10,000 vehicles per day between Jim Thorpe and Lehighton *(3)*.

According to PennDOT Carbon County maintenance personnel, this section of S.R. 209 experienced regular rockfall events in the years leading up to design and construction. The reported events have ranged from small boulder size rocks to large sheets of rock falling into the limited shoulder and travel lanes of S.R. 209 northbound. PennDOT Engineering District 5-0 recognized that this 3,000-foot section of roadway was prone to rockslides/falls due to the nature of the local geology and erosional forces at work. In June 2016, PennDOT retained Gannett Fleming, Inc., of Valley Forge, PA, to provide a preliminary geologic assessment and provide stabilization recommendations.

SITE GEOLOGY

This section of S.R. 209 parallels the Lehigh River as it meanders through the gorge between Bear Mountain and Mauch Chunk Ridge just south of Jim Thorpe, Pennsylvania. Traveling south out of Jim Thorpe, S.R. 209 begins to climb the northeast flank of Mauch Chunk Ridge, rising from approximately El. 530 to El. 765 within the project limits. A Combined Site Location and Geology Map is included as Figure 1 below.

The site lies within the Anthracite Upland section of the Ridge and Valley physiographic province. The surrounding topography has been developed through erosional processes of the regional drainage network and reflects the bedrock structural trends and relative resistance of the rocks to erosion. The road cut crosses three distinct geologic units, representing a 20-million-year interval from the Late Devonian to the Early Mississippian (360 to 340 million years ago). The exposed rock units include the Lower Mississippian Age Spechty Kopf Formation, and Duncannon and Clarks Ferry Members of the Upper Devonian Catskill Formation, as the roadway traverses northeast up Mauch Chunk Ridge.

The Clark's Ferry Member of the Catskill Formation in the vicinity of the project site is composed of gray to grayish-red medium-grained sandstone, containing interbedded quartz-rich conglomerate *(4)*. The uppermost member of the Catskill Formation, the Duncannon Member, is predominantly red sandstone interbedded with siltstone, shale, and quartz-rich conglomerate *(4)*. These coarse, resistant, ridge-forming units are well exposed along the SR 209 road cut and form the north-facing bench of Mauch Chunk Ridge on the west side of the river.

The Spechty Kopf Formation in the area of the project site is composed of gray to reddish-gray interbedded shale, sandstone, siltstone, and mudstone. The rocks comprising this formation do not form prominent ledges or ridges and tend to break down into small component grains during weathering. In general, the dominant component of the sandstone beds is quartz, of which about 70 percent is monocrystalline and 30 percent is polycrystalline. The shales and siltstones are composed of illite-sericite clay, microcrystalline silica, and variable amounts of angular, moderately strained quartz silt grains. Some organic material, presumably plant fragments, occurs in these fine-grained rocks *(5)*.

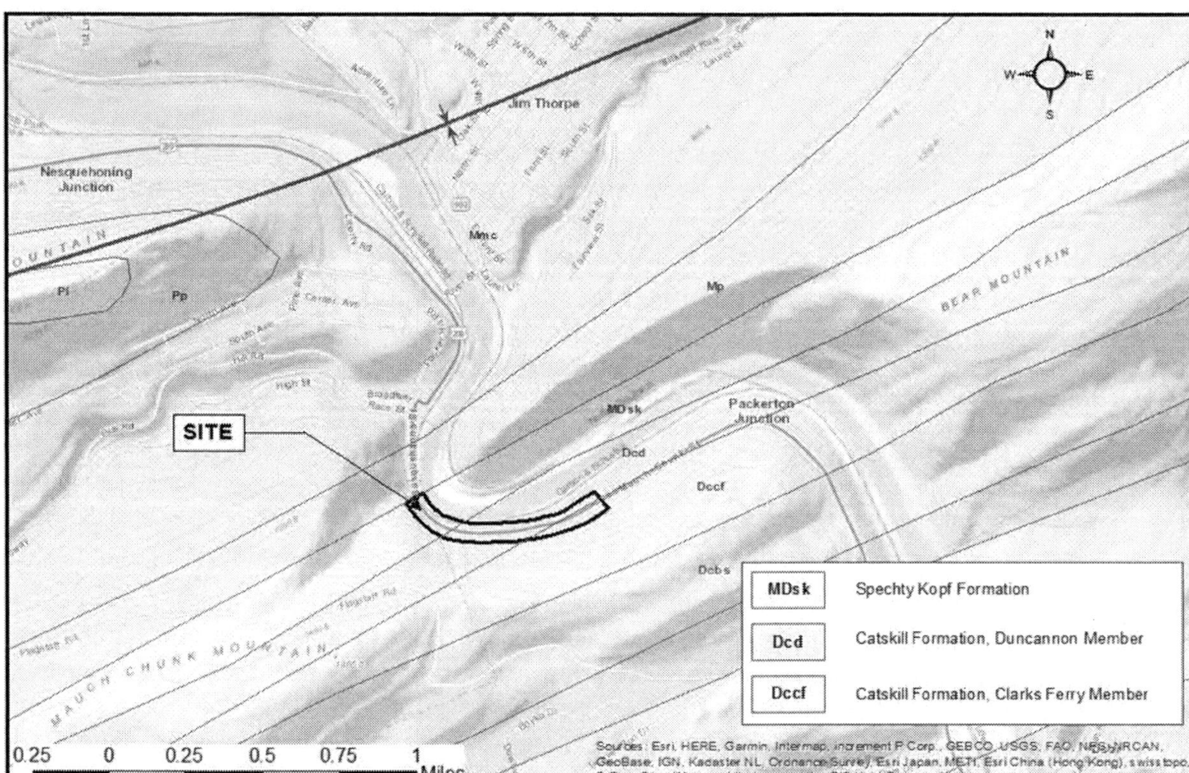

Figure 1 – Combined Site Location and Geology Map
(modified from PA DCNR, PAGEODE, Web-Mapping Application) ***(6)***

EXISTING CONDITIONS & PROJECT HISTORY

Through the project area, S.R. 209 consists of two, 11-foot-wide northbound travel lanes (passing lane and climbing lane), a single 11-foot-wide southbound lane, limited-width paved shoulders, and a variable-width raised curb area adjacent to the southbound shoulder. The northbound shoulder is typically 3 feet wide through the project area, widening to approximately 6 feet near the northeast end of the site as the climbing lane ends. No rockfall catchment area exists between the northbound shoulder and the exposed rock face. In general, the southbound shoulder varies from 1 to 2 feet and is bound by a 1- to 3-foot-high historic masonry barrier wall. Beyond the masonry barrier wall, a steep mixed soil and rock slope drops down to a single-track freight railroad line operated by Reading Blue Mountain and Northern Railroad, then continues a short distance to the Lehigh River.

On July 11, 2016, Carbon County Maintenance mechanically scaled and removed a large, visually unstable rock mass identified as Area of Concern (AOC) No. 9 (as identified during the field reconnaissance activities) from the slope face (Figure 2). The maintenance crew utilized an excavator equipped with a hydraulic hammer to pry the mass from the rock slope. According to PennDOT personnel onsite during the work, the rockfall was initiated after using only a small amount of force applied by the excavator, using the hammer tip to wedge an open vertical joint near the top of the rock mass. The work was performed under a temporary single-lane closure of the S.R. 209 northbound right-ahead travel (climbing) lane, and a temporary (approximately 30 minute) closure of all travel lanes (two northbound and one southbound) during the induced rockfall event and subsequent clean-up of the rock debris on the roadway.

Figure 2 – Mechanical Scaling of Unstable Rock Mass (July 11, 2016)

During the evening hours of September 8, 2017, a large rockfall event occurred at an area designated as AOC-6. The slope condition following the rockfall event at AOC-6 is shown in Figure 3. This event occurred after a total of 3.1 inches of precipitation fell between September 2 and 6, 2017 *(7)*. It is likely this precipitation event contributed to the rockfall event. The rockfall closed all lanes of the road for several hours while District Maintenance pushed rockfall debris into the northbound right ahead travel lane. Following this event, PennDOT initiated an accelerated construction procurement process to engage a contractor to stabilize the remaining loose material on the slope and remove the rockfall debris from the site. The contract was awarded to New Enterprise Stone and Lime, who teamed with specialty subcontractor Apex Rockfall, LLC. Approximately 55 cubic yards of rockfall material and associated debris were removed from the site.

Figure 3 – Conditions at AOC-6 following the September 8, 2017 Rockfall Event

FIELD INVESTIGATION

The formations exposed along the S.R. 209 rock cut display typical depositional and tectonic joint patterns. The strike of the bedding planes in this region trends northeast-southwest (nearly parallel with the Lehigh River and S.R. 209 along the eastern half of the project area) and dip approximately 74° to 85° northwest, toward the roadway (Figure 4). The rock units display systematic tectonic discontinuities along the length of the road cut as a result of historical uplift and folding during the Alleghanian orogeny. The discontinuities generally consist of gently-dipping (13° to 20°) longitudinal joint sets, oriented nearly perpendicular to bedding, and a steeply-dipping (70° to 85°) cross-joint set oriented orthogonal to bedding.

In addition, stress-relief displacement shear fractures are visible at various locations along the cut. The shear fractures are localized small-scale faults that resulted from shearing of rock masses as internal stresses within the rock were released. Past movement along these shear fractures is evident as slickenside (striations) features along the face of the fracture. In general, the shear fractures/shear fracture zones trend in a direction similar to bedding, and dip at approximately 40° to 50°. The shear fractures identified during field reconnaissance activities and subsequent data analysis were observed to be discontinuous through the project area. Based on field observations, the shear fractures dipping toward the roadway appear to be a primary plane of failure for past rockfall activity. The rock mass that was safely removed by PennDOT maintenance in July 2016 (AOC-9), and the rock slide that occurred in September 2017 (AOC-6), both appear to have failed as a result of steeply dipping bedding discontinuities (release joint) intersecting with the shallow angle shear fracture (slide plane) that daylights at the slope face.

Figure 4 – SR 209 Rock Cut along the Eastern Portion of Project Site Displaying Typical Joint Patterns (bedding is steeply dipping toward roadway)

In order to visually and analytically evaluate the existing cut slope, a photographic survey utilizing terrestrial based digital photogrammetry techniques was conducted. The digital photographs were downloaded and processed to provide a collage of the full length of the rock slope (photomosaic plans) and develop photogrammetric models covering observed areas of concern. A total of 8 photogrammetric models were generated over the length of the project. Surveyed control points were digitized and used to reference the photogrammetry models to real-world coordinates (northing, easting, and elevation). Digital Terrain Models (DTMs) were developed from the photogrammetry models. The orthoimages superimposed on the DTMs were used to measure the orientations of various discontinuities along the rock cut. A typical DTM generated from the photogrammetry is presented in Figure 5.

Figure 5 – Digital Photogrammetry Model No. 5 at AOC-6 (Prior to September 8, 2017 failure). Colored disks represent discontinuity orientation measurements.

The field reconnaissance and subsequent analysis of the digital photogrammetry data identified a total of 18 primary Areas of Concern (AOC). The AOC's generally consisted of:

- Various size rock masses resting atop adversely dipping discontinuities;
- Broken and partially detached rock masses, exacerbated by surface runoff, groundwater seepage, and root prying;
- Blocky rock masses containing various intersecting joints and potentially prone to breakout or toppling;
- Steeply dipping bedding planes oriented parallel to the roadway; and
- Unsupported rock mass conditions.

The AOC limits were identified in the field based on the physical extents of the adverse rock mass characteristics observed and subsequently revised based on an evaluation of the digital photogrammetric models, results of the kinematic analysis, and geotechnical stabilization treatment methods selected.

ROCK SLOPE STABILITY ANALYSES

Discontinuities are zones or planes of weakness within a rock mass. The orientation of discontinuities and shear strength along them are the primary elements that affect the stability of a rock mass. Rock blocks may separate from the rock mass if bounded by discontinuities that dip out of the slope at an angle steeper than the effective friction angle along the discontinuity. Detachment of a rock mass may also be initiated by environmental factors such as hydrostatic pressure, freeze/thaw, wind, vibration, root growth, or anthropogenic activities. A rock mass may contain numerous discontinuities but remain stable if the orientation of the discontinuities and environmental conditions are favorable. For the purposes of evaluating slope stability with respect to S.R. 209 through the project area, adverse discontinuities are the bedding planes, joints, and fractures that are oriented such that they dip out of the slope (toward the roadway) and are roughly parallel (within 30°) to the roadway.

Kinematic Analysis

Kinematic analyses are based on the geometric relationships between the rock slope orientation and structural discontinuities of the rock mass. The orientation of the slope face and discontinuities are described by the dip direction and the amount of dip as depicted in Figure 6.

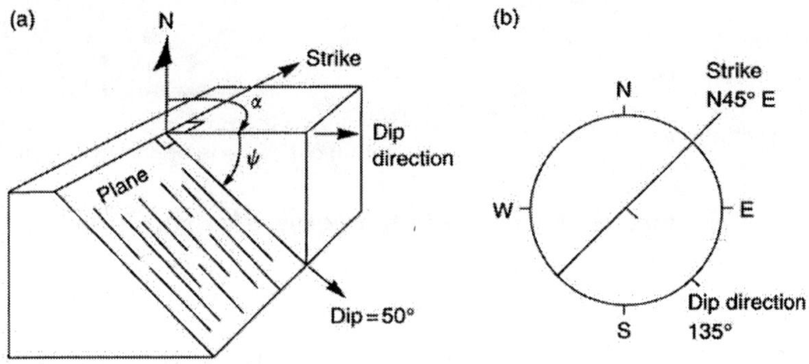

Figure 6 – Terminology defining discontinuity orientation: (a) isometric view of a discontinuity plane; (b) plan view of discontinuity plane *(8)*.

Kinematic analyses were performed using the data collected and depicted in the photogrammetric models generated as part of the photographic survey. The results of the kinematic analyses were used to identify potential modes (planar, wedge, and toppling) of rock slope failure.

Software programs were used to generate the inputs and outputs of the kinematic analyses. 3DM Analyst Lite Suite by Adam Technology was used to generate contoured pole plots of measured discontinuities on a Schmidt equal area stereonet. The contoured pole plots were used to identify major discontinuity sets and determine average orientation values for each set. RockPack III by RockWare, was utilized to generate dip vector plots of the measured discontinuities including rock slope orientation data and the estimated discontinuity interface friction angle. The dip vector plots were used to identify adverse discontinuity sets within the models.

Based on the rock type and visual discontinuity characteristics observed along the rock slope, an estimated rock mass discontinuity interface friction angle of 32° was selected for the analyses. Potential rock slope failure modes considered in the analyses included sliding of rock blocks along a single planar discontinuity, sliding of wedges formed in the slope by intersecting discontinuity planes, and toppling of rock blocks. The kinematic analysis dip vector plot for a section of the rock slope including Area of Concern No. 6 as described above is depicted in Figure 7.

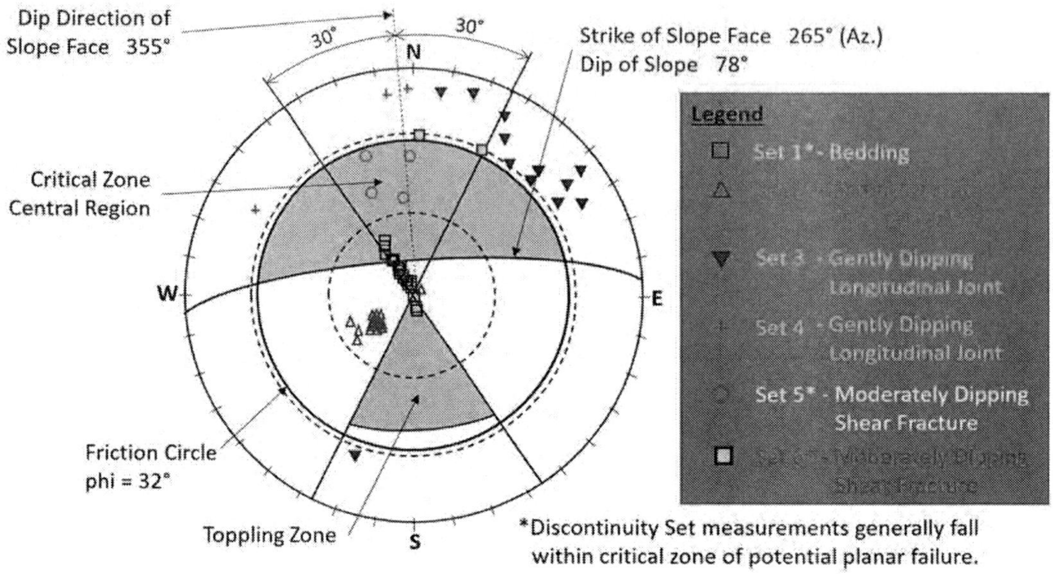

Figure 7 – Kinematic Analysis Dip Vector Plot (including AOC-6)

Limit Equilibrium Analysis

Detailed limit equilibrium analyses were performed at locations where potential failure modes were identified in the kinematic analysis. The analyses were performed to calculate a factor of safety against planar sliding, wedge failure, and toppling based on rock slope geometry, measured discontinuity orientations, estimated groundwater conditions, and estimated properties of the rock mass.

The limit equilibrium analyses were performed using RockPack III software by RockWare and traditional hand calculation methods as defined in the FHWA, 1998 Rock Slope Reference Manual *(9)*. The analyses indicated potential planar and topple modes of failure across five of eight slope sections modeled. The limit equilibrium analyses calculations were based on isolated block conditions that did not account for any cohesion or potential external resisting forces from adjacent interconnected blocks. As a result, the calculated factor of safety values in several instances was less than 1, indicating that the existing conditions are relying on other external unquantified resisting forces to maintain equilibrium. Examples of these external forces could include friction at the interface with adjacent blocks, tensile forces where blocks have not fully detached from the larger rock mass, and normal forces from outcrop protrusions below the critical block, etc.

SLOPE STABILIZATION DESIGN

The project team determined that a post-tensioned pattern bolting approach was best suited for stabilizing potential rockfall and sliding conditions across the site based on the size and irregular rock block/joint orientations observed. The intent of pattern bolting is to prevent ongoing slope relaxation while providing reinforcement to the existing rock face by increasing shear resistance along planes of weakness and interlocking fractured/jointed rock masses. Due to the amount of traffic volume along S.R. 209 and lack of a rockfall catchment area along the right-of-way, a high

-strength steel, anchored mesh system was incorporated into the overall design as a means of secondary protection against potential rock-breakouts between rock bolts and as additional resistance to surficial movements of smaller broken rock masses.

In order to calculate the anchor tension force required to stabilize the observed conditions, a limit equilibrium factor of safety design methodology, as outlined in FHWA (1998) was utilized. A combination of hand calculations and RockPack III software was used to determine the anchor parameters (bar size, length, bond length, spacing, etc.), and tension force per rock anchor required to stabilize the observed conditions with a factor of safety of 1.5. The following rock parameters were assumed in the design of the rock anchor bolts:

- Density of Rock Mass (Sandstone): 160 pcf
- Discontinuity Interface Friction Angle: 32° (Cohesion = 0)
- Allowable Grout to Rock Bond Stress: 110 psi

Based on the overall geologic conditions across the site (variable block size, steeply dipping, highly fractured/jointed) an anchor spacing of 8 feet with a diamond pattern layout was selected. The 8-foot spacing provides a good balance between the total number of anchors and system redundancy. The diamond pattern provides favorable load distribution between mesh elements (rhomboid shape) and rock bolts. The anchor design analysis yielded the following results:

- Design Tension Load: 38 kips
- Minimum Bond Length: 10 feet
- Minimum Unbonded Length: 10 feet
- Rock Bolts: Class I Corrosion Protection (PTI, 2014), 1-1/4", 75 ksi all-thread bar

Once the anchor parameters and design load were established, the limit equilibrium analyses were recalculated to include resulting stabilization scenarios to verify that a factor of safety greater than 1.5 was satisfied for the observed conditions.

The dimensioning tool RUVOLUM® Version 2015 by GeoBrugg was utilized during the design process to verify that the mesh component of the slope stabilization system would provide the resistance required to retain loose rock blocks that have potential to breakout from the slope between anchors.

In addition to pattern bolting and anchored mesh, the stabilization design included rock slope scaling and clearing vegetation over the full extent of the exposed rock face within the project limits, as-directed spot rock bolts, horizontal drains, and as-direct wire mesh treatment to stabilize upslope areas that are disturbed as a result of scaling operations. A design section, showing the typical stabilization treatment layout, is depicted in Figure 8.

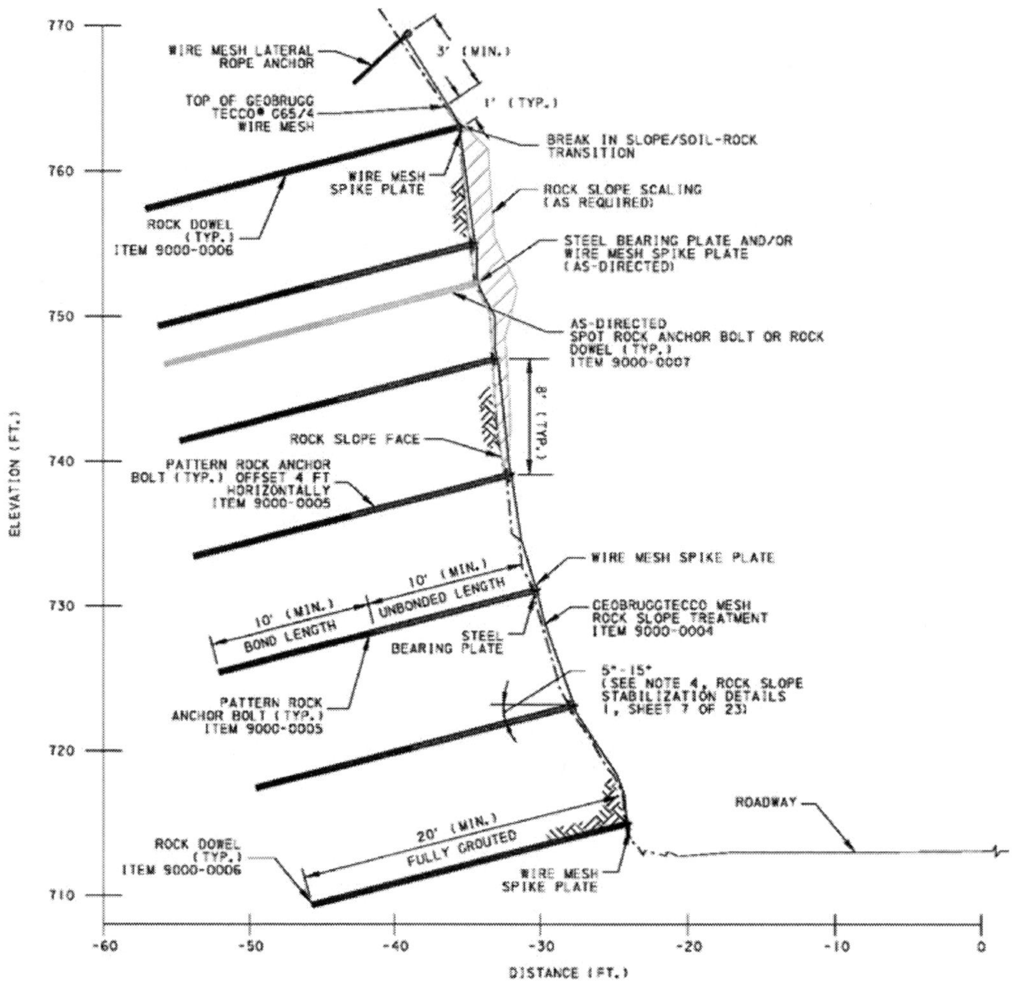

Figure 8 – Typical Design Section

In order to secure the wire mesh and boundary ropes flush to the rock face, fully grouted rock dowels fitted with wire mesh spike plates were included along the periphery of the treatment areas. Post tensioned rock anchors as described above served as the internal wire mesh anchors and fitted with traditional bearing plate hardware to transfer the design tension load to the rock face. Wire mesh spike plates were installed over the bearing plate hardware to secure the wire mesh to the rock bolt.

CONSTRUCTION

The project bid package was advertised through PennDOT's ECMS system. The successful bidder was general contractor Road-Con, Inc. (Road-Con), of West Chester, Pennsylvania. Road-Con teamed with specialty subcontractors Ameritech Slope Constructors (Ameritech), of Ashville, North Carolina, to perform the rock slope scaling work and install wire mesh facing, and Axis Stabilization (Axis), of Harleysville, Pennsylvania to perform the drilling and installation of the rock anchors and stabilization measures. Construction of rock slope stabilization was completed in nine months, between May 2019 and January 2020. Due to the height of the rock slope and proximity of the travel lanes to the slope face, all rock slope stabilization construction activities were performed under daily road closures between the hours of 8:30 AM and 3:00 PM, Monday through Friday.

An experienced geologist from Gannett Fleming familiar with the site conditions and objectives of the stabilization program, provided part-time oversight and quality control efforts during construction.

Rock Slope Scaling

Ameritech used rappelling techniques to access the slope face. Each crew consisted of two scalers and one foreman. Typical scaling arrangements referred to as "hangs" consisted of two crews working side by side from the top of the rock face down to the base. The crews used scaling bars to remove the majority of the loose rock, and 22- to 70-ton high-pressure air cushions (MatJacks) to dislodge and remove larger loose rock masses and boulders. Ameritech limited the use of the MatJacks to larger rock masses already detached from the intact rock face and/or considered potentially dangerous to disturb blocks by drilling.

In order to protect the historic masonry wall along the southbound shoulder and the Reading Blue Mountain and Northern Railroad downslope of the roadway from rockfall material, Ameritech used a temporary, 12-ft high, mobile rockfall shielding system (Figure 9). The system consisted of high-tensile strength steel wire mesh and geotextile facing, supported via wire ropes and steel H-beams resting on concrete deadman anchored pedestals.

Figure 9 – Scaling Operations Above Mobile Rockfall Shielding System

Rock Slope Stabilization Elements

The rock slope stabilization design consisted of 260, post-tensioned rock bolts; 160, fully grouted rock dowels; 3,300 square yards of GeoBrugg TECCO® G65/4 Steel Wire Mesh; 60, as directed (in the field) rock bolts; 70, 10-foot long horizontal drains; and 100 square yards of GeoBrugg TECCO® G65/3 Steel Wire Mesh. All bolts/dowels were installed to a depth of 20 feet into rock and consisted of 1.25-inch diameter, galvanized, continuous thread, 75 ksi steel bars. The batter angle of the dill holes ranged from 5° to 15° in order to optimize the applied normal force with respect to the bedding joints exposed along the roadway. Per recommendations in the Post-Tensioning Institute (PTI) Manual *(10)* and degree of potential consequence from failure, all rock bolts/dowels were fitted with double corrosion protection measures at the manufacturer's facility.

Axis performed the drilling work using excavator- and telehandler-mounted TEI HEM550 rock drills. In order to meet the project schedule and to optimize working hours during road closure, multiple operations were performed concurrently (Figure 10).

Figure 10 – Concurrent Drilling Operations

Per the designed criteria, the post-tensioned rock bolts were installed maintaining a 10-foot bond length to achieve the 38-kip design load. Completed rock bolt assemblies consisted of an 8-inch x 8-inch galvanized steel bearing plate coupled with a hexagonal nut with a hardened washer, and beveled washers as necessary to apply uniform load transfer from the anchor bar to the bearing plate. Axis selected a non-shrink neat cement flowable grout mix consisting of bagged Portland Type I cement and water with a 28-day design strength of 5,000 psi. The grout was mixed on-site with a mobile, trailer-mounted batch plant and pumped to the back of the drill hole through a full-length plastic grout tube. Verification testing was performed at the onset of installation to verify rock bolt capacity and grout-rock bond strength. Proof and performance testing were performed on the post-tensioned rock bolts to confirm the contractor's installation methods and materials.

Due to the variable sizes of rock blocks and unfavorable joint patterns observed during the field investigation, high-tensile strength steel wire mesh was installed over the areas of pattern rock bolting as a means of protection from rock-breakouts and potential surficial movements between rock bolts. The project specified GeoBrugg TECCO® G65/4 high-tensile strength steel wire mesh. TECCO® products perform as an integrated, homogeneous system, where the components work uniformly across the stabilized area ensuring forces are transferred over the entire system. Upon the completion of bolt/dowel installation and testing, Ameritech hung and secured the mesh facing panels. This work was accomplished using a combination of aerial man lifts and rappelling techniques to perform the work. A completed slope section with anchored wire mesh including a close-up photo of the post-tensioned rock bolt head section assembly consisting of a spike plate overlying a standard bearing plate is included in Figure 11.

Figure 11 – (A) Completed Slope Section with Anchored Wire Mesh (B) Close-Up View of a Post-Tensioned Rock Bolt Head Section Assembly

To improve near surface groundwater flow and promote slope drainage a total of 70, 10-foot perforated PVC horizontal drains were installed at an inclination of 5° in areas where groundwater seepage was consistently noted during the field investigation. The horizontal drains were oriented in the field to intersect projected water bearing fractures. Several drain locations encountered significant water bearing fractures and maintained some degree of flow through the duration of the project.

Field and Design Adjustments During Construction

Clearing of the vegetation and on-slope scaling activities revealed several previously unknown, broken and potentially unstable rock conditions upslope of the originally scoped project limits that required attention. These conditions included detached rock blocks within the overburden soils along the crown of the slope; a significant upper rock outcrop composed of differentially weathered shale and sandstone; and an isolated mass of loosely stacked rock blocks located more than 120 feet above the roadway. In response, Gannett Fleming engineering geologists worked closely with PennDOT District 5 Construction and Geotechnical Units and contractor personnel to evaluate the unforeseen conditions and develop a quick turn-around design addendum to remediate the unstable conditions under the current contract and within the construction schedule. The revised design included hollow-bar type soil nails and additional anchored wire mesh in the areas where detached rock masses were observed along the crown of the slope; a combination of anchored wire mesh and wire mesh drapery in the area where the differentially weathered rock outcrop was exposed; a 400-foot long GeoBrugg T35 type rockfall barrier system situated along the historic construction bench; and a custom-designed rock netting system (TECCO G65/4 mesh and cable lashing) for in-place stabilization of the isolated mass farther upslope. Scaling of the loose rock mass was not a feasible option due to the amount of material surrounding the mass and the height above the roadway.

In order to reach the additional soil nail and rock bolt locations greater than 70 feet above the roadway, Axis brought in a crane with a specialty designed flange to mount the TEI rock drill directly to the boom. Drilling operations within the isolated rock mass located more than 120 feet above the roadway is presented in Figure 12. The hybrid elevated rockfall barrier and drapery system is shown in Figure 13.

Figure 12 – Drilling Isolated Rock Mass Approximately 120 Feet Above Roadway

Figure 13 – Overview of Hybrid Elevated Rockfall Barrier and Drapery System. Additional Area of Anchored Mesh and Location of Upper Isolated Rock Mass also Shown.

Due to construction impacts on the traveling public and potential hazards associated with the onset of winter, the project was under a strict construction schedule. The contractor and subcontractors faced daily challenges associated with working on a very tall and potentially unstable slope, changing geologic and environmental conditions, and a compressed daily work window. Inclement weather interspersed throughout the timeline, including below freezing temperatures during the latter months of the project, resulted in less-than-ideal working conditions that hampered drilling and grouting efforts. Effectively managing these conditions was a major contributor to reaching the timely conclusion of the project.

CONCLUSIONS

Given the steep topography and limited access for detailed field investigation, Gannett Fleming was able to prepare an effective slope stabilization design package relying on limited site reconnaissance due to access constraints and heavy vegetation, photomosaic plans, DTM's developed from a digital photogrammetry survey, and previous rock slope stabilization design experience. Final stabilization design solutions including the combination of active slope reinforcement (pattern bolts) combined with passive protection measures (anchored wire mesh, rockfall barrier system and drapery) were dictated by the geological conditions, slope geometry, and public safety.

The construction team encountered several design and construction challenges associated with the ever-changing field conditions throughout the course of the rock slope stabilization project.

Meeting these challenges was facilitated through constant communication between PennDOT, Gannett Fleming, and the Contractors, along with detailed attention to the geologic conditions as construction progressed. Several factors contributed to the successful implementation of the stabilization elements:

1. Understanding the geologic and environmental dynamics influencing the rock slope movements.
2. Performing quick-turnaround analyses and providing an addendum to the original design to accommodate unforeseen slope conditions revealed following initial clearing and scaling activities.
3. Flexibility of the contractors to adapt construction methods to the irregular site conditions.
4. Experienced geotechnical engineers and engineering geologists familiar with the site conditions and objectives of the stabilization program on site providing direct oversight and quality control efforts.
5. Regular on-site presence of an experienced geotechnical engineer/engineering geologist to direct field adjustments (field-fitting) of the design to accommodate conditions revealed during construction.

To date, more than 2 years after completion of the stabilization work, the site appears to be performing well with no reports of rock debris on the road surface or obvious visual indicators of active movement.

REFERENCES

1. Lehigh Valley Railroad Historical Society, Lehigh Valley Railroad History, http://lvrrhs.org/history/index.htm, Accessed, May 2020.

2. Pennsylvania Highways website, U.S. Route 209 History. http://www.pahighways.com/us/US209.html, Accessed, May 2020.

3. Pennsylvania Department of Transportation (2017), 2016 Traffic Volume Map, Carbon County, Pennsylvania.

4. Dyson, J.L. (1967), Geology and mineral resources of the southern half of the New Bloomfield quadrangle, Pennsylvania: Pennsylvania Geological Survey 4th Ser., Atlas 137cd, 86 p.

5. Epstein, J.B., Sevon, W.D., and Glaesser, J.D. (1974), Geology and Mineral Resources of the Lehighton and Palmerton 7 1/2-minute Quadrangles, Pennsylvania: Pennsylvania Geological Survey 4th Ser., Atlas 195cd, 460 p.

6. Pennsylvania Department of Conservation and Natural Resources Web-Mapping Application and Resources. https://www.gis.dcnr.state.pa.us/geology/index.html

7. Weather History & Data Archive: Weather Underground." Weather Underground, www.wunderground.com/history/. Accessed, October 2017.

8. Wyllie, Duncan C. Christopher W. Mah, and Evert Hoek (2004), Rock Slope Engineering: Civil and Mining, 4th Edition, London: Spon Press

9. Federal Highway Administration (1998), Rock Slopes Reference Manual.

10. Post-Tensioning Institute, PTI DC35-14 (November 2014), Recommendations for Prestressed Rock and Soil Anchors.

Geophysical Applications for Highway Wall Design

Edward D. (Ned) Billington, PG
ESP Associates, Inc.
7011 Albert Pick Road, Suite E
Greensboro, NC 27409
Phone: 336-420-5452
nbillington@espassociates.com

C. Ryan Pastrana, GIT
ESP Associates, Inc.
7011 Albert Pick Road, Suite E
Greensboro, NC 27409
Phone: 919-215-5749
rpastrana@espassociates.com

Prepared for the 71st Highway Geology Symposium, May, 2022

Acknowledgements

The authors would like to thank the individuals/entities for their contributions in the work described:

Geotechnical Engineering Unit - North Carolina Department of Transportation, including Ms. Christina Bruinsma, PG and Mr. Kevin Miller, PG.
Paul M. Weaver, PG (reviewer) – ESP Associates, Inc.

Disclaimer

Statements and views presented in this paper are strictly those of the author(s), and do not necessarily reflect positions held by their affiliations, the Highway Geology Symposium (HGS), or others acknowledged above. The mention of trade names for commercial products does not imply the approval or endorsement by HGS.

ABSTRACT

Geophysical methods can provide valuable subsurface information for highway and bridge design or rehabilitation purposes. Example applications include approximate depth to rock, location and depth of voids and loose zones, and location of buried objects. This paper focuses on the use of seismic methods to help evaluate depth to rock for retaining wall and noise wall design.

Geophysical methods have been used for approximately 100 years to evaluate subsurface conditions, generally beginning with petroleum and mineral exploration. As geophysical equipment became smaller, more portable, and computationally more powerful, geophysical data collection and processing became more cost-effective, and began being used for near-surface, engineering applications. By the 1970s, various geophysical methods were available for engineering applications, including resistivity, seismic reflection, seismic refraction, gravity, and electromagnetic induction.

The North Carolina Department of Transportation maintains consultants under contract to provide subsurface information using intrusive and geophysical methods. One geophysical example is using seismic techniques to help evaluate depth to crystalline rock in areas of limited drill rig access. The subsurface velocity models derived from the seismic data can be correlated with intrusive data to determine the best-fit velocity to represent depth to rock. The depth-to-rock models can be used for design purposes and to make decisions on additional investigations, as needed.

INTRODUCTION

Depth to crystalline rock is an important factor when designing retaining walls in the Piedmont and Mountains of North Carolina. The North Carolina Department of Transportation (NCDOT) typically performs standard penetration testing (SPT) drilling and rock coring to determine the top of crystalline rock. Borings are generally required every 50 feet for retaining walls and every 100 feet for sound walls, and are drilled to twice the height of the wall for retaining walls and the height of the wall for sound walls (*1*).

In areas of limited drill rig access, the NCDOT can employ one of their consultants to collect geophysical data to provide data on depth to rock. Seismic refraction is performed as an alternative to drilling in areas of the foothills and mountains where the slopes are too steep to cost-effectively set up a drill rig. Seismic refraction and/or surface wave seismic also may be performed in lieu of drilling to limit lane closure time.

Seismic Theory

An impact or explosion on or in the earth generates body waves and surface waves (Figure 1). Body waves consist of compressional (P) waves that travel in a push-pull motion in the direction of propagation and shear (S) waves that have a transverse (side-to-side) motion relative to the direction of travel. Generally, P-waves have a higher velocity than S-waves. Surface waves are slower than body waves and travel coupled to the ground surface,

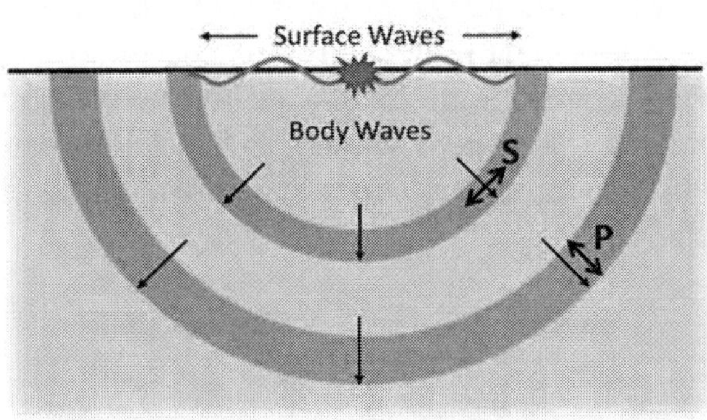

Figure 1 – Body Wave and Surface Wave Seismic Propagation.

Seismic Refraction

Seismic refraction is based on the principal of Snell's Law, where an acoustic raypath changes angle when passing through a boundary between layers of differing acoustic velocities. The relationship between the incident angle of the raypath and the refracted angle is given by:

$$\frac{\sin\theta_1}{V_1} = \frac{sin\theta_2}{V_2}.$$

As body wave energy encounters an interface between two earth materials with different velocities, some energy will be reflected up and the remainder will be transmitted (refracted) down into the underlying material (Figure 2). At a critical incident angle, the refraction angle will be 90 degrees and the raypath will travel along the velocity interface as a head wave with the velocity of the lower layer.

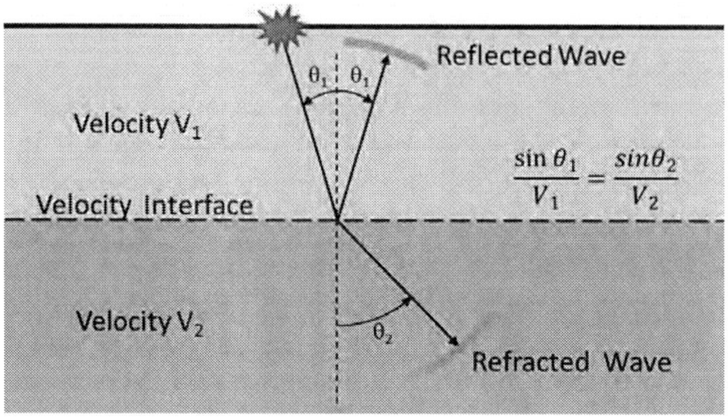

Figure 2 - Body wave reflection and refraction at velocity interface.

Assuming a series of "layers" with velocity increasing with depth, at some distance from the source, the refracted body wave energy traveling at the higher velocity will overtake the direct arrival through the surficial layer (Figure 3). Likewise, for successively deeper and faster layers, the refracted energy traveling through the deeper layer will arrive sooner than the refracted energy from the shallower and slower layer. The refraction method only considers the first arrivals of energy at each station (or geophone). Changes in soil and rock types, erosional surfaces, voids, and man-made objects can refract body wave energy.

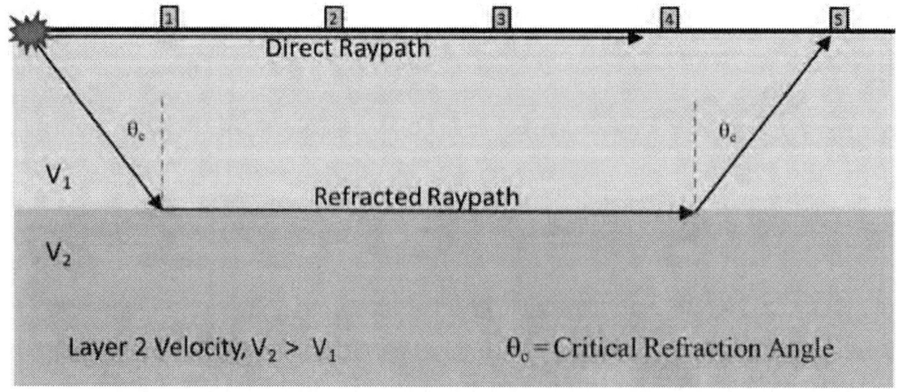

Figure 3 – Principle of Refraction where the Refracted Raypath Arrives at Geophone No. 5 Earlier than the Slower Direct Arrival.

Surface Wave Seismic

Surface waves are slower than P or S-waves and travel coupled to the ground surface, analogous to ripples on a pond. The devastating "ground roll" experienced in earthquakes is composed of surface wave energy. Surface waves typically have higher energy than P or S waves. In engineering geophysics, the retrograde elliptical Raleigh wave is the form of surface wave most often used and discussed, although Love waves have some application (*2, e.g.*). The Raleigh wave velocity is approximately 92 percent of the shear wave velocity (*3*). Given certain assumptions or other constraining data, the shear wave velocity can be derived from surface wave seismic data.

The dispersive property of Raleigh waves is what makes them useful for geophysical studies. Higher frequency components of the Raleigh wave have shorter wavelengths and travel through less of the subsurface while remaining coupled to the ground surface (Figure 4). Lower frequency components have longer wavelengths and travel through a thicker volume of the subsurface. Given that velocity changes with depth, it follows that the different frequency components of the surface wave will travel at different velocities. By separating out different frequency components and identifying their velocities, we can model the shear wave velocity of the subsurface.

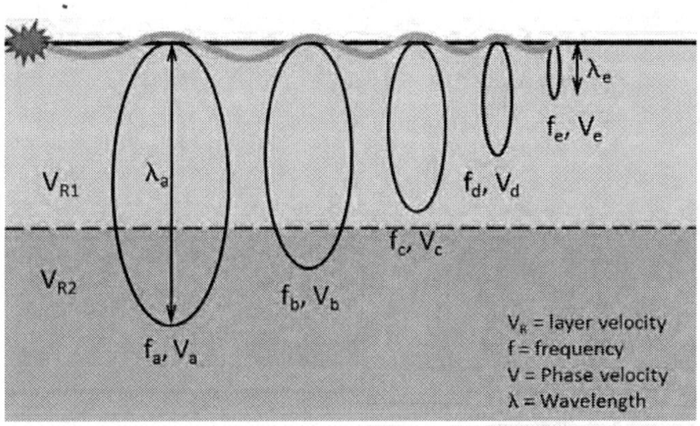

Figure 4 – Dispersive Nature of Surface Waves

Seismic Data Acquisition

The basic seismic data acquisition system consists of an explosive or weight drop energy source, a seismograph, a trigger to signal the seismograph to start recording, and a series of geophones (or hydrophones) connected to the seismograph to record the ground motion at different distances from the source. The energy source, number of channels, recording parameters, and type of geophones differ according to the type of seismic study and objectives.

Seismic Refraction

Initially developed during World War I by Ludger Mintrop to locate enemy gun emplacements, the portable seismic refraction method (using an artificial energy source) was introduced to the oil exploration industry in the early 1920s in Mexico and the United States, and primarily was used for locating salt domes (*4*). The refraction method gradually was adopted by the engineering field for exploration of bedrock and for groundwater studies (Figure 5). By the 1970's, the development of small, portable seismographs led to widespread use of the refraction method (*5*).

Figure 5 – An Early Single-channel Digital Seismograph (ES-125), Circa 1978 (Courtesy Geometrics)

Seismic refraction data is collected using a linear array of vertical geophones connected to an engineering seismograph to record first arrivals (first breaks) of compressional wave energy from a weight drop or explosive source. (Although not as common, shear wave refraction can also be performed using horizontal geophones and a shear wave energy source.) A typical data acquisition system consists of 24 geophones (8 to 12 Hz response) spaced at intervals of 5 or 10 feet with a total array (spread) length of 115 or 230 feet (Figure 6). The geophones are connected to a geophone cable that is connected to an engineering seismograph. Energy sources range from sledgehammers for shorter arrays and shallower depths to explosive sources for longer arrays and deeper depths.

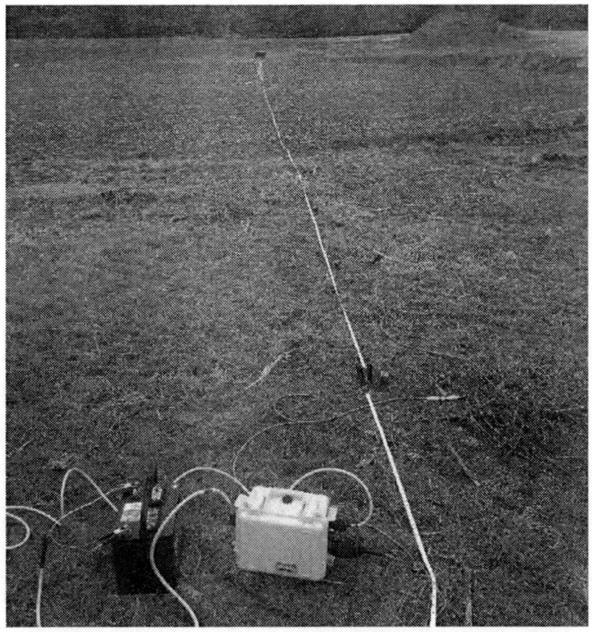

Figure 6 – 24-Channel Seismograph (Geometrics Geode, yellow case) with 8Hz Geophones Spaced 5 Feet Apart, 2014.

A key to recording quality seismic refraction data is obtaining good signal-to-noise ratio. Traffic noise is detrimental and data often has to be recorded when traffic is stopped or not passing by the spread. Geophones placed in loose material such as leaf litter or gravel will not be well coupled to the ground surface and the signal-to-noise ratio will be low. Noise can mask the first arrivals of energy, reducing the confidence of the selected first arrival time or causing the arrival times for certain traces (individual geophone time-series responses) to be skipped. Redundant data collected with multiple source locations (shot points) can reduce the effect of skipped traces or poorly picked first arrivals. The number of shot points for a single spread can range from 5 to 11, for example. The more lateral subsurface variation that is expected, the more shot points should be recorded.

Seismic refraction processing steps include frequency filtering to reduce the effect of unwanted noise, selection of first arrivals for each trace, entering array geometry and relative or absolute elevations, if needed, and modeling the subsurface compressional wave velocity. A simple two-layer model may suffice for discrete subsurface layers, such as alluvium over scoured bedrock, whereas tomographic modeling can be more appropriate for weathered bedrock terrains. While there are some references for equating compressional wave velocity to maximum depth of rippability (*6, e.g.*), a more reliable correlation may be obtained by using on-site boring data and test pits.

Refraction data can be collected on soil and asphalt surfaces but is not recommended for concrete pavement, due to the stiffness and high velocity of the concrete. Dry conditions are preferred for refraction studies, as most geophones are not weatherproof and raindrops striking geophones will cause noise in the data. Seismic refraction also can be performed underwater using a hydrophone cable.

Surface Wave Seismic

Surface wave seismic data often are used to develop one-dimensional (1D) shear wave velocity (Vs) profiles for seismic site class designation (Vs30, meters or Vs100, feet). Multiple 1D models generated from a series of array locations can be combined and presented as a 2D cross-section of shear wave velocity. Since shear wave velocity is a direct indication of the stiffness of subsurface materials, 2D models are valuable in estimating the depth to rock and delineating loose or stiff zones in the subsurface.

Surface wave seismic data can be collected in the passive method using ambient noise or in the active method using a controlled energy source. Typically, the passive method provides surface wave data in a lower frequency range (2 to 10 Hz, e.g.), while the active method generates energy with a higher frequency range. Since a broad range of frequencies can provide a more detailed Vs model, active and passive data can be combined to develop a shear wave velocity model.

Surface wave seismic data can be collected using the same equipment as is used for seismic refraction. Vertical low-frequency geophones are connected to an engineering seismograph that is triggered manually (for the passive method) or by the impact of a weight drop source on a hard surface (active method). Two-second recording lengths will suffice for the active method, while longer records of 30 seconds, for example, are needed for the passive method. A land streamer can be used on asphalt roadways, compacted soil, and closely mowed grass for cost-effective 2D production.

Processing steps for surface wave seismic data include assigning geometry of geophone locations and source location, converting the time series data to the frequency domain, selecting the dispersion curve from a frequency-velocity plot, and generating a Vs model to match the observed dispersion curve (Figure 7).

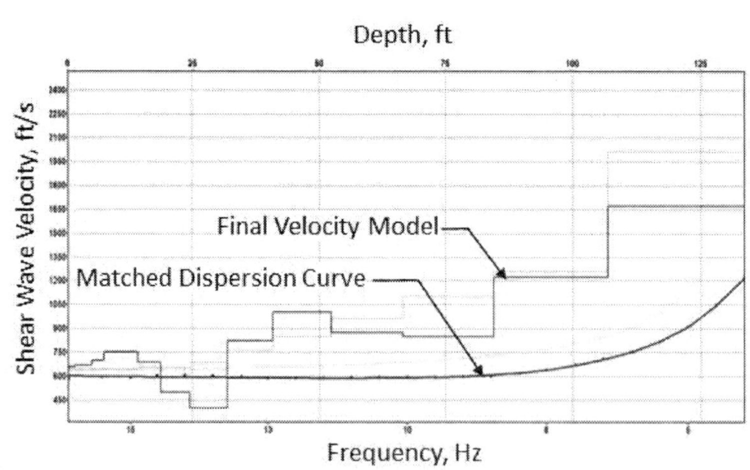

Figure 7 – Example Compressional Wave Velocity Model from Surface Wave Data.

CASE STUDY 1 – SEISMIC REFRACTION FOR PROPOSED RETAINING WALL

The NCDOT contacted ESP in early 2020 to provide subsurface information on depth to rock along a planned retaining wall location in Ashe County, NC as part of a roadway realignment and bridge replacement project. Borings had been drilled by the NCDOT along the existing roadway but as these were approximately 30 to 40 feet upslope from the planned retaining wall, they probably did not represent the subsurface conditions along the planned wall location. The existing slope was too steep for standard drilling rig access.

Data Collection

ESP collected compressional wave seismic refraction data on 6 lines: Line 1 was located along-slope following the planned retaining wall alignment and 5 lines were oriented downslope starting at the edge of existing pavement (Figure 8). The downslope lines started at or near existing borings for correlation. The refraction data were collected using a 24-channel Geode seismograph, 8 Hz geophones, and a sledgehammer/plate source (Figure 9). Four 115-foot long arrays using 24 geophones were employed for Line 1. Due to the short length of the slope, only 9 to 10 geophones were able to be used for the slope lines with array lengths of 40 to 45 feet. Wooden stakes were placed at 50-foot intervals along Line 1, and at the top, bottom, and significant slope changes on Lines 2, 3, 4, 5, and 6. The steepness of the slope required geophysical personnel to wear safety harnesses and utilize climbing ropes so they could stand safely on the slope.

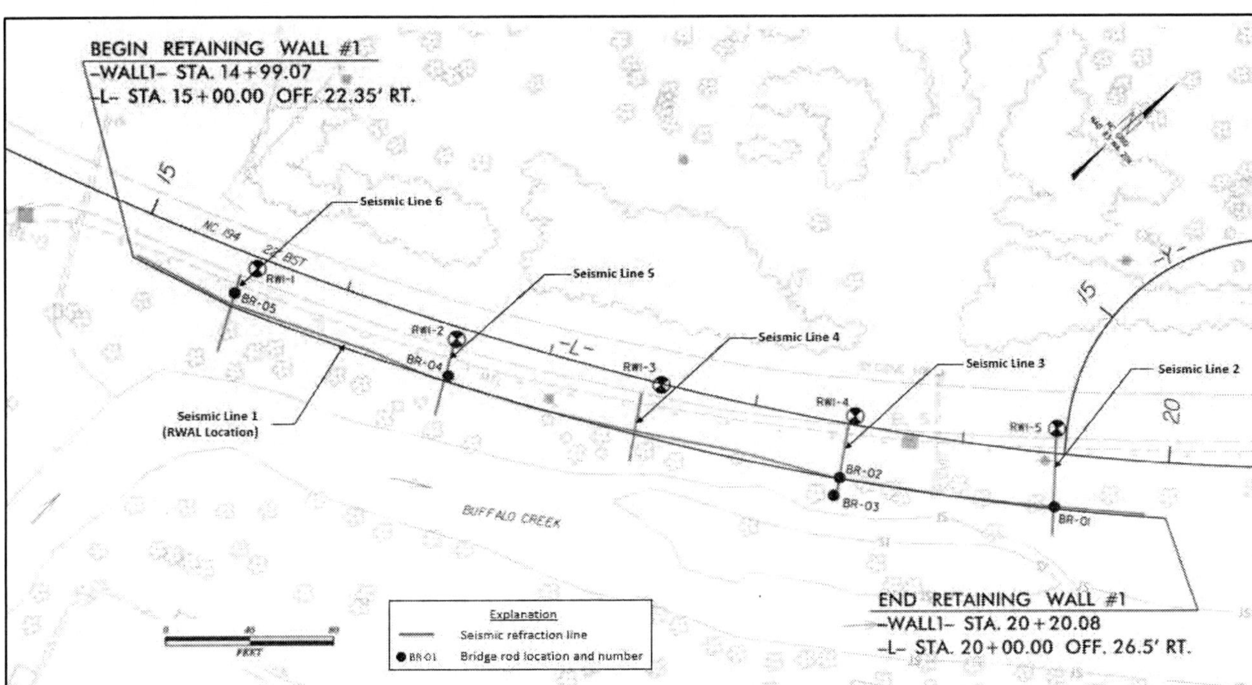

Figure 8 – Plan Map of Proposed Retaining Wall, Borings, and Seismic Lines.

Figure 9 – Photographs of Setting Up Array for Downslope Line (L) and Swinging Sledgehammer Source (R).

In addition to collecting the seismic data, we drove "bridge rods" at the intersections of Line 1 with Lines 2, 3, 5, and 6. The bridge rods consisted of driving 5-foot long, half-inch steel rods with a 16-pound slide hammer approximately vertically down into the ground until refusal. Couplers were used when more than one rod was needed. Notes were recorded as to the relative density of the materials that were driven through with the rods and the depth of refusal. Wooden stakes were placed to mark the location of the rod drives. The locations and elevations of the wooden stakes placed to mark the seismic line locations, rod drives, and existing borings were located utilizing conventional survey equipment.

Data Analysis

The seismic data were processed using the program SeisImager®, specifically, the modules Pickwin®, for picking first breaks, and Plotrefa®, for developing the tomographic velocity models (*7*). The processing steps consisted of assigning geometry, picking the first breaks, creating an elevation model from the survey point data, developing an initial model using the time-term inversion method, then performing a tomographic inversion to develop a compressional wave velocity model for each line. The velocities are presented in feet per second (ft/s).

The velocity models were correlated with the rod drives to assess the approximate depth to weathered rock and to crystalline rock. Based on this evaluation, we made the following generalized definitions.

Table 1 – Approximate Velocity-Material Relationships

Compressional Wave Velocity (ft/s)	*Corresponding Material Type*
Less than 3500	Fill and Residual Soil
3500 to 7500	Weathered Rock, WR
7500 or more	Crystalline Rock, CR

Discussion

The velocity model for Line 1 indicates that the depth to weathered rock is approximately 20 feet from STA 15+00 to 17+00 (Figure 11). After STA 17+00, the depth to weathered rock decreases to 10 feet or less. At rod drive BR-01 on the alluvial bench, the material was soft until almost refusal at 4.7 feet below ground surface (bgs). Based on the seismic velocities, it appears that BR-01 refused on crystalline rock, so there appears to be little to no weathered rock in the vicinity of BR-01; this would be expected for an alluvial stream bank where the stream had previously scoured down to crystalline rock.

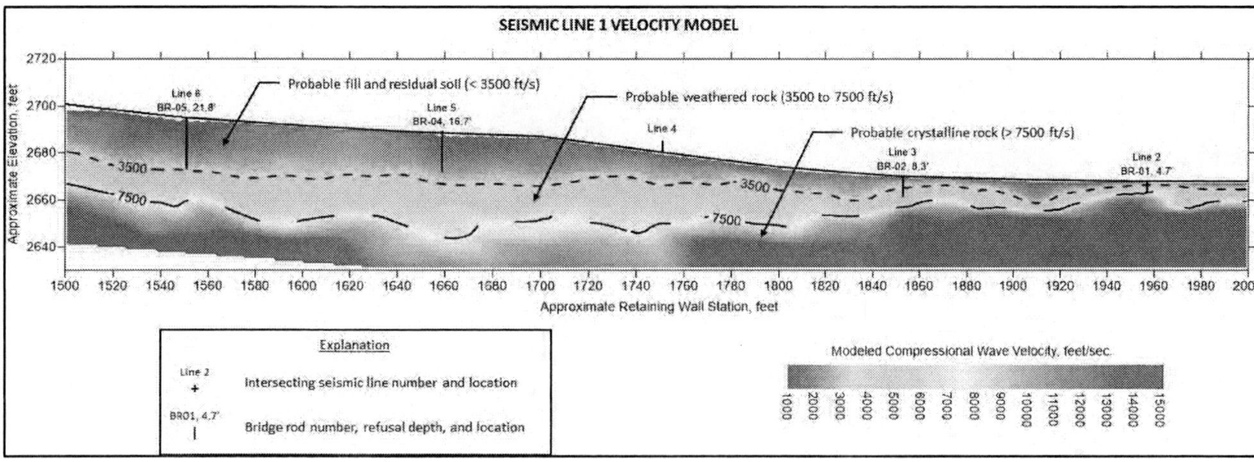

Figure 11 – Compressional-wave Velocity Model for Line 1, Along Slope

Due to the limited slope distance from the guard rail to the creek, the length of the arrays for Lines 2 through 6 were too short to obtain sufficient refracted arrivals from crystalline rock, resulting in velocity models that probably do not represent the true velocity structure of the subsurface (Figure 12). Although there is not a satisfactory match between the velocity model for Line 1 and the models for Lines 2 through 6 where they intersect, the models for Lines 2 through 6 do indicate that the depth to weathered rock decreases from STA 15+00 to STA 20+00, supporting the interpretation of Line 1, and they show a reasonable correlation with the adjacent soil test borings.

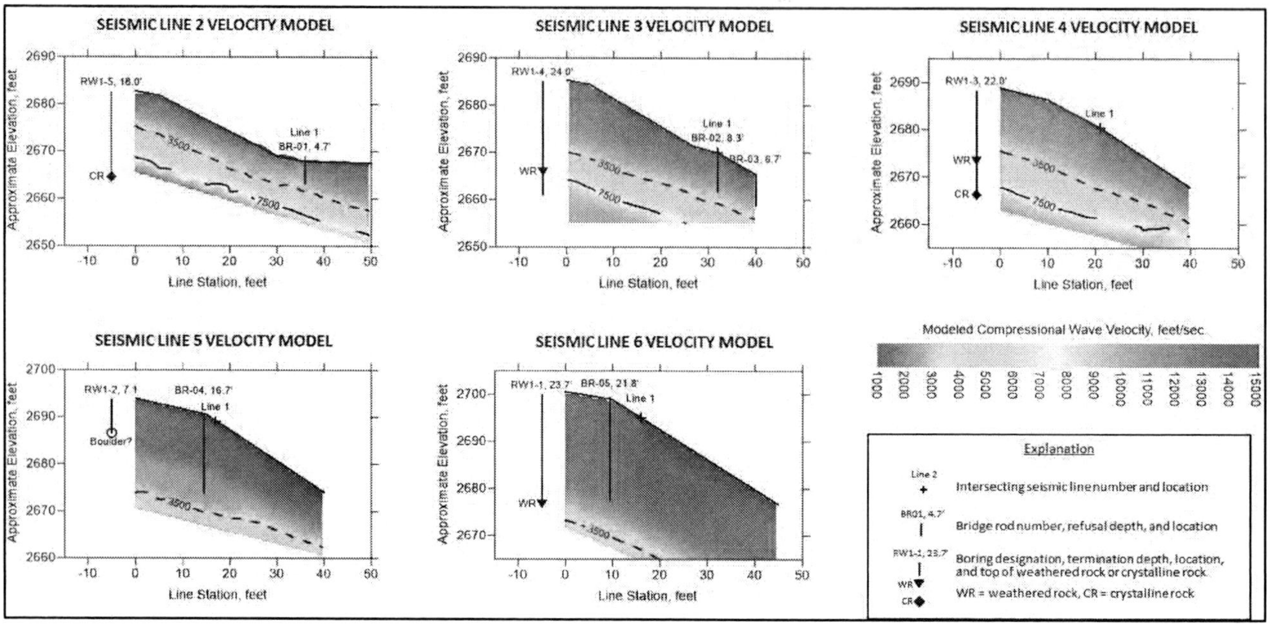

Figure 12 - Compressional-wave Velocity Models for Down-Slope Lines

CASE STUDY 2 – SURFACE WAVE SEISMIC FOR PROPOSED SOUND WALLS

In 2013, the NCDOT was planning the addition of High-Occupancy Toll (HOT) lanes to I-77 north of Charlotte. As part of the design, noise barrier walls were proposed for some sections, including in and adjacent to the rock embankment causeways in the Lake Norman area (Figure 13). The NCDOT requested that ESP collect geophysical data to help determine the approximate subsurface extent of the buried rock embankments in 5 sections, ranging from 200 feet to 400 feet in length. ESP recommended collecting surface wave seismic data to try to image the buried rock. It was expected that the shear wave velocity of the buried rock would be higher than the surrounding residual soil and roadway fill.

Figure 13 – Section of Noise Barrier Wall Constructed along I-77 by Lake Norman.

Surface Wave Seismic Data Collection

The data were collected during night-time hours along the paved shoulder of the south-bound lanes (west side) of I-77. The NCDOT provided traffic control by closing the right south-bound lane of each work area and providing a crash truck that followed us while we collected data. Data collection had to be paused while tractor-trailers were passing due to noise interference.

The seismic data were collected using a 24-channel towed seismic array (land streamer) with a geophone spacing of 2 feet for a total array length of 46 feet (Figure 14). The energy source (20-pound sledgehammer striking the asphalt surface) was located 20 feet from the nearest geophone. The land streamer was moved 20 feet at a time with data collected at each land streamer location. The data were recorded using a laptop-controlled Geometrics 24-channel Geode seismograph.

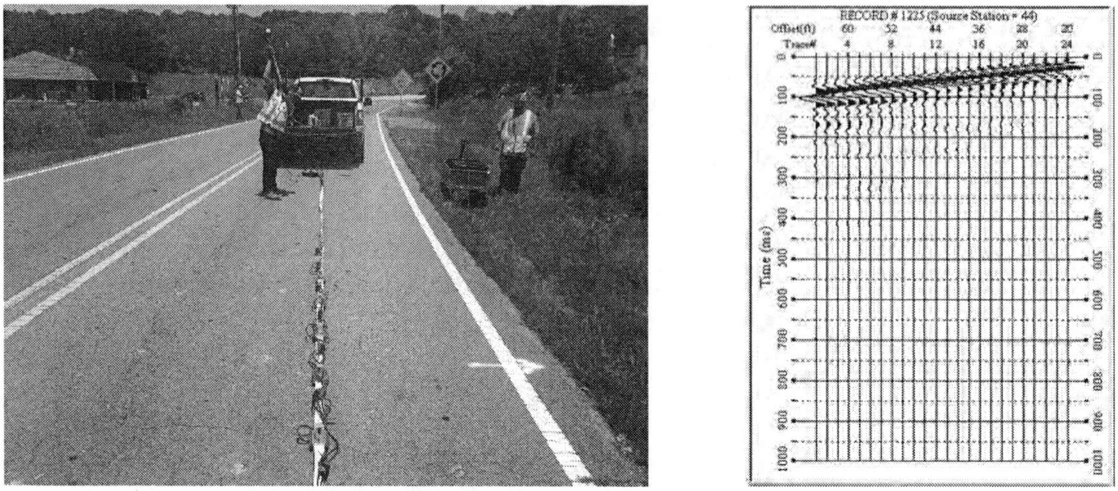

Figure 14 – Photograph of Seismic Landstreamer (from similar project) (L) and Example Seismic Record Showing Surface Wave Energy from this Project (R).

Data Analysis

The surface wave seismic data were collected and processed using the Multi-channel Analysis of Surface Waves (MASW) method. The data were recorded digitally as time-distance waveforms and then processed using the program SurfSeis, developed by the Kansas Geological Survey (*8*). The SurfSeis program converts the time-series seismic data into frequency/phase velocity, allowing the user to select the dispersion curve representing the fundamental mode of the surface wave energy (Figure 15). The program performs an inversion to create a layered earth model of the shear wave velocity that matches the observed dispersion curve in a least-squares sense.

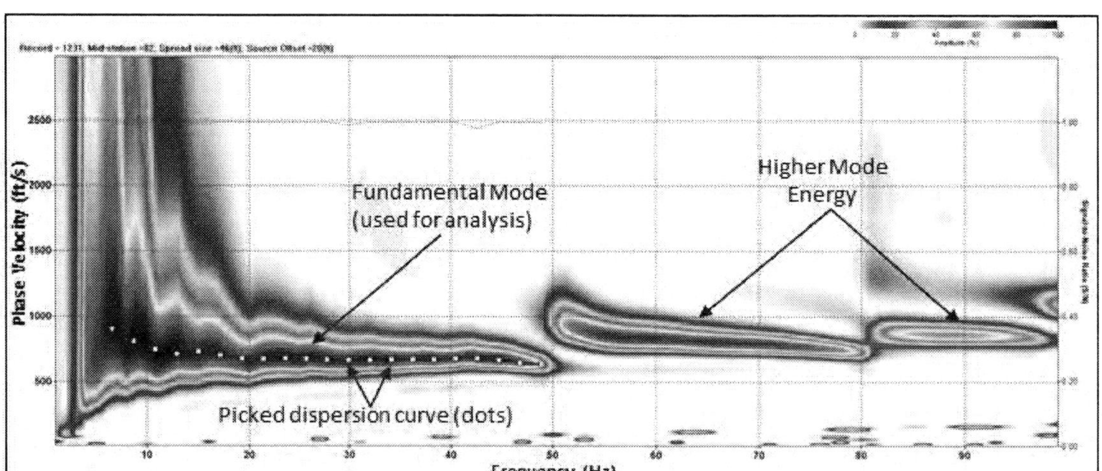

Figure 15 – Example Dispersion Curve with Fundamental Mode used for Analysis.

The MASW analysis produced a single 1D shear wave velocity model for each position of the 46-foot-long geophone array (Figure 16, e.g.). Each 1D velocity model is an average of the subsurface velocities over the length of the array position and is plotted at the center of the array position. The 1D models were combined to form a 2D model of the subsurface shear wave velocity for each line. The model data were gridded using the Kriging method in the program Surfer® and color contour plots were made of the gridded data.

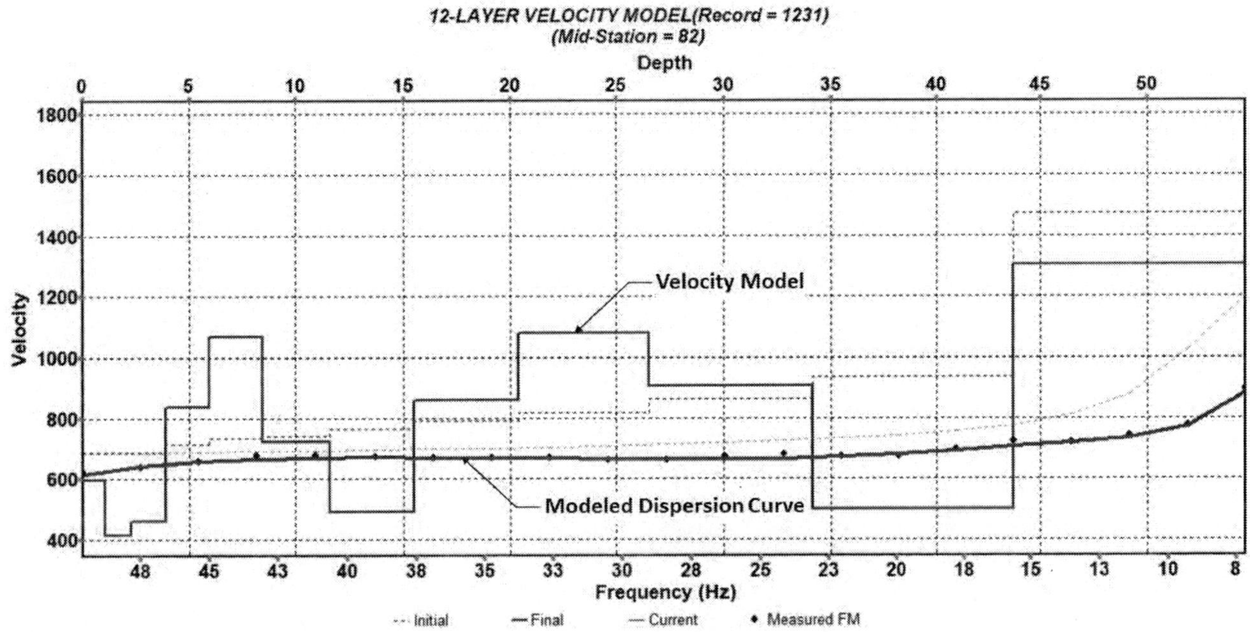

Figure 16 – Example 1D Velocity Model Showing Dispersion Curve Fit (7% RMS)

The 2D models showed a semi-continuous shallow high-velocity layer suspended in a lower velocity matrix. The models were compared to the 1996 construction drawings to help interpret the results.

Review of 1966 Roadway Construction Drawings

Our review of the 1966 roadway construction sheets indicates that three of the sections of I-77 where the MASW data were collected (Lines 1, 2, and 3) were constructed on the existing highway US-21. Comparison of culvert locations on the 1966 plans with their locations on the noise wall plans provided a conversion from the 2013 stationing to the 1966 stations, allowing a comparison of the MASW velocity models with the 1966 construction drawings.

The 1966 drawings indicate that the remaining 2 MASW lines (Lines 4 and 5) were located on new highway construction. Notes on the 1966 sheets state that "Embankment thru lake to be constructed with rock fill up to Elev. 962.0'." The station location of the intersection of elevation 962.0 feet with the existing contour was identified from the profiles and annotated on the relevant portion of the 1966 plans; this provides the approximate lateral extent of the rock fill for comparison with the shear wave velocity models for these two lines.

Example 2D MASW Models

Example MASW models are discussed for both situations: I-77 constructed over existing highway US-21 and I-77 constructed as new highway embankment.

MASW Line 2

The model for Line 2 shows a shallow relatively higher velocity layer with the depth to the top of the layer ranging from about 5 feet in the south half of the model to about 8 feet in the north half of the model (Figure 17). This layer may represent the influence of the higher velocity riprap located beneath the line location. The shallow, high velocity layers may also be caused by pavement and/or dense roadbed material from the pre-existing highway US-21.

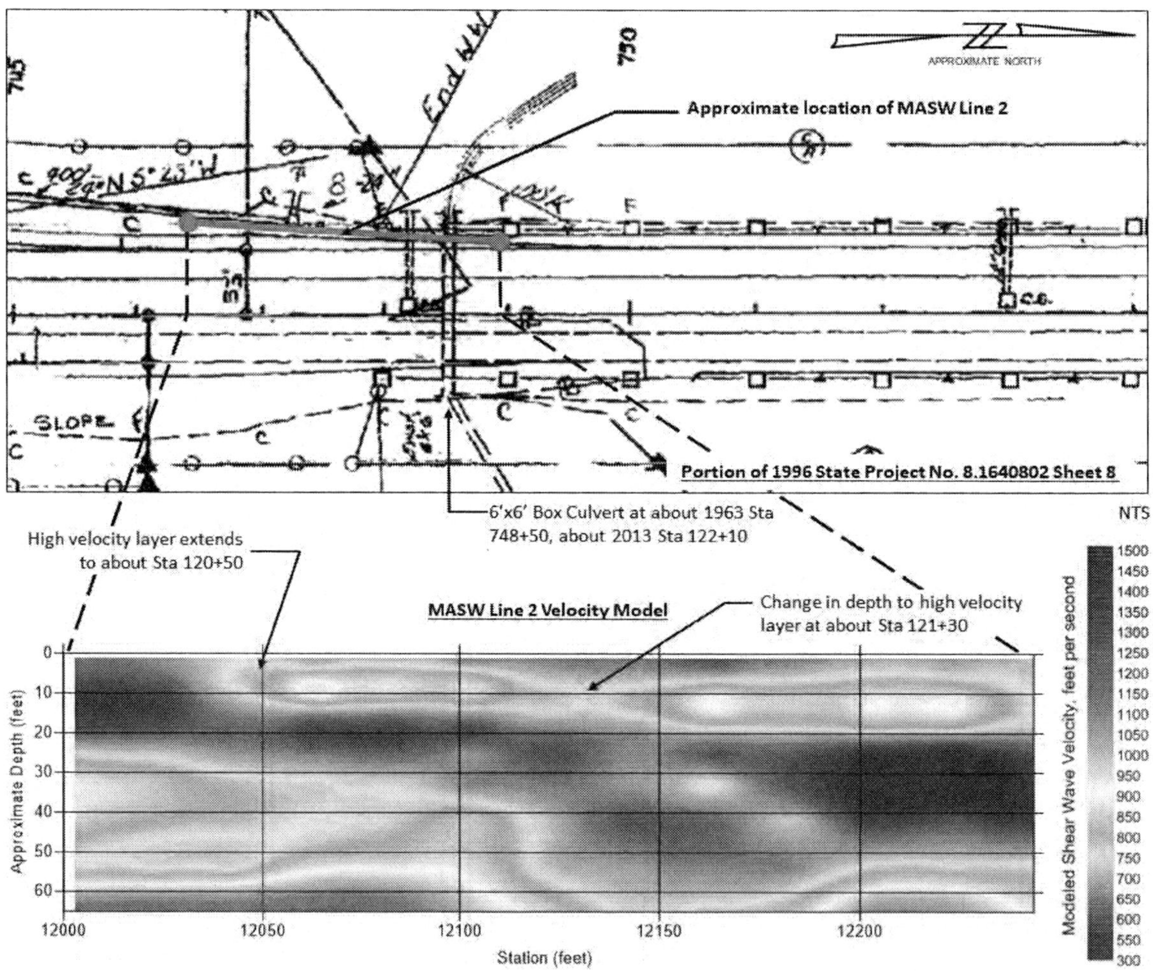

Figure 17 – MASW Line 2 Velocity Model Showing Shallow High Velocity Layer (Bottom) with Line Location Shown on 1966 Plan (Top).

MASW Line 4

The model for this line shows a shallow, relatively higher velocity layer about 8 to 10 feet below surface extending from the north end of the model to about Station 338+15 (Figure 18). It is likely that this represents the approximate lateral extent of the rock fill layer. Correlation with the 1966 drawing indicates that the rock fill would have terminated at about Station 338+00. The velocity model also shows a deeper higher velocity zone that probably represents weathered rock; the depth to this ranges from about 25 feet at the south end of the model to about 55 feet at Station 338+00 and beyond.

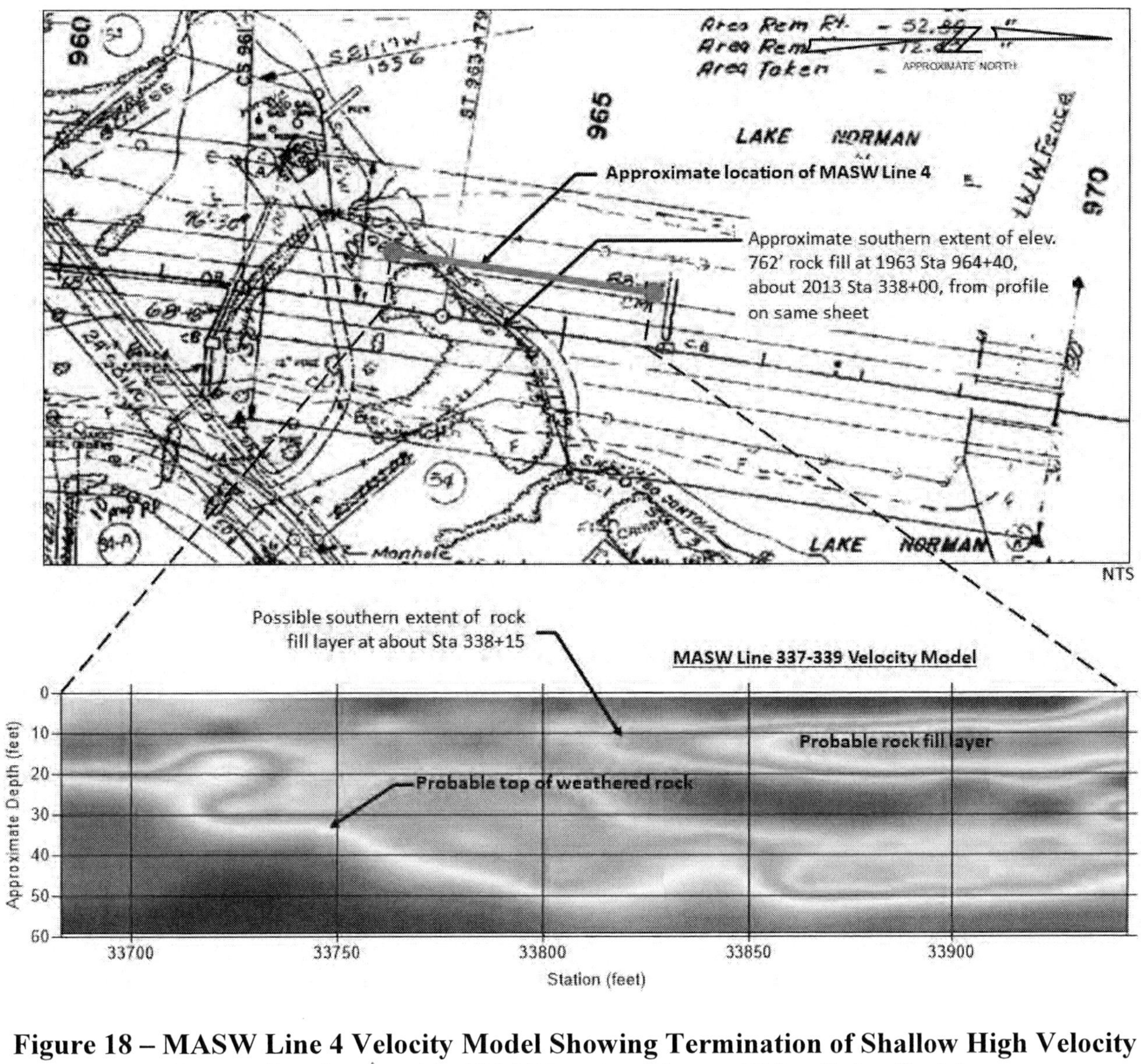

Figure 18 – MASW Line 4 Velocity Model Showing Termination of Shallow High Velocity Layer Consistent with 1966 Plan (see Figure 17 for Color Scale).

Conclusions

The example MASW model for the 1966 I-77 new construction area, Line 4, shows what appears to be the rock fill layer at a depth of about 8 to 10 feet below ground surface with the rock fill layer terminating at about Station 338+15, close to the expected termination of the rock fill based on the 1966 drawing.

The example MASW model for the 1966 I-77 construction on the existing US-21 roadway areas, Line 2, shows a shallow, relatively higher velocity layer with depths ranging from just below the ground surface to approximately 5 feet. This layer is generally thinner and lower velocity than the layer representing the rock fill on Line 4. Our interpretation of the shallow, higher velocity layer on Line 2 is that it represents a relatively thinner layer of riprap protection, or that it represents pre-existing pavement and/or compacted roadbed material from the original US-21 construction.

Based on the projected depths of the new wall construction, it is possible that the shallow, buried rock zones will interfere with the design and/or construction of the planned noise walls in some locations.

SUMMARY

The continued increase in geophysical data acquisition quality and computational inversion capability has improved the accuracy and cost-effectiveness of geophysical methods. The two case studies presented in this paper show the successful application of seismic refraction and surface wave seismic for the design of walls for new highway construction.

The combined interpretation of intrusive data and geophysical data is stronger and more reliable than either method used alone. The interpretation of geophysical data is partially dependent on constraining data such as that derived from borings, bridge rods, outcrops, and original design plans. For NCDOT projects, the interpretation of boring data often assumes consistent subsurface conditions over distances of up to 100 feet between borings. Geophysical data can be used to fill those "gaps" between borings.

REFERENCES

1. North Carolina Department of Transportation (NCDOT). *Geotechnical Investigation and Recommendations Manual,* NCDOT Geotechnical Engineering Unit, 2021.

2. Ivanov, J., R. D. Miller, D. Feigenbaum, S. L. C. Morton, S. L. Peterie, and J. B. Dunbar. *Revisiting levees in southern Texas using Love-wave multichannel analysis of surface waves with the high-resolution linear Radon transform*: Interpretation, vol. 5 (3), 2017, ppT287-T298.

3. Telford, W. M., L. P. Geldart, R. E. Sheriff, and D. A. Keys. *Applied Geophysics*, Cambridge University Press, New York, 1976.

4. Keppner, Gerhard. *Ludger Mintrop*, The Leading Edge, vol. 10 (9), 1991, pp. 21–28.

5. Green, Ronald. *The Seismic Refraction Method – A Review*, Geoexploration, vol. 12, 1974, pp. 259-284.

6. Caterpillar Inc. *Handbook of Ripping*, 12th Edition, Peoria, IL, 2000.

7. Geometrics. *SeisImager/2D*, Geometrics, San Jose, CA, 2018, Accessed March 7, 2022.

8. Kansas Geologic Survey. *Surfseis MASW Software*, The University of Kansas, Lawrence, KS, 2022, Accessed March 7, 2022.

GUARD - making flexible geohazard protection systems SMART

Tim Shevlin, R.G.
Geobrugg North America LLC
Salem, OR 97302, United States of America
+1 503 423 7258
tim.shevlin@geobrugg.com

Helene Lanter
Geobrugg Switzerland
Aachstrasse 11
Romanshorn, 8590
+41 71 466 81 81
helene.lanter@geobrugg.com

Prepared for the 71st Highway Geology Symposium, May, 2022

Disclaimer

Copyright Notice

ABSTRACT

Flexible steel protection systems against natural hazards are often difficult to access due to installation in hazardous zones, and thus inherently become difficult to monitor and maintain. Many small-scale events, such as rockfalls below the service energy limit (SEL) defined by the EAD 340059-00-0106 or debris flows under the maximum impact pressure of the net, according to EAD 340020-00-0106, can easily go unnoticed. However, the repetition of several small events into a protection system still requires regular maintenance to provide full performance in case of a maximum design event occuring. Furthermore, experience has shown that corrosion can vary greatly in small, localised areas and lead to unanticipated degradation.

A newly developed Internet of Things (IoT) device, called GUARD, has been developed aiming to provide real-time monitoring of flexible steel protection systems, allowing the concept of predictive maintenance. The second goal of the device is to move beyond repair and maintenance to the concept of predictive maintenance by evaluating local corrosivity and the associated lifetime of the protection system with a specially developed corrosion sensor. GUARD devices have been deployed recently in Europe and at six sites in North America and have been in operation since summer 2021. This paper aims to highlight monitoring with the GUARD system and the inspection concept that can be developed using it, with examples of the data collected so far in Europe and North America.

INTRODUCTION

There is an increased need for real-time information to know the immediate status or condition of things, some of which was previously difficult to obtain, but essential. This status condition information consists of data on the current use, aging, or environmental conditions of the object, and is intended to improve usability, such as early recognition of the need for maintenance or the replacement of components. The Internet of things (IoT) describes physical objects (or groups of such objects) with sensors, processing ability, software, and other technologies that connect and exchange data with other devices and systems over the Internet or other communications networks [1]. This paper aims to illustrate the purpose of IoT in the field of infrastructure protection against natural hazards by means of flexible protection solutions.

Flexible geohazard protection solutions represent the object for which it is necessary to generate status information. Until now, the condition of a flexible protection system has been determined by periodic inspections, sometimes laborious or dangerous manual work. Further, it is often the case that certain protective measures were also forgotten over time, resulting in a renewed threat to the transport infrastructure when the protective solution is not maintained. One status condition information that is of primary interest is the "filling condition" of a protection solution. Can it still provide the necessary protection if it is two-thirds full? Another condition of primary interest is the status of the protection system's aging process. Specifically, corrosion attacks the steel, and the system strength and function can decrease over time.

By using IoT technology, when this condition information is collected, maintenance work can be planned more efficiently, and it is less necessary to move into a dangerous hazard area for the purpose of periodic examinations. In addition, the aging process can be monitored and replacement of a protection solution after several decades, can be planned into the maintenance budget at an early stage.

Problem Definition

One aspect of transportation infrastructure is monitoring its condition, ideally in real-time to carry out or plan targeted maintenance. Protection against natural hazards is an important aspect that significantly influences the operation and maintenance of infrastructure. There are various protective solutions to stop natural hazards, for example flexible protective fences made of steel mesh. In the last 30 years these flexible steel rockfall and debris flow barriers have become more established worldwide as a protective solution.

Protective structures are often built-in hazardous zones, which coincide with the mountains or along coastal zones. The systems are usually located in steep and rough terrain, they are difficult to reach, and visual monitoring is often not possible. Due to access issues the inventory and maintenance of such protection systems has been neglected in many places. Some of these solutions have also been forgotten, mostly hidden by growing vegetation. However, this poses a considerable danger if, for example, a rockfall fence slowly fills up and is not cleared, if the largest possible rockfall, for which the fence was designed should then occur, the energy absorption capacity is not guaranteed.

Another scenario outside of impacts from falling rocks or a debris flow is the slow degradation of the corrosion protection exposed to the environment. Different corrosion classes are standardised and help estimate expected service life. Depending on the location and local conditions (i.e., frequent scattering of salt on the road, coastal environments), the corrosion class can be over- or underestimated, leading to over-dimensioning of the protection solution or, on the other hand, to early maintenance measures or even replacement of a protection solution that was not yet included in budget planning.

Maintenance is also event and location dependent. In practice, those responsible usually define intervals for the on-site inspection of barriers. This can mean one to several times a year. But even with frequent checks, an event can remain undetected for a long time. If a major rockfall occurs and is undetected the protective capacity of the system may be reduced, or if there is unexpected corrosion of certain system elements. Both situations subsequently lead to an unnecessary safety risk.

In order to better document inventories of flexible protection solutions, monitor them in real time, and plan maintenance work in advance, a multi-functional IoT sensor called GUARD has been developed. This paper aims to illustrate the purpose of IoT in the field of infrastructure protection against natural hazards.

IoT DEVICE GEOBRUGG GUARD

An IoT device, the GUARD, has been developed that measures the environmental conditions; (i.e., humidity, temperature, corrosion process, as well as dynamic and quasi-static load) by means of acceleration sensor and force measurement in the barrier systems' support ropes (Figure 1).

The Internet of things (IoT) describes physical objects (or groups of such objects) with sensors, processing ability, software, and other technologies that connect and exchange data with other devices and systems over the Internet or other communications networks [1]. It must be possible to retrieve the information on the physical device by means of radio frequency identification (RFID) or a quick response (QR) code. This is the case with the GUARD device, in that RFID makes it possible to upload updates to the device, as well as a QR code, which makes it possible to directly record all relevant information about the object (flexible barrier) during installation, and most importantly download status condition information during service. All these elements are accessed in a data portal via a web app.

The requirements to achieve the above are relatively high; the hardware must be reliable, have a low maintenance effort (since a high failure rate requires maintenance work on many devices that are sometimes far apart or difficult to reach), and have low energy consumption. Finally, the acquisition costs should be relatively low, since as many physical locations as possible need to be equipped. The developed GUARD fulfils all these requirements. It has a low energy consumption, the measured data are sent at least weekly or immediately in case of large dynamic events, and the device is equipped with a battery that has a life span of about 7 to 10 years, depending on where it is exposed (warm/cold, good/bad network connection). The data collected from the GUARD is transmitted via the mobile network (GSM/UMTS/LTE) and displayed in a login-protected data portal. There, the transmitted data can be evaluated and interpreted, and a warning process can be defined.

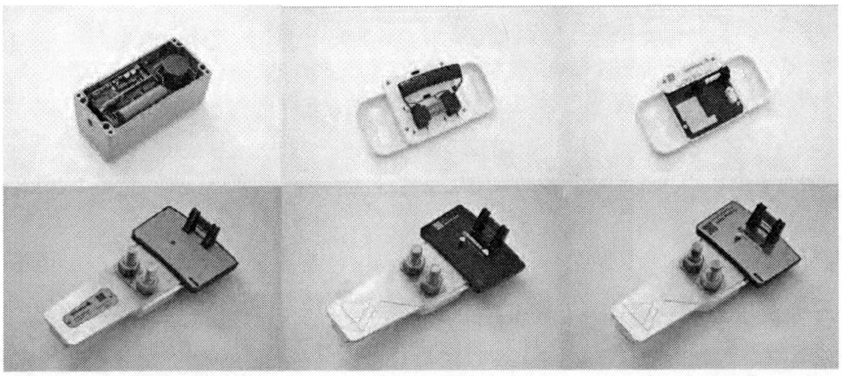

Figure 1 - GUARD hardware development over the last few years

Sensors in the GUARD

The GUARD system is equipped with a multitude of individual sensors (Table 1). The sensors include a specially developed sensor technology that measures the local corrosion conditions, temperature and humidity sensors, acceleration sensors that can report a dynamic process, and strain gauges measure the force in the support cables of the protective solution to perceive slow, pseudo-static changes in the system. The data are transmitted directly to a cloud via the mobile network (GSM, UMTS or LTE). An online platform allows viewing of the processes taking place in quasi real time (Figure 2). Responsible persons thus know the status of their barrier not only directly after an on-site inspection, but continuously from real-time transmitted data.

Table 1: the Guard sensor technology and technical specifications

Table 1	
Sensor Technology	Range
Rope force measurement	up to 30,000 kg
Acceleration	0 g to 200 g
Orientation	XYZ axis
Corrosion	Current (μA)
Temperature	- 50°C to 80°C
Humidity	0% - 100%
Energy	Battery voltage (V); running time 7 to 10 years
Signal strength	RSSI

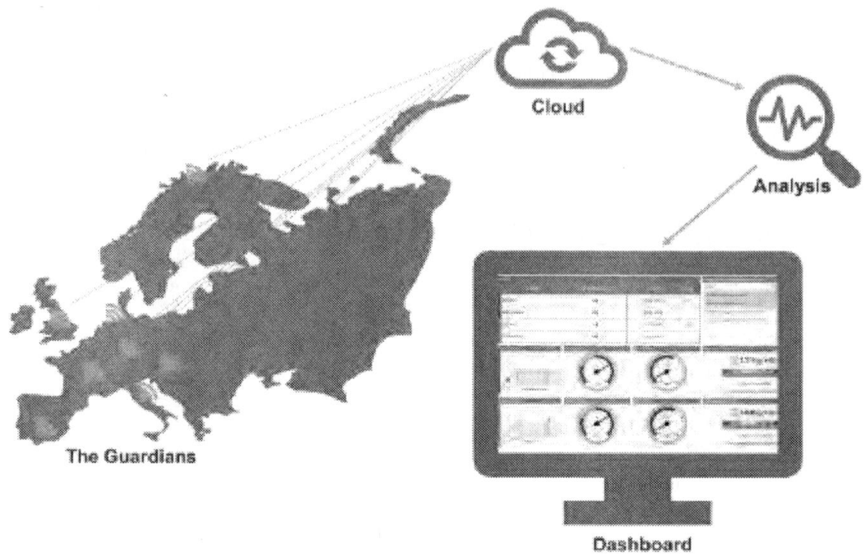

Figure 2 - Functional principle of the data transmission of GUARDs and the anecdotes of their data.

Dynamic Load Cases

The dynamic load cases, such as a rockfall, a debris flow, or tree fall are detected and measured by means of two acceleration sensors. A 0-200 g acceleration sensor is for dynamic impacts, and a 0-15 g is sensor for static loading and measurement of the orientation of the guard. These sensors are triggered to record at the time of dynamic impact for five seconds recording the peak impact and residual dynamic load. Currently the collection and interpretation of data at several locations is required to identify the magnitude and exact location of an impact. As a rockfall protection structure can be several hundred meters long, as well as estimation of the size of the stone or the volume of the mudflow may be difficult. In the long-term, the data collected with the development of algorithms should enable more precise statements to be made about the possible location and size of an impact.

Static Load Cases

Static load cases, such as slowly increasing snow cover or the load of filled material after a debris flow, etc., are determined by means of measurement of force in a support rope. The Guard is equipped with strain gauges that work with the three connection points to the rope (Figure 3). As the barrier is slowly loaded with debris, the rope is tensioned, and the force of the rope can be determined via strain gauges.

Figure 3 – The GUARD attached to the support rope by the wire rope clamp and touching the two ends allows measurement of the force in the rope.

Corrosion Sensor

Besides dynamic, gravitational natural events, corrosion is the most important factor for a reduced service life of flexible geohazard protection infrastructure [2]. Corrosion is problematic in the field of natural hazard protection because the functionality of protection systems depends on the full integrity of their components.

The corrosion sensor in the GUARD was tested in a climate chamber and on various natural test sites. The results in the climate chamber and the results on the test sites indicate a proportionality between the measured current and the weight loss on the corrosion sensor. Over 200 sensors have been used so far and initial results seem to confirm the trend. Further conclusions can be drawn if the devices are used outdoors for a longer period of time.

Remaining sensors and displaying the data

The remaining sensors, such as temperature and humidity allow a plausibility check (do the temperatures correspond to the environment). As the Guard device has sensors recording the voltage of the battery and the signal strength of the mobile network, and a status display of the respective device to enable scheduling any required maintenance on the device itself at an early stage. The data are clearly displayed on the online platform and provides a variety of decisive information on the current condition of the protection solution. The calculated galvanization loss rates of the corrosion sensor are also displayed, as well as the converted deflection of the rope as a force in Newtons.

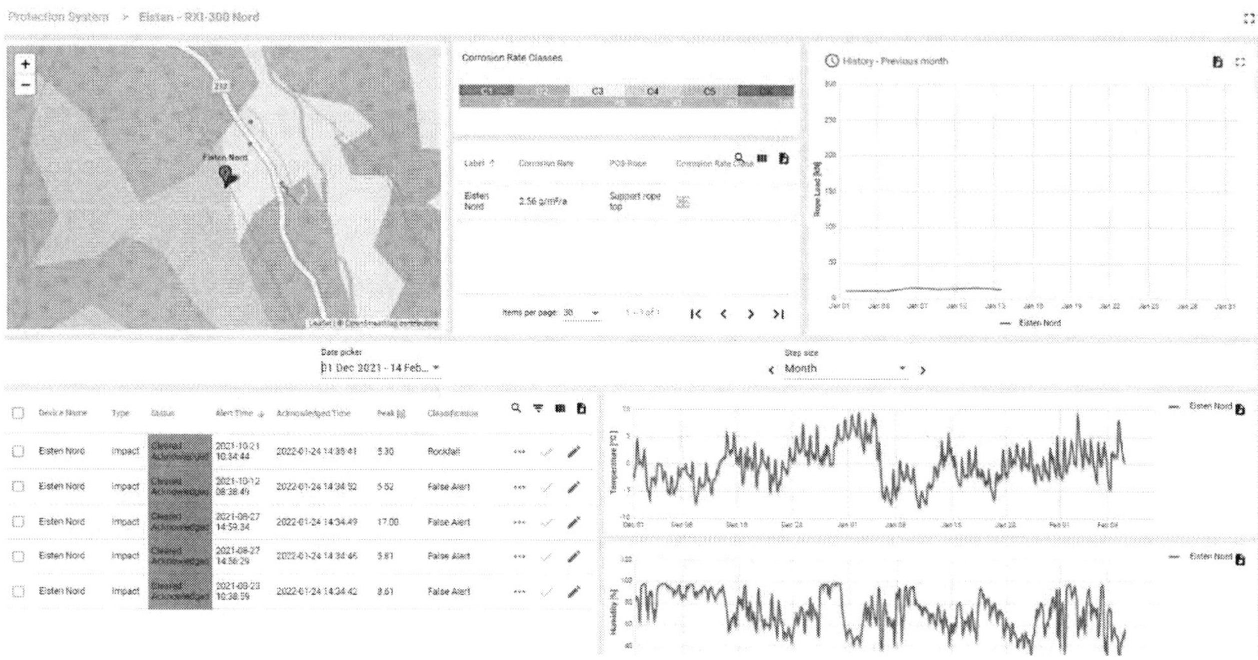

Figure 4 – Example: Overview of a flexible protection system on the platform showing the GUARD locations, estimated Corrosion Rate Classes, rope loads, temperature and humidity line graphs.

GUARD APPLICATIONS:

Predictive Maintenance

One aim of the GUARD is to enable the transition from repair and maintenance to predictive maintenance by assessing local corrosivity. The corrosion sensor constantly monitors the environmental conditions by measuring changes in current and allows a status report to be made regarding the service life of an installed flexible protection system, leading to the concept of predictive maintenance.

Worldwide field experience has shown that the corrosion classes according to EN ISO 12944-2 (EN ISO 14713-1) [3] can vary greatly over short distances and can lead to unexpected corrosion. Therefore, the understanding of microclimates relative to corrosion needs to be improved. Currently, the corrosiveness of an environment is defined according to EN ISO 12944-2 and described in 6 different corrosion classes from C1 to CX (Table 2). These six environmental descriptions leave much room for interpretation.

Unfortunately, these classes are very general and based only on regional climatic aspects. Further, the lifetime prediction of wire zinc coatings according to ISO 9223:2012-05 [4], ranges widely within an atmospheric class. For example, the C3 category 5-15 g/m2/year which means there is a factor of 3 from the lowest to highest rate when calculating based on this the theoretical lifetime. For the C4 category the factor is 2 with a range of 15-30 g/m2/year.

Table 2: Typical atmospheric corrosion environments related to corrosion classes according to EN ISO 12944-2

Corrosivity category C Corrosion rate for zinc (based upon one year exposures), r_{corr} (µm·a^{-1}) and corrosion level	Typical environments (examples)	
	Indoor	Outdoor
C1 $r_{corr} \leqslant 0,1$ Very low	Heated spaces with low relative humidity and insignificant pollution, e.g. offices, schools, museums	Dry or cold zone, atmospheric environment with very low pollution and time of wetness, e.g. certain deserts, central Arctic/Antarctica
C2 $0,1 < r_{corr} \leqslant 0,7$ Low	Unheated spaces with varying temperature and relative humidity. Low frequency of condensation and low pollution, e.g. storage, sport halls	Temperate zone, atmospheric environment with low pollution (SO_2 < 5 µg/m^3), e.g.: rural areas, small towns. Dry or cold zone, atmospheric environment with short time of wetness, e.g. deserts, sub-arctic areas
C3 $0,7 < r_{corr} \leqslant 2$ Medium	Spaces with moderate frequency of condensation and moderate pollution from production process, e.g. food-processing plants, laundries, breweries, dairies	Temperate zone, atmospheric environment with medium pollution (SO_2: 5 µg/m^3 to 30 µg/m^3) or some effect of chlorides, e.g. urban areas, coastal areas with low deposition of chlorides, subtropical and tropical zones with atmosphere with low pollution
C4 $2 < r_{corr} \leqslant 4$ High	Spaces with high frequency of condensation and high pollution from production process, e.g. industrial processing plants, swimming pools	Temperate zone, atmospheric environment with high pollution (SO_2: 30 µg/m^3 to 90 µg/m^3) or substantial effect of chlorides, e.g. polluted urban areas, industrial areas, coastal areas without spray of salt water, exposure to strong effect of de-icing salts, subtropical and tropical zones with atmosphere with medium pollution
C5 $4 < r_{corr} \leqslant 8$ Very high	Spaces with very high frequency of condensation and/or with high pollution from production process, e.g. mines, caverns for industrial purposes, unventilated sheds in subtropical and tropical zones	Temperate and subtropical zones, atmospheric environment with very high pollution (SO_2: 90 µg/m^3 to 250 µg/m^3) and/or important effect of chlorides, e.g. industrial areas, coastal areas, sheltered positions on coastline
CX $8 < r_{corr} \leqslant 25$ Extreme	Spaces with almost permanent condensation or extensive periods of exposure to extreme humidity effects and/or with high pollution from production process, e.g. unventilated sheds in humid tropical zones with penetration of outdoor pollution including airborne chlorides and corrosion-stimulating particulate matter	Subtropical and tropical zones (very high time of wetness), atmospheric environment with very high pollution (SO_2 higher than 250 µg/m^3), including accompanying and production pollution and/or strong effect of chlorides, e.g. extreme industrial areas, coastal and offshore areas with occasional contact with salt spray

The result is the predicted lifespan of a protective structure, for example, can be between 30 and 90 years according to the defined climate and standard EN ISO 12944-2 [3]. Without ongoing measurements, the shortest value must be assumed, which can cause unnecessary costs and is also not convincing in terms of sustainability. With direct ongoing measurements from the sensors part of the GUARD system, the infrastructure manager knows the real corrosion and can act accordingly.

These classes offer general guidance, but the corrosion process is more complex and depends on several factors that can vary greatly locally. Factors that create a microclimate that differs from the corrosivity classification based on regional climate are, for example, an industrial plant that emits polluted air, the presence of local water rich in chloride or sulphur, areas that are always in the shade and therefore wetter, or, on the other hand, very dry areas with some salt input that is not regularly washed off. A very specific example is the de-icing of roads in winter that also induces a more severe microclimate along the first meter above the road. This leads to accelerated corrosion due to salt input, although in an alpine environment one would usually think that the corrosivity class must be C2. The need to develop a special corrosion sensor seemed to be of utmost importance to define and monitor such microclimatic areas around protection systems.

REAL-TIME MONITORING EXAMPLES

The first Guard systems were installed at several rockfall and debris flow barriers across Europe, and six sites have been equipped since summer 2021 in North America. The locations were selected based on known frequent impacts and highly corrosive areas.

Corrosion Estimates

Along the most northern coast of Norway there is avalanche and rockfall protection netting for protecting the coastal highway (Figure 5). Due to the proximity to the sea, this site could easily be interpreted as having a C4 or C5 atmospheric condition according to the EN ISO 14713-1 descriptions (Table 2). The GUARD system provides direct estimation of corrosion rates and more precise environmental classification. As shown in Figure 5 the GUARD-defined corrosion rate indicates a lower than estimated C3 environment and identifies variable microclimates across the site with higher corrosion rates at the lowest elevation and proximity to the ocean.

Figure 5: Example of corrosion sensor data showing microclimate variation of estimated galvanization coating loss with elevation and proximity to the sea, as well as variability of corrosion rates in a single installation.

REMOTE MONITORING

A rockfall protection net protecting a road in Switzerland was equipped with three guards in 2020 (Figure 6). As can be seen in the figures, this flexible protection system is a typical example of vegetation overgrowing a protection system. Despite the barrier's proximity to the infrastructure being protected, it is increasingly disappearing under the growing vegetation and is slowly being filled with small debris and foliage (Figures 6 and 7). Figure 8 shows a filled barrier with a sizable tree growing through the primary ring net and a lack of access or a forgotten protection system and the need for remote monitoring.

Figure 6 – GUARD mounted on the support rope of a rockfall protection structure

DYNAMIC IMPACTS:

On 16 June 2020, a small rockfall occurred. It was a boulder with edge lengths of about 100 cm x 100 cm x 40 cm and a mass of about 1,000 kg. A GUARD installed in the field adjacent to the impact recorded the rockfall event: Acceleration 10.1 g, at 18:00:32 (Figure 9 and 10). The event immediately triggered an alert sending a SMS and an e-mail message about the impact via the online GUARD platform. These alerts gave the system owner an immediate alert regarding the magnitude of the impact and the ability to determine the appropriate maintenance measures needed by those responsible.

Figure 7 – Rockfall protection barrier disappearing into the vegetation

Figure 8 – Barrier filled slowly over time without regular inspections. Note bent tree growing though ring net.

Figure 8 – Impact on 16.06.2020

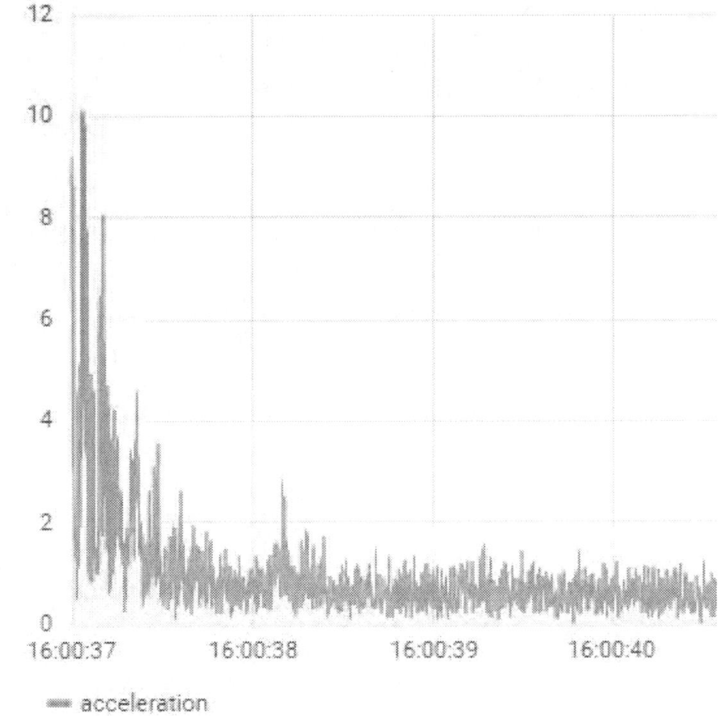

Figure 9 – Absolute acceleration (g) of rockfall on 16.06.2020

On the 4th of January 2022, an impact alarm was registered in a protection system along the Columbia River Highway in Oregon that turned out to be a 3ft and a 2ft block. A GUARD installed in the field adjacent to the impacts recorded the rockfall event: Highest detected acceleration 5.5 g, at 01:09:20 (Figure 13 and 14). The events immediately triggered SMS and e-mail messages about the impact via the online platform. The intensity of the acceleration peak allows a decision regarding whether to visit the site rapidly and whether maintenance is needed, such that the barrier is always able to resist a potential subsequent design load impact.

Figure 13 – Impacts on the 04.01.2022. Note rock next to the support post. Rocks in foreground are not rockfall, but placed to block parking.

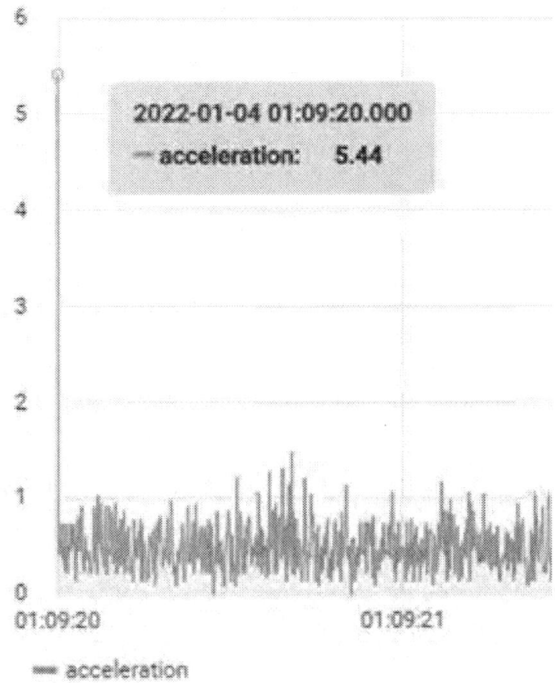

Figure 14 - Absolute acceleration (g) of rockfall on 04.01.2022

COLLECTING DATA WOLRDWIDE

The GUARD sensors and their prototypes have been deployed over the past five years on 40 sites in 13 countries in Europe (Figure 15). In addition, many flexible protection barriers are equipped with GUARDs in North America, Australia, and New Zealand. In addition to the monitoring service, the aim is to use the collected data to improve corrosion and impact interpretations by developing algorithms to automate data interpretation. The data will also provide a basis for planning more needs-based inspections and making lifetime estimations more accurate in the future.

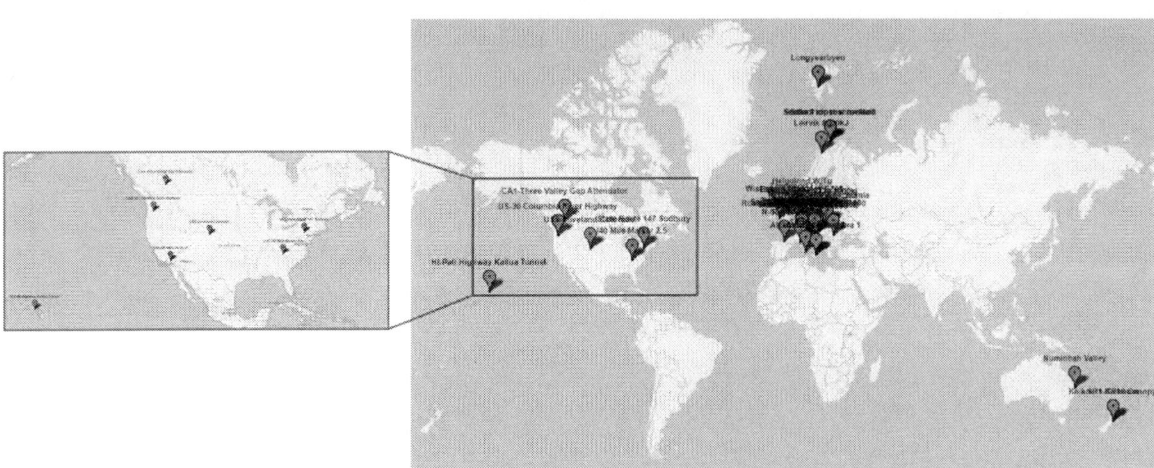

Figure 15 – Platform print-screen with an overview of worldwide devices

CONCLUSION

This paper on the GUARD device presents the development of an IoT device for monitoring flexible protection systems against natural hazards to protect infrastructure. The GUARD can be installed quickly in a few minutes - on systems from any manufacturer. With its independent power supply, it works for up to ten years without on-site device maintenance. The GUARD provides the most important information to ensure that protective measures function reliably. It has been tested under a wide range of conditions at various locations around the world.

This IoT solution should ensure 24/7 monitoring making it possible to carry out fewer inspections or more timely inspections on demand. This reduces the inspection costs of the geohazard mitigation system and increases the safety level by eliminating the physical time workers are present in the danger zone. Predictive maintenance is also possible by evaluating the local corrosivity and estimating the associated lifespan of the protection system. Over time, events are logged, and important conclusions can be drawn by combining other data sets such as wildlife, weather data, and air pollution impacts relative to rockfall, debris flow, and corrosion. This monitoring solution makes it possible to achieve smart infrastructures of existing and new buildings in the field of natural hazard prevention.

REFERENCES:

[1] "Internet of Things." Wikipedia, Wikimedia Foundation, 26 Apr. 2021, en.wikipedia.org/wiki/Internet_of_things.

[2] Hofmann, H., Hörtnagl, A., Sorg, M., von Wartburg, J., 2020. Development of a digital device for monitoring and predictive maintenance of flexible steel protection systems against natural hazards. Proceedings of the 14th Congress Interpraevent 2020.

[3] ISO 9223:2012-05 Corrosion of metals and alloys - Corrosivity of atmospheres - Classification, determination and estimation

[4] Corrosion protection of steel by coatings and coatings 4; DIN EN ISO 12944-1 to DIN EN ISO 12944-8; 1998 Beuth

S.R. 0081 Rock Slope Stabilization, Lackawanna County, Pennsylvania

Daniel F. Martt, P.G.,

Retired
331 Chessbriar Dr.
Bethel Park, PA 15102
(412)-854-4122
danmartt1952@gmail.com

Sebastian Lobos-Guerrero, P.E., Ph.D.

American Geotechnical and Environmental Services, Inc.
4 Grandview Circle
Canonsburg, PA 15102
(724) 916-0300
sebastianl@agesinc.com

Prepared for the71st Highway Geology Symposium, May, 2022

Acknowledgements

The authors would like to thank the individuals for the accomplishments in the work described:
Neil Styler- American Geotechnical and Environmental Services, Inc.
K.P. Chopra- American Geotechnical and Environmental Services, Inc
Donna Marsh, Administrative Assistant, American Geotechnical and Environmental Services, Inc.

Disclaimer

Statements and views presented in this paper are strictly those of the author(s), and do not necessarily reflect positions held by their affiliations, the Highway Geology Symposium (HGS), or others acknowledged above. The mention of trade names for commercial products does not imply the approval or endorsement by HGS.

Copyright Notice

Abstract

A section of four lane highway in northeastern Pennsylvania constructed in the 1960's included a significant rock cut consisting primarily of sandstone. The project excluded provisions for major rockfall when constructed, probably because the rock appeared to be competent. Over the years freeze-thaw along joints and over-break fractures reduced the integrity of the cut significantly, increasing the rock fall potential along the north bound lanes. A study was undertaken to remediate the situation. A review of available geologic literature, results of earlier core drilling, geologic mapping, and a field survey including limited rock testing were completed. A remediation treatment was devised consisting of flattening the slopes and installing passive rock nails with high strength steel mesh where sliding was found to be kinematically possible. Soil nailing of the upper, more weathered slopes was found to be necessary in some segments to keep the cut within the right of way. The project involved approximately 11,500 linear feet of rock nails and approximately 68,000 ft^2 of steel mesh. Approximately 13,166 linear feet of soil nails were needed for the upper slope reinforcement.

Background of Study

The study involves a four lane Interstate Highway found in Lackawanna County, Pennsylvania (Figure 1). According to available historic aerial photos, this section of the S.R. 0081 was built by 1967. Previously, older roads and a railroad followed the sinuous valley on the western slope of the wider Wyoming-Lackawanna Valley (Figure 2). The narrow valley (from about 700-1100 feet wide) was cut into the northern, bedrock slope of the valley. The rock cut here varied from about 33 to greater than 60 feet in height.

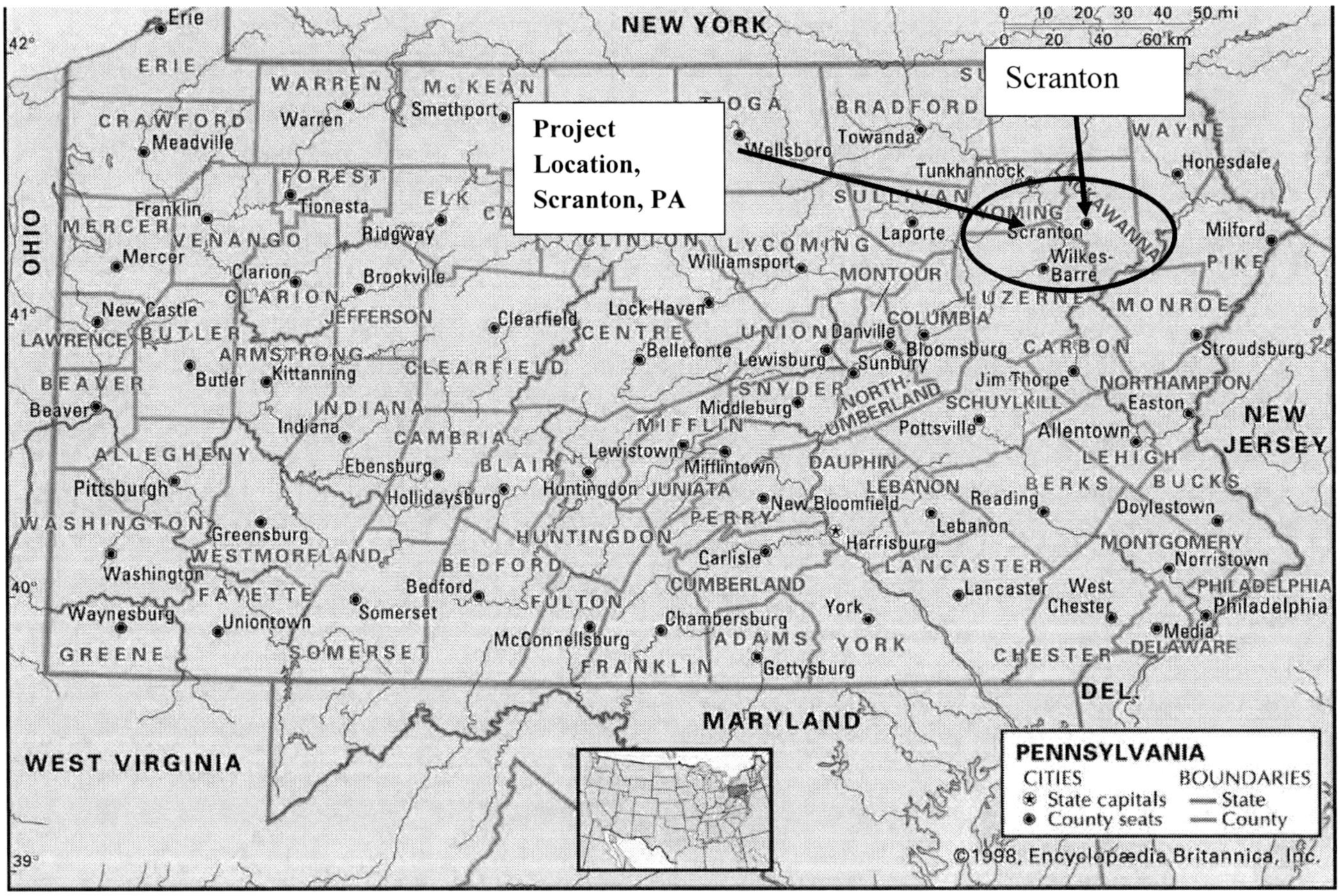

FIGURE 1 PROJECT LOCATION

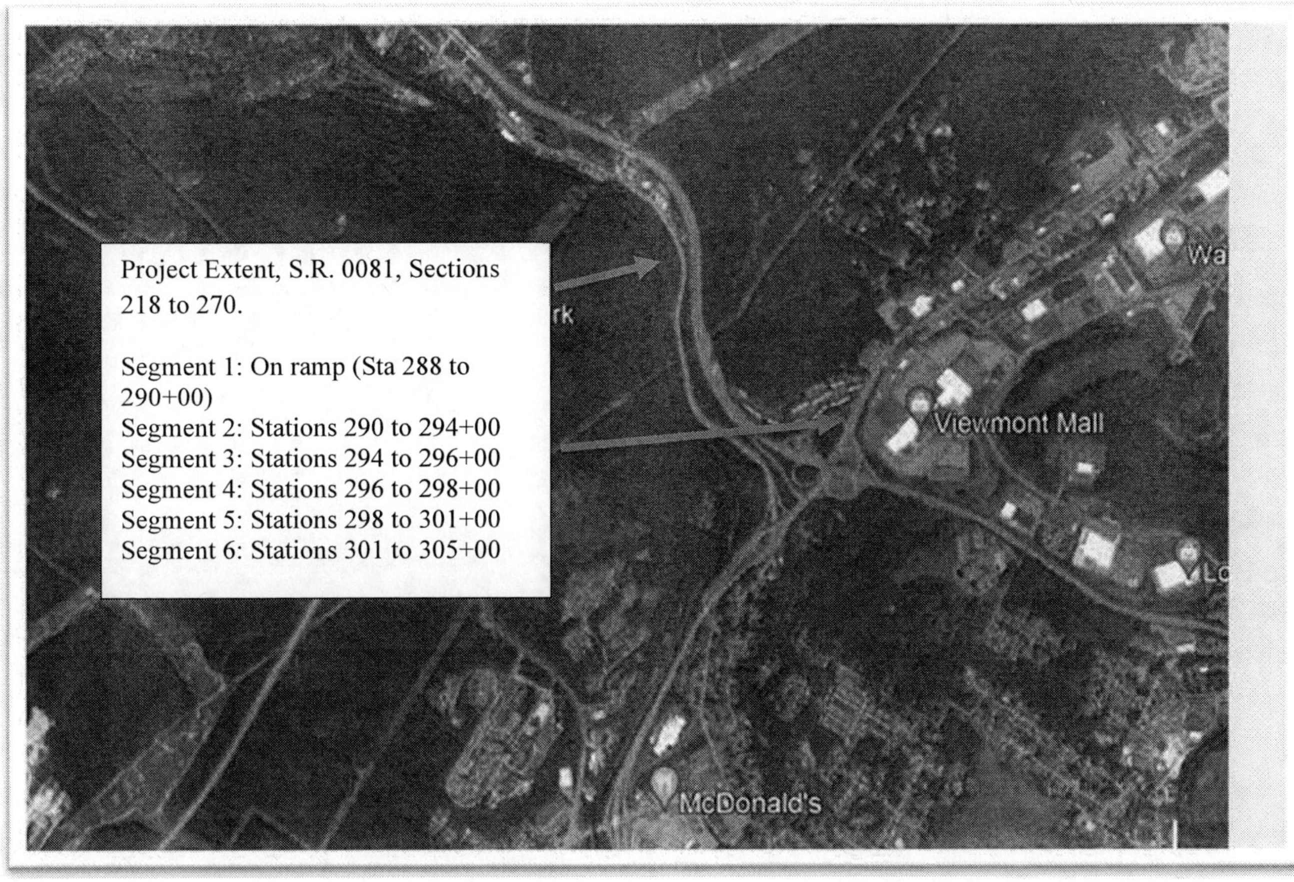

FIGURE 2 PROJECT VICINITY AND EXTENT (GOOGLE EARTH PRO 7.3.4)

A photo (Figure 3) taken in 2009 shows the proximity of the northbound lanes to the unstable rock slope, as well as an overall view of the cut along the slope. The crests of the rock slopes were covered in colluvium and rockfall debris that fell on the shoulder and occasionally on the highway**.** A steep cut at the edge of the shoulder, restricted site distance, and minimal rockfall protection presented an unacceptable risk to the traveling public. For this reason, a study by the Pennsylvania Department District 4 was started in 2009 to develop a slope remediation option.

FIGURE 3 VIEW OF NORTHBOUND LANE OF S.R. 0081

The Pennsylvania Department of Transportation contracted a design consultant (HRI, Inc.) to develop a design-build contract for remediation of the cut. The object of this study was to:

- Conduct a geotechnical investigation including borings and mapping of discontinuities in the cut.

- Develop a conceptual slope stabilization plan including typical treatments and limit of treatment.

- Submit specification for a design-build contract, including conceptual treatments.

After preliminary studies by others (1,2), the firm of American Geotechnical and Environmental Services, Inc., (A.G.E.S. Inc.) of Canonsburg, Pennsylvania was selected as the lead geotechnical designer.

Methodology

The methods used in the design were the following:

- A review of earlier reports and mapping including the Pennsylvania Geologic Survey (7), Field Conference of Pennsylvania Geologists (8) and design memorandums by others (1,2). The reports included background geology, logs from borings performed along the cut, and stereonet plots of discontinuity mapping performed on the rock cut.
- Site reconnaissance and mapping of the rock slopes, measuring the strike and dip of discontinuities and including a survey of the orientation and roughness of the joint surface (Figure 4).
- Evaluation of the results with, dividing the slope into segments to account for variability in discontinuity orientation along and heights along the length of the cut.
- Establishing rock quality properties along the various segments using the results of core testing (completed previously by others), laboratory testing and evaluation of joint surface condition.
- Using the results of the office, field, and laboratory studies, evaluate the stability of the cut for kinematically unstable blocks with stereonets..
- Designing a passive, fully grouted steel dowel reinforcement system to increase shear resistance along the critical joint system.
- Designing an anchored mesh system to prevent sloughing of rock debris from the slope to the highway.
- Submission of the design for review by others, including the design consultant and the owner, and
- Design of a soil nail treatment for the upper slopes of the project, using the results of test pitting to find the limits of soil and weathered rock.

FIGURE 4 FIELD DISCONTINUITY SURVEY

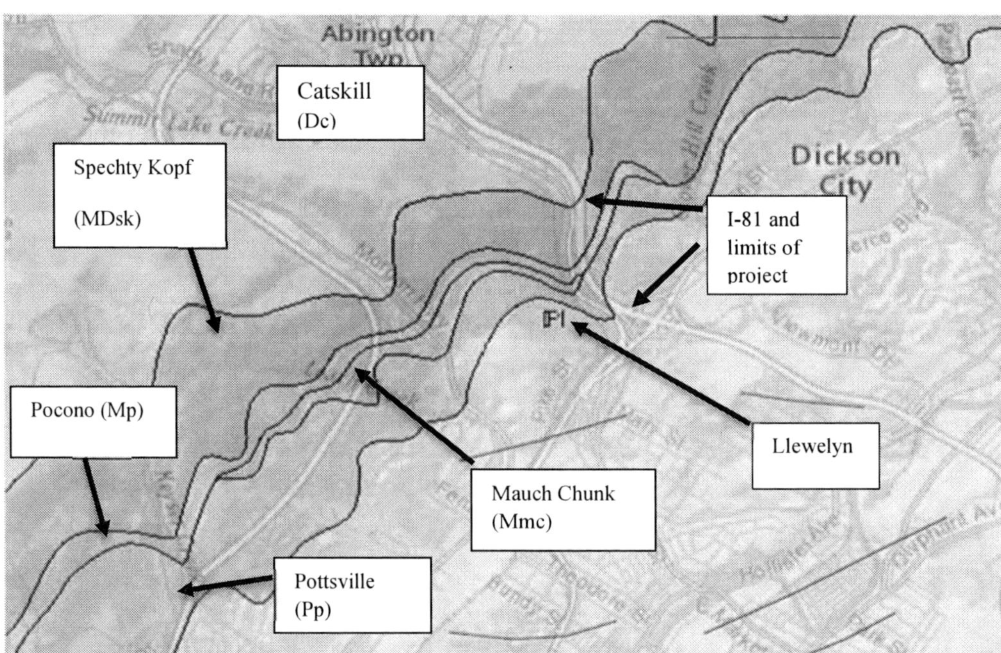

FIGURE 5 GEOLOGIC MAP (red lines are anticlines)

Background Geology

The project lies in the Northern Anthracite Field of the Appalachian Mountain Section of the Valley and Ridge physiographic province. The Northern Anthracite Field is characterized as a narrow to wide canoe shaped valley with irregular to linear hills and a valley enclosed by a steep, mountain rim. The general geologic structure is made up of a broad, double plunging syncline with faults and smaller folds.

The soil covering of the slopes in the area was found to be very shallow. The glacial till covering the slopes was largely removed by erosion and gelifluction of till deposits that flowed into the valley. The soil cover is within ± 6 feet thick in the vicinity of the project. Surficial geological mapping by Braun (5) also showed the valley in which the rock cut is located was a low area in thick glacial deposits which later became a glacial meltwater channel. It is believed deep weathering occurred in the valley walls due to glacial and postglacial climate conditions that caused frost shattering of exposed rock

The bedrock of the rock slopes (7, 9) is made up of four groups or formations, the Spechty Kopf (Mississippian/Devonian age), Pocono (Mississippian), the Pottsville Group (lower Pennsylvanian) and the Llewellyn (Pennsylvanian) (Figure 5, from PA Geode). The Mississippian aged Mauch Chunk does not extend into the project according to available geologic sources and mapping. In summary, the rock expected along the cut was sandstone with some weaker shale and siltstone layers; due to the past climate conditions, deep weathering and jointing was expected. According to Geyer and Wilshusen (6), the general slope stability of the formations can be expected to be good unless hard sandstone overlies weaker siltstone and shale layers. Evidence of valley stress release jointing parallel to the various cut orientations is clear due to the prolonged exposure of the valley walls (8).

Field Discontinuity Study

A site visit was made in early 2011 (3) to evaluate the rock face, do preliminary stereo nets, and a division of the project based on height and joint orientation. Six (6) segments were delineated. Segments 1-3 start along a northbound on ramp for the four-lane highway and end where prominent tight folding and faulting are encountered along the cut (approximately 800 feet). The folded and faulted section is approximately 200 feet in width (designated as Segment 4). Segments 5 and 6 start at the end of Segment 4 and end where the rock cut tapers down, and failures are not kinematically possible (approximately 600 feet in width.) The results of the visit were:

- Upon viewing the site in the field, 6 segments, based on joint orientation and height of slope were selected.
- Segments 1, 2, 3, 5 & 6 have discontinuities of similar orientation.
- Some prominent slope joints are visible in all the segments (Example, Joint 2, Figure 6).
- Segment 4 is tightly folded and faulted and has overhanging strong rock over weaker beds.

FIGURE 6 PROMINENT JOINT 2 AT STATION 300+00

- The joint survey conducted by A.G.E.S., Inc. is in general agreement with past surveys (2)

The following main discontinuities along the rock face (excluding Segment 4) were found along the rock face (Table 1 and Figure 7).

TABLE 1

PRINCIPLE DISCONTINUITIES AND ORIENTATIONS (Segments 1-3 & 5-6)

Discontinuty ID	Dip/Dip Direction
1	83/192
2	68/172(considered adverse)
3	79/014
4	76/088
5	17/152 (bedding)

Joints 1 and 3 are the same set with different dip orientations as are Joints 2 and 4. Joint 5 is the bedding. Based on available stereo nets (2), site photographs and roadway plans, Joint 2 is well developed and prominent along the various segments. The joint is parallel with the cut face and the cause of the many rock block failures observed along the shoulder (3).

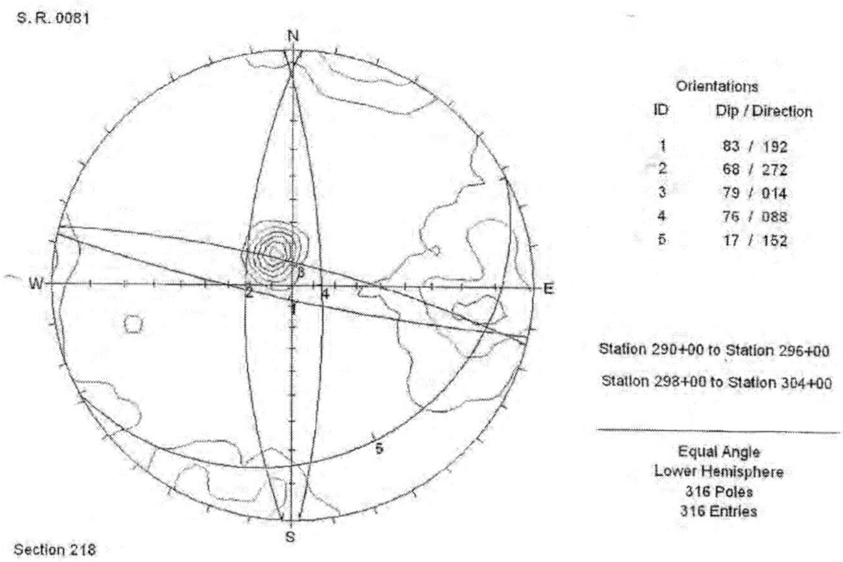

FIGURE 7 STEREO NET FOR SEGMENTS 1-3 & 5-6

A second visit concentrated on the condition of this joint along the entire rock slope, including the spacing, roughness, joint wall hardness and weathering characteristics. More strike and dip readings were taken allowing the selection of the dip angle for Joint 2 to be used in all the segments. It was noted the joint varied in dip angle in the different selected segments,

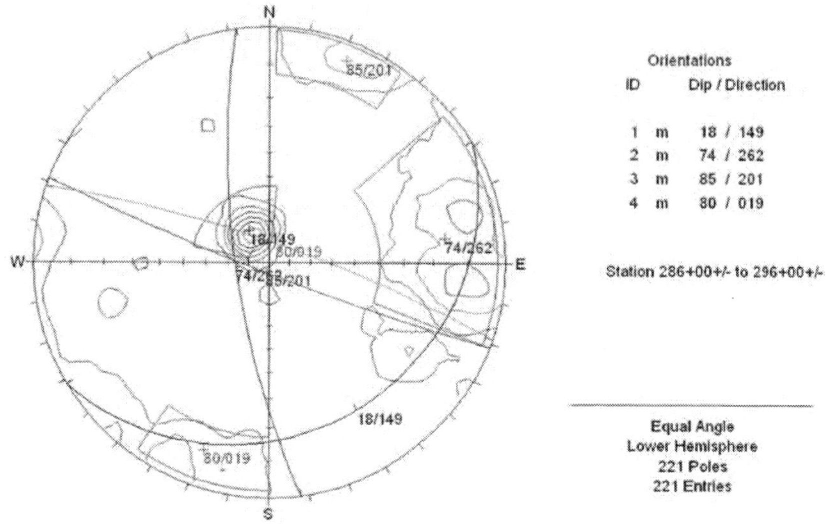

FIGURE 8 STEREO NET FOR SEGMENTS 1-3

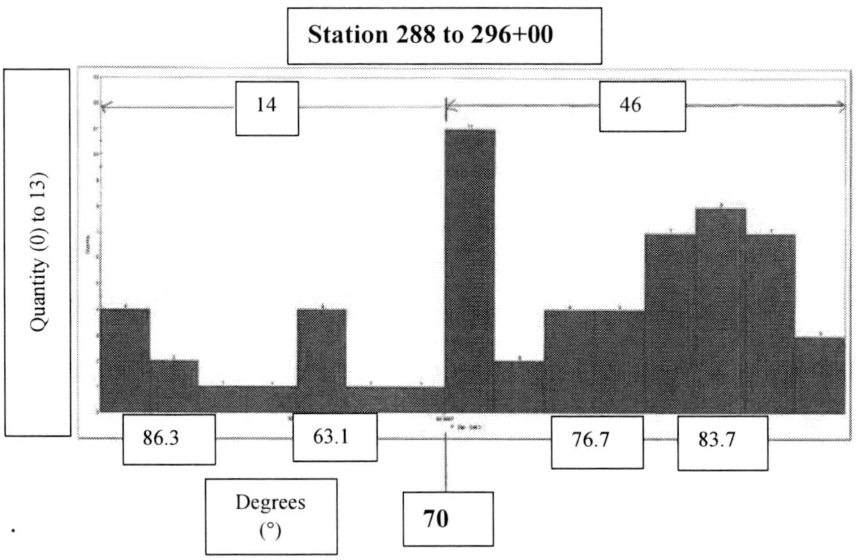

FIGURE 9 HISTOGRAM FOR SEGMENTS 1-3

For Segments 1-3, a total of 60 readings on Joint 2 surfaces were taken along the 1200-foot-long section. The stereo net for Segments 1-3 is shown on Figure 8. Based on the stereo net, a histogram of Joint 2 measurements in Segments 1-3 were plotted as dip magnitude vs. quantity (Figure 9). Forty-six (46) of the 60 readings (77%) had a dip magnitude of more than 70 degrees.

Therefore, if the rock slope is cut at 70 degrees, joints of lesser magnitude are contained, and global failures are resisted. Conservatively, consider the joint set will extend the entire height of the rock slope. This condition was not observed in the field, but most of the potential failures are contained and eliminated if the face is cut at this angle.

The stereo net for Segment 4 (Figure 9) shows the scatter of readings typical of tightly folded and faulted bedrock. However, there is a trend in the northeast corner of the stereo net which shows a similar prominent joint as in Segment 1. The average orientation of the prominent joint in Segment 2 is 55/250. Figure 10 is a histogram of 21 readings of this average, and 76% have a dip magnitude of greater than 50 degrees. Therefore, use 50 degrees as the design cut for Segment 2. The friction angle is conservatively reduced to 25 degrees in this segment due to the distortion and weathering of the rock (10).

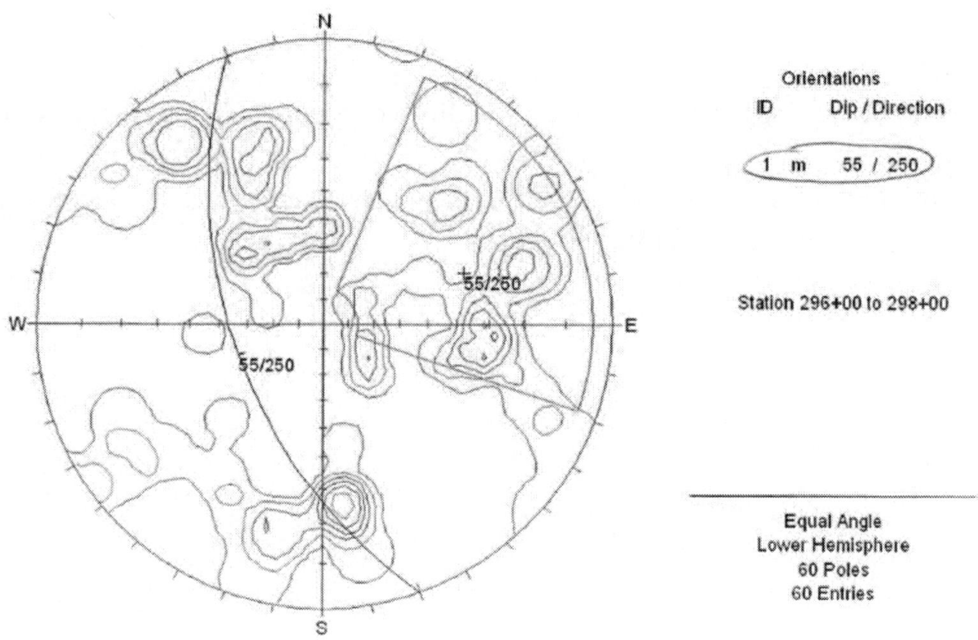

FIGURE 10 STEREO NET FOR SEGMENT 4

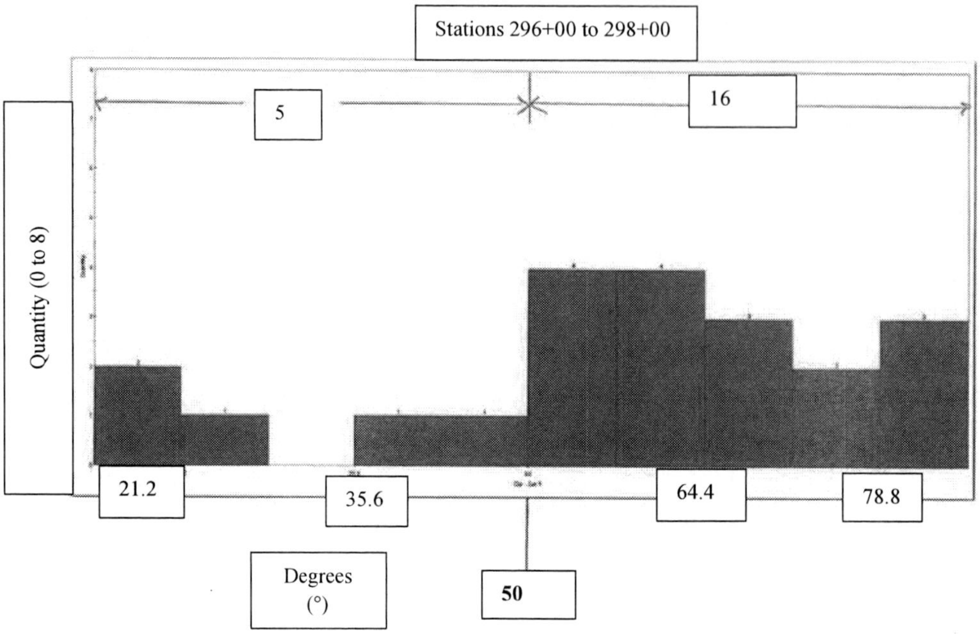

FIGURE 11 HISTOGRAM FOR SEGMENT 4

Figure 11 shows the readings from Stations 298 to 304 (Segments 5 and 6); the most prominent joint along this segment had an orientation of 64/278 degrees. Using the same method as before, it was found from Figure 12 that 48 of 73 readings have a dip greater than 57 degrees. Therefore, 57 degrees was the analysis slope for these segments.

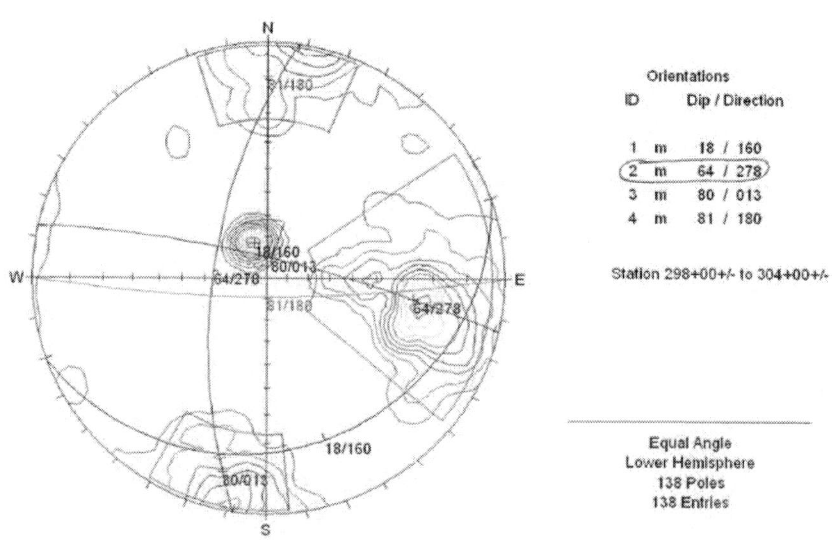

FIGURE 12 STEREO NET FOR SEGMENTS 5- 6

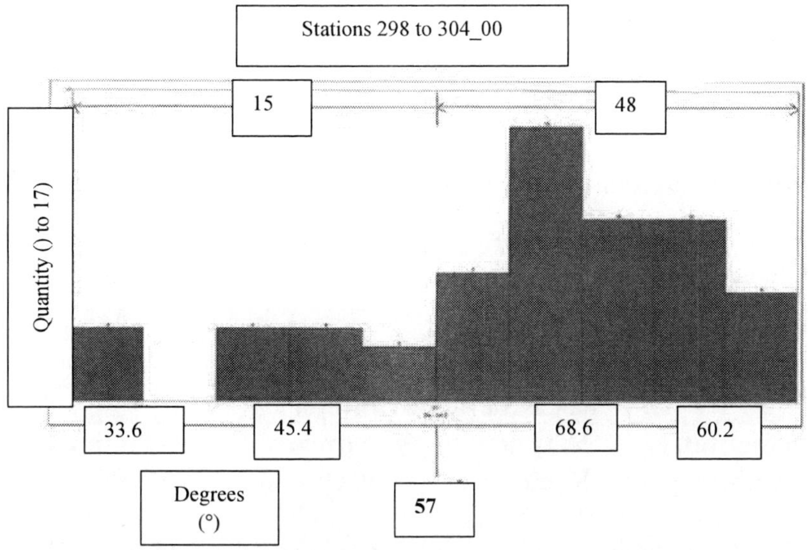

FIGURE 13 HISTOGRAM FOR SEGMENTS 5 -6

For the most prominent joint in all the segments, only one end of the joint was visible, and the surface was generally 10 to 30 feet in length. The surface of the joint was rough with minor asperities, and no evidence of water seepage except between Segments 2 and 3. The joint surfaces were very hard and slightly weathered to fresh.

Laboratory Testing

The results of unconfined compression tests on sandstones and conglomerate samples from the cut by others had results ranging from 904 to more than 1500 TSF (tons per ft^2) (2). Therefore, the design was based on the discontinuities and not the rock strength.

The slake durability of shales and siltstones taken from drilled core and from the cut, both by others (2) and A.G.E.S., Inc. (4) ranged from 80 to 98.5%, so severe undercutting of harder layers by siltstones and shales is not expected. Field observations confirmed this conclusion.

Design Criteria

The design for the remediation was based on shear pin design as presented in a memorandum by A.G.E.S., Inc. (4), with reinforcement with fully grouted untensioned dowels (11), the AASHTO LFRD specifications for steel structures (12), and the FHWA Manual for Design and Construction of Soil Nail Walls (13). Passive shear pins will be placed along the slope in a 10 ft. by 10 ft. pattern. The shear pin lengths will extend beyond the critical design joint set and adequately contain the steel mesh designed by the manufacturer to contain any rock layers loosened along the discontinuities. Conservatively, the rock slopes are modeled as if the entire height of the rock slope is along the controlling joint. This is not seen in the field, but all joints of lesser dip are eliminated. Table 2 shows the properties calculated along the segments, which vary in slope height steepness and strength. The section of rock slope prior to Segment 1 (Station 284 to 290) did not require analysis or remediation, because the cut angles are flatter than dip angles of the joints. The slope protection is designed as a stabilization of surficial blocks and rock wedges on the cut face due to jointing and undercutting of softer layers. The anchors are not installed to stabilize potential deep-seated failures, as none were found during the various studies.

Table 2

Rock Slope Parameters

Analysis Section	Representative Stations	Approx. Rock Cut Height (ft)	Approx. Rock Cut Angle (degrees	Friction angle at Joint (degrees)	Analysis Dip Angle (degrees)
2	290+00 to 294+00	26 to 33	58 to 79	30	70
3	294+00 to 296+00	42 to 46	79	30	70
4	296+00 to 298+00	53 to 61	68	25	50
5	298+00 to 301+50	Max. 50	68	30	57
6	301+50 to 305+00	Max. 39	68	30	57

The rock slope will be cut back away from the travel lanes The cut slope angle will be found by the statistically steepest dip angle according to histograms for the segments as shown in Figures 9, 11, and 13.

Calculations

The normal use of soil nails is to counteract a rotational or linear force. In this case, however, the use of soil nails as passive shear pins is only used to contain the discontinuities. After removal of the excess rock, the weights of the various rock wedges along the proposed cut were calculated to ensure the dowel length needed to contain it. The joint along the different segments was assumed to start at the toe of the slope and daylight at the top of the slope, for each segment. This condition is considered the worst possible condition for rock slope stability; therefore, the properties given are conservative. The factors of safety were based on the ratio of driving and resisting forces along the slope, or:

$$\mathbf{F.S.} = \sum R_F / \sum D_F$$

The ratios should calculate at 1.5 or better. The performance ratio (P.R.) is found by multiplying the resistance factor defined by the Pennsylvania Department of Transportation design manual times the resisting forces and then dividing by the load factors multiplied by the driving forces, or:

$$\mathbf{P.R.} = \sum \varphi_F * R_F / \sum \varphi_F * D_F$$

the performance ratio should be 1.0 or better. Resisting forces ($\sum R_F$) are the frictional resistance along the block wedges and the shear force provided by the nails. Driving forces ($\sum D_F$) are provided by the retained rock masses. Table 3 shows the design criteria for the various segments

The model uses the shear strength of doweled joints with fully grouted dowels installed in pre-drilled holes encapsulated with grout. The high strength steel mesh is designed

Table 3
Design Criteria for Various Segments

Analysis Segment	Analyzed Section Height (ft)	Analyzed No. of Nails per Vertical Section	Vertica Spacing of Nails (ft)	Horizontal Spacing of Nails (ft)	Factor of Safety (Min 1.5)	Performance Ration (Min 1.0)	Required Bar Size
2	33	4	10	10	2.0	1.1	No. 8
3	46	6	10	10	1.8	1.2	No. 8
4	61	7	10	10	1.6	1.0	No. 8
5	50	6	10	10	1.6	1.0	No. 8 and 10
6	39	5	10	`10	1.6	1.0	No. 8

to be installed over the rock slope contained by pins in a 10 x 10-foot pattern to hold possible rock failures. In all cases, the pins were longer than needed for the recommended steel mesh design.

Due to the larger wedges (higher slopes) between Stations 298+50 to 301+50 (Segment 5), the required performance ratio for #8 bars was not reached; therefore, #10 bars will be used on the top and bottom nail rows.

Soil Nails on Upper Slopes

For the soil nails in the upper part of the cut, needed to ensure the project stayed within the right of way, test pits were excavated to find any weak areas in the slope and to find what material the nails will be placed in. The soil nail wall was designed with Goldnail software (a widely used program for design.

During the calculations it was found the second or third row of nails would bear more strain, and therefore larger bars were used in these rows. The performance bars used in the pins varied in length and have strength of 75 or 150 ksi depending on location. Regular grout was used to encase and protect the nails. Corrugated pipe was also used to protect the steel against corrosion.

The nails were installed in 6-inch diameter holes and grouted during construction. Typical cross sections for each segment are shown in Figures 14 and 15.

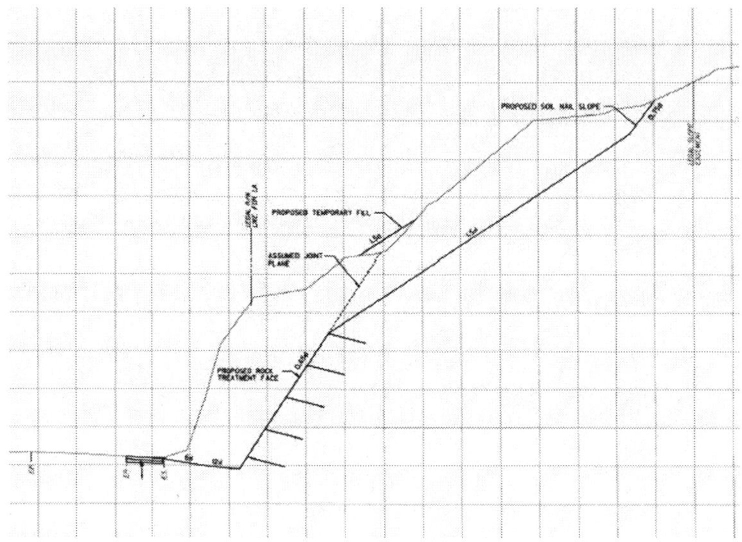

FIGURE 14 STATION 299+00 LOWER NAIL WALL SECTION

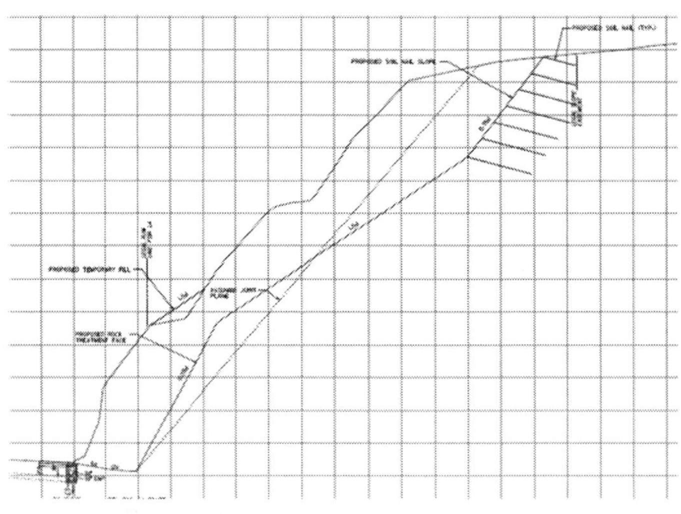

FIGURE 15 UPPER SOIL NAIL WALL STATION 297+00

Finished Product

Approximately 13, 200 liner feet of soil nails were installed. Five percent of the production was tested to twice their design bond strength, and ten nails were evaluated to more than their ultimate strength.

FIGURE 16 COMPLETED PROJECT IN SEGMENT 3

Summary

- By finding the discontinuity statistically abundant in a rock slope and cutting the slope to that angle, the problem of discontinuities with lesser magnitude are mitigated.
- if deep seated failures are found or suspected, passive shear pins placed at a sufficient depth behind the critical discontinuity can be used to block any kinematically possible failures. Calculations of the factor of safety and the performance ratio of the pins to the sheer forces are needed for the case where the cut angle is steeper than the critical discontinuity.
- High strength steel mesh can be used to hold the rock against any potential failures laterally and vertically along with the passive pinning.

References:

Unpublished References

1) Geomechanics, Inc., 2009, "*Design Memorandum: Geotechnical Aspects of Rock Slope Drainage Problem, Segment 1914/0000 to Segment 1914/1950 Northbound.*" (Lackawanna County, S.R. 0081 Section 218, Geomechanics Project 07074).
2) Geomechanics, Inc. 2010, *"Design Memorandum, Rock Cut Slope Stability, Station 284+00 To Station 305+00 ± Northbound."* (Lackawanna County, S.R. 0081 Section 218, Geomechanics Project 07074).
3) A.G.E.S., Inc., undated, "*Analysis of Joint Sets, S.R. 0081, Sections 218/270, Rock Slope Stabilization, Lackawanna County, Pennsylvania,* A.G.E.S., Inc. Project 12016."

4) A.G.E.S., Inc., 2012, "*S.R. 0081, Sections 218/270 Rock Slope Cut Stabilization, Lackawanna County, Pennsylvania, A.G.E.S., Inc. Project 12016, ECMS No. 75128*: Re: Rock Nail Calculation."

Pennsylvania Geological Survey Publications

5) Braun, D.D., 2006, "*Surficial Geology of the Scranton 7.5 Minute Quadrangle, Lackawanna County, Pennsylvania*," Pennsylvania Geological Survey, 4th Series, Open File Report OFSM 06-07.0, Harrisburg, Pennsylvania, 14 pp, 1 map.
6) Geyer, A.R., and Wilshusen, J.P., 1982, *Engineering Characteristics of the Rocks of Pennsylvania*, Department of Environmental Resources, Office of Resources Management, Bureau of Topographic and Geologic Survey, Environmental Geology Report 1, Harrisburg, Pennsylvania, 297 pp.
7) Pennsylvania Department of Conservation and Natural Resources, "*DCNR Interactive Map Resources, PaGEODE*" (PA Geological Survey Interactive Map) https://www.gis.dcnr.state.pa.us/geology/index.html:

Conference Proceedings

8) Ferguson, H.R., and Hamel, J.V., 1981, "*Valley Stress Release in Flat Lying Sedimentary Rock*," Proceedings of the International Symposium on Weak Rock, Tokyo, Japan

Books:

9) Edmunds, W.E., Leader," *Stop 10, U.S. 6-11N Roadcut in Leggett's Gap: Pocono, Pottsville, and Llewellyn Stratigraphy*" in Inners, J.D., editor, 1997, *Geology of the Wyoming-Lackawanna Valley and its Mountain Rim, Northeastern Pennsylvania, 62nd Annual Field Conference of Pennsylvania Geologists*, Field Conference of Pennsylvania Geologists, Inc., Harrisburg, Pennsylvania, 200 pp.
10) Hoek, E.H., and Bray, J, 1981, *Rock Slope Engineering (revised 3rd Edition)*, Institute of Mining and Metallurgy, E.& F.N. Spon, New York, New York, 358 pp.
11) Wyllie, D.C., and Mah, C.W., 2004, *Rock Slope Engineering Civil and Mining*, 4th Edition, Spon Press, New York, New York, 408 pp.

Manuals

12) AASHTO LRFDBDS-9 *LRFD Bridge Design Specifications, 9th Edition, Includes Errata by* American Association of State and Highway Transportation Officials, 2020
13) FHWA, 1996, *Manual for Design and Construction Monitoring of Soil Nail Walls* Published Date: 1996-11-01Report Number: FHWA-SA-96-069 https://rosap.ntl.bts.gov/view/dot/42092.

Advancements and Unknowns in the Design of Flexible Facings for Slope Improvement

Jonathan D. Blanchard, P.E., John D. Duffy P.G., C.E.G.
and Michael S. Finegan. P.E.

Yeh and Associates
391 Front Street, Suite D, Grover Beach, CA 93433
(805) 878-7784
jblanchard@yeh-eng.com

Prepared for the 71st Highway Geology Symposium, May 2022

Acknowledgements

The authors would like to thank these individuals for their contributions in the work described:

Khamis Haramy, Federal Highway Administration, Central Federal Lands Highway Division
Marilyn Dodson, Federal Highway Administration, Central Federal Lands Highway Division

Disclaimer

Statements and views presented in this paper are strictly those of the author(s), and do not necessarily reflect positions held by their affiliations, the Highway Geology Symposium (HGS), or others acknowledged above. The mention of trade names for commercial products does not imply the approval or endorsement by HGS.

ABSTRACT

Slope stabilization and earth retention systems now commonly include flexible facing elements composed of wire mesh to save cost, incorporate aesthetic and context sensitive features, and allow faster construction compared to more traditional reinforced concrete or shotcrete facings. Flexible facing systems were introduced to slope stabilization as rockfall barriers and drapery. Anchoring wire mesh onto slopes to improve stability, mitigate erosion and provide retention has become common practice. Despite the increasing frequency of these installations, there is still limited consensus and often disagreement regarding how these systems should be designed and analyzed, where and when it is appropriate to use flexible facings, and how design and construction practices influence the performance of these systems. This paper provides a summary of recent advancements in flexible facing design. A simplified design approach and methodology is proposed that provides guidance to know when a flexible facing is and is not appropriate based on the design requirements and ground conditions.

INTRODUCTION

Flexible facing systems have become a common part of design and construction projects involving slope stabilization, temporary shoring, and erosion protection. Ground anchors are always used to anchor the flexible facing to the slope. Ground anchor systems generally consist of a series of grouted steel threaded bars embedded in a slope to improve slope stability or provide earth retention. A facing placed over the slope can provide additional retention of the ground between the ground anchors, erosion resistance, and confinement around the head of the ground anchor. Flexible facings composed of wire mesh, geosynthetics, or rolled erosion control product with ground anchors offer a method for stabilizing slopes that is often less expensive, easier to construct, and faster to install than reinforced concrete facings for soil nail type retaining walls. Those systems using wire mesh as the flexible facing are the focus of this paper.

Design methods and the mechanics of how these systems interact with a slope are typically based on past-experience, anecdotal solutions, or design methods for proprietary systems that have not been fully vetted by design practitioners and agencies. A goal for this paper is to help understand and develop a design methodology for using flexible facings on retaining structures. An engineer should be able to reasonably estimate loads and resistance commonly used to check criteria used for slope stabilization and earth retention systems, understand the performance goals and tolerances of those systems, and allow consideration of alternative items and materials specified for a specific design.

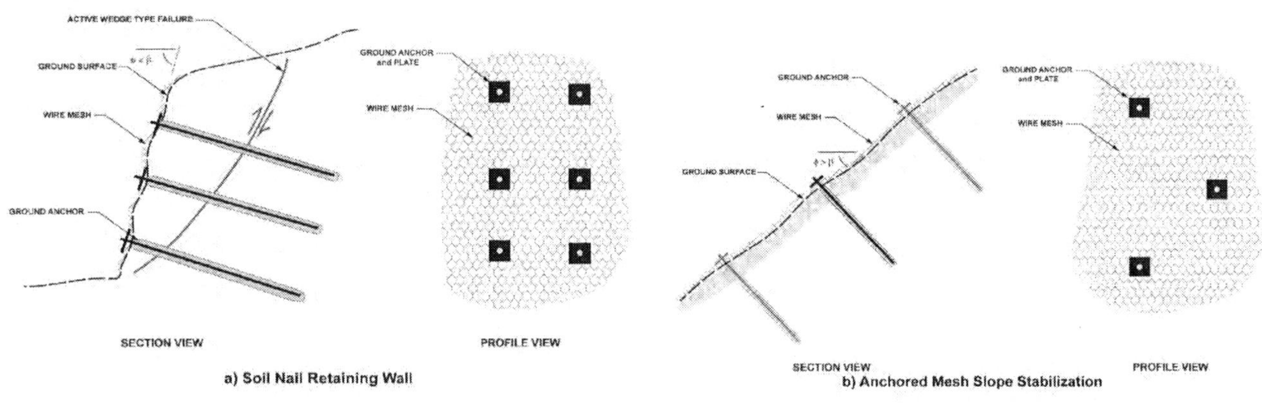

Figure 1: Retaining and Non-Retaining Flexible Facing Systems

A key consideration for design is whether flexible facing can be used as a retaining wall design or only to improve surficial slope stability. The system in Figure 1a shows a typical cross section for soil nail retaining walls with flexible facing that is presumed to resist lateral earth pressure the same as conventional soil nail walls with a reinforced concrete facing. The system in Figure 1b shows a typical cross section for an "anchored mesh" system and is designed mainly to improve surficial slope stability, resist erosion, and retain a mantle of unstable soil or loose rock. The resistance to slope instability provided by both systems develops passively in response to slope movement.

Flexible faced retaining walls can experience bulging and slope movements around the ground anchors and above the top of the wall. Case histories showing successful stabilization of vertical slopes with flexible facings are typically supporting cemented or cohesive soil or rock that are generally self-supporting and are not acting as a retaining wall. The Kansas Department of Transportation (Pokharel et al. 2011) performed research and modeling to evaluate the feasibility of designing soil nail retaining walls with flexible facing and concluded that even relatively small walls could experience large deformation of the facing before resistance to lateral earth pressures and settlement of the ground surface behind the walls could be mobilized.

Wire mesh essentially provides catchment between soil nails. Flexible facings are typically successful where an anchored mesh type system is laid on relatively competent and stable slopes, where the potential failure surface is slope-parallel or constrained by the ground anchor spacing and is shallow, or where the slope is inclined near or below the angle of repose (ϕ') and the facing is not subject to lateral earth pressures and therefore considered non-retaining. A flexible anchored mesh system is composed of ground anchors and wire mesh facing that develops resistance passively and is not well suited for stabilization of large or deep-seated landslides.

GENERAL CONSIDERATIONS AND MAIN COMPONENTS

The concept for improving slope stability with flexible facings is influenced by the same factors that influence a conventional soil nail retaining wall design. The soil nails, facing, and

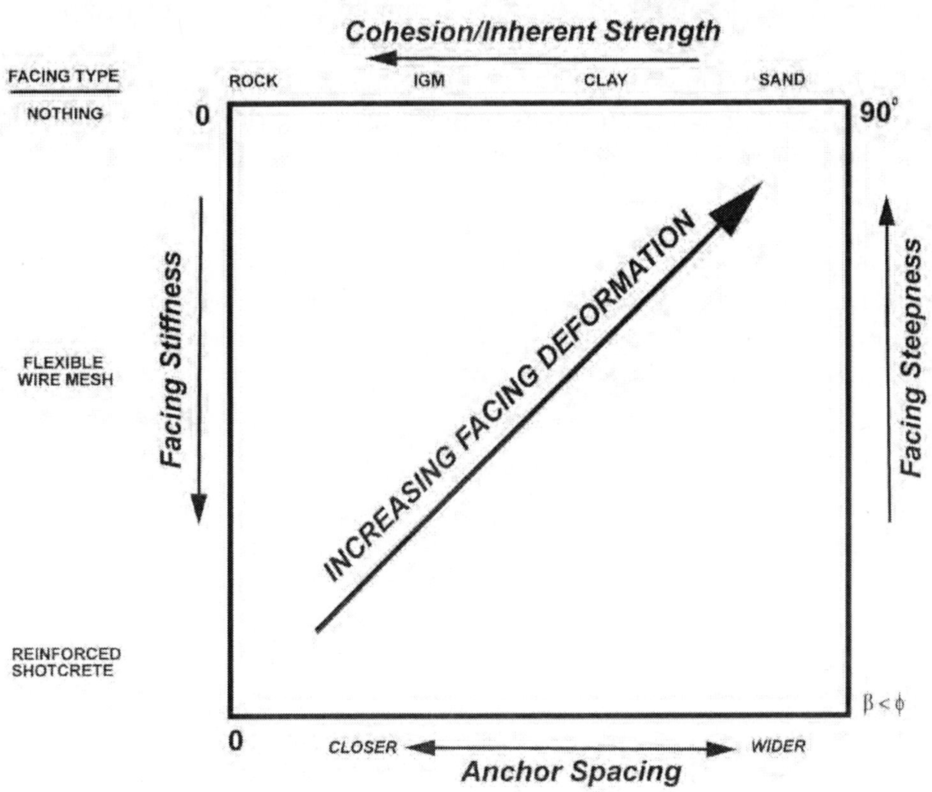

Figure 2: Factors Influencing Deformation of Flexible-Faced Systems

connections between the components of the system develop resistance only in response to ground movement. The system consists of mechanical components including soil nails, a bearing plate at the nail head, and the flexible wire mesh facing. Interaction of these components creates a reinforced earth mass that can be designed to achieve specific strength and deflection tolerances that are unique to the ground and slope conditions it will support as shown in Figure 2. These interactions remain poorly defined and are most often handled qualitatively.

Slope Assessment

The design of slope stabilization or earth retention systems should begin with an assessment of the slope, characterization of geotechnical properties of the slope materials, and defining goals, objectives, and standards for design. Assessing the stability of the unimproved slope provides the basis for what slope improvements and stabilization measures are needed. The slope assessment typically consists of field reconnaissance and mapping, exploration and testing, stability analyses and finding a suitable slope stabilization solution. The assessment defines the characteristics of the slope, depth of potential movement, areas where specific blocks or unstable rock should be stabilized, the spacing and embedment of the soil nails, and quantifies the anticipated improvement in slope stability.

A flexible facing is mainly suited for improving slope stability or retention of shallow surficial soils, the outer several feet of a slope, or helping to secure blocks of rock or boulders. Flexible facing systems will deform with the same characteristics of the materials that the slope is composed of. These systems are best suited for stabilizing slopes where the inherent strength or cohesion of the slope material is enough to allow the facing to be properly placed on a relatively stable surface and secured. These slopes are often composed of weathered rock or colluvium or are placed on flatter slopes that may be vulnerable to erosion but are otherwise inherently stable. Placing flexible facings on slopes with some degree of inherent stability helps reduce the potential for future slope instability associated with ongoing weathering and erosion.

It is difficult to place wire mesh on unstable soil. Cohesionless sand can run and flow like sugar between and around the soil nails and cause large deformations in the facing, debond around anchors, and result in soil movement above the facing. Large or deep-seated landslides will likely have to deform significantly, perhaps several feet or more for a large landslide, to develop resistance in a passive system like anchored wire mesh.

Wire Mesh

Wire mesh is the most common type of flexible facing being used for slope stabilization. The mesh generally lies relatively loosely on the slope face and is secured in place by ground anchors. The flexible nature of the mesh allows it to be somewhat molded to an irregular slope face, around boulders or blocks that need to be retained, or over and under ledges or overhangs. Ground anchors can be added to help to conform to irregularities and improve contact on the slope and reduce tenting of the mesh. Generally, the mesh is not 100 percent in contact with the slope face and the amount of contact varies with the stiffness of the mesh and irregularity of the slope. Geosynthetics and rolled erosion control products are other types of flexible facing facings primarily used to mitigate erosion, and while not directly the focus of this paper, their application is particularly well-suited to mitigating soil erosion on moderate and graded slopes, so those alternatives should also be considered when selecting a design solution. Seeding and rolled erosion control products are often placed in combination with the wire mesh.

Wire mesh is fabricated of various grades and gauges of woven steel wires. Wire can be high tensile strength or mild steel. The steel can be galvanized for corrosion resistance, or colored or coated to meets aesthetic considerations particular to the context of a site. Wire mesh openings are on the order of 3 to 4 inches. Figure 3 shows different types of wire mesh, and cable nets commonly used as flexible facing. Similar types of wire mesh are used for rockfall protection systems. Each type has different stiffness, strength, and application. Single and double twist are the most used wire meshes for flexible facing on slopes. Cable mesh typically has openings 6 to 12 inches and is backed by a wire mesh to prevent fines from passing through.

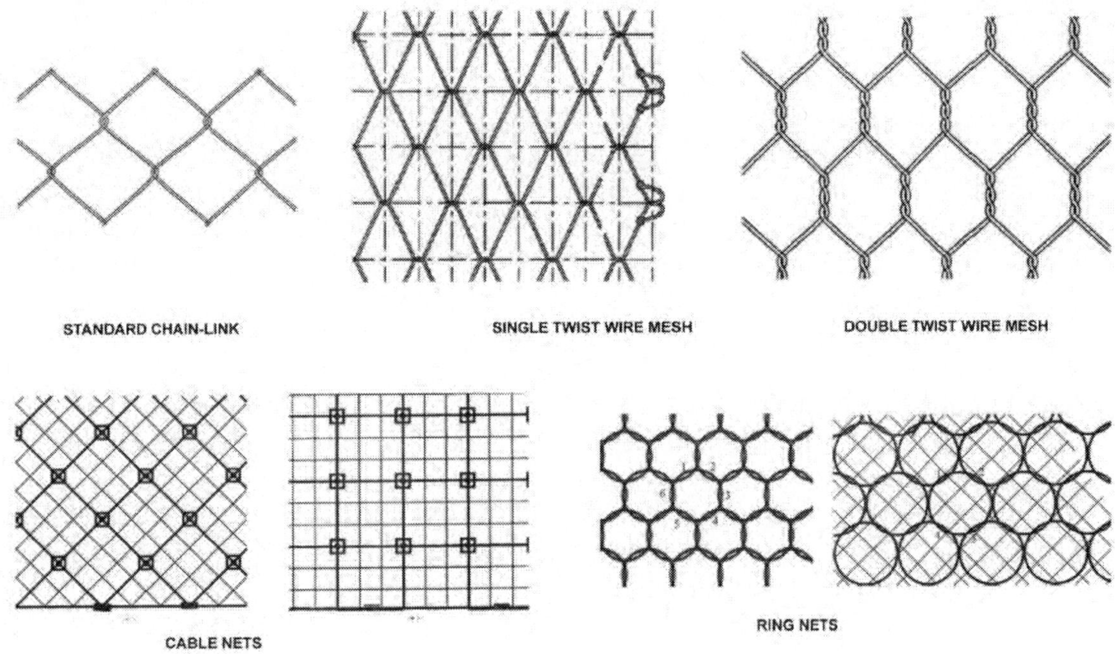

Figure 3: Types of Flexible Face

The two meshes fixed together stiffens and strengthens the combined mesh. Cable mesh is well suited to conforming the mesh to highly irregular or blocky slopes. Ring nets are extremely flexible and are used to dissipate energy from rockfall or debris flows and maintain integrity even when stretched to several meters of displacement but are not used as flexible facing.

All of the wire mesh is considered flexible; however, each tends to be noticeably stiffer when bending is parallel to the axis of the twists. The mesh should be identified by size, type and strength. For example: *3mm, single twist, high strength steel wire mesh* or *3mm, double twist, mild strength steel wire mesh*. Standardizing these terms allows the designer to be able to specify a specific type of mesh, better understand the difference in systems when comparing case histories, and what engineering properties are associated with the different types.

Facing Types for Soil Nail Retaining Walls

Wire mesh is not the only choice when considering an appropriate facing for a soil nail retaining wall or slope stabilization project. The selection and design of the facing for a soil nail type system should consider the loads to be resisted and the function of the facing as well as the potential for erosion, global slope movement, and potential instability of the soil between the nails. The type of facing should be selected that is best suited for slope conditions and purpose for the soil nail or slope stabilization system being designed. The following four categories are generally the types of facings that can be considered in association with ground stabilization using soil nails.

1. **No Facing.** Arching and interaction between soil nails can allow mobilization of soil resistance as a ground modification technique to strengthen slopes. These systems are commonly used in fin-piles or "stich piles" where interaction and arching between the nails reinforces the soil mass to improve slope stability and resist "flow through" between nails. These systems do not retain soil or resist erosion. This system may be appropriate if the slope between the nails has inherent stability, can rely on existing vegetation between the nails to resist erosion and provide surficial stability, and nail spacings or characteristics of the slope allow stability to be provided by the nails only. These types of systems are mostly used for shallow slumps, to improve surficial stability or stabilize specific blocks or layers of unstable soil or rock.

2. **Soft Facing.** The main function of soft facings is usually to control erosion or to provide turf reinforcement. Rolled erosion control products are not relied on for any retention or resistance to earth pressures between the nails. The soft facing is essentially the same as a no-facing system except the soft facing allows eventual slope stabilization by helping vegetation establish. These types of systems also provide no retention or catchment of the soil between the nails. Soft facings are most appropriate for moderate or graded slopes that are stable, and the purpose of the facing is to allow vegetation to establish.

3. **Flexible Facing.** Flexible facings are typically steel wire mesh that provides catchment and passive tensile resistance as a membrane to stabilize earth, blocks, boulders, or rocks between ground anchors. Resistance is passive because the tensile resistance of the facing material is not mobilized until the slope moves. While stresses on a conventional shotcrete facing are limited and reduce the lateral pressure on the facing between the soil nails (see Figure 2), a flexible facing catches the material and pressures may increase as continued slope movement adds material to the catchment. The analysis of the flexible should consider the maximum forces and deformation that could be imposed on the wire mesh by unstable blocks or slumps occurring between the soil nails.

4. **Hard Facing.** Hard facings are considered structural elements with moment resistance that resists outward deformation and transfers shear forces to the nail head as part of an earth retention system. Hard facings are generally composed of reinforced shotcrete, cast-in-place concrete, prefabricated concrete, or a combination of these materials. Their main function is to prevent soil loss, prevent debonding near the head of the soil nail due to raveling of the slope face, and limit soil deformation between the soil nails with movement that is essentially imperceptible. Hard facings also increase the resistance at

the nail heads against slope instability. Hard facings should be used when the soil nail system will act as a retaining wall.

Ground Anchors

Anchored Wire Mesh. Ground anchors secure the flexible facing to the slope face and are the reinforcing elements used for improving slope stability. Various design approaches for retaining structures use soil nail anchors with specific lengths and spacings to resist lateral earth pressures and improve slope stability, similar to how a configuration of pin piles or plate piles can be designed to improve slope stability without a facing element. A flexible-faced system composed of anchored wire mesh will use ground anchors to resist translational or surficial slope instability on the outer portions of the slope, and provide the anchorage needed to secure the wire mesh to the slope face. The designer should consider each of these functions, identify the design for a retaining structure or anchored mesh for shallow instabilities, then identify the depth, spacing, capacity, and type of ground anchors that are needed for slope stability. These anchors may range from common ground anchors composed of a steel rebar grouted into a drilled hole to provide slope stability, driven or screw type anchors with a known amount of pullout capacity, or shallow anchors with limited capacity that need only to pin the mesh securely to the slope.

Retaining Structures. Soil nails become stabilizing elements in reinforced earth. Slope stability is improved by anchoring a mass of earth behind the critical failure plane with soil nails, while the resistance along soil nails in front of the failure surface helps distribute earth pressures through interaction between the nails to form the reinforced mass. Key considerations for design include how outward movement is resisted by the soil nail while the facing provides confinement around the nail head to prevent the reinforced earth from stripping off the nail head and debonding the soil nail. A conventional soil nail retaining wall includes a hard facing that retains the soil between the nails prevents the soil from debonding around the outer portion of the anchor and preserves the reinforced earth mass. Flexible facings are generally not suited for that task because they deform significantly in response to out-of-plane loads or require very close nail spacings to limit deformation of the facing, which may not be practical or economical to install when compared to a soil nail wall with a hard facing.

The magnitude of the load transfer that can occur between nail heads and a hard or flexible facing is why a flexible facing is not well suited for retaining wall design. The force at the nail head (To) for a hard facing is estimated to be approximately 50 to 60 percent of the maximum stress in the nail (Tmax). The maximum stress in the soil nail is estimated from active earth pressure calculations or slope stability analyses and is dependent on the spacing and lengths of the soil nails. A hard facing is then designed with a moment connection between the head of the soil nail and facing that can resist nail head resistance (To) and transfer those forces into the hard facing with minimal deflection. The resistance at the head of the soil nail and from the reinforced concrete facing is mobilized passively in response to outward soil movement, typically limited to about 0.005H, where H is the retained height of the slope. FHWA Geotechnical Engineering Circular No. 7 (Lazarte et al 2015) describes the specific methodology for designing soil nail lengths, bar sizes, spacings and facings for a soil nail retaining wall with a hard reinforced concrete facing. Figure 4 shows a schematic section at the head of a soil nail from GEC No.7 that shows the pressures and deflection that the facing should resist to retain the soil around the nail head and between the soil nails.

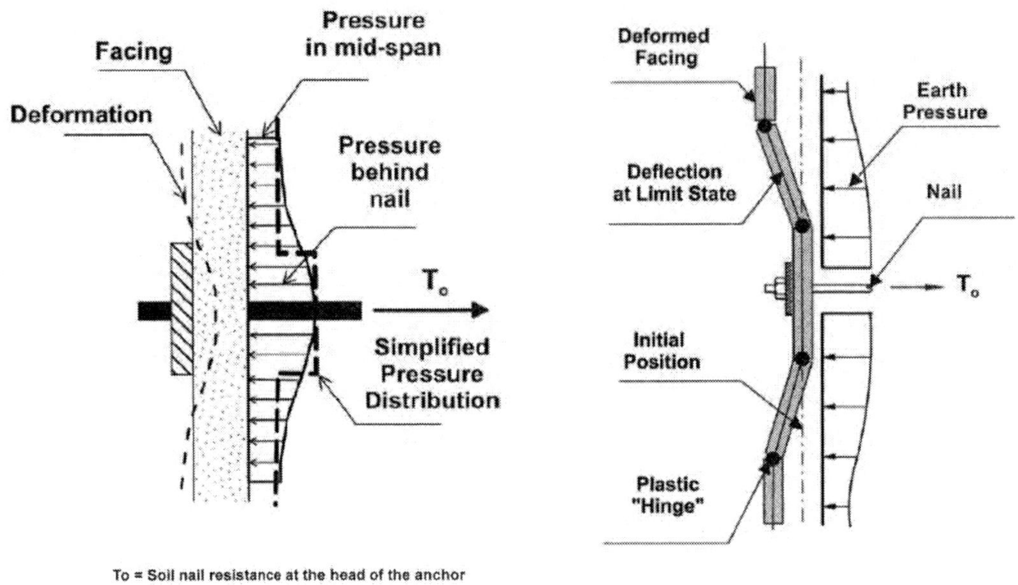

Figure 4: Pressure Distribution on Soil Nail Facing

A flexible-faced retaining wall should ideally support those same earth pressures as a wall with a reinforced concrete facing, except the nail head resistance (To) is limited by the size of the anchor plate and has no moment connection to the facing. A hard-faced soil nail wall can be designed to resist thousands of pounds of force, while the bearing resistance from an anchor plate on a flexible may only be about 100 to 300 pounds. Past practices that assume flexible facings could be tensioned in a manner that puts active pressure on the slope face have been mostly dismissed. While the initial soil nail layout and lengths for a retaining wall with a flexible or hard facing maybe analyzed similarly, a flexible facing being "flexible" does not develop resistance at the slope face at small strains, and therefore the resistance of the facing at the head of the soil nail is essentially 0.

Figure 5 shows the tensile stress distribution along a soil nail connected to a facing versus one that is not connected to a facing based on research by Shui and Chen (2005). The implication of these different stress distributions is that higher tensile stresses are resisted at the head of the soil nails that are connected to a hard facing than those that are not. The facing also resists destabilizing forces between soil nails and limits deformation of the facing by transferring the soil pressure on the facing to the head of the soil nail. The flexible facing does not have the moment connections to resist movement between the nail head and facing, or the ability to confine the soil around the nail head to resist out-of-plain forces as occurs in a soil nail wall with a hard facing. Soil nail systems with flexible facing are more suitable for flatter, non-retaining, situations.

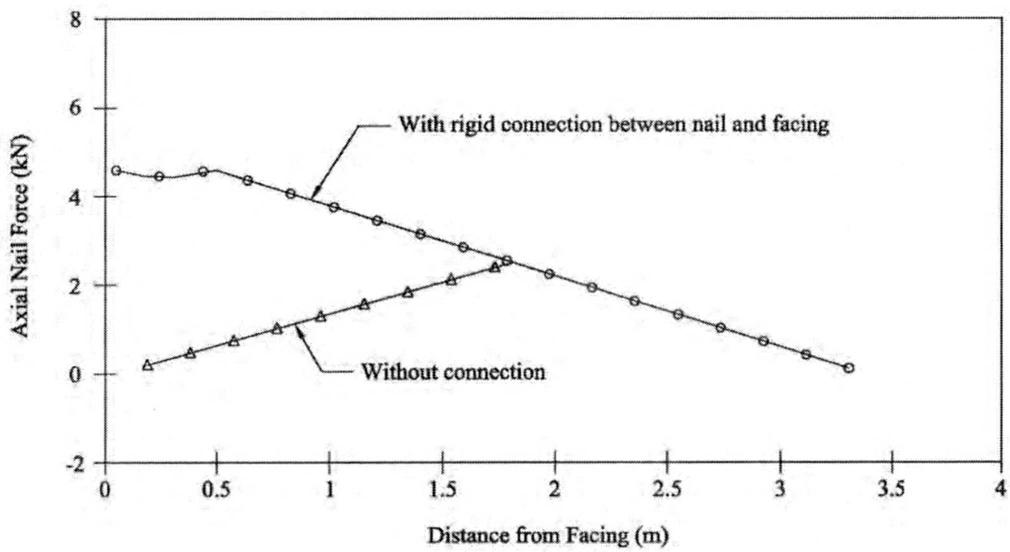

Figure 5: Distribution of Axial Force along a soil nail

DESIGN APPROACH

Slope stability is mainly improved by strengthening provided by ground anchors. While wire mesh is the most recognized component of a flexible facing system and attributed to stabilizing a slope; oddly enough, wire mesh is not considered when calculating the resisting forces or factor of safety for slope stability. The wire mesh provides catchment of material between soil nails and appears to play an important role in providing erosion protection, securing blocks of rock or boulders in place, and improving surficial slope stability even though current practice does not account for those contributions in the calculations for slope stability. Maximizing the contact between the wire mesh and the ground is needed to acknowledge those benefits for slope stability. The recommended approach is therefore to design flexible facings to help stabilize slopes in stiff or dense soil or rock with enough inherent stability for the slope height and inclination being considered to allow the facing system to be placed and/or are easily stabilized with ground anchors.

Slope Face and Inclination

Flexible facings should not be placed on slopes that are unstable, moving or subject to lateral earth pressures. Design the flexible faced system for a slope inclination that can be stabilized relying on the strength of the soil or the ability of the ground anchor patten to improve surficial slope stability. Generally, the slope should have a factor of safety of at least 1.0 at the design slope inclination and time of construction to allow for proper placement of the flexible facing. Slope improvements are generally not performed on a slope with active movement regardless of the mitigation approach being considered. Flexible facings can be and are

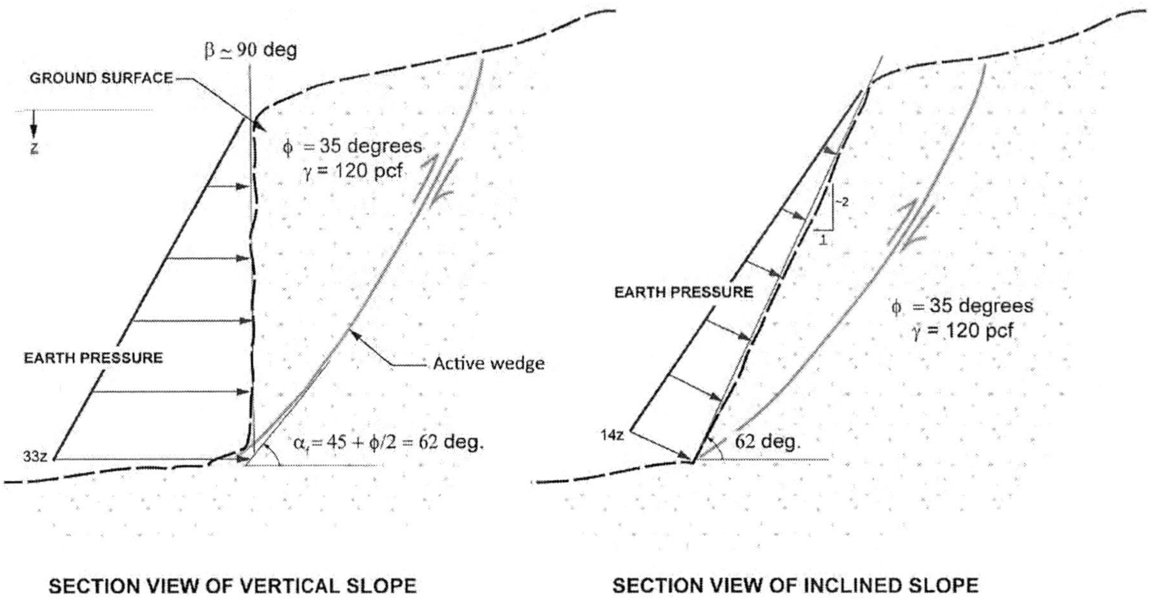

Figure 6: Slope Inclination vs. Lateral Earth Pressure

commonly designed for steeper or vertical only when there is sufficient cohesion or strength in the soil or rock to maintain a stable slope at that inclination or the slope has been stabilized for global stability prior to placing the facing.

The reduction in lateral earth pressure for a slope face flattened behind the active wedge is illustrated for a cohesionless soil in Figure 6. Rankine earth pressure theory defines the active wedge for a vertical slope as beyond an angle (α) steeper than $45° + \phi/2$. Reducing the slope face to an inclination flatter than the active wedge prior to installing anchored wire mesh helps eliminate lateral earth pressures and allow the soil cohesion or apparent cohesion to resist slope movement. For cohesionless soil (clean sand or gravel), the slope would likely need to be flattened to at least the angle of repose to allow for placement of the wire mesh and slope stabilization. Slope stability analyses should be used to help define finished slope inclinations, estimate nail spacings for slope stability, and evaluate whether the slope between ground anchors remains stable. Flattening the inclination will allow a slope to be stabilized more easily and reduce lateral earth pressures so that they may be more easily resisted by cementation or cohesion within the soil. Generally, the slope inclination should be below the active wedge to reduce the potential for slope movement during construction and reduce the potential for outward lateral earth pressures to develop post-construction.

Ground Anchor Spacing

Ground anchors are the primary strengthening element of slope stabilization systems with flexible facings. However, ground anchors may or may not be relied upon to improve slope stability. A minimal anchor spacing (no more than 10 feet typically) is considered suitable where the primary function of the ground anchor is to secure the flexible facing to the slope to resist erosion and help vegetation become established. Spacings closer than 10 feet are used when needed for slope stability. Enough ground anchors should be provided to reduce undulations in the wire mesh, maximize contact between the wire mesh and the ground surface, and reduce tenting around slope irregularities. Anchors that are not functioning to stabilize the slope should be designed to provide a minimal pullout resistance (about 4 or 5 kips each) to ensure the anchors are durable, have sufficient capacity to secure the facing for the long-term. The specified capacity of ground anchors that resist surficial or global slope instability should be estimated from slope stability analyses.

Conventional Spacing

Figure 7 shows a typical section of a slope that is stabilized with ground anchors. A ground anchor spacing is typically estimated assuming arching occurs to three diameters around each ground anchor to stabilize a slope to depths of up to about 6 feet. Arching effectively results in a larger ground anchor diameter that resists the soil movement around and beyond the limits of the ground anchor to increase the effective ground anchor diameter (B′) to typically three times the actual ground anchor diameter (b). An estimate of B′ = 3b is a common spacing used for the design of soldier piles, shear pins, fin piles, and micropiles for resisting lateral ground forces. The ground anchor resists translation or surficial slope instability essentially the same as a micropile. The vertical spacing and number of rows of ground anchors needed to stabilize the slope over its full height can easily be estimated using conventional computer programs used to analyze slope stability. For flexible facings, staggered or diamond shaped configurations are typically used to create a layout with sufficient coverage to anchor the wire mesh and provide slope stability.

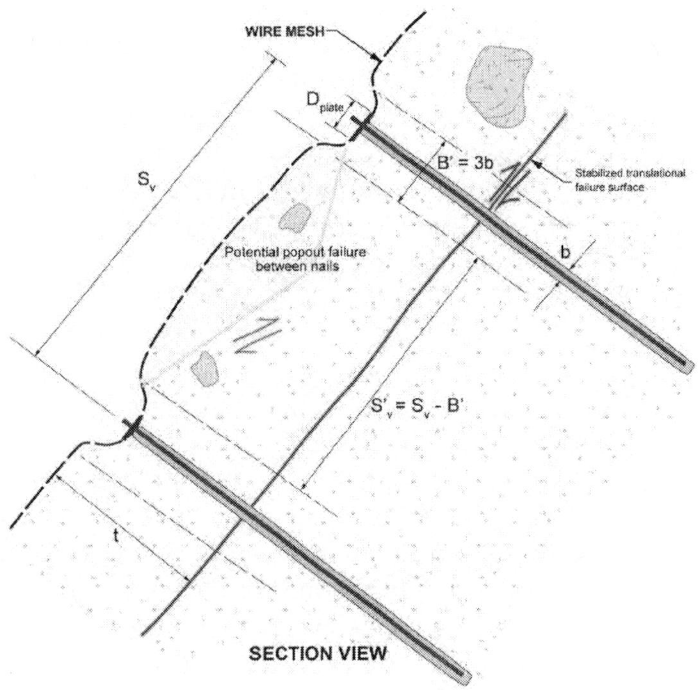

Figure 7: Anchored Mesh

The pullout resistance is primarily developed by the tensile capacity of the ground anchor below the failure plane. Turner and Halvorson (2013) recommend methods to estimate the lateral capacity of micropiles, essentially ground anchor, that develop the lateral resistance from the pullout capacity of the ground anchor in tension. The ground anchor resistance develops passively in response to slope movement and eventually mobilized as pullout resistance from below the slide plane. The ground anchor can then be sized for the needed tensile stress and checked for shear or be coupled with a non-liner p-y type pile analysis or structural calculation to estimate an allowable ground anchor capacity for a specific amount of lateral deflection. Anchoring the wire mesh to the head of the ground anchor likely influences the lateral capacity as discussed in the following section of this paper; however, current practice assumes the anchor head is free to rotate and not able to resist bending.

Pressure Cone Spacing

Geobrugg (Cata el al 2020) presents a design approach that assumes a pressure cone develops around the ground anchor plate. Geobrugg developed this theory based on arching observations and measurements around the anchor plate and ground anchor head during a series of large-scale tests performed in a soil-filled box. Geobrugg recommends the anchor plate be countersunk below the slope face with a hydraulic press. The pressure cone is then estimated to develop from edge of the crater around the anchor plate and project down through the slide to the failure plane, at approximately 1h:2v (horizontal to vertical). The method assumes 100 percent of the post tensioned load used to set their anchor (spike) plate into the slope is transferred through the unstable mass to the failure plane. That normal force on the failure plane is then assumed to resist sliding. Specific analyses are performed using their proprietary Ruvolum® software and the methodology is relatively unique compared to the arching that is assumed to develop around a ground anchors or micropile design. Current practice assumes that the resistance in the ground anchor, anchor plate and facing develops passively in response to slope movement. The limitations and specifics in the mechanics of the design approach using a pressure cone are not completely explained at this time. The arching observed in the tests could perhaps be explained by arching around the soils instead of from active pressure being imposed on the slope facing by tensioning of the mesh and embedding the anchor plate.

Similarly, Koerner (2014) describes the pullout resistance of a driven anchor plate (such as a duckbill or manta ray plate) used for rolled geosynthetic, similar to currently available or rolled erosion control products like Armormat® and Pyramat® by Propex, that appears to result in a similar zone of influence around the anchors. Koerner however attributes the influence around the anchor from a cone developed above the plate of a driven anchor, and accounts for an increase in confinement on the slope developed by counter sinking the anchor plate into the slope to tension the geosynthetic, and states that retensioning may be necessary to maintain this pressure. This approach is delivered qualitatively, and whether the confinement is realistic or reliable for a permanent slope stabilization system is uncertain.

Recommended Spacing

It seems reasonably conservative to estimate the ground anchor spacing assuming arching develops to 3b around a ground anchor. Application of proprietary software solutions should be done carefully with an understanding of the loads and assumptions that govern the design of the slope stabilization system. The pressure cone and mobilization of resistance behind the anchor plate should be considered to occur passively, as downslope movement develops resistance in the ground anchors and ground anchor plates. The anchor plate at the head of the ground anchor is important if the flexible facing system will develop any interaction with the ground anchors, anchor plate, and soil because no confinement at the ground anchor head is offered by the flexible facing on the slope alone.

Flexible Facing

Current practice generally relies on wire mesh to resist erosion and allow vegetation to establish on the slope while the ground anchors and anchor spacing provide slope stability. Slope movements can impose forces on the facing causing the wire mesh to deform, burst, or tear from the anchors. The design should follow the load path of unstable slope conditions that may develop to estimate the forces that the wire mesh and anchoring system must resist. The unstable slope conditions that could act on the wire mesh are generally from translational slope movement or creep, a pop-out or rotational failure between the ground anchors, or a wedge or block type failure occurring between ground anchors. These surfaces should be estimated from slope stability analyses and/or the characteristics and size of the rocks that may be caught by the flexible facing. Proprietary software from Geobrugg (Ruvolum) and Maccaferri (MACRO) can help estimate the punching forces and ground anchor systems needed for their specific wire mesh products. Deformations and movement of the flexible facing for slope stabilization applications is generally not noticeable if the facing is placed on a relatively stable slope and not subject to forces that would cause it to bulge or fail.

Drag Forces

Some literature suggests that interface friction between the ground and a wire mesh laying on a slope provides drag resistance against surficial stability, erosion and raveling of the slope face. Quantifying drag forces has proven challenging because of the difference in soil properties at the slope face, is no normal force on the mesh to promote friction, and the wire mesh is typically not in full contact with the slope face Muhunthan et al (2005)). Even with drag, the wire mesh is not in full contact with the slope face and the normal force provided by the weight of the mesh is small. The drag component maybe more significant where the ground is rocky, on boulders, or weathered rock slopes where interactions between the mesh and those larger blocks either by protrusion through the mesh or envelopment reduces the potential for those larger particles to roll out of slope. For this condition, the large rock inclusions give the mesh something to grab onto and likely allow planar stresses through the mesh to be mobilized. Current practice does not include any provision for such drag.

In—plane resistance

A common observation is that the wire mesh can be easily lifted off the slope face by hand between anchors even when anchor plates are sunk behind the slope face, and tie-wires and cables are lashed over the mesh. However, the same mesh deforms very little when pulled parallel to the plane of the mesh and underlying slope face. The in-plane strength of wire mesh can be quite rigid, likely mobilizes more quickly and develops at much smaller strains compared to the out-of-plane direction. The anchoring of the wire to the head of the ground anchor may partially fix the location of the head, resist rotation, and could possibly provide greater bending resistance than if the head of the ground anchor were considered free to rotate.

A previous study presented to HGS by Koutsourais and Deana (2018, from Maccaferri) reviewed various design methods and software used in the design of anchored wire mesh systems. The study included a slope analysis performed using a finite element model using Plaxis®. with consideration of the stabilizing effect of a wire mesh facing to improve the estimated factor of safety for slope stability. Limit equilibrium analyses were limited to estimating anchors loads, lengths and spacings for the ground anchor part of the design, while Koutsourais and Deana used Plaxis® to perform a more complete analysis considering tangible components of the flexible facing and anchors (i.e. tension in the wire mesh, shear and bending moment in the anchor plate and ground anchor).

Koutsourais and Deana (2018) compared slope stability analyses for an assumed 3-foot-thick translation failure sliding on a 75-degree infinite slope in soil having an internal friction angle of 38 degrees and cohesion of 400 pounds per square foot. They analyzed the slope using the computer models Ruvolum®, MACRO, SLIDE (by Rocscience for limit equilibrium analysis), and Plaxis® with and without considering wire mesh. The Plaxis model considered the steel's tensile strength in the wire mesh laid parallel to the slope face with no flexural stiffness, and the mesh hinged with no moment transfer at the anchor heads. Drag between the mesh and slope face was not considered. Their published results are shown in Figure 9. The wire mesh contributed significantly toward improving slope stability. However, Plaxis® is not a typical tool in a geotechnical triage kit and is not known for productivity or being easily tailored to site specific variables associated with slopes being stabilized with anchored wire mesh, and the details of the Plaxis® model, assumptions and limitations were not disclosed by the authors.

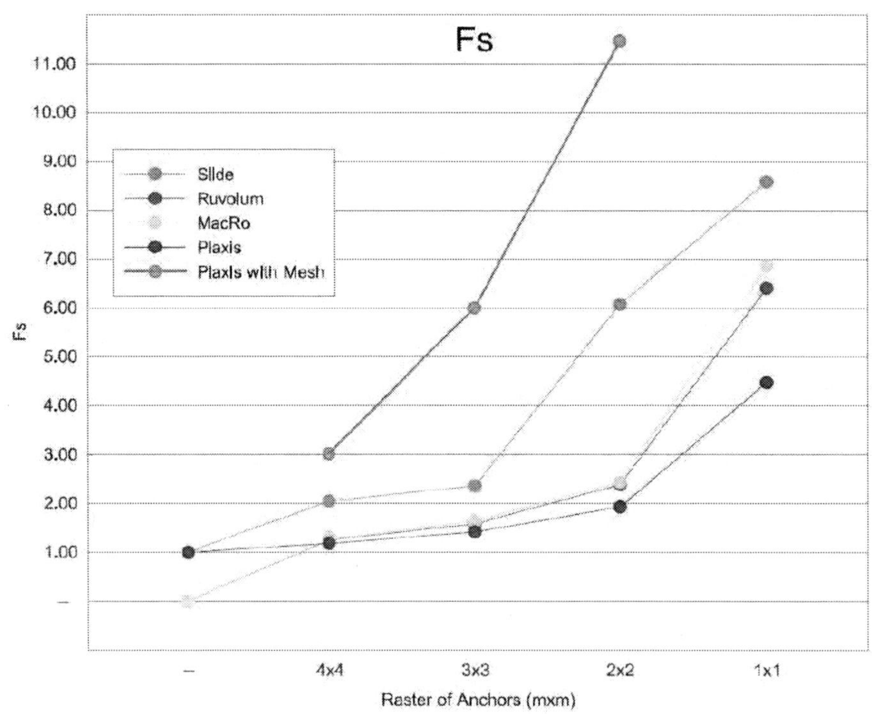

Figure 8: Comparison of Analytical Methods (Koutsourais and Deana 2018)

These results; however, suggest that the contribution of the wire mesh may be significant and explain the successes that have been achieved for stabilizing slopes with anchored wire mesh. The improved stability could be associated with both the in-plane stiffness of the wire and increased ground anchor capacity that occurs by fixing or semi-fixing the anchor head. The in-plane resistance of the wire mesh is unaccounted for in current practice but likely plays an important role in the interaction between the slope and ground anchor.

Punching

Punching Resistance (P) is the amount of force that wire mesh can resist by catchment between anchor points. Punching forces occur when there is slope instability and wasting of slope material between the ground anchors. Evaluation of punching forces is not a focus of this paper, mainly because anchored mesh systems should be placed on stable slopes (having a factor of safety of at least 1) or the slope is stabilized by the anchors prior to placing the flexible facing. Punching forces should not develop that would cause the flexible to rupture or tear off the head of ground anchors. Proprietary programs such as Ruvolum®, (Geobrugg) and MACRO, (Maccaferri) can be used to estimate punching forces, if needed. The design should also consider potentially unstable blocks or wedges of rock, or global slip outs and slides that may be larger than those considered by the software. The designer should select the strength of the mesh that is needed to support the punching force associated with the soil or rock falling into it when it is appropriate for the design. The punching force should be transferred through the mesh to the anchor point without breaking. The mesh is secured to the anchor head by a metal anchor plate that helps distribute the load to the strands of wire in the mesh so that they do not shear or break in tension at the anchor head.

Deformation

Deformation or bulging is the primary response of a flexible facing to slope instability. Similar to the discussion of punching forces, the potential for excessive deformation and bulging of the wire mesh is reduced when the slope is stabilized by the ground anchors prior to placing the flexible facing. Studies and tests, such as those by Pokharel et al. (2011), have been conducted to evaluate the behavior of meshes using various sized samples with a range of constraint conditions. The mesh starts to appreciably resist load only after the application of significant load and deformation. Deformation of the facing and the potential for raveling of the slope behind the wire mesh flexible facings is reduced when the flexible facings are placed on slopes with at least some inherent stability or are stabilized with the ground anchor prior to placing the flexible facing.

DESIGN APPLICATIONS

Design should consist of assessing the slope, selecting a ground anchor spacing and finished slope inclination that will provide slope stability and limit the potential for excessive deformation of the slope face, and selecting a wire mesh for the flexible facing that will resist erosion, allow vegetation to establish on the slope, and help secure loose blocks of rock or boulders on the slope face. The following presents a discussion of examples of where anchored wire mesh can be used to improve slope stability relative to specific site conditions.

Case	Example
ϕ-c Soil: Stiff clay, clayey sand or gravel, some silty sand with inherent cohesion or cementation. Slope has factor of safety of at least 1.0 at design slope inclination. Slide debris and unstable material (observe along base of slope) is removed prior to placing the mesh. Critical failure surface is typically from surficial instability or toe failure. Ground anchor spacing and depth can provide additional stability to meet slope stability criteria; however, overall approach is to develop a weather-resistant facing on the slope using wire mesh and vegetation. Wire mesh may be combined with temporary erosion control mats placed below the wire mesh and vegetation to stabilize slope face and provide long-term stability.	
Cohesionless Soil: Clean sand or gravel with no cohesion or cementation. Slope has factor of safety of 1.0 at the angle of repose. Vertical slopes are only temporarily stable from moisture and vulnerable to collapse. Critical failure surface is surficial instability commonly manifested as sand flows near the slope face and generally long shallow surfaces. Wire mesh combined with rolled erosion control products and planting help stabilize sandy soil and resist long term erosion.	
Severe erosion in rocky ground in colluvium, residual soil or weathered rock. Slope has factor of safety of at least 1.0 at design slope inclination. Slide debris and unstable material is removed prior to placing the mesh. Slope is inherently stable but erosion around blocks of rock and weathering results in slipouts and rockfalls. Ground anchors are primarily used to anchor wire mesh to the slope face. Wire mesh holds blocks, boulders and rock in place helping to reduce erosion and rockfall.	

Case	Example
Rock Slopes: Fracture rock of various types and hardness with stability primarily controlled by rock strength and discontinuities. Instability is mainly manifested by rockslides and rockfall associated with structural discontinuities within the rock (joints, fractures, bedding) or unstable wedges and blocks of rock. Analyze slope with discontinuity and rockfall analyses. Anchored mesh is typically not appropriate for these slopes because catchment of rockfall within the wire mesh above the road is problematic to remove and maintain. Rock bolting, doweling, and slope drapery systems can be designed to improve slope stability and provide catchment for rockfall.	
Slopes well below angle of repose: Graded or soil slopes that are relatively stable but may have isolated erosion or instability due to concentrated runoff, severe storm event, springs, or saturation during spring thaw. Employ typical erosion control, surface drainage and methods appropriate for stable or graded slopes. Consider need for maintenance (mowing) that may not be conducive to wire mesh or other methods.	
Deep-seated Landslide: Large, deep-seated landslides and earth flows Slide is characterized by deep-seated movement, may have multiple failure plains, is active and may be moving. Stabilization is not appropriate for an anchored wire mesh system. Characterization and analysis is complex and requires a more comprehensive engineered solution than provided by a typical anchored wire mesh system design.	 https://www.usgs.gov/media/images/2005-landslide-conchita-ca

The slope assessment is typically concluded by recommending or selecting a slope improvement solution appropriate for the site, ensuring the system achieves the design objectives and is constructable within the available funding for the project. Alternatives should be considered as part of this process, and a flexible facing system should be used when the evaluation shows there is a need and benefit to using the system. An anchored mesh type system is well-suited for a permanent slope where analysis shows that the slope is generally stable, the design will not need to resist significant lateral earth pressures, deformation of the flexible facing is not a concern or concerns can be eliminated by limiting the steepness of the finished slope or the slope is or can be made stable with the addition of the ground anchors. Anchored mesh systems are often successful when stabilizing a shallow thicknesses of colluvium, bouldery soil, or weathered rock or on flatter slopes composed of erodible soil that can be stabilized with relatively light forces. Anchored wire mesh has been found to help maintain and improve the stability of those types of slopes over time.

CONCLUSIONS

The design of slope improvements using flexible mesh is not a one-size fits all solution and should consider all factors that influence slope stability:

- the height and steepness of the slope,
- the strength of the materials,
- creep,
- erodibility,
- whether the slope improvements are temporary or permanent, and
- interaction of the wire mesh and anchors with the slope.

Quantitative modeling to estimate a ground anchor spacing for slope stability is needed for design, as well as considerations for erodibility and rockfall within the matrix that will be left mostly unsupported between the anchors.

The combination of the wire mesh and vegetation are key to providing long term stability. Maximizing the contact of the wire mesh with the ground is important to fully achieve the benefits of using wire mesh to improve slope stability and resist erosion. The wire mesh can help secure blocks of rock or boulder and prevent further erosion that may occur if rocks were allowed to roll out of the slope exposing fresh soil to erosion.

Wire mesh does not resist out of plane slope movement but has a relatively high in-plane stiffness. Current practice does not include considerations for drag, in-plane stiffness of the mesh, or whether the wire helps the head of ground anchor resist rotation. These factors likely contribute more to improve slope stability than is considered in current practice.

REFERENCES:

Cata, M., Flum, D., Roduner, A., Rüegger R. and Wartmann, S. (Cata el al 2020), *TECCO® Slope Stabilization System and Ruvolum® Dimensioning Method,* New Edition 2020, AGH University of Science and Technology, Romanshorn, Switzerland.

Koerner, R. (2014), "In-Situ Stabilization of Soil Slopes Using Geosynthetics", *International Journal of Geosynthetics and Ground Engineering,* (2015) 1:2 DO 10.01007/s-40891-014-0002-2, accepted October 14, 2014.

Koutsourais, M. and Deana, M. (2018), *Design of Pinned Drapery Systems for Rockfall Protection*, Proceedings of the 69th Highway Geology Symposium, Portland, Maine.

Lazarte, C.A. Robinson, H. Gómez, J., Baxter, A., Cadden, A.; Berg, R. (2015), *Soil Nail Walls – Reference Manual*, Geotechnical Engineering Circular No. 7, Report No. FHWA-NHI-14-007, National Highway Institute, U.S. Department of Transportation Federal Highway Administration, Washington, DC 20590, dated February 2015.

Muhunthan, B., Shu S., Sasiharan, N., Hattamleh, O., Badger, T. Lowell, S. and Duffy, J. (Muhunthan et al 2005), *Design Guidelines for Wire Mesh/Cable Net Slope Protection,* Report No. WA-RD- 612.2, prepared for Washington State Transportation Commission, Department of Transportation with cooperation with Federal Highway Administration.

Sanat Pokharel, S. Parsons, R., Pierson, M., Han, J. and Willems, I. (Pokharel et al. 2011), *Use of Flexible Facing for Soil Nail Walls,* A cooperative transportation research program between Kansas Department of Transportation, Kansas State University Transportation Center, and The University of Kansas; Report No. K-Tran KU-10-6, November 2011.

Shiu. Y.K. and Chang, G.W.K., (2005). *Soil Nail Head Review*, GEO Report No. 175, Geotechnical Engineering Office, Civil Engineering and Development Department, The Government of the Hong Kong Special Administrative Region.

Turner, J.P., and Halvorson, M. (2013), "Design Method for Slide-Stabilizing Micropile Walls", Proceedings: *Geo-Congress 2013*, American Society of Civil Engineers, San Diego, California, conference dates March 3 through 7, 2013.

Migrating Mud Pot - Emergency Responses to Protect Critical Transportation Infrastructure

Jim Bailey LHG, R.G.
Shannon & Wilson Inc.
400 N 34th Street, Suite 100
Seattle WA. 98103
425.422.9013
Jim.Bailey@shanwil.com

R. Travis Deane P.E., G.E
Shannon & Wilson Inc.
100 North First Street, Suite 200
Burbank, CA 91502
rtd@shanwil.com

Prepared for the 71st Highway Geology Symposium, May, 2022

Acknowledgements

The author(s) would like to thank the individuals/entities for their contributions in the work described:

David K. Lynch, Ph.D, Physicist and Consulting Geologist, Thule Scientific

Disclaimer

Statements and views presented in this paper are strictly those of the author(s), and do not necessarily reflect positions held by their affiliations, the Highway Geology Symposium (HGS), or others acknowledged above. The mention of trade names for commercial products does not imply the approval or endorsement by HGS.

Copyright Notice

ABSTRACT

The Salton Sea, located in southern California, is the southern terminus of the San Andreas fault and a locale for sediment hosted, low temperature geothermal features. Commonly known as mud pots, these features are believed to form in this area by decarbonation reactions involving sedimentary carbonate that generate carbon dioxide (CO_2) gas.

In early 2018 one of these mud pots began migrating toward a critical Union Pacific rail line, a fuel pipeline and California Highway 111 paralleling the east side of the Salton Sea. This was the first time a mud pot had been observed migrating. The mud pot produces a sediment slurry at approximately 30 to 40 gallons per minute, eroding soils in the direction of the railroad tracks and Highway.

Initial actions included multi-method geophysical surveys, dewatering of the mud pot caldera, and installation of a sheet pile wall. After Imperial County declared an emergency, three deep borings/wells were drilled to depths up to 800 feet deep. The borings were used to determine the feasibility of depressurizing one or more aquifers that might be contributing to the flow. Drilling conditions were challenging due to high concentrations of CO_2, H2S, daytime temperatures up to 115^0 F, and occurrence of high-pressure gas and water.

The Mud Pot has since moved past the railroad tracks and is now threatening California 111. The State took several measures to protect the road but it was not successful. The road alignment has recently been moved to the west while the mud pot movement continues.

INTRODUCTION

Just east of the Salton Sea, two heavily used railroad tracks move freight from the ports of Southern California south and east to other parts of the country. This seismically active area is located at the southern end of the San Andreas Fault. Associated with the seismic activity are gas driven features called mud pots, or mud volcanoes (Figure 1).

Figure 2: Typical mud pot

Although the geologic mechanisms controlling these features are poorly understood, they likely originate from thousands of feet below the alluvial filled Salton Sea valley. Carbon dioxide gas generated at depth from carbonaceous rocks appears to rise along active fault lines, dragging groundwater to the surface.

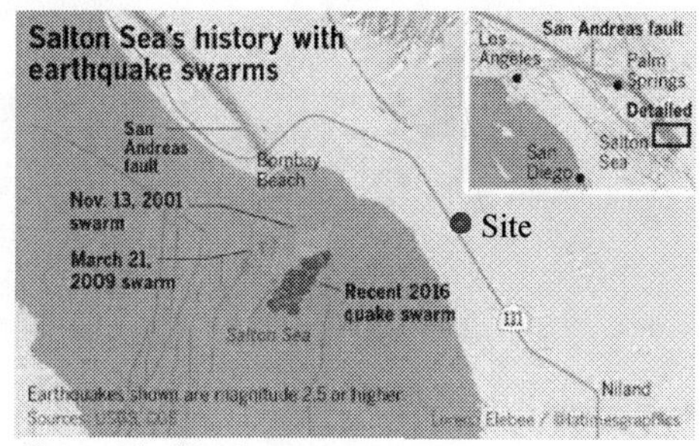

Figure 1: Site Location

Mud pots are common in this area of the Salton Sea basin and can appear and disappear over time but were believed to be stationary. In 2016 one of these mud pots, Wister mud pot, began to migrate relatively quickly to the southwest of its historical location. At that time, it was approximately 300 feet northeast of the railroad tracks, a gas pipeline & California Highway 111. The geographic and geologic setting of this mud pot is shown in Figure 2.

MOVEMENT TOWARD CRITICAL INFRASTRUCTURE

In the spring of 2018, the railroad became concerned about the continued migration of the mud pot toward its tracks. The initial response was to complete a geologic and hydrogeologic evaluation of the site to determine if there was a potential geotechnical mitigation option to protect the railroad tracks from continued movement of the mud pot. Looking at historical aerial photographs from 2016 to 2018 a general migration path was estimated (Figure 3). Next geophysical testing was performed to develop a conceptual subsurface model of what was controlling the mud pot movement. The geophysical testing characterized the subsurface conditions along several horizontal surface lines using High-Resolution S-wave Reflection. The results appeared to show a relatively homogenous subsurface profile with two distinct, near-horizontal dense layers in the upper half of the imaged depth along one profiled line just northeast of where the mud pot had passed. The dense layers were disrupted by linear, near-vertical faults (GeoVision, 2018). Using this data and discussions with international mud pot experts a conceptual model was developed for the site conditions (Figure 4).

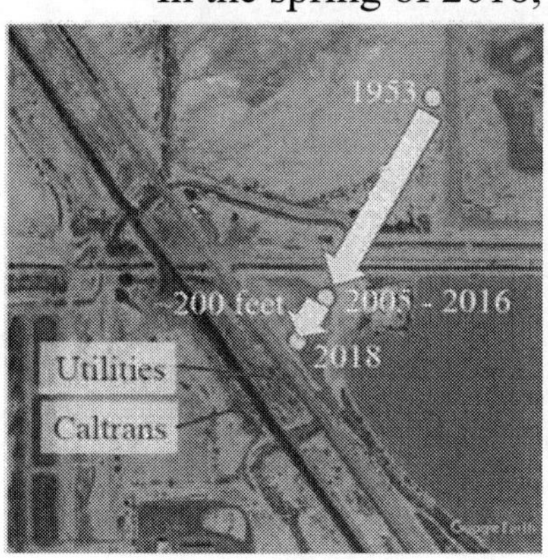

Figure 3: Mud Pot Migration

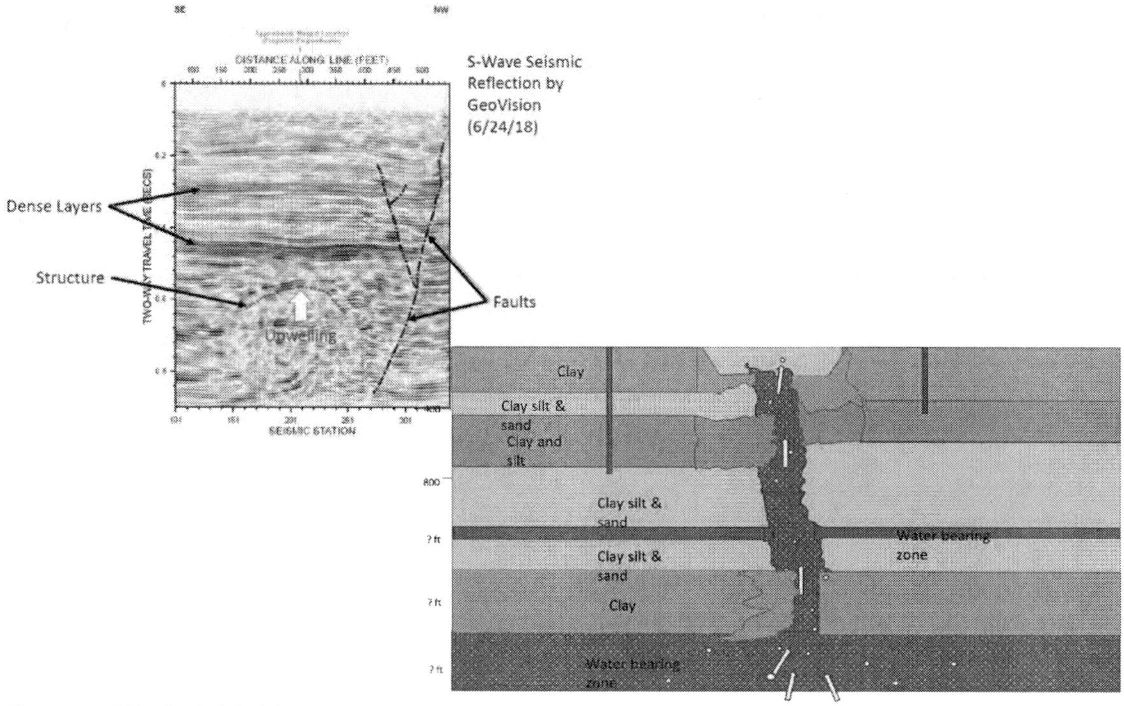

Figure 4: Conceptual Geologic Model

In May of 2018 the mud pot was a large actively bubbling feature approximately 80 feet from the active rail line (Figure 5). Concerns about erosion to the rail bed necessitated efforts to mitigate or control the mud pots movement until a permanent solution could be developed.

Figure 5: Mud Pot Approaching Tracks May 2018

INTERIM MITIGATION MEASURES

The geologic features controlling the mud pot migration precluded any permanent mitigation approach that would prevent the eventual impact on the railroad, gas pipeline and California Highway 111. The movement could not be stopped but its erosional effects might be delayed giving additional time to temporarily relocate the critical infrastructure until the mud pot stopped or moved beyond the area of concern.

The erosional impacts of the mud pot were being driven by the movement of CO2 gas as it discharged from the fault or lineament trace it was following. Two mitigation measures were initially implemented to slow the surficial erosion; lowering the water level in the active mud pot caldera, and driving sheet piles in front of the mud spring's path. The sheet piles would not prevent the mud springs continued movement but serve as a temporary erosional barrier while the critical infrastructure was relocated.

The sheet piles were installed in June 2018 and consisted of a 100-foot-long barrier across the path of the mud pot (Figure 6). The sheet piles were driven into dense plastic clays to a refusal depth of 75 feet. Large rock rip rap was placed on the leading edge of the mud spring caldera to add additional erosion protection.

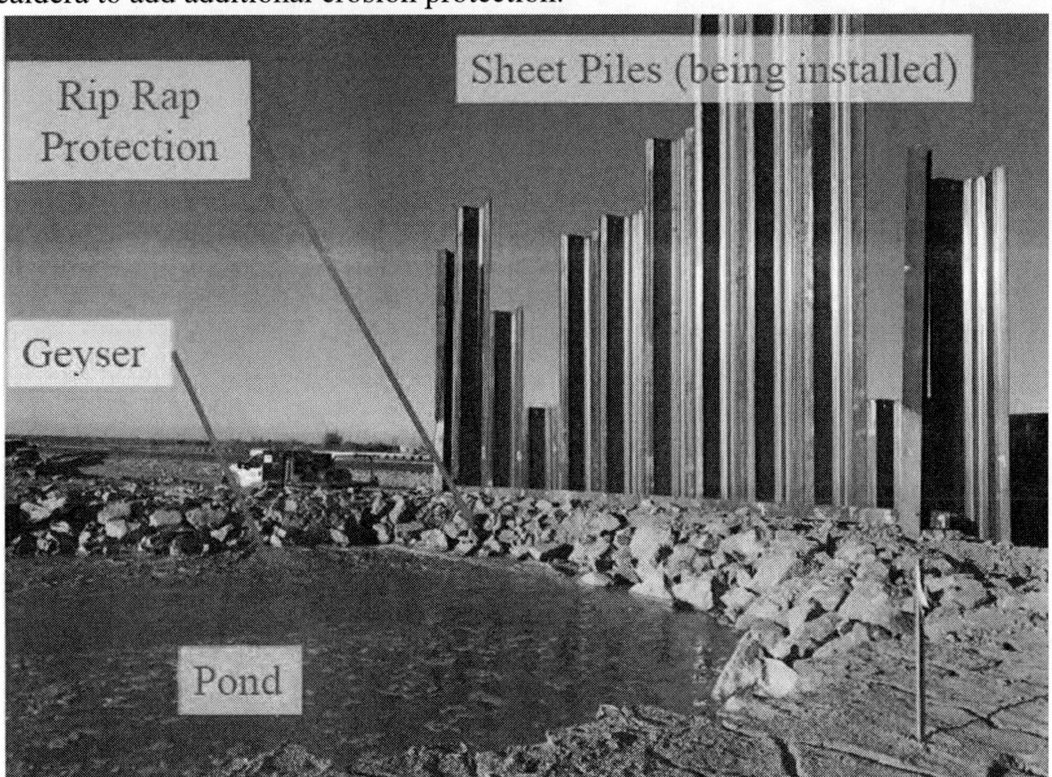

Figure 6: Installation of Sheet Pile Barrier

Once the sheet piles were in place the water in the Caldera was lowered approximately 25 feet using large centrifugal pumps at rate of up to 30 gallons per minute, 24-hours a day. The pumping resulted in a large, dewatered basin where the mud pot had been and was currently located (Figure 7). The mud spring approached the sheet piles in mid-July 2018 and remained contained behind the sheet piles for over three months. During this period three pressure relief wells were installed in an attempt to decrease the volume of water being expelled from aquifers near the surface by the high-pressure CO2 gas.

Figure 7: Dewatered Mud Pot Caldera

The first pressure relief well (B-1) was installed in the location where the geophysical testing had identified an upwelling in the subsurface approximately 300 feet below ground surface. This well encountered high pressure water conditions at the anticipated depth and a screen and pump were installed. There appeared to be a slight decrease in activity from the adjacent mud pot after installation of the first relief well. Two additional relief wells B-2 and B-3) were then installed as close as feasible to the active face of the mud pot near the sheet pile wall (Figure 8). The second well B-2 was drilled to a depth of 800 feet but did not encounter any water bearing zones, just high-pressure CO_2 gas. The third well B-3 was drilled to a depth of 600 feet but no water was encountered.

Figure 8: Location of Pressure Relief Wells

During construction of the relief wells, work to relocate the gas pipe line and one of the rail tracks began. A new shoofly track was constructed at the west edge of the railroad right-of-way. The pipeline company moved their line to the north and east sides of the mud spring's former path. Buried fiber optic and signal lines were put above ground on temporary power poles. The mud pot continued stay on the northeast side of the sheet piles, swallowed the rip rap and eroded all the soil in front of the sheet piles after three months (Figure 9).

Figure 9: Mud Pot September 2018

In October 2018 the mud pots active area moved to the other side of the sheet pile wall adjacent to the abandoned rail line. Train traffic was diverted from the main line tracks to the newly completed western shoofly track. Once the mud pot had moved beyond the sheet pile wall, pumping of the water ceased and the large caldera was backfilled with rip rap and soil. The railroad company then proceeded to construct an eastern shoofly track over the former caldera area that was just backfilled. The eastern shoofly was put into operation by the first of November 2018. It is important to note that during the entire time the mud pot has been moving, the railroad continued to operate at least one of their tracks. The mitigation measures appeared to be successful in slowing the surface expression of the mud pot while critical infrastructure was moved.

The mud pot continued its mostly westward movement the remainder of 2018 and into 2019. By July of 2019 the mud pot was centered over the former western main line rail track (Figure 10).

Figure 10: Mud Pot July 2019

CALIFORNIA HIGHWAY 111

Beginning in the fall of 2018 the California Department of Transportation (CALTRANS) began their own investigations of mitigation measures to protect Highway 111, the main north-south highway on the east side of the Salton Sea. Their initial effort was to mimic what the railroad had done to minimize the surficial erosional effects from the leading edge of the mud pot. In the spring of 2019, CALTRANS began installation of a sheet pile wall on the east side of the highway right of way (Figure 11).

Figure 11:CALTRANS Sheet Pile Installation

In addition to the new sheet pile wall, CALTRANS installed an extensive drainage system on the east side of the wall to intercept and divert flow from the mud pot once it reached the highway right of way.

The mud pot movement slowed somewhat in 2019 but continued to track toward the western edge of the railroad right-of-way by the end of January 2020. In August 2020, Caltrans closed the state highway for several weeks while a detour road was constructed to the west (Figure 12). As it had done to the railroad sheet pile wall, the mud pot breached the CALTRANS sheet pile wall in the fall of 2020.

Figure 12: California Highway 111 Detour

In March 2021, the mud pot movement brought it to the edge of the abandoned section of state Highway 111. The elevated section of the detour was approximately 100 feet east of the new detour (Figure 13). The mud pot movement had now slowed to a forward rate of about 3 feet

Figure 13: Mud Pot Position March 18, 2021

per month. This rate was down from a rate of about 10 feet a month in 2018 and 2019. By December of 2021 the mud pot had moved to just under the paved section of the original Highway 111 alignment (Figure 14). At the current rate of movement, the mud pot will likely cross the old highway 111 road in 2022 and once this happens CALTRANS plans to rebuild SR-111 back to the east close to the original alignment for Highway 111. Of course the mud pots movement is still not well understood and it could decide to change direction or become stationary like all the other mud pots in the area.

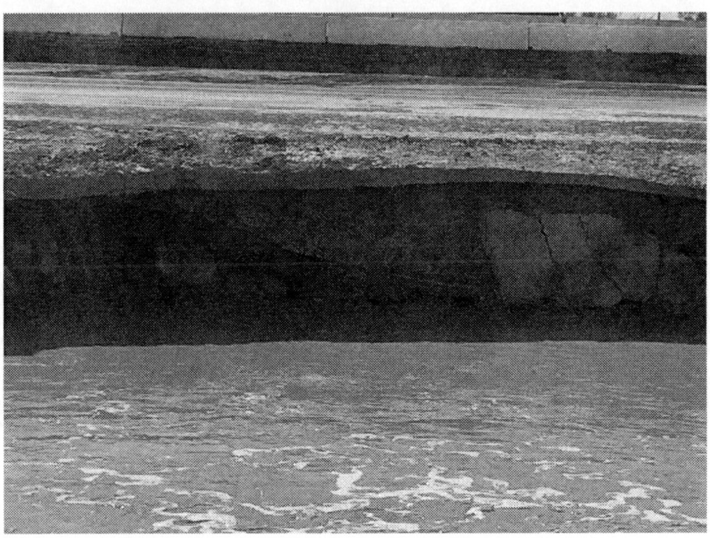

Figure 14:Mud Pot December 2021

REFERENCES:

- GeoVision (2018), "Geophysical Survey – Mudpot Investigation, Gillespie Road and Highway CA-111, Mundo, California," Project No. 18203, June 24.
- Google Earth (2016), earth.google.com/web/.
- Lynch, David K. and Kenneth W. Hudnut (2008), "The Wister Mud Pot Lineament: Southeastward Extension or Abandoned Strand of the San Andreas Fault?," Bulletin of the Seismological Society of America, Vol. 98, No. 4, pp. 1720-1729, August. *Research*, U.S. Department of Transportation, 1981.

Highway Geology Symposium
C/O John Pilipchuk
1589 Mail Service Center
Raleigh, NC, 27699-1589

ISBN 978-1-7138-5552-1

CURRAN ASSOCIATES INC.
proceedings.com